The Council of State Governments

STATE DIRECTORY

Directory III—

Administrative Officials 2017

The Council of State Governments
1776 Avenue of the States
Lexington, KY 40511

Contact the Publication Sales Department at
1-800-800-1910 or sales@csg.org to order:

Directory I—Elective Officials 2017,

Directory II—Legislative Leadership, Committees and Staff 2017

Directory III—Administrative Officials 2017

or mailing lists of state government officials.

Since 1933, The Council of State Governments has served our nation's state leaders by providing a forum for "sharing capitol ideas." As the only state services organization spanning all three branches of government, CSG offers a unique look into the issues shaping state policy and legislation from the national and regional perspectives. This unique arrangement contributes to a strong national presence for CSG, creating unparalleled opportunities to network, collaborate and form problem-solving partnerships.

The Council of State Governments

David Adkins, Executive Director CEO

1776 Avenue of the States ▪ Lexington, KY 40511 ▪ (859) 244-8000 ▪ Fax: (859) 244-8001 ▪ www.csg.org

---

Eastern Office
Wendell M. Hannaford, Director
22 Cortlandt Street, 22nd Floor
New York, NY 10007
(212) 482-2320
Fax: (212) 482-2344
www.csg-erc.org

Midwestern Office
Michael H. McCabe, Director
701 East 22nd Street, Suite 110
Lombard, IL 60148
(630) 925-1922
Fax: (630) 925-1930
www.csgmidwest.org

Southern Office
Colleen Cousineau, Director
P.O. Box 98129
Atlanta, GA 30359
(404) 633-1866
Fax: (404) 633-4896
www.slcatlanta.org

Western Office
Edgar E. Ruiz, Director
1107 9th Street, Suite 730
Sacramento, CA 95814
(916) 553-4423
Fax: (916) 446-5760
www.csgwest.org

Washington Office
444 N. Capitol Street, N.W., Suite 401
Washington, DC 20001
(202) 624-5460
Fax: (202) 624-5452
www.csgdc.org

Editorial Staff

Kelley Arnold ▪ Jessica Clay ▪ Eric Lancaster ▪ Heather Perkins

Special thanks to the CSG regional offices and the clerks and secretaries of the legislature for each state.

Printed in the United States of America
ISBN #978-0-87292-707-0
Price: $65.00

Table of Contents

How to Use This Directory

This annual directory provides basic information about elected and appointed officials with primary responsibility in more than 110 state government functions. The directory includes names, addresses, telephone, fax and email addresses. The information is organized alphabetically by function (e.g., Labor) and by state and U.S. jurisdiction name. Generally, there is one entry per function for each state or U.S. jurisdiction. State names and jurisdictions are not listed if there is not a corresponding entry for a given section.

CSG collected the information for the 2017 directory between April and June 2017. The data contained in this volume was compiled through one of three methods. First, national associations were given the opportunity to provide a roster for the directory. For those categories that did not have rosters provided, the information was gathered through two other methods. Each state and territory was sent a survey requesting updated information for their administrative officials. If states did not respond to the surveys, CSG staff collected the updated information from state-sponsored websites or phone calls to state offices.

Party Abbreviations

D	Democrat
R	Republican
REFORM	Reform
C	Covenant
I	Independent
L	Libertarian
S	Statehood
ICM	Independent Citizen Movement
DFL	Democratic-Farmer-Labor
NP	Nonpartisan
P	Progressive
NPP	New Progressive Party
PDP	Popular Democratic Party
PIP	Puerto Rican Independent Party
RA	Rural Alaskan
TRIBAL	Delegate representing a Native American tribe
U	Unenrolled

Adjutant General

The executive or administrative head of the state's military service.

ALABAMA
Major General Perry G. Smith Sr.
Adjutant General
National Guard
1720 Congressman W.L. Dickinson Drive
Montgomery, AL 36109
P: (334) 271-7200
F: (334) 213-7511
E: perry.g.smith@us.army.mil

ALASKA
Major General Laurel J. Hummel
Adjutant General & Commissioner
Department of Military & Veterans Affairs
P.O. Box 5800
Fort Richardson, AK 99505
P: (907) 428-6003
F: (907) 428-6019
E: laurie.hummel@alaska.gov

ARIZONA
Major General Michael T. McGuire
Adjutant General
Department of Emergency & Military Affairs
5636 East McDowell Road
Phoenix, AZ 85008
P: (602) 267-2700
F: (602) 267-2715

ARKANSAS
Major General Mark Berry
Adjutant General
Military Department
Camp Robinson
North Little Rock, AR 72199
P: (501) 212-5100
F: (510) 212-5009

CALIFORNIA
Major General David Baldwin
Adjutant General
Military Department
Joint Force Headquarters
9800 Goethe Road
Sacramento, CA 95827
P: (916) 854-3000
F: (916) 854-3671
E: david.s.baldwin@us.army.mil

COLORADO
Major General Michael A. Loh
Adjutant General
Department of Military Affairs
6848 South Revere Parkway
Centennial, CO 80112
P: (720) 250-1500

CONNECTICUT
Major General Thaddeus J. Martin
Adjutant General
Military Department
State Armory
360 Broad Street
Hartford, CT 06105
P: (860) 524-4953
F: (860) 524-4898
E: thad.martin@us.army.mil

DELAWARE
Major General Carol A. Timmons
Adjutant General
National Guard
250 Airport Road
New Castle, DE 19720
P: (302) 326-7000

DISTRICT OF COLUMBIA
Major General George M. Degnon
Acting Adjutant General
National Guard
2001 East Capitol Street, Southeast
Washington, DC 20003
P: (202) 685-9798

FLORIDA
Major General Michael Calhoun
Adjutant General
National Guard
82 Marine Street
St. Augustine, FL 32084
P: (904) 823-0100
F: (904) 823-0149
E: michael.a.calhoun4.mil@mail.mil

GEORGIA
Major General Joe Jarrard
Adjutant General
National Guard
1000 Halsey Avenue, Building 447
Marietta, GA 30062
P: (678) 569-6060

GUAM
Mr. Roderick R. Leon Guerrero
Adjutant General
National Guard
430 Army Drive, Building 300
Barrigada, GU 96913
P: (671) 735-0400
F: (671) 734-4081

HAWAII
Major General Arthur "Joe" Logan
Adjutant General
Department of Defense
3949 Diamond Head Road
Honolulu, HI 96816
P: (808) 733-4246
F: (808) 733-4499

IDAHO
Major General Gary L. Sayler
Adjutant General
National Guard
4040 West Guard Street, Building 600
Boise, ID 83705
P: (208) 272-5755
F: (208) 422-6179
E: saylerg@imd.idaho.gov

ILLINOIS
Major Richard J. Hayes Jr.
Adjutant General
National Guard
1301 North MacArthur Boulevard
Springfield, IL 62702
P: (217) 761-3500
F: (217) 761-3736

INDIANA
Major General Courtney Carr
Adjutant General
Adjutant General's Office
2002 South Holt Road
Indianapolis, IN 46241
P: (317) 247-3559
F: (317) 247-3540
E: courtney.carr@us.army.mil

IOWA
Major General Timothy E. Orr
Adjutant General
Office of the Adjutant General
7105 Northwest 70th Avenue
Johnston, IA 50131
P: (515) 252-4211
F: (515) 252-4787
E: timothy.e.orr4.mil@mail.mil

KANSAS
Major General Lee E. Tafanelli (R)
Adjutant General
Adjutant General's Department
5920 Southeast Coyote Drive
Building 2005, Room 229
Topeka, KS 66619
P: (785) 646-1190
F: (785) 274-1682
E: ng.ks.ksarng.list.staff-pao@mail.mil

KENTUCKY
Major General Stephen Hogan
Adjutant General
Department of Military Affairs
100 Minuteman Parkway
Frankfort, KY 40601
P: (502) 607-1713
F: (502) 607-1271

LOUISIANA
Major General Glenn Curtis
Adjutant General
National Guard
6400 St. Claude Avenue
New Orleans, LA 70117
P: (318) 641-5600
F: (318) 641-3865
E: glenn.curtis@us.army.mil

MAINE
Brigadier General Douglas Farnham
Adjutant General
Office of the Adjutant General
Camp Keyes
Augusta, ME 04333
P: (207) 262-4205
F: (207) 626-4509

MARYLAND
Major General Linda L. Singh
Adjutant General
Military Department
5th Regiment Armory
219 29th Division Street
Baltimore, MD 21201
P: (410) 576-6000
F: (410) 576-6079
E: linda.l.singh.mil@mail.mil

MASSACHUSETTS
Major General Gary W. Keefe
Adjutant General
National Guard
2 Randolph Road
Hanscom AFB, MA 01731
P: (339) 202-3999

Adjutant General

MICHIGAN
Major General Gregory J. Vadnais
Director & Adjutant General
Department of Military & Veterans Affairs
3411 North Martin Luther King Boulevard
Lansing, MI 48906
P: (517) 481-8083
F: (517) 481-8125
E: VadnaisG@michigan.gov

MINNESOTA
Major General Richard C. Nash
Adjutant General
National Guard
20 West 12th Street
St. Paul, MN 55155
P: (651) 268-8919
F: (651) 282-4541
E: rick.nash@us.army.mil

MISSISSIPPI
Major General Janson D. Boyles
Adjutant General
National Guard
1410 Riverside Drive
Jackson, MS 39202
P: (601) 313-6232

MISSOURI
Major General Stephen L. Danner
Adjutant General
National Guard
2302 Militia Drive
Jefferson City, MO 65101
P: (573) 638-9500
F: (573) 638-9722
E: stephen.l.danner@us.army.mil

MONTANA
Major General Matthew T. Quinn
Adjutant General
Department of Military Affairs
1956 Mt. Majo Street
P.O. Box 4789
Fort Harrison, MT 59636
P: (406) 324-3010
F: (406) 324-4800

NEBRASKA
Major General Daryl L. Bohac
Adjutant General
National Guard
2433 Northwest 24th Street
Lincoln, NE 68524
P: (402) 309-8104
F: (402) 309-7147
E: daryl.l.bohac.mil@mail.mil

NEVADA
NAME ERROR
Adjutant General
National Guard
2460 Fairview Drive
Carson City, NV 89701
P: (775) 887-7302
F: (775) 887-7315
E: william.ross.burks@us.army.mil

NEW HAMPSHIRE
Major General William N. Reddel III
Adjutant General
National Guard
1 Minuteman Way
Concord, NH 03301
P: (603) 225-1200
F: (603) 225-1257
E: william.n.reddel.mil@mail.mil

NEW JERSEY
NAME ERROR
Adjutant General
Department of Military & Veterans' Affairs
P.O. Box 340
Trenton, NJ 08625
P: (609) 530-6957
F: (609) 530-7191

NEW MEXICO
Brigadier General Andrew E. Salas
Adjutant General
Office of the Adjutant General
47 Bataan Boulevard
Santa Fe, NM 87508
P: (505) 474-1210
F: (505) 474-1355

NEW YORK
Major General Anthony P. German
Adjutant General
Division of Military & Naval Affairs
330 Old Niskayuna Road
Latham, NY 12110
P: (518) 786-4502

NORTH CAROLINA
Major General Gregory A. Lusk
Adjutant General
National Guard
4105 Reedy Creek Road
Raleigh, NC 27609
P: (919) 664-6101
F: (919) 664-6430
E: greg.lusk@us.army.mil

NORTH DAKOTA
Major General Alan Dohrmann
Adjutant General
National Guard
P.O. Box 5511
Bismarck, ND 58506
P: (701) 333-2000
F: (701) 333-2017
E: alan.dohrmann@us.army.mil

OHIO
Major General Mark Bartman
Adjutant General
National Guard
2825 West Dublin Granville Road
Columbus, OH 43235
P: (614) 336-7070
F: (614) 336-7074

OKLAHOMA
Major General Robbie Asher
Adjutant General
National Guard
3501 Military Circle
Oklahoma City, OK 73111
P: (405) 228-5000

OREGON
Major General Michael E. Stencel
Adjutant General
Office of the Adjutant General
P.O. Box 14350
Salem, OR 97309
P: (503) 584-3991
F: (503) 584-3987
E: tagor@mil.state.or.us

PENNSYLVANIA
Brigadier General Anthony Carrelli
Adjutant General
Department of Military & Veterans Affairs
Fort Indiantown Gap
Annville, PA 17003
P: (717) 861-8500
F: (717) 861-8481

PUERTO RICO
Major General Marta Carcana
Adjutant General
Office of the Adjutant General
P.O. Box 3786
San Juan, PR 00902
P: (787) 724-1295

RHODE ISLAND
Mr. Christopher Callahan
Adjutant General
National Guard
645 New London Avenue
Cranston, RI 02920
P: (401) 275-4102
F: (401) 275-4338

SOUTH CAROLINA
Major General Robert E. Livingston Jr.
Adjutant General
National Guard
1 National Guard Road
Columbia, SC 29201
P: (803) 299-4200
F: (803) 806-4468
E: bob.livingston@us.army.mil

SOUTH DAKOTA
Major General Timothy A. Reisch
Adjutant General
Department of the Military
425 East Capitol Avenue
Pierre, SD 57501
P: (605) 773-4984
F: (605) 737-6677
E: tim.reisch@us.army.mil

TENNESSEE
Major General Terry M. Haston
Adjutant General
Military Department
P.O. Box 41502
Nashville, TN 37204
P: (615) 313-3004
F: (615) 313-3100
E: terry.max.haston@us.army.mil

TEXAS
Major General John F. Nichols
Adjutant General
Adjutant General's Department
P.O. Box 5218
Austin, TX 78703
P: (512) 782-5006
F: (512) 782-5578
E: john.f.nichols1@us.army.mil

U.S. VIRGIN ISLANDS
Brigadier General Deborah Howell
Adjutant General
National Guard
RR#1, Box 9201
Kingshill, VI 00850
P: (340) 712-7711
F: (340) 712-7709

UTAH
Major General Jefferson S. Burton
Adjutant General
Office of the Adjutant General
12953 South Minuteman Drive
Draper, UT 84020
P: (801) 432-4194
F: (801) 432-4677
E: jeffburton@utah.gov

VERMONT
Major General Steven A. Cray
Adjutant General
Department of Military
789 Vermont National Guard Road
Colchester, VT 05446
P: (802) 338-3124
F: (802) 338-3425

VIRGINIA
Brigadier General Timothy Williams
Adjutant General
National Guard
5901 Beulah Road
Sandston, VA 23150
P: (804) 236-7880
F: (804) 236-7901

WASHINGTON
Major General Bret D. Daugherty
Adjutant General
Department of Military
Building 1, 1 Militia Drive
Camp Murray, WA 98430
P: (253) 512-8000
F: (253) 512-8497
E: bret.daughtery@mil.wa.gov

WEST VIRGINIA
Major General James A. Hoyer
Adjutant General
Army National Guard
1703 Coonskin Drive
Charleston, WV 25311
P: (304) 561-6318
F: (304) 561-6327
E: james.a.hoyer.mil@mail.mil

WISCONSIN
Major General Donald P. Dunbar
Adjutant General
Department of Military Affairs
2400 Wright Street
Madison, WI 53708
P: (608) 242-3000
F: (608) 242-3111
E: donald.p.dunbar@us.army.mil

WYOMING
Major General K. Luke Reiner
Adjutant General
Military Department
5410 Bishop Boulevard
Cheyenne, WY 82009
P: (307) 772-5234
F: (307) 772-5010
E: luke.reiner@us.army.mil

Administration

Umbrella agency of administration that coordinates administrative services provided to state agencies.

ALABAMA
Mr. Clinton Carter
Director of Finance
Department of Finance
State Capitol
600 Dexter Avenue, Suite N-105
Montgomery, AL 36130
P: (334) 242-7160
F: (334) 353-3300
E: clinton.carter
@finance.alabama.gov

ALASKA
Mr. Sheldon Fisher
Commissioner
Department of Administration
P.O. Box 110200
Juneau, AK 99811
P: (907) 465-2200
E: Sheldon.Fisher
@alaska.gov

ARIZONA
Mr. Craig C. Brown
Director
Department of Administration
100 North 15th Avenue, Suite 401
Phoenix, AZ 85007
P: (602) 542-1500
E: craig.brown@azdoa.gov

CALIFORNIA
Mr. Daniel C. Kim
Director
Department of General Services
707 Third Street
West Sacramento, CA 95605
P: (916) 376-5012
E: daniel.kim@dgs.ca.gov

COLORADO
Ms. June Taylor
Executive Director
Department of Personnel & Administration
1525 Sherman Street, 5th Floor
Denver, CO 80203
P: (303) 866-3000
E: june.taylor@state.co.us

CONNECTICUT
Ms. Melody A. Currey
Commissioner
Department of Administrative Services
450 Columbus Boulevard
Hartford, CT 06103
P: (860) 713-5100
F: (860) 713-7481
E: Melody.Currey@ct.gov

DELAWARE
Mr. Brian Maxwell
Director
Office of Management & Budget
Haslet Armory
122 Martin Luther King Boulevard South
Dover, DE 19901
P: (302) 739-4204
E: brian.maxwell
@state.de.us

DISTRICT OF COLUMBIA
Mr. Christopher Weaver
Director
Department of General Services
2000 14th Street, Northwest, 8th Floor
Washington, DC 20009
P: (202) 727-2800
E: dgs@dc.gov

FLORIDA
Ms. Erin Rock
Interim Secretary
Department of Management Services
4050 Esplande Way, Suite 250
Tallahassee, FL 32399
P: (850) 414-1159
E: erin.rock
@dms.myflorida.com

GEORGIA
Mr. Christopher Nunn
Commissioner
Department of Administrative Services
200 Piedmont Avenue, 1804 West Tower
Atlanta, GA 30334
P: (404) 656-5514
E: christopher.nunn
@doas.ga.gov

HAWAII
Mr. Roderick Becker
Comptroller
Department of Accounting & General Services
1151 Punchbowl Street, Room 412
Honolulu, HI 96813
P: (808) 586-0400
F: (808) 586-0775
E: roderick.k.becker
@hawaii.gov

IDAHO
Mr. Robert L. Geddes
Director
Department of Administration
650 West State Street, Room 100
Jordan Building, P.O. Box 83720
Boise, ID 83720
P: (208) 332-1824
F: (208) 334-5315
E: bob.geddes@adm.idaho.gov

ILLINOIS
Mr. Michael Hoffman
Director
Department of Central Management Services
401 South Spring, Suite 715
Springfield, IL 62706
P: (217) 782-2141
E: michael.hoffman
@illinois.gov

INDIANA
Ms. Jessica Robertson
Commissioner
Department of Administration
402 West Washington Street, Room W479
Indianapolis, IN 46204
P: (317) 234-3185
E: jrobertson@idoa.in.gov

IOWA
Ms. Janet Phipps
Director
Department of Administrative Services
1305 East Walnut Street
Hoover Building, 3rd Floor
Des Moines, IA 50319
P: (515) 725-2205
E: janet.phipps@iowa.gov

KANSAS
Ms. Sarah L. Shipman
Secretary
Department of Administration
1000 Southwest Jackson, Suite 500
Topeka, KS 66612
P: (785) 296-3011
E: sarah.shipman@ks.gov

KENTUCKY
Mr. William Landrum III
Secretary
Finance & Administration Cabinet
383 Capitol Annex
Frankfort, KY 40601
P: (502) 564-4240
E: william.landrum@ky.gov

LOUISIANA
Mr. Jay Dardenne
Commissioner of Administration
Division of Administration
1201 North Third Street, Suite 7-210
Baton Rouge, LA 70802
P: (225) 342-7000
E: Jay.Dardenne@la.gov

MAINE
Mr. Richard W. Rosen
Commissioner
Department of Administration & Financial Services
78 State House Station
Augusta, ME 04333
P: (207) 624-7800
F: (207) 624-7804
E: richard.rosen@maine.gov

MARYLAND
Mr. Ellington E. Churchill Jr.
Cabinet Secretary
Department of General Services
301 West Preston Street, Room 1401
Baltimore, MD 21201
P: (410) 767-4960
E: ellington.churchill2
@maryland.gov

MASSACHUSETTS
Ms. Kristen Lepore
Secretary
Executive Office for Administration & Finance
State House, Room 373
Boston, MA 02133
P: (617) 727-2040
F: (617) 727-2779
E: kristen.lepore
@state.ma.us

MICHIGAN
Mr. David Behen
Director
Department of Technology, Management & Budget
320 South Walnut Street, 2nd Floor
P.O. Box 30026
Lansing, MI 48909
P: (517) 373-1004
E: behend@michigan.gov

MINNESOTA
Mr. Matt Massman
Commissioner
Department of Administration
116 Veterans Service Building
20 West 12 Street
St. Paul, MN 55155
P: (651) 201-3421
F: (651) 297-7909
E: Matt.Massman@state.mn.us

MISSISSIPPI
Ms. Laura Jackson
Executive Director
Department of Finance & Administration
501 North West, 701 Woolfolk Building
P.O. Box 267
Jackson, MS 39205
P: (601) 359-3402
F: (601) 359-5525
E: laura.jackson@dfa.ms.gov

MISSOURI
Ms. Sarah Steelman
Commissioner
Office of Administration
201 West Capitol Avenue, Room 125
P.O. Box 809
Jefferson City, MO 65102
P: (573) 751-1851
E: sarah.steelman@oa.mo.gov

MONTANA
Mr. John Lewis
Director
Department of Administration
125 North Roberts Street, Room 155
P.O. Box 200101
Helena, MT 59620
P: (406) 444-3033
F: (406) 444-6194
E: johnlewis@mt.gov

NEBRASKA
Mr. Byron L. Diamond
Director
Department of Administrative Services
1526 K Street, Suite 250
Lincoln, NE 68508
P: (402) 471-2331
E: byron.diamond@nebraska.gov

NEVADA
Mr. Patrick Cates
Director
Department of Administration
515 East Musser Street
Room 300
Carson City, NV 89701
P: (775) 684-0294
F: (775) 684-0260
E: pcates@admin.nv.gov

NEW HAMPSHIRE
Ms. Vicki Quiram
Commissioner
Department of Administrative Services
25 Capitol Street
State House Annex, Room 120
Concord, NH 03301
P: (603) 271-3201
F: (603) 271-6600
E: vicki.quiram@nh.gov

NEW JERSEY
Mr. Michael Tyger
Acting Director
Division of Administration
Department of the Treasury
P.O. Box 221
Trenton, NJ 08625
P: (609) 633-2826
E: michael.tyger@treasury.nj.gov

NEW MEXICO
Mr. Ed Burckle
Cabinet Secretary
General Services Department
P.O. Box 6850
Santa Fe, NM 87502
P: (505) 827-2000
E: ed.burckle@state.nm.us

NEW YORK
Ms. RoAnn M. Destito
Commissioner
Office of General Services
41st Floor, Corning Tower
Empire State Plaza
Albany, NY 12242
P: (518) 474-3899
E: roann.destito@ogs.ny.gov

NORTH CAROLINA
Ms. Machelle Sanders
Secretary
Department of Administration
116 West Jones Street, Suite 5106
MSC 1301
Raleigh, NC 27699
P: (919) 807-2425
E: machelle.sanders@doa.nc.gov

NORTH DAKOTA
Ms. Pam Sharp
Director
Office of Management & Budget
600 East Boulevard Avenue
Department 110
Bismarck, ND 58505
P: (701) 328-4606
F: (701) 328-3230
E: psharp@nd.gov

OHIO
Mr. Robert Blair
Director
Department of Administrative Services
30 East Broad Street, 40th Floor
Columbus, OH 43215
P: (614) 466-6511
F: (614) 644-8151
E: jackie.murray@das.ohio.gov

OKLAHOMA
Mr. Dan Ross
Administrator
Capital Assets Management
Will Rogers Office Building
2401 North Lincoln Boulevard, Suite 206
Oklahoma City, OK 73105
P: (405) 521-2124
F: (405) 521-6873
E: dan.ross@omes.ok.gov

OREGON
Ms. Katy Coba
Chief Operating Officer
Department of Administrative Services
155 Cottage Street, Northeast
Salem, OR 97301
P: (503) 373-0914
E: katy.m.coba@oregon.gov

PENNSYLVANIA
Ms. Sharon Minnich
Secretary
Governor's Office of Administration
207 Finance Building
Harrisburg, PA 17102
P: (717) 783-0247
E: sminnich@pa.gov

RHODE ISLAND
Mr. Michael DiBiase
Director
Department of Administration
One Capitol Hill
Providence, RI 02908
P: (401) 222-2280
E: michael.dibiase@doa.ri.gov

SOUTH CAROLINA
Ms. Marcia S. Adams
Executive Director
Department of Administration
1200 Senate Street, Suite 600
Columbia, SC 29201
P: (803) 734-8120
F: (803) 734-2117
E: marcia.adams@admin.sc.gov

SOUTH DAKOTA
Mr. Scott Bollinger
Commissioner
Bureau of Administration
320 North Nicollet
C/o 500 East Capital Avenue
Pierre, SD 57501
P: (605) 773-3688
E: scott.bollinger@state.sd.us

TENNESSEE
Mr. Bob Oglesby
Commissioner
Department of General Services
22nd Floor, 312 8th Avenue, North
Nashville, TN 37243
P: (615) 741-2081
E: bob.oglesby@tn.gov

TEXAS
Mr. Harvey Hilderbran
Executive Director
Facilities Commission
1711 San Jacinto
Austin, TX 78701
P: (512) 463-3446
E: Harvey.Hilderbran@tfc.state.tx.us

UTAH
Ms. Tani Pack Downing
Executive Director
Department of Administrative Services
350 North State Street
Salt Lake City, UT 84114
P: (801) 538-3010
E: tdowning@utah.gov

VERMONT
Ms. Susanne Young
Secretary of Administration
Agency of Administration
109 State Street
Montpelier, VT 05609
P: (802) 828-3322
E: susanne.young@vermont.gov

Administration

VIRGINIA
Mr. Christopher L. Beschler
Director
Department of General Services
1100 Bank Street, Suite 420
Richmond, VA 23219
P: (804) 786-3311
E: christopher.beschler
@dgs.virginia.gov

WASHINGTON
Mr. Christopher Liu
Director
Department of Enterprise
Services
P.O. Box 41401
Olympia, WA 98504
P: (360) 407-9201
E: chris.liu@des.wa.gov

WEST VIRGINIA
Mr. John Myers
Acting Director
Department of Administration
1900 Kanawha Boulevard East,
Building 1
Room E-119
Charleston, WV 25305
P: (304) 558-4331
E: john.a.myers@wv.gov

WISCONSIN
Mr. Scott Neitzel
Secretary
Department of Administration
10th Floor, 101 East Wilson
Street
Madison, WI 53703
P: (608) 266-1741
E: scott.neitzel
@wisconsin.gov

WYOMING
Mr. Dean Fausset
Director
Department of Administration &
Information
2001 Capitol Avenue
Cheyenne, WY 82002
P: (307) 777-6414
F: (307) 777-3633
E: dean.fausset@wyo.gov

Aging

Develops and strengthens services for the aged and conducts or promotes research into their problems.

ALABAMA
Mr. Neal Morrison
Commissioner
Department of Senior Services
201 Monroe Street, Suite 350
P.O. Box 301851
Montgomery, AL 36130
P: (334) 242-4985
F: (334) 242-5594

ALASKA
Mr. Duane Mayes
Director
Senior & Disabilities Services
Department of Health & Social Services
550 West 8th Street
Anchorage, AK 99501
P: (907) 269-2083
F: (907) 269-3688
E: duane.mayes@alaska.gov

AMERICAN SAMOA
Ale Tifimalae
Chief
Territorial Administration on Aging
American Samoa Government
Pago Pago, AS 96799
P: (684) 633-1251
F: (684) 633-2533

ARIZONA
Mr. Charles Shipman
Interim Assistant Director
Division of Aging & Adult Services
Department of Economic Security
1789 West Jefferson, (S/C 001A)
Phoenix, AZ 85007
P: (602) 542-4446
F: (602) 542-6575

ARKANSAS
Mr. Craig Cloud
Director, Division of Aging and Adult Services
Department of Human Services
700 Main Street, 5th Floor, S530
P.O. Box 1437, Slot S530
Little Rock, AR 72203
P: (501) 682-2441
F: (501) 682-8155

CALIFORNIA
Ms. Lora Connolly
Director
Department of Aging
1300 National Drive, #200
Sacramento, CA 95834
P: (916) 419-7500
F: (916) 928-2267
E: lconnoll@aging.ca.gov

COLORADO
Mr. Todd Coffey
Acting Director
Commission on Aging
Department of Human Services
1575 Sherman Street, 10th Floor
Denver, CO 80203
P: (303) 866-2750
F: (303) 866-2696
E: Todd.Coffey@state.co.us

CONNECTICUT
Ms. Elizabeth B. Ritter
Commissioner
State Department on Aging
Department of Social Services
55 Farmington Avenue, 12th Floor
Hartford, CT 06106
P: (860) 424-5992
F: (860) 424-5301
E: Elizabeth.Ritter
@cga.ct.gov

DELAWARE
Mr. Al Griffth
Acting Director
Division of Services for Aging & Adults with Physical Disabilities
1901 North DuPont Highway
New Castle, DE 19720
P: (302) 255-9351
F: (302) 255-9354
E: al.griffith@state.de.us

DISTRICT OF COLUMBIA
Ms. Laura Newland
Director
Office on Aging
500 K Street, Northeast
Washington, DC 20002
P: (202) 724-5622
F: (202) 724-4979

FLORIDA
Mr. Jeffrey Bragg
Secretary
Department of Elder Affairs
4040 Esplanade Way, Suite 315
Tallahassee, FL 32399
P: (850) 414-2000
F: (850) 414-2004

GEORGIA
Ms. Abby Cox
Director
Division of Aging Services
Department of Human Services
2 Peachtree Street, Northwest, 9th Floor
Atlanta, GA 30303
P: (404) 657-5258
F: (404) 657-5285

GUAM
Mr. Arthur U. San Agustin
Senior Citizens Administrator, Division of Senior Citizens
Department of Public Health & Social Services
130 University Drive, Suite 8
University Castle Mall
Mangilao, GU 96913
P: (671) 735-7011
F: (671) 735-7316
E: chiefdsc
@dphss.govguam.net

HAWAII
Ms. Terri Byers
Director
Executive Office on Aging
No. 1 Capitol District
250 South Hotel Street, Suite 406
Honolulu, HI 96813
P: (808) 586-0100
F: (808) 586-0185

IDAHO
Mr. Judy Taylor
Administrator
Commission on Aging
341 West Washington, 3rd Floor
P.O. Box 83720
Boise, ID 83720
P: (208) 334-3833 Ext. 226
F: (208) 334-3033

ILLINOIS
Ms. Jean Bohnoff
Director
Department on Aging
One Natural Resources Way, Suite 100
Springfield, IL 62702
P: (217) 785-2870
F: (217) 785-4477

INDIANA
Ms. Yonda Synder
Director, Division of Aging
Family & Social Services Administration
402 West Washington Street
P.O. Box 7083
Indianapolis, IN 46207
P: (317) 232-7123
F: (307) 232-7867

IOWA
Ms. Linda J. Miller
Director
Department of Aging
Jessie Parker Building
510 East 12th Street, Suite 2
Des Moines, IA 50319
P: (515) 725-3301
F: (515) 725-3300

KANSAS
Mr. Tim Keck
Secretary
Department for Aging & Disability Services
New England Building
503 South Kansas Avenue
Topeka, KS 66603
P: (785) 296-4986
F: (785) 296-0256
E: tim.keck@kdads.ks.gov

KENTUCKY
Ms. Lala Williams
Deputy Commissioner
Department for Aging & Independent Living
Cabinet for Health & Family Services
275 East Main Street, 3E-E
Frankfort, KY 40621
P: (502) 564-6930
F: (502) 564-4595

LOUISIANA
Ms. Karen Ryder
Assistant Director
Governor's Office of Elderly Affairs
525 Florida, 4th Floor
Baton Rouge, LA 70801
P: (225) 342-7100
F: (225) 342-7133

MAINE
Mr. Daniel Sylvester
Director
Office of Aging & Disability Services
Department Health & Human Services
41 Anthony Avenue
Augusta, ME 04333
P: (207) 287-9200
E: daniel.sylvester
@maine.gov

MARYLAND
Ms. Rona E. Kramer
Secretary
Department of Aging
301 West Preston Street, Suite 1007
Baltimore, MD 21201
P: (410) 767-1100
F: (410) 333-7943

Aging

MASSACHUSETTS
Ms. Alice Bonner
Secretary
Executive Office of Elder Affairs
One Ashburton Place
Boston, MA 02108
P: (617) 222-7417
F: (617) 727-9368

MICHIGAN
Mr. Richard Kline
Acting Director
Office of Services to the Aging
300 East Michigan Avenue, 3rd Floor
Lansing, MI 48913
P: (517) 373-8230
F: (517) 373-4092

MINNESOTA
Ms. Kari Benson
Director
Board on Aging
Department of Human Services
P.O. Box 64976
St. Paul, MN 55164
P: (651) 431-2500

MISSISSIPPI
Ms. Sandra McClendon
Director
Division of Aging & Adult Services
Department of Human Services
750 North State Street
Jackson, MS 39202
P: (601) 359-4929
F: (601) 359-4370

MISSOURI
Ms. Celesta Hartgraves
Director
Division of Senior & Disability Services
Department of Health & Senior Services
P.O. Box 570
Jefferson City, MO 65102
P: (573) 526-3626
F: (573) 751-8687

MONTANA
Mr. Charles Rehbein
Aging Services Bureau Chief, Office on Aging
Senior & Long Term Care Division
Public Health & Human Services
111 Sanders Street, P.O. Box 4210
Helena, MT 59604
P: (406) 444-7788
F: (406) 444-7743
E: crehbein@mt.gov

NEBRASKA
Ms. Cynthia Brammeier
Administrator
State Unit on Aging, State Health & Human Services
301 Centennial Mall, South
P.O. Box 95026
Lincoln, NE 68509
P: (402) 471-4624
F: (402) 471-4619

NEVADA
Mr. Eddie Ableser
Administrator
Aging & Disability Services Division
3416 Goni Road, Building D, Suite 132
Carson City, NV 89706
P: (775) 301-0904
F: (775) 687-4264
E: edwardableser@adsd.nv.gov

NEW HAMPSHIRE
Ms. Sheri Rockburn
Acting Associate Commissioner
Department of Health & Human Services
Brown Building
129 Pleasant Street
Concord, NH 03301

NEW JERSEY
Ms. Laura Otterbourg
Director
Division of Aging Services
222 South Warren Street
P.O. Box 700
Trenton, NJ 08625
P: (609) 292-9265
F: (609) 292-3824

NEW MEXICO
Mr. Myles Copeland
Secretary
Aging & Long-Term Services Department
2550 Cerrillos Road
Santa Fe, NM 87505
P: (505) 476-4799
F: (505) 476-4750

NEW YORK
Mr. Greg Olsen
Acting Director
State Office for the Aging
Two Empire State Plaza
Albany, NY 12223
P: (518) 474-7012
F: (518) 474-1398

NORTH CAROLINA
Ms. Suzanne Merrill
Director
Division of Aging & Adult Services
Department of Health & Human Services
2101 Mail Service Center, 693 Palmer Dr.
Raleigh, NC 27699
P: (919) 855-3400
F: (919) 733-0443

NORTH DAKOTA
Ms. Nancy Nikolas-Maier
Director
Aging Services Division
Department of Human Services
1237 West Divide Avenue, Suite 6
Bismarck, ND 58501
P: (701) 328-4607
F: (701) 328-8744

NORTHERN MARIANA ISLANDS
Mr. Melvin Faiao
Acting Director
Commonwealth of the Northern Mariana Islands
Office on Aging
P.O. Box 502178
Saipan, MP 96950
P: (670) 233-1320
F: (670) 233-1327

OHIO
Ms. Stephanie Loucka
Director
Department of Aging
246 North High Street, 1st Floor
Columbus, OH 43215
P: (614) 466-1055
F: (614) 995-1049

OKLAHOMA
Mr. Lance A. Robertson
Director
Aging Services Division
Department of Human Services
2401 Northwest 23rd Street, Suite 40
Oklahoma City, OK 73107
P: (405) 521-2281
F: (405) 521-5805
E: lance.robertson@okdhs.org

OREGON
Ms. Ashley Carson-Cottingham
Director
Aging & People with Disabilities Program
Department of Human Services
500 Summer Street, Northeast, E12
Salem, OR 97301
P: (503) 945-5858
F: (503) 373-7823

PENNSYLVANIA
Ms. Teresa Osborne
Secretary
Department of Aging
555 Walnut Street, 5th Floor
Harrisburg, PA 17101
P: (717) 783-6128
F: (717) 783-6842

PUERTO RICO
Dr. Carmen Delia Sanchez Salgado
Ombudsman
Office for Elderly Affairs
P.O. Box 191179
San Juan, PR 00919
P: (787) 721-6121
F: (787) 725-2919

RHODE ISLAND
Mr. Charles J. Fogarty
Director
Division of Elderly Affairs
Hazard Building, #74
35 Howard Avenue
Cranston, RI 02920
P: (401) 462-0565
F: (401) 462-0503

SOUTH CAROLINA
Mr. Darryl Broome
Director
Office of Aging
Department of Health & Human Services
1301 Gervais Street
Columbia, SC 29201
P: (803) 734-9900
F: (803) 734-9886

Ms. Lisa Osvold
Senior Administrator
Aging Division
Department of Health
6101 Yellowstone Road, Suite 186
Cheyenne, SC 82001
P: (307) 777-7995
F: (307) 777-5340

SOUTH DAKOTA
Ms. Beth Dokken
Deputy Division Director
Office of Adult Services & Aging
Department of Social Services
700 Governors Drive
Pierre, SD 57501
P: (605) 773-3656
F: (605) 773-6834

TENNESSEE
Mr. Jim Shulman
Executive Director
Commission on Aging & Disability
Andrew Jackson Building
500 Deaderick Street, Suite 825
Nashville, TN 37243
P: (615) 741-2056 Ext. 134
F: (615) 741-3309
E: jim.shulman@tn.gov

TEXAS
Mr. Jon Weizenbaum
Commissioner
Department of Aging & Disability Services
701 West 51st Street
P.O. Box 149030
Austin, TX 78714
P: (512) 438-3011
F: (512) 438-3011

U.S. VIRGIN ISLANDS
Mr. Felicia Blyden
Commissioner
Department of Human Services
3011 Golden Rock
Christiansted
St. Croix, VI 00802
P: (340) 718-2980

UTAH
Mr. Nels Holmgren
Director
Division of Aging & Adult Services
Department of Human Services
195 North 1950 West, 3rd Floor
Salt Lake City, UT 84116
P: (801) 538-3921
F: (801) 538-4395
E: nholmgren@utah.gov

VERMONT
Ms. Monica Caserta Hutt
Commissioner
Department of Disabilities, Aging & Independent Living
Weeks Building
103 South Main Street
Waterbury, VT 05676
P: (802) 871-3350
F: (802) 871-3281

VIRGINIA
Mr. James Rothrock
Commissioner
Department for Aging & Rehabilitative Services
8004 Franklin Farms Drive
Henrico, VA 23229
P: (804) 662-7010
F: (804) 662-7644

WASHINGTON
Mr. Bill Moss
Acting Secretary
Department of Social & Health Services
1115 Washington Street, Southeast
Olympia, WA 98504
P: (800) 737-0617
F: (360) 407-0304

WEST VIRGINIA
Mr. Robert Roswall
Commissioner
Bureau of Senior Services
3003 Town Center Mall
1900 Kanawha Boulevard, East
Charleston, WV 25305
P: (304) 558-3317
F: (304) 558-5609

WISCONSIN
Ms. Carrie Molke
Director, Bureau on Aging & Disability Resources
Department of Health Services
One West Wilson Street, Room 551
P.O. Box 7851
Madison, WI 53707
P: (608) 267-5267
F: (608) 267-3203

Agriculture

Enforces agriculture laws and administers agricultural programs in the state.

ALABAMA
The Honorable John McMillan (R)
Commissioner
Department of Agriculture & Industries
Richard Beard Building
1445 Federal Drive
Montgomery, AL 36107
P: (334) 240-7100
F: (334) 240-7190

ALASKA
Mr. Arthur J. Keyes IV
Director
Division of Agriculture
Department of Natural Resources
1800 Glenn Highway, Suite 12
Palmer, AK 99645
P: (907) 761-3867
F: (907) 745-7112
E: Arthur.Keyes@alaska.gov

AMERICAN SAMOA
Ms. Lealao Purcell
Director
Department of Agriculture
American Samoa Government
Industrial Parkway
Tafuna, AS 96779
P: (684) 699-9272

ARIZONA
Mr. Mark W. Killian
Director
Department of Agriculture
1688 West Adams
Phoenix, AZ 85007
P: (602) 542-5729
F: (602) 542-5420

ARKANSAS
Mr. Wes Ward
Secretary of Agriculture
Agriculture Department
1 Natural Resources Drive
Little Rock, AR 72205
P: (501) 683-4851
F: (501) 683-4852

CALIFORNIA
Ms. Karen Ross
Secretary
Department of Food & Agriculture
1220 N Street, Suite 400
Sacramento, CA 95814
P: (916) 654-0433
F: (916) 654-0403

COLORADO
Mr. Don Brown
Commissioner
Department of Agriculture
305 Interlocken Parkway
Broomfield, CO 80021
P: (303) 869-9000
F: (303) 466-2867

CONNECTICUT
Mr. Steven Reviczky
Commissioner
Department of Agriculture
165 Capitol Avenue
Hartford, CT 06106
P: (860) 713-2501
F: (860) 713-2514

DELAWARE
Mr. Michael T. Scuse
Secretary
Department of Agriculture
2320 South DuPont Highway
Dover, DE 19901
P: (302) 698-4500

FLORIDA
The Honorable Adam H. Putnam (R)
Commissioner
Department of Agriculture & Consumer Services
The Capitol, PL-10
400 South Monroe Street
Tallahassee, FL 32399
P: (850) 488-3022
F: (850) 922-4936

GEORGIA
Mr. Gary Black
Commissioner
Department of Agriculture
19 Martin Luther King Jr. Drive, SW
204 Agricultural Building
Atlanta, GA 30334
P: (404) 656-3600
F: (404) 651-8206

GUAM
Ms. Mariquita F. Taitague
Director
Department of Agriculture
163 Dairy Road
Mangilao, GU 96913
P: (671) 734-3942
F: (671) 734-6569

HAWAII
Mr. Scott Enright
Chairperson
Department of Agriculture
1428 South King Street
Honolulu, HI 96814
P: (808) 973-9560
F: (808) 973-9613

IDAHO
Ms. Celia R. Gould
Director
State Department of Agriculture
2270 Old Penitentiary Road
P.O. Box 790
Boise, ID 83701
P: (208) 332-8500
F: (208) 332-2170

INDIANA
Mr. Ted McKinney
Director
State Department of Agriculture
One North Capitol Avenue
Suite 600
Indianapolis, IN 46204
P: (317) 232-8770
F: (317) 232-1362

IOWA
Mr. Bill Northey
Secretary of Agriculture
Department of Agriculture & Land Stewardship
Wallace Building
502 East 9th Street
Des Moines, IA 50319
P: (515) 281-5321
F: (515) 281-6236

KANSAS
Ms. Jackie McClaskey
Secretary
Department of Agriculture
1320 Research Park Drive
Manhattan, KS 66502
P: (785) 564-6700
F: (785) 564-6777

KENTUCKY
The Honorable Ryan Quarles (R)
Commissioner of Agriculture
Department of Agriculture
105 Corporate Drive, Suite A
Frankfort, KY 40601
P: (502) 573-0282
F: (502) 573-0046
E: ag.web@ky.gov

LOUISIANA
Dr. Michael G. Strain
Commissioner
Department of Agriculture & Forestry
5825 Florida Boulevard, Suite 2000
Baton Rouge, LA 70806
P: (225) 922-1234
F: (225) 923-4880
E: commissioner@ldaf.state.la.us

MAINE
Mr. Walter E. Whitcomb
Commissioner
Department of Agriculture, Conservation & Forestry
Harlow Building - AMHI Complex
28 State House Station
Augusta, ME 04333
P: (207) 287-3419
F: (207) 287-7548
E: dacf@maine.gov

MARYLAND
Mr. Joe Bartenfelder
Secretary
Department of Agriculture
50 Harry S. Truman Parkway
Annapolis, MD 21401
P: (410) 841-5880
F: (410) 841-5914
E: joe.bartenfelder@maryland.gov

MASSACHUSETTS
Mr. John Lebeaux
Commissioner
Department of Agricultural Resources
251 Causeway Street, Suite 500
Boston, MA 02114
P: (617) 626-1720
F: (617) 626-1850

MICHIGAN
Ms. Jamie Clover Adams
Director
Department of Agriculture & Rural Development
525 West Allegan Street
P.O. Box 30017
Lansing, MI 48909
P: (517) 284-5716
F: (517) 335-1423

MINNESOTA
Mr. Dave Frederickson
Commissioner
Department of Agriculture
Freeman Office Building
625 Robert Street North
St. Paul, MN 55155
P: (651) 201-6219
F: (651) 201-6118

MISSISSIPPI
The Honorable Cindy Hyde-Smith (R)
Commissioner
Department of Agriculture & Commerce
121 North Jefferson Street
Jackson, MS 39201
P: (601) 359-1100
F: (601) 354-7710

MISSOURI
Mr. Chris Chinn
Director
Department of Agriculture
1616 Missouri Boulevard
P.O. Box 630
Jefferson City, MO 65102
P: (573) 751-5617

MONTANA
Mr. Anson Tebbetts
Secretary
Department of Agriculture, Food & Markets
116 State Street
Montpelier, MT 05620
P: (802) 828-2430

Mr. Ben Thomas
Director
Department of Agriculture
302 North Roberts
Helena, MT 59620
P: (406) 444-3144
E: agr@mt.gov

NEBRASKA
Mr. Greg Ibach
Director
Department of Agriculture
301 Centennial Mall South
P.O. Box 94947
Lincoln, NE 68509
P: (402) 471-2341
F: (402) 471-6876

NEVADA
Mr. Jim Barbee
Director
Department of Agriculture
405 South 21st Street
Sparks, NV 89431
P: (775) 353-3600
F: (775) 668-1178

NEW HAMPSHIRE
Ms. Lorraine Merrill
Commissioner
Department of Agriculture, Markets & Food
P.O. Box 2042
Concord, NH 03302
P: (603) 271-3551
F: (603) 271-1109

NEW JERSEY
Mr. Douglas H. Fisher
Secretary of Agriculture
Department of Agriculture
P.O. Box 330
John Fitch Plaza
Trenton, NJ 08625
P: (609) 292-3976
F: (609) 292-3978

NEW MEXICO
Mr. Jeff Witte
Director/Secretary
Department of Agriculture
MSC 3189
P.O. Box 30005
Las Cruces, NM 88003
P: (575) 646-3007
F: (575) 646-8120

NEW YORK
Mr. Richard A. Ball
Commissioner
Department of Agriculture & Markets
10B Airline Drive
Albany, NY 12235
P: (518) 457-2771
F: (518) 457-3087

NORTH CAROLINA
Mr. Steve Troxler
Commissioner
Department of Agriculture & Consumer Services
1001 Mail Service Center
Raleigh, NC 27699
P: (919) 707-3000
F: (919) 733-1141

NORTH DAKOTA
Mr. Doug Goehring
Commissioner
Department of Agriculture
600 East Boulevard Avenue
Department 602
Bismarck, ND 58505
P: (701) 328-2231
F: (701) 328-4567
E: ndda@nd.gov

OHIO
Mr. David Daniels
Director
Department of Agriculture
8995 East Main Street
Reynoldsburg, OH 43068
P: (614) 466-2732
F: (614) 466-6124

OKLAHOMA
Mr. Jim Reese
Secretary
Department of Agriculture, Food & Forestry
2800 North Lincoln Boulevard
Oklahoma City, OK 73105
P: (405) 522-5719
F: (405) 522-0909

OREGON
Ms. Alexis Taylor
Director
Department of Agriculture
635 Capitol Street, Northeast
Salem, OR 97301
P: (503) 986-4552

PENNSYLVANIA
Mr. Russell Redding
Secretary
Department of Agriculture
2301 North Cameron Street
Harrisburg, PA 17110
P: (717) 772-2853
F: (717) 705-8402

PUERTO RICO
Mr. Carlos A. Flores Ortega
Secretary
Department of Agriculture
1309 Ave. Fernandez Juncos
Pda. 19 1/2
San Jaun, PR 00908
P: (787) 722-0871

RHODE ISLAND
Mr. Kenneth Ayars
Chief
Division of Agriculture
Department of Environmental Management
235 Promenade Street, Room 370
Providence, RI 02908
P: (401) 222-2781 Ext. 4500
F: (401) 222-6047

SOUTH CAROLINA
Mr. Hugh E. Weathers
Commissioner
Department of Agriculture
Wade Hampton Office Building
P.O. Box 11280
Columbia, SC 29211
P: (803) 734-2179
F: (803) 734-2192

SOUTH DAKOTA
Mr. Michael Jaspers
Secretary
Department of Agriculture
523 East Capitol
Pierre, SD 57501
P: (605) 773-5425

TENNESSEE
Mr. Jai Templeton
Commissioner
Department of Agriculture
Melrose Station
P.O. Box 40627
Nashville, TN 37204
P: (615) 837-5100
F: (615) 837-5333

TEXAS
The Honorable Sid Miller (R)
Commissioner
Department of Agriculture
P.O. Box 12847
Capitol Station
Austin, TX 78711
P: (512) 463-7567
F: (512) 463-1104

U.S. VIRGIN ISLANDS
Mr. Carlos A. Robles
Commissioner
Department of Agriculture
#1 Estate Lower Love Kingshill
St. Croix, VI 00850
P: (340) 778-0991

UTAH
Ms. LuAnn Adams
Commissioner
Department of Agriculture & Food
350 North Redwood Road
P.O. Box 146500
Salt Lake City, UT 84114
P: (801) 538-7100
F: (801) 538-7126

VIRGINIA
Ms. Sandy Adams
Commissioner
Department of Agriculture & Consumer Services
102 Governor Street
Richmond, VA 23219
P: (804) 786-3501
F: (804) 371-2945

WASHINGTON
Mr. Derek Sandison
Director
State Department of Agriculture
1111 Washington Street, Southeast
P.O. Box 42560
Olympia, WA 98504
P: (360) 902-1887
F: (360) 902-2092

Agriculture

WEST VIRGINIA
The Honorable Kent
Leonhardt (R)
Commissioner
Department of Agriculture
1900 Kanawha Boulevard, East
State Capitol, Room E-28
Charleston, WV 25305
P: (304) 558-3550
F: (304) 558-2203

WISCONSIN
Mr. Ben Brancel
Secretary
Department of Agriculture,
Trade & Consumer Protection
2811 Agriculture Drive
P.O. Box 8911
Madison, WI 53708
P: (608) 224-5012
F: (608) 224-5045

WYOMING
Mr. Doug Miyamoto
Director
Department of Agriculture
2219 Carey Avenue
Cheyenne, WY 82002
P: (307) 777-6569
F: (307) 777-6593

Alcohol and Substance Abuse

Plans, establishes and administers programs for the prevention, treatment, and rehabilitation of alcohol and/or drug and other abusers.

ALABAMA
Ms. Diane Baugher
Associate Commissioner
Division of Mental Health & Substance Abuse Services
100 North Union Street
P.O. Box 301410
Montgomery, AL 36130
P: (334) 242-3454
F: (334) 242-0725

ALASKA
Mr. Randall Burns
Director
Division of Behavioral Health
Department of Health & Social Services
3601 C Street, Suite 878
Anchorage, AK 99503
P: (907) 269-3600
F: (907) 269-3623
E: randall.burns@alaska.gov

AMERICAN SAMOA
Dr. Taeaoafua Meki Solomona
Director
Department of Human & Social Services
P.O. Box 997534
Pago Pago, AS 96799
P: (684) 633-1664
F: (684) 633-7449
E: mtsolomona@dhss.as

ARIZONA
Dr. Cara M. Christ
Director
Department of Health Services
150 North 18th Avenue
Phoenix, AZ 85007
P: (602) 542-1025
F: (602) 542-0833

ARKANSAS
Ms. Paula Stone
Interim Director
Division of Behavioral Health Services
305 South Palm Street
Little Rock, AR 72205
P: (501) 686-9981
F: (501) 686-9182
E: paula.stone
@dhs.arkansas.gov

CALIFORNIA
Ms. Karen Baylor
Deputy Director
Mental Health & Substance Use Disorder Services
Department of Health Care Services
P.O. Box 997413
Sacramento, CA 95899
P: (916) 440-7800
F: (916) 440-7404
E: karen.baylor@dhcs.ca.gov

COLORADO
Dr. Nancy VanDeMark
Director
Office of Behavioral Health
Department of Human Services
1575 Sherman Street, 8th Floor
Denver, CO 80203
P: (303) 866-5700
F: (303) 866-5563
E: nancy.vandemark
@state.co.us

CONNECTICUT
Dr. Miriam E. Delphin-Rittmon
Commissioner
Department of Mental Health & Addiction Services
410 Capitol Avenue
P.O. Box 341431
Hartford, CT 06134
P: (860) 418-6676
F: (860) 418-6691
E: Miriam.delphin-rittmon
@ct.gov

DELAWARE
Dr. Michael A. Barbieri
Director, Division of Substance Abuse & Mental Health
Department of Health & Social Services
1901 North DuPont Highway
Main Building
New Castle, DE 19720
P: (302) 255-9399
F: (302) 255-4427
E: michael.barbieri
@state.de.us

DISTRICT OF COLUMBIA
Dr. Tanya Royster
Director
Department of Behavioral Health
64 New York Avenue, Northeast
Washington, DC 20002
P: (202) 673-2246
E: tanya.royster@dc.gov

FLORIDA
Mr. Mike Carroll
Secretary
Department of Children & Families
1317 Winewood Boulevard
Building 1, Room 202
Tallahassee, FL 32399
P: (850) 487-1111
F: (850) 922-2993
E: mike.carroll
@myflfamilies.com

GEORGIA
Ms. Judy Fitzgerald
Commissioner
Department of Behavioral Health & Developmental Disabilities
2 Peachtree Street, Northwest
Suite 24.290
Atlanta, GA 30303
P: (404) 463-7945
F: (770) 408-5480
E: judy.fitzgerald
@dbhdd.ga.gov

GUAM
Mr. Rey Vega
Director
Department of Mental Health & Substance Abuse
790 Gov. Carlos Camancho Road
Tamuing, GU 96913
P: (671) 647-1901
F: (671) 647-6948
E: rey.vega
@mail.dmhsa.guam.gov

IDAHO
Mr. Ross Edmunds
Administrator
Division of Behavioral Health
Department of Health & Welfare
450 West State Street
Boise, ID 83720
P: (208) 334-5726
F: (208) 334-5998
E: edmundsr@dhw.idaho.gov

ILLINOIS
Mr. James T. Dimas
Secretary
Department of Human Services
100 South Grand Avenue, 3rd Floor
Springfield, IL 62702
P: (217) 557-2134
F: (217) 557-1647

INDIANA
Mr. Kevin Moore
Director
Division of Mental Health & Addiction
Family & Social Services Administration
402 West Washington Street, Room W353
Indianapolis, IN 46204
P: (317) 232-7860
F: (317) 233-1986
E: kevin.moore@fssa.in.gov

IOWA
Ms. Brenda Dobson
Interim Division Director
Health Promotion & Chronic Disease Prevention
Lucas State Office Building
321 East 12th Street
Des Moines, IA 50319
P: (515) 281-7769
F: (515) 281-4958
E: brenda.dobson
@idph.iowa.gov

KANSAS
Ms. Susan Fout
Commissioner
Behavioral Health Services
Aging & Disability Services
503 South Kansas Avenue
Topeka, KS 66603
P: (785) 368-7338
E: susan.fout@ks.gov

LOUISIANA
Dr. James Hussey
Assistant Secretary/Medical Director; MH Commissioner
Office of Behavioral Health
Department of Health
P.O. Box 629
Baton Rouge, LA 70821
P: (225) 342-8916
F: (225) 342-3875
E: James.Hussey@LA.gov

MAINE
Mr. Sheldon Wheeler
Director
Office of Substance Abuse & Mental Health Services
Department of Health & Human Services
41 Anthony Avenue
Augusta, ME 04333
P: (207) 287-2595
F: (207) 287-4334
E: Sheldon.wheeler
@maine.gov

Alcohol and Substance Abuse

MARYLAND
Dr. Barbara Bazron
Executive Director
Behavioral Health Administration, Department of Health & Mental Hygiene
Spring Grove Hospital Center
Dix Building, 55 Wade Avenue
Catonsville, MD 21228
P: (410) 402-8452
F: (410) 402-8441
E: barbara.bazron@maryland.gov

MASSACHUSETTS
Ms. Allison Bauer
Director of Substance Abuse Services
Department of Public Health
Office of Health & Human Services
250 Washington Street
Boston, MA 02108
P: (617) 624-5111

MICHIGAN
Ms. Lynda Zeller
Deputy Director
Mental Health & Substance Abuse Administration
Department of Community Health
320 South Walnut Street
Lansing, MI 48913
P: (517) 335-0196
F: (517) 335-4798
E: zellerl2@michigan.gov

MINNESOTA
Mr. Brian Zirbes
Deputy Director
Alcohol & Drug Abuse Division
540 Cedar Street
P.O. Box 64977
St. Paul, MN 55164
P: (651) 431-4928
F: (651) 431-7449
E: Brian.Zirbes@state.mn.us

MISSISSIPPI
Dr. Jerri Avery
Director
Bureau of Alcohol & Drug Services
801 Robert E. Lee Building
239 North Lamar Street
Jackson, MS 39201
P: (601) 359-6220
F: (601) 359-6295

NEBRASKA
Ms. Sheri Dawson
Acting Director
Division of Behavioral Health
Department of Health & Human Services
301 Centennial Mall South, 3rd Floor
Lincoln, NE 68509
P: (402) 471-8553
F: (402) 471-9449
E: sheri.dawson@nebraska.gov

NEVADA
Ms. Cody Phinney
Administrator
Division of Public & Behavioral Health
4150 Technology Way
Carson City, NV 89706
P: (775) 684-4200
F: (775) 684-4211
E: cphinney@health.nv.gov

NEW HAMPSHIRE
Mr. Joseph P. Harding
Director
Bureau of Drug & Alcohol Services
Department of Health & Human Services
105 Pleasant Street
Concord, NH 03301
P: (603) 271-6738
F: (603) 271-6105
E: jharding@dhhs.state.nh.us

NEW JERSEY
Ms. Valerie Mielke
Assistant Commissioner
Division of Mental Health & Addiction Services
Department of Human Services
P.O. Box 700
Trenton, NJ 08625
P: (609) 292-3717
F: (609) 341-2302
E: Valerie.mielke@dhs.state.nj.us

NEW MEXICO
Mr. Brent Earnest
Cabinet Secretary
Human Services Department
P.O. Box 2348
Santa Fe, NM 87504
P: (505) 827-7750
F: (505) 827-6286

NEW YORK
Ms. Arlene Gonzalez-Sanchez
Commissioner
Office of Alcoholism & Substance Abuse Services
1450 Western Avenue
Albany, NY 12203
P: (518) 473-3460
F: (518) 457-5474
E: communications@oasas.ny.gov

NORTH DAKOTA
Ms. Kris Storbeck
Substance Abuse Treatment Administrator
Behavioral Health Division
Department of Human Services
1237 West Divide Avenue, Suite 1C
Bismarck, ND 58501
P: (701) 328-8920
F: (701) 328-8969
E: kstorbeck@nd.gov

NORTHERN MARIANA ISLANDS
Ms. Roxanne P. Diaz
Director
Division of Public Health Services
P.O. Box 500409
Saipan, MP 96950
P: (670) 236-8703
E: chcpublichealth@gmail.com

OHIO
Ms. Tracy J. Plouck
Director
Department of Mental Health & Addiction Services
30 East Broad Street, 36th Floor
Columbus, OH 43215
P: (614) 466-2337
F: (614) 752-9453
E: tracy.plouck@mha.ohio.gov

OKLAHOMA
Ms. Jessica Hawkins
Prevention Services Director
Department of Mental Health & Substance Abuse Services
1200 Northeast 13th Street
P.O. Box 53277
Oklahoma City, OK 73152
P: (405) 522-5952
F: (405) 522-3650
E: Jhawkins@odmhsas.org

OREGON
Dr. Pam Martin
Director
Addictions & Mental Health Division
State Health Authority
500 Summer Street Northeast, E86
Salem, OR 97301
P: (503) 945-5879
F: (503) 378-8467
E: pamela.a.martin@dhsoha.state.or.us

PENNSYLVANIA
Mr. Gary Tennis
Secretary
Department of Drug & Alcohol Programs
Health & Welfare Building, Room 903
Harrisburg, PA 17120
P: (717) 214-1937
F: (717) 214-1939

SOUTH CAROLINA
Ms. Sara Goldsby
Interim Director
Department of Alcohol & Other Drug Abuse Services
1801 Main Street, 4th Floor
P.O. Box 8268
Columbia, SC 29202
P: (803) 896-8371
F: (803) 896-5557
E: sgoldsby@daodas.sc.gov

SOUTH DAKOTA
Ms. Tiffany Wolfgang
Division Director
Division of Behavioral Health Services
Department of Social Services
811 East 10th Street, Department 9
Sioux Falls, SD 57103
P: (605) 367-5078
F: (605) 367-5239
E: Tiffany.Wolfgang@state.sd.us

TENNESSEE
Ms. Marie Williams
Commissioner
Department of Mental Health & Substance Abuse Services
Andrew Jackson Building
Nashville, TN 37243
P: (615) 253-3049
F: (615) 532-6514
E: Marie.Williams@tn.gov

TEXAS
Ms. Lauren Lacefield Lewis
Assistant Commissioner of Mental Health & Substance Abuse
Mental Health & Substance Abuse Services
P.O. Box 149347
Austin, TX 78714
P: (512) 206-5145
F: (512) 206-5306
E: lauren.lacefieldlewis@dshs.state.tx.us

UTAH
Mr. Doug Thomas
Director
Division of Substance Abuse & Mental Health
Department of Human Services
195 North 1950 West
Salt Lake City, UT 84116
P: (801) 538-4298
F: (801) 538-9892
E: dothomas@utah.gov

VERMONT
Ms. Barbara A. Cimaglio
Deputy Commissioner
Department of Health
108 Cherry Street
Burlington, VT 05402
P: (802) 951-1258
F: (802) 863-7425
E: Barbara.Cimaglio@vermont.gov

VIRGINIA
Dr. Jack Barber
Interim Commissioner
Department of Behavioral Health & Developmental Services
1220 Bank Street
P.O. Box 1797
Richmond, VA 23218
P: (804) 786-3921
F: (804) 371-6638
E: jack.barber@dbhds.virginia.gov

WEST VIRGINIA
Mr. Damon Iarossi
Deputy Commissioner
Bureau for Behavioral Health & Health Facilities
Department of Health & Human Resources
350 Capitol Street, Room 350
Charleston, WV 25301
P: (304) 356-4811
F: (304) 558-1008
E: Damon.E.Iarossi@wv.gov

WISCONSIN
Ms. Joyce Allen
Director, Bureau of Prevention Treatment & Recovery
Division of Mental Health & Substance Abuse Services
1 West Wilson Street, Room #850
Madison, WI 53707
P: (608) 266-1351
F: (608) 266-2579
E: joyce.allen@wisconsin.gov

WYOMING
Ms. Chris Newman
Senior Administrator
Behavioral Health Division
Department of Health
6101 Yellowstone Road, Suite 220
Cheyenne, WY 82002
P: (307) 777-6494
F: (307) 777-5849
E: chris.newman@wyo.gov

Alcoholic Beverage Control

Administers and enforces the laws governing the manufacturing, distribution, and dispensing of alcoholic beverages.

ALABAMA
Mr. H. Mac Gipson
Administrator
Alcoholic Beverage Control Board
2715 Gunter Park Drive West
Montgomery, AL 36109
P: (334) 277-0569
F: (334) 277-2150

ALASKA
Ms. Erika McConnell
Director
Alcohol & Marijuana Control Office
State Office Building, 9th Floor
333 Willoughby Avenue
Anchorage, AK 99801
P: (907) 465-2330

ARIZONA
Mr. John Cocca
Director
Department of Liquor Licenses & Control
800 West Washington Street, 5th Floor
Phoenix, AZ 85007
P: (602) 542-9032
F: (602) 542-5707

ARKANSAS
Mr. Boyce Hamlet
Director, ABC Enforcement
Alcoholic Beverage Control Division
1509 West 7th Street
Little Rock, AR 72201
P: (501) 682-8174
F: (501) 682-2221
E: boyce.hamlet@dfa.arkansas.gov

Mr. Bud Roberts
Director, ABC Administration
Alcoholic Beverage Control Division
1509 West 7th Street
Little Rock, AR 72201
P: (501) 682-1105
F: (501) 682-2221
E: ABCAdmin@dfa.state.ar.us

CALIFORNIA
Ms. Ramona Prieto
Acting Director
State Alcoholic Beverage Control
3927 Lennane Drive, Suite 100
Sacramento, CA 95834
P: (916) 419-2512
F: (916) 419-2599
E: ramona.prieto@abc.ca.gov

COLORADO
Mr. Patrick Maroney
Director
Liquor & Tobacco Enforcement Division
Department of Revenue
1881 Pierce Street, Suite 108
Lakewood, CO 80214
P: (303) 205-2934
F: (303) 205-2341

CONNECTICUT
Mr. John Suchy
Director
State Division of Liquor Control
165 Capitol Avenue
Hartford, CT 06106
P: (860) 713-6217
F: (860) 713-7235
E: John.Suchy@ct.gov

DELAWARE
Mr. John H. Cordrey
Commissioner
State Alcoholic Beverage Control
Carvel State Building
820 North French Street
Wilmington, DE 19801
P: (302) 577-5222
F: (302) 577-3204
E: john.cordrey@state.de.us

DISTRICT OF COLUMBIA
Mr. Fred Moosally
Director
Alcoholic Beverage Regulation Administration
2000 14th Street Northwest
Suite 400-South
Washington, DC 20009
P: (202) 442-4355
F: (202) 442-9563
E: abra@dc.gov

FLORIDA
Mr. Thomas Philpot
Director
Division of Alcoholic Beverages & Tobacco
1940 North Monroe Street
Tallahassee, FL 32399
P: (850) 717-1107
F: (850) 922-5175

GEORGIA
Mr. Howard A. Tyler
Director, Alcohol & Tobacco Division
Department of Revenue
1800 Century Center Boulevard, Northeast
Room 4235
Atlanta, GA 30345
P: (404) 417-4902
F: (404) 417-4901
E: atdiv@dor.ga.gov

HAWAII
Mr. Franklin Don Pacarro Jr.
Administrator
Liquor Commission, City & County of Honolulu
711 Kapiolani Boulevard, Suite 600
Honolulu, HI 96813
P: (808) 768-7303
F: (808) 768-7311

Mr. Gerald T. Rapozo
Director
Liquor Control Commission, County of Kauai
4444 Rice Street, Suite 120
Lihue, HI 96766
P: (808) 241-4966
F: (808) 241-6585
E: liquor@kauai.gov

Mr. Gerald Takase
Director
Department of Liquor Control, County of Hawaii
Hilo Lagoon Centre
101 Aupuni Street, Suite 230
Hilo, HI 96720
P: (808) 961-8218
F: (808) 961-8684
E: cohdlc@co.hawaii.hi.us

IDAHO
Mr. Jeffrey R. Anderson
Director
State Liquor Division
1199 Shoreline Lane, Suite 100
P.O. Box 6537
Boise, ID 83707
P: (208) 334-2600
F: (208) 947-9401
E: info@idaholottery.com

Captain Brad Doty
Bureau Chief, ABC
Alcohol Beverage Control
State Police
700 South Stratford Drive, Suite 115
Meridian, ID 83642
P: (208) 884-7062
F: (208) 884-7096

ILLINOIS
Mr. Donvan Borvan
Executive Director
Liquor Control Commission
100 West Randolph Street, Suite 7-801
Chicago, IL 60601
P: (312) 814-1801
F: (312) 814-2241

INDIANA
Mr. David Cook
Chair
Alcohol & Tobacco Commission
302 West Washington Street, Room E114
Indianapolis, IN 46204
P: (317) 232-2462
F: (317) 234-1520

IOWA
Mr. Stephen Larson
Administrator
Alcoholic Beverages Division
1918 Southeast Hulsizer Road
Ankeny, IA 50021
P: (515) 281-7402
F: (515) 281-7372
E: larson@iowabd.com

KANSAS
Ms. Debbi Beavers
Interim Director
Department of Revenue
Docking State Office Building
915 Southwest Harrison, Room 214 North
Topeka, KS 66625
P: (785) 296-3139
F: (785) 296-7185
E: debbi.beavers@kdor.ks.gov

KENTUCKY
Ms. Christine Trout
Commissioner
Department of Alcoholic Beverage Control
1003 Twilight Trail, Suite A-2
Frankfort, KY 40601
P: (502) 564-4850
F: (502) 564-1442
E: christine.trout@ky.gov

LOUISIANA
Ms. Juana Marine-Lombard
Commissioner
Office of Alcohol & Tobacco Control
Department of Revenue
8585 Archives Avenue, Suite 220
Baton Rouge, LA 70809
P: (225) 925-4054
F: (225) 925-3975

MAINE
Mr. Gregg Mineo
Director
State Liquor & Lottery Commission
10 Water Street
Hallowell, ME 04333
P: (207) 287-3721

MARYLAND
The Honorable Peter Franchot (D)
Comptroller
Office of the Comptroller
L.L. Goldstein Treasury Building
80 Calvert Street, P.O. Box 466
Annapolis, MD 21404
P: (410) 260-7801
F: (410) 974-3808
E: mdcomptroller@comp.state.md.us

Mr. Jeffrey A. Kelly
Director
Field Enforcement Division
80 Calvert Street
Annapolis, MD 21404
P: (410) 260-7104
F: (410) 974-5564
E: jakelly@comp.state.md.us

MASSACHUSETTS
Mr. Ralph Sacramone
Executive Director
Alcoholic Beverage Control Commission
239 Causeway Street, First Floor
Boston, MA 02114
P: (617) 727-3040 Ext. 731
F: (617) 727-1510

MICHIGAN
Mr. Andrew J. Deloney
Chair
Liquor Control Commission
525 West Allegan
Lansing, MI 48933
P: (517) 284-6310
F: (517) 763-0057
E: ajdeloney@michigan.gov

MINNESOTA
Ms. Carla Cincotta
Director
Alcohol & Gambling Enforcement Division
445 Minnesota Street, Suite 222
St. Paul, MN 55128
P: (651) 201-7534

MISSISSIPPI
Mr. Herb Frierson
Commissioner
Department of Revenue
P.O. Box 1033
Jackson, MS 39215
P: (601) 923-7000
F: (601) 923-7423

Ms. Patsy Holeman
Director
Alcoholic Beverage Control Division
P.O. Box 540
Madison, MS 39130
P: (601) 856-1302
F: (601) 856-1390

MISSOURI
Mr. Keith Hendrickson
Chief of Enforcement
Division of Alcohol & Tobacco Control
Department of Public Safety
1738 East Elm Street
Jefferson City, MO 65101
P: (573) 526-2772
F: (573) 526-4369
E: keith.hendrickson@dps.mo.gov

MONTANA
Ms. Shawna Helfert
Administrator, Liquor Control Division
Department of Revenue
Sam W. Mitchell Building
125 North Roberts Street, 3rd Floor
Helena, MT 59601
P: (406) 444-1464
F: (406) 444-0718
E: shelfert@state.mt.gov

NEBRASKA
Mr. Hobert B. Rupe
Executive Director
Liquor Control Commission
301 Centennial Mall South, 5th Floor
Lincoln, NE 68509
P: (402) 471-2574
F: (402) 471-2814
E: hobert.rupe@nebraska.gov

NEVADA
Ms. JoLynn Smith
Supervisor
Department of Taxation
1550 East College Parkway, Suite 115
Carson City, NV 89706
P: (775) 684-2029
F: (775) 684-2020

NEW HAMPSHIRE
Mr. Joseph W. Mollica
Chair
State Liquor Commission
Storrs Street - Robert J. Hart Building
Concord, NH 03302
P: (603) 271-3134
F: (603) 271-1107
E: joseph.mollica@liquor.state.nh.us

NEW JERSEY
Mr. Jonathan Orsen
Acting Director
Division of Alcoholic Beverage Control
Department of Law & Public Safety
140 East Front Street, 5th Floor
Trenton, NJ 08625
P: (609) 984-2830
F: (609) 633-6078

NEW MEXICO
Ms. Mary Kay Root
Director
Alcohol & Gaming Division
Regulation & Licensing Department
2550 Cerrillos Road, 2nd Floor
Santa Fe, NM 87505
P: (505) 476-4550
F: (505) 476-4595
E: MaryKay.Root@state.nm.us

NEW YORK
Mr. Vincent Bradley
Chair
State Liquor Authority
80 South Swan Street, Suite 900
Albany, NY 12210
P: (518) 473-6559

NORTH CAROLINA
Mr. Robert A. Hamilton
Chief Administrator
Alcoholic Beverage Control Commission
4307 Mail Service Center
Raleigh, NC 27699
P: (919) 779-8323
F: (919) 662-3583

NORTH DAKOTA
Mr. Blane Braunberger
Supervisor, Alcoholic Beverages
Office of State Tax Commission
600 East Boulevard Avenue
Department 127
Bismarck, ND 58505
P: (701) 328-3011
F: (701) 328-1283
E: bbraunberger@nd.gov

OHIO
Mr. Jim Canepa
Interim Superintendent
Division of Liquor Control
6606 Tussing Road
Reynoldsburg, OH 43068
P: (614) 995-3420
F: (614) 644-2480

OKLAHOMA
Mr. A. Keith Burt
Director
Alcoholic Beverage Laws Enforcement Commission
3812 North Santa Fe
Suite 200
Oklahoma City, OK 73118
P: (405) 521-3484
F: (405) 521-6578
E: kburt@able.ok.gov

OREGON
Mr. Steve Marks
Executive Director
Liquor Control Commission
9079 Southeast McLoughlin Boulevard
Portland, OR 97222
P: (503) 872-5062
F: (503) 872-5266

PENNSYLVANIA
Mr. Charles Mooney
Executive Director
Liquor Control Board
Northwest Office Building
901 Capitol Street
Harrisburg, PA 17124
P: (717) 787-7114
F: (717) 772-3725

RHODE ISLAND
Ms. Maria D'Alessandro
Deputy Director & Superintendent
Division of Commercial Licensing - Liquor Enforcement & Compliance
1511 Pontiac Avenue
Cranston, RI 02920
P: (401) 462-9527
F: (401) 462-9645
E: maria.dalessandro@dbr.ri.gov

SOUTH CAROLINA
Ms. Tammy Young
Supervisor, ABL Section
Alcoholic Beverage Licensing
Department of Revenue
300 Outlet Pointe Boulevard, Suite A
Columbia, SC 29210
P: (803) 898-5864
F: (803) 898-5899

Alcoholic Beverage Control

SOUTH DAKOTA
Mr. Michael Houdyshell
Director
Department of Revenue
445 East Capital Avenue
Pierre, SD 57501
P: (605) 773-3311
F: (605) 773-6729

TENNESSEE
Mr. Clayton Byrd
Executive Director
Alcoholic Beverage Commission
500 James Robertson Parkway
Davy Crockett Tower, 3rd Floor
Nashville, TN 37243
P: (615) 741-7628
F: (615) 741-0847
E: clayton.byrd@tn.gov

TEXAS
Ms. Sherry Cook
Executive Director
Alcoholic Beverage Commission
5806 Mesa Drive
Austin, TX 78731
P: (512) 206-3366
F: (512) 206-3203
E: sherry.cook@tabc.state.tx.us

UTAH
Mr. Salvador Petilos
Executive Director
Department of Alcoholic Beverage Control
1625 South 900 West
Salt Lake City, UT 84130
P: (801) 977-6800
F: (801) 977-6888
E: spetilos@utah.gov

VERMONT
Mr. Patrick Mooney
Commissioner
Department of Liquor Control
13 Green Mountain Drive
Montpelier, VT 05620
P: (802) 828-4929
E: patrick.delaney@vermont.gov

VIRGINIA
Mr. Jeffrey Painter
Chair
State Alcoholic Beverage Control
2901 Hermitage Road
Richmond, VA 23220
P: (804) 213-4404
F: (804) 213-4411

WASHINGTON
Ms. Jane Rushford
Board Chair
State Liquor Control Board
3000 Pacific Avenue, Southeast
Olympia, WA 98504
P: (360) 664-1711
F: (360) 586-3190

WEST VIRGINIA
Mr. Fredric L. Wooton
Commissioner
Alcohol Beverage Control Administration
900 Pennsylvania Avenue, 4th Floor
Charleston, WV 25302
P: (304) 356-5501
E: fredric.l.wooton@wv.gov

WISCONSIN
Ms. Justin Shemanski
Criminal Investigation Section Chief
Department of Revenue
2135 Rimrock Road
Madison, WI 53713
P: (608) 266-0286
F: (608) 261-6240
E: justin.shemanski@revenue.wi.gov

WYOMING
Mr. Greg Cook
Administrator
Liquor Distribution Division
Department of Revenue
6601 Campstool Road
Cheyenne, WY 82002
P: (307) 777-6448
F: (307) 777-6255
E: greg.cook@wyo.gov

Arbitration and Mediation

Promotes the settlement of a variety of labor disputes.

ALABAMA
Mr. Fitzgerald Washington
Secretary
Department of Labor
649 Monroe Street
Montgomery, AL 36131
P: (334) 242-8055
E: fwashington@labor.alabama.gov

ALASKA
Ms. Heidi Drygas
Commissioner
Department of Labor & Workforce Development
P.O. Box 111149
Juneau, AK 99811
P: (907) 465-2700
F: (907) 465-2784
E: heidi.drygas@alaska.gov

AMERICAN SAMOA
Mr. Esenaeiaso J. Liu
Director
Department of Human Resources
Executive Office Building
AP Lutali, 2nd Floor
Pago Pago, AS 96799
P: (684) 644-4485
F: (684) 633-1139
E: eseneiaso.liu@hr.as.gov

COLORADO
Ms. Ellen Golombek
Executive Director
Department of Labor & Employment
633 17th Street, Suite 201
Denver, CO 80202
P: (303) 318-8017
F: (303) 318-8047
E: Ellen.Golombek@state.co.us

CONNECTICUT
Mr. Scott D. Jackson
Commissioner
Department of Labor
200 Folly Brook Boulevard
Westerfield, CT 06109
P: (860) 263-6000
F: (850) 263-6529
E: scott.jackson@ct.gov

DELAWARE
Mr. John McMahon
Secretary of Labor
Department of Labor
4425 North Market Street
Wilmington, DE 19802
P: (302) 761-8000
F: (302) 761-6621
E: john.mcmahon@state.de.us

FLORIDA
Ms. Donna Maggart Poole
Chair
Public Employees Relations Commission
4708 Capital Circle Northwest
Suite 300
Tallahassee, FL 32303
P: (850) 488-8641
F: (850) 488-9704

GEORGIA
The Honorable Mark Butler (R)
Commissioner
Department of Labor
148 International Boulevard Northeast
Atlanta, GA 30303
P: (404) 232-7300
F: (404) 656-2683
E: commissioner@gdol.ga.gov

GUAM
Mr. Manuel Q. Cruz
Director
Department of Labor
Government of Guam
P.O. Box 9970
Tamuning, GU 96931
P: (671) 475-7044
F: (671) 674-6517

Mr. Tony A. Lamorena V
Director
Civil Service Commission
P.O. Box 3156
Hagatna, GU 96932
P: (671) 647-1855
F: (671) 647-1867

IDAHO
Mr. Kenneth D. Edmunds
Director
Department of Labor
317 West Main Street
Boise, ID 83735
P: (208) 332-3570
F: (208) 334-6430
E: kenneth.edmunds@labor.idaho.gov

ILLINOIS
Ms. Kimberly Stevens
Executive Director
Labor Relations Board
160 North LaSalle Street, Suite S-400
Chicago, IL 60601
P: (217) 785-3111

INDIANA
Mr. Rick J. Ruble
Commissioner
Department of Labor
402 West Washington Street, Room W195
Indianapolis, IN 46204
P: (317) 232-2655
F: (317) 233-3790
E: rruble@dol.in.gov

IOWA
Mr. Michael A. Mauro
Commissioner
Division of Labor Services
150 Des Moines Street
Des Moines, IA 50309
P: (515) 725-5601
F: (515) 281-4698
E: michael.mauro@iwd.iowa.gov

KANSAS
Ms. Lana Gordon
Secretary of Labor
Department of Labor
401 Southwest Topeka Boulevard
Topeka, KS 66603
P: (785) 296-5000
F: (785) 368-5289
E: lana.gordon@dol.ks.gov

KENTUCKY
Ms. Jodie L. Martin
Program Coordinator
Labor-Management Relations & Mediation
1047 U.S. Highway 127 South
Suite 4
Frankfort, KY 40601
P: (502) 564-3203
F: (502) 696-1897
E: jodie.martin@ky.gov

LOUISIANA
Ms. Ava Dejoie
Executive Director
Workforce Commission
1001 North 23rd Street
P.O. Box 94094
Baton Rouge, LA 70804
P: (225) 342-3111
F: (225) 342-3778
E: owd@lwc.la.gov

MAINE
Ms. Jeanne Paquette
Commissioner
Department of Labor
54 State House Station
Augusta, ME 04333
P: (207) 623-7900
F: (207) 623-7934
E: jeanne.paquette@maine.gov

MASSACHUSETTS
Ms. Susan M. Jeghelian
Executive Director
Office of Public Collaboration
100 Morrissey Boulevard
McCormack Building, 1st Floor, Room 627
Boston, MA 02125
P: (617) 287-4047
F: (617) 287-4049
E: susan.jeghelian@umb.edu

MICHIGAN
Ms. Ruthanne Okun
Director
Bureau of Employment Relations
Cadillac Place, Suite 2-750
3026 West Grand Boulevard
Detroit, MI 48202
P: (313) 456-3519
F: (313) 456-3511
E: okunr@michigan.gov

MINNESOTA
Mr. Todd Doncavage
Acting Commissioner
Bureau of Mediation Services
1380 Energy Lane, Suite 2
St. Paul, MN 55108
P: (651) 649-5431
E: todd.doncavage@state.mn.us

MONTANA
Mr. John Lewis
Director
Department of Administration
125 North Roberts Street, Room 155
P.O. Box 200101
Helena, MT 59620
P: (406) 444-3033
F: (406) 444-6194
E: johnlewis@mt.gov

Arbitration and Mediation

NEBRASKA
Ms. Annette Hord
Clerk/Administrator
Commission of Industrial Relations
301 Centennial Mall South
P.O. Box 94864
Lincoln, NE 68509
P: (402) 471-2934
F: (402) 471-6597
E: annette.hord@nebraska.gov

NEVADA
Mr. Philip E. Larson
Chair
Local Government Employee-Management Relations Board
Department of Business & Industry
2501 East Sahara Avenue, Suite 203
Las Vegas, NV 89104
P: (702) 486-4504
F: (702) 486-4355
E: emrb@business.nv.gov

NEW HAMPSHIRE
Mr. Ken Merrifield
Commissioner
Department of Labor
95 Pleasant Street
Concord, NH 03301
P: (603) 271-3176

NEW JERSEY
Dr. Aaron R. Fichtner
Acting Commissioner
Department of Labor & Workforce Development
1 John Fitch Plaza
P.O. Box 110
Trenton, NJ 08625
P: (609) 292-1070
E: aaron.fichtner@dol.state.nj.us

NEW MEXICO
Ms. Celina Bussey
Secretary
Department of Workforce Solutions
401 Broadway, Northeast
P.O. Box 1928
Albuquerque, NM 87103
P: (505) 841-8405
F: (505) 841-8491
E: celina.bussey@state.nm.us

NORTH CAROLINA
The Honorable Cherie K. Berry (R)
Commissioner
Department of Labor
1101 Mail Service Center
Raleigh, NC 27699
P: (919) 733-7166
F: (919) 733-7640
E: cherie.berry@labor.nc.gov

NORTH DAKOTA
Ms. Michelle Kommer
Commissioner of Labor
Department of Labor & Human Rights
600 East Boulevard Avenue
Department 406
Bismarck, ND 58505
P: (701) 328-2660
F: (701) 328-2031
E: mkommer@nd.gov

OHIO
Mr. Robert Blair
Director
Department of Administrative Services
30 East Broad Street, 40th Floor
Columbus, OH 43215
P: (614) 466-6511
F: (614) 644-8151
E: jackie.murray@das.ohio.gov

OKLAHOMA
Ms. Melissa McLawhorn Houston
Commissioner of Labor
Department of Labor
3017 North Stiles, Suite 100
Oklahoma City, OK 73105
P: (405) 521-6101
F: (405) 521-6018
E: labor.info@labor.ok.gov

OREGON
Mr. Adam L. Rhynard
Chair
Employment Relations Board
Old Garfield School Building, Suite 400
528 Cottage Street, Northeast
Salem, OR 97301
P: (503) 378-3807
F: (503) 373-0021
E: Adam.Rhynard@oregon.gov

PENNSYLVANIA
Ms. Kathy M. Manderino
Secretary
Department of Labor & Industry
651 Boas Street
Harrisburg, PA 17121
P: (717) 787-5279
F: (717) 787-8826

PUERTO RICO
Mr. Carlos J. Saavedra Gutierrez
Secretary
Department of Labor & Human Resources
P.O. Box 195540
San Juan, PR 00919
P: (787) 754-5353
F: (787) 753-9550

SOUTH CAROLINA
Ms. Emily Farr
Director
Department of Labor, Licensing & Regulation
110 Centerview Drive
P.O. Box 11329
Columbia, SC 29211
P: (803) 896-4300
F: (803) 896-4393
E: ContactLLR@llr.sc.gov

SOUTH DAKOTA
Ms. Marcia Hultman
Cabinet Secretary
Department of Labor & Regulation
123 West Missouri Avenue
Pierre, SD 57501
P: (605) 773-5395
F: (605) 773-6184
E: marcia.hultman@state.sd.us

TENNESSEE
Mr. Burns Phillips
Commissioner
Department of Labor & Workforce Development
220 French Landing Drive
Nashville, TN 37243
P: (844) 224-5818
F: (615) 741-5078
E: burns.phillips@tn.gov

TEXAS
Mr. Larry E. Temple
Executive Director
Workforce Commission
101 East 15th Street
Austin, TX 78778
P: (512) 463-0735
F: (512) 475-2321
E: larry.temple@twc.state.tx.us

UTAH
Mr. Jaceson Maughan
Commissioner
Labor Commission
P.O. Box 146600
Salt Lake City, UT 84114
P: (801) 530-6800
E: laborcom@utah.gov

VERMONT
Mr. Timothy J. Noonan
Executive Director
Labor Relations Board
133 State Street
Monpelier, VT 05633
P: (802) 828-2700
F: (802) 828-2392
E: tim.noonan@vermont.gov

VIRGINIA
Mr. Todd Haymore
Secretary of Commerce & Trade
Office of Commerce & Trade
1111 East Broad Street
P.O. Box 1475
Richmond, VA 23218
P: (804) 786-7831
F: (804) 371-0250
E: Todd.Haymore@governor.virginia.gov

WASHINGTON
Mr. Joel Sacks
Director
Department of Labor & Industries
P.O. Box 44000
Olympia, WA 98504
P: (360) 902-5800
F: (360) 902-5798
E: joel.sacks@lni.wa.gov

WEST VIRGINIA
Mr. David W. Mullins
Commissioner
Division of Labor
Department of Commerce
749 B, Building 6, Capitol Complex
Charleston, WV 25305
P: (304) 558-7890
F: (304) 558-2415

WISCONSIN
Mr. Ray Allen
Secretary
Department of Workforce Development
201 East Washington Avenue (GEF-1)
Room A-400, P.O. Box 7946
Madison, WI 53707
P: (608) 266-3131
F: (608) 266-1784
E: sec@dwd.wisconsin.gov

Archives

Identifies, acquires, preserves and makes available state government records of continuing historical and research value.

ALABAMA
Mr. Steve Murray
Director
Department of Archives & History
624 Washington Avenue
P.O. Box 300100
Montgomery, AL 36130
P: (334) 242-4441
E: steve.murray@archives.alabama.gov

ALASKA
Ms. Karen Gray
Acting State Archivist
State Archives
P.O. Box 110525
Juneau, AK 99811
P: (907) 465-2275
F: (907) 465-2465
E: karen.gray@alaska.gov

AMERICAN SAMOA
Mr. James Hemphill
Territorial Archivist
Office of Archives & Records Management
American Samoa Government
Pago Pago, AS 96799
P: (684) 699-6848
F: (684) 699-6849
E: James.Himphill@la.as.gov

ARIZONA
Dr. Ted Hale
Director
Archives, Records Management & Capitol Museum
State Library, Archives & Public Records
1700 West Washington Street, 7th Floor
Phoenix, AZ 85007
P: (602) 926-4035

ARKANSAS
Ms. Lisa Speer
Director
State Archives
One Capitol Mall, Suite 2B215
Little Rock, AR 72201
P: (501) 682-6900
F: (501) 682-6916
E: lisa.speer@arkansas.gov

CALIFORNIA
Ms. Nancy Lenoil
Chief
State Archives
1020 O Street
Sacramento, CA 95814
P: (916) 653–7715
F: (916) 653–7363
E: nlenoil@sos.ca.gov

COLORADO
Ms. Aly Jabrocki
State Archivist
State Archives
Department of Personnel & Administration
1525 Sherman Street
Denver, CO 80203
P: (303) 866-5687
F: (303) 866-2257
E: aly.jabrocki@state.co.us

CONNECTICUT
Ms. Lizette Pelletier
State Archivist
State Library & Archives
231 Capitol Avenue
Hartford, CT 06106
P: (860) 566-1100 Ext. 304
E: lizette.pelletier@ct.gov

DELAWARE
Mr. Stephen M. Marz
Director
Public Archives
121 Martin Luther King Jr. Blvd., North
Dover, DE 19901
P: (302) 744-5000
F: (302) 739-8436
E: stephen.marz@state.de.us

DISTRICT OF COLUMBIA
Ms. Rebecca Katz
Administrator
District of Columbia Archives
1300 Naylor Court, Northwest
Washington, DC 20001
P: (202) 671-1105
F: (202) 727-6076
E: rebecca.katz@dc.gov

FLORIDA
Mr. Gerard Clark
Bureau Chief
Archives & Record Management
R.A. Gray Building
Tallahassee, FL 32399
P: (850) 245-6639
F: (850) 245-6744
E: Gerard.Clark@DOS.MyFlorida.com

GEORGIA
Mr. Christopher M. Davidson
Director
The Georgia Archives
5800 Jonesboro Road
Morrow, GA 30260
P: (678) 364-3710
F: (678) 364-3860
E: Christopher.Davidson@usg.edu

HAWAII
Mr. Adam Jansen
State Archivist
State Archives
Kekauluohi Bldg., Iolani Palace Grounds
364 South King Street
Honolulu, HI 96813
P: (808) 586-0329
F: (808) 586-0330
E: adam.jansen@hawaii.gov

IDAHO
Mr. David Matte
State Archivist
State Archives
2205 Old Penitentiary Road
Boise, ID 83712
P: (208) 514-2328
F: (208) 334-2626
E: david.matte@ishs.idaho.gov

ILLINOIS
Mr. David A. Joens
Director
State Archives
Margaret Cross Norton Building
Capitol Complex
Springfield, IL 62756
P: (217) 782-4682
F: (217) 524-3930
E: djoens@ilsos.net

INDIANA
Mr. Jim Corridan
Director/State Archivist
Commission on Public Records
402 West Washington Street, Room W472
Indianapolis, IN 46204
P: (317) 232-3380
F: (317) 233-1713
E: jcorridan@icpr.IN.gov

IOWA
Mr. Anthony Jahn
State Archivist
Historical Society of Iowa
Capitol Complex
East 6th & Locust Street
Des Moines, IA 50319
P: (515) 281-4895
F: (515) 282-0502
E: anthony.jahn@iowa.gov

KENTUCKY
Ms. Beth Shields
State Archivist & Records Administrator
Department for Libraries & Archives
300 Coffee Tree Road
Frankfort, KY 40602
P: (502) 564-8300
E: beth.shields@ky.gov

LOUISIANA
Dr. Florent Hardy Jr.
State Archivist
State Archives
Office of the Secretary of State
3851 Essen Lane
Baton Rouge, LA 70809
P: (225) 922-1200
F: (225) 922-0433
E: florent.hardy@sos.louisiana.gov

MAINE
Mr. Dave Cheever
State Archivist
State Archives
84 State House Station
Augusta, ME 04333
P: (207) 287-5790
F: (207) 287-6035
E: david.cheever@maine.gov

MARYLAND
Mr. Timothy D. Baker
State Archivist
State Archives
350 Rowe Boulevard
Annapolis, MD 21401
P: (410) 260-6402
F: (410) 974-2525
E: tim.baker@maryland.gov

MASSACHUSETTS
Dr. John D. Warner Jr.
Archivist of the Commonwealth
State Archives
Secretary of the Commonwealth
220 Morrissey Boulevard
Boston, MA 02125
P: (617) 727-2816
F: (617) 288-8429
E: john.warner@sec.state.ma.us

MICHIGAN
Mr. Mark Harvey
State Archivist
Archives of Michigan
Library & Historical Center
702 West Kalamazoo Street
Lansing, MI 48913
P: (517) 373-1415
E: HarveyM@michigan.gov

Archives

MINNESOTA
Mr. Shawn Rounds
State Archivist
State Archives
Historical Society
345 West Kellogg Boulevard
St. Paul, MN 55102
P: (651) 259-3265
F: (651) 296-9961
E: shawn.rounds@mnhs.org

MISSISSIPPI
Mr. David Pilcher
Director
Archives & Records Services Division
P.O. Box 571
Jackson, MS 39205
P: (601) 576-6823
E: dpilcher@mdah.ms.gov

MISSOURI
Mr. John Dougan
State Archivist
State Archives
600 West Main Street
P.O. Box 1747
Jefferson City, MO 65102
P: (573) 751-3280
F: (573) 526-7333
E: archref@sos.mo.gov

MONTANA
Jodie Foley
State Archivist
Historical Society, Research Center
225 North Roberts Street
Helena, MT 59620
P: (406) 444-7482
F: (406) 444-5297
E: jofoley@mt.gov

NEBRASKA
Ms. Gayla Koerting
State Archivist
Historical Society
P.O. Box 82554
Lincoln, NE 68501
P: (402) 471-4783
E: gayla.koerting@nebraska.gov

NEVADA
Ms. Cynthia Laframboise
State Archives Manager
State Library & Archives
100 North Stewart Street
Carson City, NV 89701
P: (775) 684-3410
F: (775) 684-3311
E: claframboise@admin.nv.gov

NEW HAMPSHIRE
Mr. Brian Nelson Burford
Director & State Archivist
Division of Archives & Records Management
Department of State
71 South Fruit Street
Concord, NH 03301
P: (603) 271-2236
F: (603) 271-2272
E: Brian.Burford@sos.nh.gov

NEW JERSEY
Mr. Joseph Klett
Chief of Archives
Division of Archives & Records Management
225 W. State Street, Level 2
P.O. Box 307
Trenton, NJ 08625
P: (609) 292-9507
F: (609) 292-9105
E: joseph.klett@sos.state.nj.us

NEW MEXICO
Ms. Melissa Salazar
Interim State Records Administrator
Commission on Public Records
1205 Camino Carlos Rey
Santa Fe, NM 87507
P: (505) 476-7902
E: melissa.salazar@state.nm.us

NEW YORK
Mr. Thomas J. Ruller
Interim State Archivist
State Archives
Cultural Education Center, Room 9D46
Albany, NY 12230
P: (518) 473-7091
F: (518) 473-7058
E: tom.ruller@mail.nysed.gov

NORTH CAROLINA
Ms. Sarah Koonts
Director of Archives & Records
Office of Archives & History
4614 Mail Service Center
Raleigh, NC 27699
P: (919) 807-7339
F: (919) 715-7274
E: sarah.koonts@ncdcr.gov

NORTH DAKOTA
Ms. Ann B. Jenks
State Archivist
State Historical Society
612 East Boulevard Avenue
Bismarck, ND 58505
P: (701) 328-2666
F: (701) 328-3710
E: ajenks@nd.gov

NORTHERN MARIANA ISLANDS
Mr. Samuel Crawford
Territorial Archivist
CNMI Archives
P.O. Box 501250
Saipan, MP 96950
P: (670) 237-6799
E: samuel.crawford@marianas.edu

OHIO
Mr. Fred Previts
State Archivist
Historical Society
800 East 17th Avenue
Columbus, OH 43211
P: (614) 297-2536
F: (614) 297-2546
E: fprevits@ohiohistory.org

OKLAHOMA
Ms. Jan Davis
Administrator
Archives & Records
Department of Libraries
200 Northeast 18th Street
Oklahoma City, OK 73105
P: (405) 522-3191
E: jdavis@oltn.odl.state.ok.us

OREGON
Ms. Mary Beth Herkert
State Archivist
State Archives
Secretary of State
800 Summer Street, Northeast
Salem, OR 97310
P: (503) 378-5196
F: (503) 373-0953
E: mary.e.herkert@state.or.us

PENNSYLVANIA
Mr. David Carmichael
State Archivist
Historical & Museum Commission
350 North Street
Harrisburg, PA 17120
P: (717) 783-5796
E: dcarmichea@pa.gov

SOUTH CAROLINA
Dr. Eric Emerson
State Historic Preservation Officer
Department of Archives & History
8301 Parklane Road
Columbia, SC 29223
P: (803) 896-6187
F: (803) 896-6167
E: eemerson@scdah.state.sc.us

SOUTH DAKOTA
Ms. Chelle Somsen
State Archivist
State Archives
State Historical Society
900 Governors Drive
Pierre, SD 57501
P: (605) 773-5521
F: (605) 773-6041
E: chelle.somsen@state.sd.us

TENNESSEE
Mr. Charles A. Sherrill
State Librarian & Archivist
State Library & Archives
403 7th Avenue, North
Nashville, TN 37243
P: (615) 741-7996
F: (615) 532-9293
E: Chuck.Sherrill@tn.gov

TEXAS
Mr. Jelain Chubb
State Archivist
State Library & Archives Commission
State Library & Archives Commission
P.O. Box 12516
Austin, TX 78711
P: (512) 463-5467
E: jchubb@tsl.texas.gov

U.S. VIRGIN ISLANDS
Ms. Ingrid Bough
Territorial Director of Libraries, Archives & Museums
Division of Libraries, Archives & Museums
C/o Florence Williams Public Library
1122 King Street, Christiansted
St. Croix, VI 00820
P: (304) 773-5715
F: (304) 773-5327
E: ingrid.bough@dpnr.vi.gov

UTAH
Ms. Patricia
Smith-Mansfield
Director
Division of State Archives &
Records Service
346 South Rio Grande
Salt Lake City, UT 84101
P: (801) 531-3850
F: (801) 531-3854
E: pmansfie@utah.gov

VERMONT
Ms. Tanya Marshall
State Archivist & Director
Archives & Records
Administration
1078 U.S. Route 2, Middlesex
Montpelier, VT 05633
P: (802) 828-0405
F: (802) 828-3710
E: tanya.marshall
@sec.state.vt.us

VIRGINIA
Ms. Sandra Treadway
State Librarian
The Library of Virginia
800 East Broad Street
Richmond, VA 23219
P: (804) 692-3535
F: (804) 692-3594
E: Sandra.Treadway
@lva.virginia.gov

WASHINGTON
Mr. Steve Excell
State Archivist
Office of the Secretary of State
State Archives
P.O. Box 40238
Olympia, WA 98504
P: (360) 586-1492
E: steve.excell@sos.wa.gov

WEST VIRGINIA
Mr. Joe Geiger
Director, Archives & History
Division of Culture & History
The Culture Center, Capitol
Complex
1900 Kanawha Boulevard, East
Charleston, WV 25305
P: (304) 558-0230
F: (304) 558-2779
E: Joe.N.Geiger@wv.gov

WISCONSIN
Mr. Matt Blessing
Director
Library-Archives Division
816 State Street
Madison, WI 53706
P: (608) 264-6480
F: (608) 264-6486
E: matt.blessing
@wisconsinhistory.org

WYOMING
Mr. Michael Strom
State Archivist
Department of State Parks &
Cultural Resources
2301 Central Avenue
Cheyenne, WY 82002
P: (307) 777-7020
F: (307) 777-7044
E: michael.strom@wyo.gov

Attorney General

The chief legal officer of the state who represents the state or its offices in all litigation.

ALABAMA
The Honorable Steve Marshall (R)
Attorney General
Office of the Attorney General
501 Washington Avenue
P.O. Box 300152
Montgomery, AL 36130
P: (334) 242-7300

ALASKA
The Honorable Jahna Lindemuth (I) (appointed)
Attorney General
Office of the Attorney General
1031 West 4th Avenue, Suite 200
Anchorage, AK 99501
P: (907) 269-5602
F: (907) 465-2075

AMERICAN SAMOA
The Honorable Talauega V. Ale (appointed)
Attorney General
Office of the Attorney General
American Samoa Government
Executive Office Building, Utulei
Pago Pago, AS 96799
P: (684) 633-4163

ARIZONA
The Honorable Mark Brnovich (R)
Attorney General
Office of the Attorney General
1275 West Washington Street
Phoenix, AZ 85007
P: (602) 542-4266
F: (602) 542-4085

ARKANSAS
The Honorable Leslie Rutledge (R)
Attorney General
Office of the Attorney General
323 Center Street, Suite 200
Little Rock, AR 72201
P: (800) 482-8982
F: (501) 682-8084

CALIFORNIA
The Honorable Xavier Becerra (D)
Attorney General
Office of the Attorney General
1300 I Street, Suite 1740
Sacramento, CA 95814
P: (916) 445-9555

COLORADO
The Honorable Cynthia Coffman (R)
Attorney General
Office of the Attorney General
Ralph L. Carr Colorado Judicial Center
1300 Broadway, 10th Floor
Denver, CO 80203
P: (720) 508-6000
F: (720) 508-6030
E: attorney.general@state.co.us

CONNECTICUT
The Honorable George C. Jepsen (D)
Attorney General
Office of the Attorney General
55 Elm Street
Hartford, CT 06106
P: (860) 808-5318

DELAWARE
The Honorable Matthew Denn (D)
Attorney General
Office of the Attorney General
Carvel State Office Building
820 North French Street
Wilmington, DE 19801
P: (302) 577-8338
E: matthew.denn@state.de.us

DISTRICT OF COLUMBIA
The Honorable Karl A. Racine (appointed)
Attorney General
Office of the Attorney General
441 4th Street, Northwest
Suite 1100S
Washington, DC 20001
P: (202) 727-3400
F: (202) 347-8922
E: oag@dc.gov

FLORIDA
The Honorable Pam Bondi (R)
Attorney General
Office of the Attorney General
The Capitol, PL 01
Tallahassee, FL 32399
P: (850) 414-3300
F: (954) 712-4826

GEORGIA
The Honorable Chris Carr (R)
Attorney General
Office of the Attorney General
40 Capitol Square, Southwest
Atlanta, GA 30334
P: (404) 656-3300
F: (404) 657-8733

GUAM
The Honorable Elizabeth Barrett-Anderson
Attorney General
Office of the Attorney General
590 South Marine Corps Drive
ITC Building, Suite 706
Tamuning, GU 96913
P: (671) 475-3324
F: (671) 472-2493
E: law@guamag.org

HAWAII
The Honorable Doug Chin (D) (appointed)
Attorney General
Office of the Attorney General
425 Queen Street
Honolulu, HI 96813
P: (808) 586-1500

IDAHO
The Honorable Lawrence Wasden (R)
Attorney General
Office of the Attorney General
Statehouse
Boise, ID 83720
P: (208) 334-2400
F: (208) 854-8071

ILLINOIS
The Honorable Lisa Madigan (D)
Attorney General
Office of the Attorney General
James R. Thompson Center
100 West Randolph Street
Chicago, IL 60601
P: (312) 814-3000

INDIANA
The Honorable Curtis Hill (R)
Attorney General
Office of the Attorney General
Indiana Government Center South
302 West Washington Street, 5th Floor
Indianapolis, IN 46204
P: (317) 232-6201
E: chill@in.gov

IOWA
The Honorable Tom Miller (D)
Attorney General
Office of the Attorney General
Hoover State Office Building
1305 East Walnut
Des Moines, IA 50319
P: (515) 281-5164
F: (515) 281-4209

KANSAS
The Honorable Derek Schmidt (R)
Attorney General
Office of the Attorney General
120 Southwest 10th Avenue, 2nd Floor
Topeka, KS 66612
P: (785) 296-2215
F: (785) 296-6296

KENTUCKY
The Honorable Andy Beshear (D)
Attorney General
Office of the Attorney General
700 Capitol Avenue
Capitol Building, Suite 118
Frankfort, KY 40601
P: (502) 696-5300
F: (502) 564-2894

LOUISIANA
The Honorable Jeffrey Landry (R)
Attorney General
Office of the Attorney General
P.O. Box 94095
Baton Rouge, LA 70804
P: (225) 326-6000
F: (225) 326-6797

MAINE
The Honorable Janet T. Mills (D)
Attorney General
Office of the Attorney General
State House Station 6
Augusta, ME 04333
P: (207) 626-8800

MARYLAND
The Honorable Brian E. Frosh (D)
Attorney General
Office of the Attorney General
200 Saint Paul Place
Baltimore, MD 21202
P: (410) 576-6300
F: (410) 576-6404
E: oag@oag.state.md.us

MASSACHUSETTS
The Honorable Maura Healey (D)
Attorney General
Office of the Attorney General
1 Ashburton Place
Boston, MA 02108
P: (617) 727-2200

MICHIGAN
The Honorable Bill Schuette (R)
Attorney General
Office of the Attorney General
525 West Ottawa Street
P.O. Box 30212
Lansing, MI 48909
P: (517) 373-1110

MINNESOTA
The Honorable Lori Swanson (DFL)
Attorney General
Office of the Attorney General
Suite 102, State Capital
75 Dr. Martin Luther King, Jr. Boulevard
St. Paul, MN 55155
P: (651) 296-3353
F: (651) 297-4193
E: Attorney.General@ag.state.mn.us

MISSISSIPPI
The Honorable Jim Hood (D)
Attorney General
Office of the Attorney General
Department of Justice
P.O. Box 220
Jackson, MS 39205
P: (601) 359-3680
E: msag05@ago.state.ms.us

MISSOURI
The Honorable Joshua D. Hawley
Attorney General
Office of the Attorney General
Supreme Court Building
207 West High Street
Jefferson City, MO 65101
P: (573) 751-3321

MONTANA
The Honorable Tim Fox (R)
Attorney General
Office of the Attorney General
Justice Building
215 North Sanders
Helena, MT 59620
P: (406) 444-2026
F: (406) 444-3549
E: contactdoj@mt.gov

NEBRASKA
The Honorable Doug Peterson (R)
Attorney General
Office of the Attorney General
State Capitol
P.O. Box 98920
Lincoln, NE 68509
P: (402) 471-2682
F: (402) 471-3297

NEVADA
The Honorable Adam Paul Laxalt (R)
Attorney General
Office of the Attorney General
Old State Capitol Building
100 North Carson Street
Carson City, NV 89701
P: (775) 684-1100
F: (775) 684-1108
E: aginfo@ag.state.nv.us

NEW HAMPSHIRE
The Honorable Gordon MacDonald (appointed)
Attorney General
Office of the Attorney General
33 Capitol Street
Concord, NH 03301
P: (603) 271-3658
F: (603) 271-2110

NEW JERSEY
NAME ERROR (appointed)
Attorney General
Office of the Attorney General
Richard J. Hughes Justice Complex
25 Market Street, Box 080
Trenton, NJ 08625
P: (609) 292-8740

NEW MEXICO
The Honorable Hector H. Balderas (D)
Attorney General
Office of the Attorney General
P.O. Drawer 1508
Santa Fe, NM 87504
P: (505) 490-4060
F: (505) 827-5826

NEW YORK
The Honorable Eric T. Schneiderman (D)
Attorney General
Office of the Attorney General
Department of Law
The Capitol, 2nd Floor
Albany, NY 12224
P: (518) 474-7330

NORTH CAROLINA
The Honorable Josh Stein (D)
Attorney General
Office of the Attorney General
Department of Justice
P.O. Box 629
Raleigh, NC 27602
P: (919) 716-6400
F: (919) 716-6750
E: jstein@ncdoj.gov

NORTH DAKOTA
The Honorable Wayne Stenehjem (R)
Attorney General
Office of the Attorney General
State Capitol
600 East Boulevard Avenue
Bismarck, ND 58505
P: (701) 328-2210
F: (701) 328-2226
E: wstenehjem@nd.gov

NORTHERN MARIANA ISLANDS
The Honorable Edward Manibusan
Attorney General
Office of the Attorney General
Administration Building
P.O. Box 10007
Saipan, MP 96950
P: (670) 664-2341

OHIO
The Honorable Mike DeWine (R)
Attorney General
Office of the Attorney General
State Office Tower
30 East Broad Street
Columbus, OH 43266
P: (614) 466-4320

OKLAHOMA
The Honorable Mike Hunter (R)
Attorney General
Office of the Attorney General
313 Northeast 21st Street
Oklahoma City, OK 73105
P: (405) 521-3921

OREGON
The Honorable Ellen Rosenblum (D)
Attorney General
Office of the Attorney General
Justice Building
1162 Court Street, Northeast
Salem, OR 97301
P: (503) 378-6002
F: (503) 378-4017

PENNSYLVANIA
The Honorable Josh Shapiro (D)
Attorney General
Office of the Attorney General
16th Floor, Strawberry Square
Harrisburg, PA 17120
P: (717) 787-3391
F: (717) 787-8242

PUERTO RICO
The Honorable Wanda Vazquez Garced
Attorney General
Office of the Attorney General
P.O. Box 902192
San Juan, PR 00902
P: (787) 721-2900

RHODE ISLAND
The Honorable Peter F. Kilmartin (D)
Attorney General
Office of the Attorney General
150 South Main Street
Providence, RI 02903
P: (401) 274-4400

SOUTH CAROLINA
The Honorable Alan Wilson (R)
Attorney General
Office of the Attorney General
Rembert C. Dennis Office Building
P.O. Box 11549
Columbia, SC 29211
P: (803) 734-3970

SOUTH DAKOTA
The Honorable Marty J. Jackley (R)
Attorney General
Office of the Attorney General
1302 East Highway 14, Suite 1
Pierre, SD 57501
P: (605) 773-3215
F: (605) 773-4106
E: atghelp@state.sd.us

TENNESSEE
The Honorable Herbert Slatery III (appointed)
Attorney General
Office of the Attorney General
425 5th Avenue North
Nashville, TN 37243
P: (615) 741-3491
F: (615) 741-2009

Attorney General

TEXAS
The Honorable Ken Paxton (R)
Attorney General
Office of the Attorney General
Capitol Station
P.O. Box 12548
Austin, TX 78711
P: (512) 463-2100
F: (512) 475-2994
E: ken.paxton@texasattorneygeneral.gov

U.S. VIRGIN ISLANDS
The Honorable Claude E. Walker (appointed)
Attorney General
Office of the Attorney General
34-38 Kronprinsdens Gade
GERS Building, 2nd Floor
St. Thomas, VI 00802
P: (340) 774-5666 Ext. 107

UTAH
The Honorable Sean D. Reyes (R)
Attorney General
Office of the Attorney General
State Capitol, Room 236
Salt Lake City, UT 84114
P: (801) 538-9600
F: (801) 538-1121
E: uag@utah.gov

VERMONT
The Honorable TJ Donovan (D)
Attorney General
Office of the Attorney General
109 State Street
Montpelier, VT 05609
P: (802) 828-3171
F: (802) 828-3187

VIRGINIA
The Honorable Mark R. Herring (D)
Attorney General
Office of the Attorney General
202 North Ninth Street
Richmond, VA 23219
P: (804) 786-2071

WASHINGTON
The Honorable Bob Ferguson (D)
Attorney General
Office of the Attorney General
1125 Washington Street, Southeast
P.O. Box 40100
Olympia, WA 98504
P: (360) 753-6200
F: (360) 664-0228
E: bob.ferguson@atg.wa.gov

WEST VIRGINIA
The Honorable Patrick Morrisey (R)
Attorney General
Office of the Attorney General
State Capitol
1900 Kanawha Boulevard, East
Charleston, WV 25305
P: (304) 558-2021
F: (304) 558-0140

WISCONSIN
The Honorable Brad Schimel (R)
Attorney General
Office of the Attorney General, Department of Justice
State Capitol, Room 114 East
P.O. Box 7857
Madison, WI 53707
P: (608) 266-1221

WYOMING
The Honorable Peter K. Michael (appointed)
Attorney General
Office of the Attorney General
State Capitol Building
Cheyenne, WY 82002
P: (307) 777-7841
F: (307) 777-6869

Auditor

Determines that governmental funds are handled appropriately and assesses how effectively government organizations are achieving their purposes.

Information provided by:

National Association of State Auditors, Comptrollers & Treasurers
Kinney Poynter
Executive Director
449 Lewis Hargett Circle
Suite 290
Lexington, KY 40503
P: (859) 276-1147
F: (859) 278-0507
kpoynter@nasact.org
www.nasact.org

ALABAMA
Mr. Ronald L. Jones
Chief Examiner
Department of Examiners of Public Accounts
50 North Ripley Street, Room 3201
Montgomery, AL 36104
P: (334) 242-9200
F: (334) 353-1436
E: ron.jones@examiners.alabama.gov

ALASKA
The Honorable Kris Curtis
Legislative Auditor
Division of Legislative Audit
P.O. Box 113300
Juneau, AK 99811
P: (907) 465-3830
F: (907) 465-2347

AMERICAN SAMOA
Ms. Liua Fatuesi
Territorial Auditor
Territorial Audit Office
Executive Office Building
AP Lutali - 2nd Floor
Pago Pago, AS 96799
P: (684) 633-5191
F: (684) 633-1039

ARIZONA
The Honorable Debra K. Davenport
Auditor General
Office of the Auditor General
2910 North 44th Street, Suite 410
Phoenix, AZ 85018
P: (602) 553-0333
F: (602) 553-0051
E: ddavenport@azauditor.gov

ARKANSAS
Mr. Roger A. Norman
Legislative Auditor
Legislative Audit
State Capitol
500 Woodlane Street, Suite 172
Little Rock, AR 72201
P: (501) 683-8600
F: (501) 683-8605
E: roger.norman@arklegaudit.gov

CALIFORNIA
The Honorable Elaine M. Howle
State Auditor
Office of the State Auditor
621 Capitol Mall, Suite 1200
Sacramento, CA 95814
P: (916) 445-0255 Ext. 342
F: (916) 323-0913
E: elaineh@bsa.ca.gov

COLORADO
The Honorable Diane E. Ray
State Auditor
Office of the State Auditor
1525 Sherman Street, 7th Floor
Denver, CO 80203
P: (303) 869-2800
F: (303) 869-3060
E: diane.ray@state.co.us

CONNECTICUT
The Honorable John C. Geragosian
State Auditor
Office of the Auditors of Public Accounts
State Capitol
210 Capitol Avenue
Hartford, CT 06106
P: (860) 240-8651
F: (860) 240-8655
E: john.geragosian@cga.ct.gov

Mr. Robert J. Kane
Office of the Auditors of Public Accounts
State Capitol
210 Capitol Avenue
Hartford, CT 06106
P: (860) 240-8653
F: (860) 240-8655

DELAWARE
The Honorable R. Thomas Wagner Jr. (R)
Auditor of Accounts
Office of the Auditor of Accounts
401 Federal Street
Townsend Building, Suite 1
Dover, DE 19901
P: (302) 739-5055
F: (302) 739-6707
E: r.thomas.wagner@state.de.us

DISTRICT OF COLUMBIA
The Honorable Kathleen Patterson
Auditor
Office of the Auditor
717 14th Street, Northwest, 9th Floor
Washington, DC 20005
P: (202) 727-3600
F: (202) 724-8814
E: kathleen.patterson@dc.gov

FLORIDA
Ms. Sherrill Norman
Auditor General
Office of the Auditor General
Pepper Building, Room G-75
111 West Madison Street
Tallahassee, FL 32399
P: (850) 412-2722
F: (850) 488-6975
E: sherrillnorman@aud.state.fl.us

GEORGIA
Mr. Greg S. Griffin
State Auditor
Department of Audits and Accounts
270 Washington Street, Southwest
Suite 4-113
Atlanta, GA 30334
P: (404) 656-2174
F: (404) 651-9448
E: griffin@audits.ga.gov

GUAM
The Honorable Doris Flores Brooks
Public Auditor
Office of Public Accountability
DNA Building, Suite 401
238 Archbishop Flores Street
Hagatna, GU 96910
P: (671) 475-0390, Ext. 207
F: (671) 472-7951
E: dfbrooks@guamopa.com

IDAHO
Mr. Rakesh Mohan
Director
Office of Performance Evaluations
954 West Jefferson Street
10th Street Entrance, 2nd Floor
Boise, ID 83720
P: (208) 332-1470
F: (208) 332-1471
E: rmohan@ope.idaho.gov

Ms. April Renfro
Division Manager
Legislative Services, Audit Division
700 West Jefferson Street
P.O. Box 83720
Boise, ID 83720
P: (208) 334-4826
F: (208) 334-2034
E: arenfro@lso.idaho.gov

ILLINOIS
Mr. Frank J. Mautino
Auditor General
Office of the Auditor General
Iles Park Plaza
740 East Ash Street
Springfield, IL 62703
P: (217) 782-3536
F: (217) 785-8222
E: auditor@mail.state.il.us

INDIANA
Mr. Paul D. Joyce
State Examiner
State Board of Accounts
200 West Washington Street
Room E-418
Indianapolis, IN 46204
P: (317) 232-2524
F: (317) 232-4711

IOWA
Ms. Mary Mosiman
Auditor of State
Office of the Auditor of State
Room 111, State Capitol Building
Des Moines, IA 50319
P: (515) 281-5835
F: (515) 242-6134

KANSAS
Mr. Scott E. Frank
Legislative Post Auditor
Legislative Division of Post Audit
800 Southwest Jackson Street
Suite 1200
Topeka, KS 66612
P: (785) 296-5180
F: (785) 296-4482
E: scott.frank@lpa.ks.gov

Auditor

KENTUCKY
The Honorable Mike Harmon (R)
Auditor of Public Accounts
Office of the Auditor of Public Accounts
209 St. Clair Street
Frankfort, KY 40601
P: (502) 564-5841
F: (502) 564-2912

LOUISIANA
The Honorable Daryl G. Purpera
Legislative Auditor
Legislative Auditor
1600 North 3rd Street
P.O. Box 94397
Baton Rouge, LA 70804
P: (225) 339-3839
F: (225) 339-3870
E: dpurpera@lla.la.gov

MAINE
The Honorable Pola Buckley
State Auditor
Office of the State Auditor
66 State House Station
Augusta, ME 04333
P: (207) 624-6250
F: (207) 624-6273

MARYLAND
Mr. Thomas J. Barnickel III
Legislative Auditor
Office of Legislative Audits
301 West Preston Street, Room 1202
Baltimore, MD 21201
P: (410) 946-5900
F: (410) 946-5998
E: tbarnickel@ola.state.md.us

MASSACHUSETTS
The Honorable Suzanne M. Bump (D)
Auditor of the Commonwealth
Office of the Auditor of the Commonwealth
State House, Room 230
Boston, MA 02133
P: (617) 727-2075
F: (617) 727-3014
E: suzanne.bump@sao.state.ma.us

MICHIGAN
The Honorable Doug Ringler
Auditor General
Office of the Auditor General
201 North Washington Square
Victor Center, Suite 600
Lansing, MI 48913
P: (517) 334-8050
F: (517) 334-8079
E: dringler@audgen.michigan.gov

MINNESOTA
Mr. James Nobles
Legislative Auditor
Office of the Legislative Auditor
658 Cedar Street, Room 140
St. Paul, MN 55155
P: (651) 296-4708
F: (651) 296-4712
E: james.nobles@state.mn.us

The Honorable Rebecca Otto (DFL)
State Auditor
Office of the State Auditor
525 Park Street, Suite 500
St. Paul, MN 55103
P: (615) 296-2551
F: (615) 296-4755
E: rebecca.otto@state.mn.us

MISSISSIPPI
Mr. James A. Barber
Executive Director
Joint Committee on Performance Evaluation & Expenditure Review
501 North West Street, Suite 301-A
Jackson, MS 39215
P: (601) 359-1226
F: (601) 359-1420

The Honorable Stacey E. Pickering (R)
State Auditor
Office of the State Auditor
Woolfolk Building, Suite 801
501 North West Street, P.O. Box 956
Jackson, MS 39205
P: (601) 576-2641
F: (601) 576-2650
E: stacey.pickering@osa.ms.gov

MISSOURI
Ms. Nicole Galloway
State Auditor
Office of the State Auditor
State Capitol, Room 121
Jefferson City, MO 65102
P: (573) 751-4824
F: (573) 751-6539

MONTANA
Mr. Angus Maciver
Legislative Auditor
Legislative Audit Division
State Capitol Building, Room 160
P.O. Box 201705
Helena, MT 59620
P: (406) 444-3122
F: (406) 444-9784
E: amaciver@mt.gov

NEBRASKA
The Honorable Charlie Janssen (R)
State Auditor
Office of the Auditor of Public Accounts
Room 2303, State Capitol
P.O. Box 98917
Lincoln, NE 68509
P: (402) 471-2111
F: (402) 471-3301
E: charlie.janssen@nebraska.gov

NEVADA
Mr. Rocky J. Cooper
Legislative Auditor
Legislative Counsel Bureau
401 South Carson Street
Carson City, NV 89701
P: (775) 684-6815
F: (775) 684-6435

NEW HAMPSHIRE
Mr. Michael Kane
Legislative Budget Assistant
Office of Legislative Budget Assistant
State House, Room 102
107 North Main Street
Concord, NH 03301
P: (603) 271-2389
F: (603) 271-1097

NEW JERSEY
Mr. Philip Degnan
Acting State Comptroller
Office of the State Comptroller
P.O. Box 024
Trenton, NJ 08625
P: (609) 984-2888
F: (609) 292-2017

The Honorable Stephen M. Eells
State Auditor
Office of the State Auditor
P.O. Box 067
Trenton, NJ 08625
P: (609) 847-3470
F: (609) 633-0834
E: seells@njleg.org

NEW MEXICO
The Honorable Timothy Keller (D)
State Auditor
Office of the State Auditor
2540 Camino Edward Ortiz, Suite A
Santa Fe, NM 87507
P: (505) 476-3800
F: (505) 827-3512
E: timothy.keller@osa.state.nm.us

Mr. Charles Sallee
Deputy Director for Program Evaluation
Legislative Finance Committee
325 Don Gaspar Street, Suite 101
Santa Fe, NM 87501
P: (505) 986-4550
F: (505) 986-4644
E: charles.sallee@nmlegis.gov

NEW YORK
The Honorable Thomas P. DiNapoli (D)
Comptroller
Office of the State Comptroller
110 State Street
Albany, NY 12236
P: (518) 474-4040
F: (518) 474-3004
E: tdinapoli@osc.state.ny.us

Mr. Andrew SanFilippo
Office of the State Comptroller - State & Local Accountability
110 State Street
Albany, NY 12236
P: (518) 474-4040
F: (518) 473-8940

NORTH CAROLINA
The Honorable Beth Wood (D)
State Auditor
Office of the State Auditor
2 South Salisbury Street
20601 Mail Service Center
Raleigh, NC 27699
P: (919) 807-7500
F: (919) 807-7600
E: Beth_Wood@ncauditor.net

NORTH DAKOTA
The Honorable Josh Gallion (R)
State Auditor
Office of the State Auditor
600 East Boulevard, 3rd Floor
Bismarck, ND 58505
P: (701) 328-2241
F: (701) 328-1406
E: jgallion@nd.gov

NORTHERN MARIANA ISLANDS
Mr. Michael S. Pai
Public Auditor
Office of the Public Auditor
P.O. Box 501399
Saipan, MP 96950
P: (670) 322-6481
F: (670) 322-7812
E: mpai@opacnmi.com

OHIO
The Honorable David A. Yost (R)
Auditor of State
Office of Auditor of State
88 East Broad Street, 5th Floor
P.O. Box 1140
Columbus, OH 43216
P: (614) 466-4514
F: (614) 466-4490
E: contactus@auditor.state.oh.us

OKLAHOMA
The Honorable Gary Jones (R)
State Auditor & Inspector
Office of the State Auditor & Inspector
2300 North Lincoln Boulevard
State Capitol Building, Room 100
Oklahoma City, OK 73105
P: (405) 521-3495
F: (405) 521-3426
E: gjones@sai.ok.gov

OREGON
Mr. Kip Memmott
Division of Audits
255 Capitol Street, Northeast
Suite 500
Salem, OR 97310
P: (503) 986-2355
F: (503) 378-4829

PENNSYLVANIA
The Honorable Eugene DePasquale (D)
Auditor General
Department of the Auditor General
Finance Building
613 North Street, Room 229
Harrisburg, PA 17120
P: (717) 787-2543
F: (717) 783-4407
E: auditorgen@auditorgen.state.pa.us

Mr. Philip R. Durgin
Executive Director
Legislative Budget & Finance Committee
400 Finance Building
P.O. Box 8737
Harrisburg, PA 17105
P: (717) 783-1600
F: (717) 787-5487
E: pdurgin@palbfc.us

PUERTO RICO
Ms. Yesmin Valdivieso
Comptroller
Office of the Comptroller
P.O. Box 366069
San Juan, PR 00936
P: (787) 250-3300
F: (787) 751-6768
E: ocpr@ocpr.gov.pr

RHODE ISLAND
Mr. Dennis E. Hoyle
Auditor General
Office of the Auditor General
33 Broad Street, Suite 201
Providence, RI 02903
P: (401) 222-2435 Ext. 3038
F: (401) 222-2111
E: ag@oag.ri.gov

SOUTH CAROLINA
Mr. George L. Kennedy III
State Auditor
Office of the State Auditor
1401 Main Street, Suite 1200
Columbia, SC 29201
P: (803) 253-4160 Ext. 203
F: (803) 343-0723
E: gkennedy@osa.sc.gov

Mr. Earle Powell
Director
Legislative Audit Council
1331 Elmwood Avenue, Suite 315
Columbia, SC 29201
P: (803) 253-7612
F: (803) 253-7639

SOUTH DAKOTA
Mr. Martin Guindon
Auditor General
Department of Legislative Audit
500 East Capitol Avenue
Pierre, SD 57501
P: (605) 773-3595
F: (605) 773-6454
E: marty.guindon@state.sd.us

TENNESSEE
Mr. Justin P. Wilson
Comptroller of the Treasury
Office of the Comptroller of the Treasury
505 Deaderick Street, Suite 1500
Nashville, TN 37243
P: (615) 741-2501
F: (615) 741-7328
E: justin.wilson@tn.gov

TEXAS
Ms. Lisa Collier
First Assistant State Auditor
State Auditor's Office
Robert E. Johnson Building
1501 North Congress Avenue
Austin, TX 78701
P: (512) 936-9500
F: (512) 936-9400

U.S. VIRGIN ISLANDS
Mr. Steven G. Van Beverhoudt
Inspector General
Office of the Inspector General
2315 Kronprindsens Gade #75
Charlotte Amalie
St. Thomas, VI 00802
P: (340) 774-3388
F: (340) 774-6431
E: svanbeverhoudt@viig.org

UTAH
Mr. John Schaff
Auditor General
Office of the Legislative Auditor General
W315 State Capitol Complex
P.O. Box 140151
Salt Lake City, UT 84114
P: (801) 538-1033 Ext. 103
F: (801) 538-1063
E: jschaff@utah.gov

VERMONT
The Honorable Douglas R. Hoffer (D)
State Auditor
Office of the State Auditor
132 State Street
Montpelier, VT 05633
P: (802) 828-2281
F: (802) 828-2198
E: doug.hoffer@state.vt.us

VIRGINIA
Mr. Hal Greer
Director
Joint Legislative Audit & Review Commission
General Assembly Building
910 Capitol Street, Suite 1100
Richmond, VA 23218
P: (804) 371-4589
F: (804) 371-0101

Ms. Martha Mavredes
Auditor of Public Accounts
Office of the Auditor of Public Accounts
P.O. Box 1295
Richmond, VA 23218
P: (804) 225-3350
F: (804) 225-3357
E: martha.mavredes@apa.virginia.gov

WASHINGTON
Mr. Keenan Konopaski
Legislative Auditor
Joint Legislative Audit & Review Committee
1300 Quince Street, Southeast
Olympia, WA 98504
P: (360) 786-5187
F: (360) 786-5180
E: keenan.konopaski@leg.wa.gov

The Honorable Pat McCarthy (D)
State Auditor
Office of the State Auditor
P.O. Box 40021
Olympia, WA 98504
P: (360) 902-0370
F: (360) 753-0646
E: auditor@sao.wa.gov

Auditor

WEST VIRGINIA
Mr. Aaron Allred
Legislative Manager &
Legislative Auditor
Legislative Auditor's Office
State Capitol Complex
Building 1, Room E-132
Charleston, WV 25305
P: (304) 347-4800
F: (304) 347-4815
E: aaron.allred
@wvlegislature.gov

WISCONSIN
Mr. Joe Chrisman
State Auditor
Legislative Audit Bureau
22 East Mifflin Street, Suite 500
Madison, WI 53703
P: (608) 266-2818
F: (608) 267-0410
E: joe.chrisman
@legis.wisconsin.gov

WYOMING
Mr. Jeffrey C. Vogel
Director
Department of Audit
Herschler Building
3rd Floor, East Wing
Cheyenne, WY 82002
P: (307) 777-5312
F: (307) 777-5341
E: jvogel
@wyaudit.state.wy.us

Banking

Administers laws regulating the operation of banking institutions in the state.

ALABAMA
Mr. Mike Hill
Superintendent
Banking Department
P.O. Box 4600
Montgomery, AL 36103
P: (334) 242-3452
F: (334) 242-3500
E: mike.hill@banking.alabama.gov

ALASKA
Ms. Kevin Anselm
Director
Division of Banking & Securities
P.O. Box 110807
Juneau, AK 99811
P: (907) 465-2521
F: (907) 465-1230
E: kevin.anselm@alaska.gov

AMERICAN SAMOA
Ms. Ruth Matagi-Faatili
Director
Development Bank of American Samoa
DBAS Building
Pago Pago, AS 96799
P: (684) 633-4031
F: (684) 633-1163

ARIZONA
Mr. Robert Charlton
Superintendent of Financial Institutions
Department of Financial Institutions
2910 North 44th Street, Suite 310
Phoenix, AZ 85018
P: (602) 771-2770
F: (602) 381-1225
E: rcharlton@azdfi.gov

ARKANSAS
Ms. Candace Franks
Commissioner
State Banking Department
400 Hardin Road, Suite 100
Little Rock, AR 72211
P: (501) 324-9019
F: (501) 324-9028
E: cfranks@banking.state.ar.us

CALIFORNIA
Ms. Jan Lynn Owen
Commissioner
Department of Business Oversight
1515 K Street, Suite 200
Sacramento, CA 95814
P: (866) 275-2677
F: (916) 322-1559

COLORADO
Mr. Chris Myklebust
Commissioner
Division of Banking
Department of Regulatory Agencies
1560 Broadway, Suite 950
Denver, CO 80202
P: (303) 894-2336
F: (303) 894-7886
E: chris.myklebust@state.co.us

CONNECTICUT
Mr. Jorge Perez
Commissioner
Department of Banking
260 Constitution Plaza
Hartford, CT 06103
P: (860) 240-8100

DELAWARE
Mr. Robert A. Glen
Commissioner
Office of State Bank Commissioner
555 East Lockerman Street
Dover, DE 19901
P: (302) 739-4235
F: (302) 739-3609
E: bankcommissioner@state.de.us

DISTRICT OF COLUMBIA
Mr. Stephen C. Taylor
Commissioner
Department of Insurance, Securities & Banking
Government of the District of Columbia
810 First Street Northeast, Suite 701
Washington, DC 20002
P: (202) 727-8000
F: (202) 535-1196
E: disb@dc.gov

FLORIDA
Mr. Jeremy W. Smith
Director
Division of Financial Institutions
200 East Gaines Street
Tallahassee, FL 32399
P: (850) 487-9687

GEORGIA
Mr. Kevin Hagler
Commissioner
Department of Banking & Finance
2990 Brandywine Road, Suite 200
Atlanta, GA 30341
P: (770) 986-1633
F: (770) 986-1654
E: khagler@dbf.state.ga.us

GUAM
Mr. John P. Camacho
Director
Department of Revenue & Taxation
Director's Office
P.O. Box 23607
GMF, GU 96921
P: (671) 635-1817
F: (671) 633-2643
E: john.camacho@revtax.guam.gov

HAWAII
Ms. Iris Ikeda Catalani
Commissioner
Division of Financial Institutions
King Kalakaua Building
335 Merchant Street, Room 221
Honolulu, HI 96813
P: (808) 586-2820
F: (808) 586-2818
E: dfi@dcca.hawaii.gov

IDAHO
Ms. Mary Hughes
Chief
Financial Institutions Bureau
800 Park Boulevard, Suite 200
P.O. Box 83720
Boise, ID 83720
P: (208) 332-8030
F: (208) 332-8097
E: mary.hughes@finance.idaho.gov

ILLINOIS
Ms. Kerri Doll
Director
Division of Banking
320 West Washington Street
5th Floor
Springfield, IL 62786
P: (217) 558-4938

INDIANA
Mr. Tom Fite
Public Finance Director
Department of Financial Institutions
30 South Meridian Street
Suite 300
Indianapolis, IN 46204
P: (317) 453-2177
F: (317) 232-7655
E: tfite@dfi.IN.gov

IOWA
Mr. Ronald L. Hansen
Superintendent
Division of Banking
200 East Grand Avenue, Suite 300
Des Moines, IA 50309
P: (515) 281-4014
F: (515) 281-4862
E: rhansen@idob.state.ia.us

KANSAS
Ms. Michelle W. Bowman
Commissioner
Office of the State Banking Commissioner
700 Southwest Jackson, Suite 300
Topeka, KS 66603
P: (785) 296-2266
F: (785) 296-0168

KENTUCKY
Mr. Charles A. Vice
Commissioner
Department of Financial Institutions
1025 Capital Center Drive, Suite 200
Frankfort, KY 40601
P: (502) 573-3390
F: (502) 573-8787
E: charles.vice@ky.gov

LOUISIANA
Mr. John P. Ducrest
Commissioner
Office of Financial Institutions
8660 United Plaza Boulevard, Suite 200
P.O. Box 94095
Baton Rouge, LA 70804
P: (225) 925-4660
F: (225) 925-4524
E: ofila@ofi.la.gov

Banking

MAINE
Mr. Lloyd P. LaFountain III
Superintendent
Bureau of Financial Institutions
Professional & Financial Regulation
36 State House Station
Augusta, ME 04333
P: (207) 624-8570
F: (207) 624-8590
E: lloyd.p.lafountain.III@maine.gov

MARYLAND
Mr. Gordon Cooley
Commissioner of Financial Regulation
Division of Financial Regulation
500 North Calvert Street, Room 402
Baltimore, MD 21202
P: (410) 230-6001
F: (410) 333-0475
E: gordon.cooley@maryland.gov

MASSACHUSETTS
Mr. Terence A. McGinnis
Commissioner
Division of Banking
1000 Washington Street, 10th Floor
Boston, MA 02118
P: (617) 956-1500
F: (617) 956-1599

MICHIGAN
Mr. Patrick M. McPharlin
Director
Department of Insurance & Financial Services
530 West Allegan Street, 7th Floor
P.O. Box 30220
Lansing, MI 48909
P: (517) 284-8800
F: (517) 284-8837
E: difs-info@michigan.gov

MINNESOTA
Ms. Sarah Butler
Acting Deputy Commissioner
Financial Institutions Division
85 7th Place East, Suite 500
St. Paul, MN 55101
P: (651) 539-1720
F: (651) 539-1547
E: sarah.butler@state.mn.us

MISSISSIPPI
Ms. Charlotte Corley
Commissioner
Department of Banking and Consumer Finance
P. O. Box 12129
Jackson, MS 39236
P: (601) 321-6901

MISSOURI
Ms. Debbie Hardman
Commissioner of Finance
Division of Finance
Truman State Office Building, Room 630
P.O. Box 716
Jefferson City, MO 65102
P: (573) 751-3242
F: (573) 751-9192
E: finance@dof.mo.gov

MONTANA
Ms. Melanie Hall
Commissioner
Division of Banking & Financial Institutions
301 South Park, Suite 316
P.O. Box 200546
Helena, MT 59620
P: (406) 841-2920
F: (406) 841-2930
E: mghall@mt.gov

NEBRASKA
Mr. Mark Quandahl
Director
Department of Banking & Finance
1526 K Street, Suite 300
P.O. Box 95006
Lincoln, NE 68509
P: (402) 471-2845
E: mark.quandahl@nebraska.gov

NEVADA
Mr. George E. Burns
Commissioner
Financial Institutions Division
Department of Business & Industry
2785 East Desert Inn Road, Suite 180
Las Vegas, NV 89121
P: (702) 486-4120
F: (702) 486-4563
E: gburns@fid.state.nv.us

NEW HAMPSHIRE
Mr. Jerry Little
Bank Commissioner
Banking Department
53 Regional Drive, Suite 200
Concord, NH 03301
P: (603) 271-3561

NEW JERSEY
Mr. Richard J. Badolato
Commissioner
Department of Banking & Insurance
State of New Jersey
20 West State Street, P.O. Box 325
Trenton, NJ 08625
P: (609) 292-7272
F: (609) 984-5273
E: commissioner@dobi.state.nj.us

NEW MEXICO
Mr. Christopher Moya
Acting Director
Financial Institutions Division
2550 Cerrillos Road, 3rd Floor
Santa Fe, NM 87505
P: (505) 476-4885
F: (505) 476-4670

NEW YORK
Ms. Maria T. Vullo
Superintendent
Department of Financial Services
One State Street
New York, NY 10004
P: (212) 709-3500
F: (212) 709-3520

NORTH CAROLINA
Mr. Ray Grace
Commissioner of Banks
Banking Commission
316 West Edenton Street
4309 Mail Service Center
Raleigh, NC 27699
P: (888) 384-3811
F: (919) 733-6918
E: rgrace@nccob.gov

NORTH DAKOTA
Mr. Robert J. Entringer
Commissioner
Department of Financial Institutions
2000 Schafer Street, Suite G
Bismarck, ND 58501
P: (701) 328-9933
F: (701) 328-0290
E: rentring@nd.gov

OHIO
Mr. Kevin R. Allard
Superintendent
Division of Financial Institutions
Department of Commerce
77 South High Street, 21st Floor
Columbus, OH 43215
P: (614) 728-8400
F: (614) 728-0380
E: Web.dfi@com.ohio.gov

OKLAHOMA
Mr. Mick Thompson
Commissioner
State Banking Department
2900 North Lincoln Boulevard
Oklahoma City, OK 73105
P: (405) 521-2782
F: (405) 522-2993
E: mick.thompson@banking.ok.gov

OREGON
Ms. Laura N. Cali Robison
Insurance Commissioner/Chief Actuary
Department of Consumer & Business Services
Financial Regulation, P.O. Box 14480
350 Winter Street, Northeast
Salem, OR 97309
P: (503) 947-7980
F: (503) 378-4351
E: laura.n.cali@oregon.gov

PENNSYLVANIA
Ms. Robin Weissmann
Secretary
Department of Banking & Securities
Market Square Plaza
17 North 2nd Street, Suite 1300
Harrisburg, PA 17101
P: (717) 787-2665
F: (717) 787-8773
E: dobssecretary@pa.gov

PUERTO RICO
Mr. Ivelisse Colon Berrios
Acting Commissioner of Financial Institutions
Office of the Commissioner of Financial Institutions
Commonwealth of Puerto Rico
P.O. Box 11855
San Juan, PR 00910
P: (787) 723-3131
F: (787) 723-4042
E: ivelissec@ocif.pr.gov

RHODE ISLAND
Ms. Elizabeth Kelleher Dwyer
Superintendent
Banking Regulation Division
Department of Business Regulation
1511 Pontiac Avenue, Building 69-2
Cranston, RI 02920
P: (401) 462-9617
F: (401) 462-9602
E: elizabeth.dwyer@dbr.ri.gov

SOUTH CAROLINA
Mr. Robert L. Davis
Commissioner of Banking
Office of the Commissioner of Banking
1205 Pendleton Street, Suite 305
Columbia, SC 29201
P: (803) 734-2001
F: (803) 734-2013

SOUTH DAKOTA
Mr. Bret Afdahl
Director
Division of Banking
Department of Labor & Regulation
1601 North Harrison Avenue, Suite 1
Pierre, SD 57501
P: (605) 773-3421
F: (866) 326-7504
E: banking@state.sd.us

TENNESSEE
Mr. Greg Gonzales
Commissioner
Department of Financial Institutions
414 Union Street, Suite 1000
Nashville, TN 37219
P: (615) 741-5603
F: (615) 253-6306
E: Greg.Gonzales@tn.gov

TEXAS
Mr. Charles G. Cooper
Commissioner
Department of Banking
2601 North Lamar Boulevard
Austin, TX 78705
P: (512) 475-1325
F: (512) 475-1313
E: executive@dob.texas.gov

UTAH
Mr. G. Edward Leary
Commissioner
Department of Financial Institutions
324 South State Street, Suite 201
P.O. Box 146800
Salt Lake City, UT 84114
P: (801) 538-8830
F: (801) 538-8894
E: ELEARY@utah.gov

VERMONT
Mr. Michael Pieciak
Commissioner
Department of Financial Regulation
89 Main Street
Montpelier, VT 05620
P: (802) 828-3301
F: (802) 828-3306
E: michael.pieciak@vermont.gov

VIRGINIA
Mr. E. Joseph Face Jr.
Commissioner of Financial Institutions
Bureau of Financial Institutions
1300 East Main Street, 8th Floor
P.O. Box 640
Richmond, VA 23218
P: (804) 371-9657
F: (804) 371-9416
E: joe.face@scc.virginia.gov

WASHINGTON
Ms. Roberta Hollinshead
Director of Banks
Division of Banks
Department of Financial Institutions
P.O. Box 41200
Olympia, WA 98504
P: (360) 902-8704
F: (360) 753-6070
E: banks@dfi.wa.gov

Ms. Gloria Papiez
Director
Department of Financial Institutions
P.O. Box 41200
Olympia, WA 98504
P: (360) 902-8700
F: (360) 586-5068
E: confsec@dfi.wa.gov

WEST VIRGINIA
Ms. Dawn Holstein
Acting Commissioner & Director of Depository Institutions
Division of Financial Institutions
Board of Banking & Financial Institution
900 Pennsylvania Avenue, Suite 306
Charleston, WV 25302
P: (304) 558-2294
F: (304) 558-0442
E: dholstein@wvdob.org

WISCONSIN
Ms. Cheryll Olson-Collins
Administrator
Division of Banking
P.O. Box 7876
Madison, WI 53707
P: (608) 261-7578
F: (608) 267-6889
E: cheryll.olsoncollins@dfi.wisconsin.gov

WYOMING
Mr. Albert L. Forkner
State Banking Commissioner
Division of Banking
Herschler Building, 3rd Floor, East Wing
122 West 25th Street
Cheyenne, WY 82002
P: (307) 777-7797
F: (307) 777-3555
E: albert.forkner@wyo.gov

Borders Management

Oversees and regulates the flow of transportation and immigration over state and international borders.

AMERICAN SAMOA
The Honorable Talauega V. Ale
Attorney General
Office of the Attorney General
American Samoa Government
Executive Office Building, Utulei
Pago Pago, AS 96799
P: (684) 633-4163

FLORIDA
Mr. Rick Swearingen
Commissioner
Department of Law Enforcement
2331 Phillips Road
P.O. Box 1489
Tallahassee, FL 32302
P: (850) 410-7011
E: RickSwearingen@fdle.state.fl.us

GUAM
Mr. Pedro A. Leon Guerrero Jr.
Director
Customs & Quarantine Agency
Building 13-16, 17 Mariner Drive, Tiyan
Barrigada, GU 96932
P: (671) 475-6202
F: (671) 475-6227

KANSAS
Colonel Mark Bruce
Superintendent
Highway Patrol
122 Southwest 7th Street
Topeka, KS 66603
P: (785) 296-6800
F: (785) 296-3049

MASSACHUSETTS
Colonel Richard D. McKeon
Superintendent
State Police
Office of Public Safety & Security
470 Worcester Road
Framingham, MA 01702
P: (508) 820-2300
F: (617) 727-6874

MINNESOTA
Ms. Ramona Dohman
Commissioner
Department of Public Safety
445 Minnesota Street, Suite 199
St. Paul, MN 55101
P: (651) 201-7160
F: (651) 297-5728
E: Mona.Dohman@state.mn.us

MISSOURI
Mr. Charles A. Juden
Director
Department of Public Safety
Office of the Director
P.O. Box 749
Jefferson City, MO 65102
P: (573) 751-4905
F: (573) 751-5399

MONTANA
The Honorable Tim Fox (R)
Attorney General
Department of Justice
Justice Building
215 North Sanders
Helena, MT 59620
P: (406) 444-2026
F: (406) 444-3549
E: contactdoj@mt.gov

NEW HAMPSHIRE
Mr. John J. Barthelmes
Commissioner
Department of Safety
James H. Hayes Safety Building
33 Hazen Drive
Concord, NH 03305
P: (603) 223-3889
F: (603) 271-3903
E: john.barthelmes@dos.nh.gov

NORTH DAKOTA
Mr. Greg Wilz
Director, Division of Homeland Security
Department of Emergency Services
Fraine Barracks Lane, Building 35
P.O. Box 5511
Bismarck, ND 58506
P: (701) 328-8100 Ext. 8101
F: (701) 995-0446
E: gwilz@nd.gov

SOUTH CAROLINA
Ms. Christy Hall
Interim Secretary of Transportation
Department of Transportation
Silas N. Pearman Building
955 Park Street
Columbia, SC 29201
P: (803) 737-2314
F: (803) 737-2038
E: HallCA@dot.state.sc.us

U.S. VIRGIN ISLANDS
Mr. David W. Mapp
Acting Executive Director
Port Authority
8074 Lindbergh Bay
P.O. Box 301707
St. Thomas, VI 00803
P: (340) 774-1629
F: (340) 774-0025
E: info@viport.com

UTAH
Mr. Chad Sheppick
Director
Motor Carriers Division
Department of Transportation
4501 South 2700 West, P.O. Box 148240
Salt Lake City, UT 84114
P: (801) 965-4156
F: (801) 965-4847
E: csheppick@utah.gov

VIRGINIA
Mr. John F. Reinhart
CEO & Executive Director
Port Authority
600 World Trade Center
Norfolk, VA 23510
P: (757) 683-2103
F: (757) 683-8500
E: jreinhart@portofvirginia.com

WASHINGTON
Major General Bret D. Daugherty
Adjutant General
Department of Military
Building 1, 1 Militia Drive
Camp Murray, WA 98430
P: (253) 512-8000
F: (253) 512-8497
E: bret.daughtery@mil.wa.gov

Budget

Collects and analyzes budget requests and supporting materials and prepares the executive budget documents.

ALABAMA
Mr. Kelly Butler
State Budget Officer
Executive Budget Office
State House, 11 South Union Street
Montgomery, AL 36130
P: (334) 242-7160
F: (334) 242-3776
E: kelly.butler@budget.alabama.gov

ALASKA
Ms. Pat Pitney
Director
Office of Management & Budget
P.O. Box 110020
Juneau, AK 99811
P: (907) 465-4660
F: (907) 465-2090
E: pat.pitney@alaska.gov

ARIZONA
Mr. Lorenzo Romero
Director
Strategic Planning & Budgeting
1700 West Washington, Suite 500
Phoenix, AZ 85007
P: (602) 542-5381
F: (602) 542-5381
E: romero@az.gov

ARKANSAS
Mr. Larry Walther
Director
Department of Finance & Administration
1509 West 7th Street
DFA Building, Room 401
Little Rock, AR 72201
P: (501) 682-2242
F: (501) 682-1029
E: larry.walther@dfa.arkansas.gov

CALIFORNIA
Mr. Michael Cohen
Director
Department of Finance
915 L Street
Sacramento, CA 95814
P: (916) 445-3878
E: michael.cohen@dof.ca.gov

COLORADO
Mr. Henry Sobanet
Director
Governor's Office of State Planning & Budgeting
111 State Capitol Building
Denver, CO 80203
P: (303) 866-3317
F: (303) 866-3044
E: henry.sobanet@state.co.us

CONNECTICUT
Mr. Benjamin Barnes
Secretary
Office of Policy & Management
450 Capitol Avenue
Hartford, CT 06106
P: (860) 418-6500
F: (860) 418-6487
E: Ben.Barnes@Ct.gov

DELAWARE
Mr. Michael S. Jackson
Director
Office of Management & Budget
Haslet Armory
122 Martin Luther King Boulevard, South
Dover, DE 19901
P: (302) 739-4206
E: michael.s.jackson@state.de.us

Mr. Brian Maxwell
Director
Office of Management & Budget
Haslet Armory
122 Martin Luther King Boulevard South
Dover, DE 19901
P: (302) 739-4204
E: brian.maxwell@state.de.us

FLORIDA
Ms. Cynthia Kelly
State Budget Director
Office of Policy & Budget
Executive Office of the Governor
1702 The Capitol
Tallahassee, FL 32399
P: (850) 487-1880

GEORGIA
Ms. Teresa MacCartney
Director
Governor's Office of Planning & Budget
2 Capitol Square, 5th Floor
Atlanta, GA 30334
P: (404) 656-3820
F: (404) 656-3828
E: teresa.maccartney@opb.state.ga.us

HAWAII
The Honorable Wesley Machida
Director of Finance
Department of Budget & Finance
P.O. Box 150
Honolulu, HI 96810
P: (808) 586-1518
F: (808) 586-1976
E: hi.budgetandfinance@hawaii.gov

IDAHO
Ms. Jani Revier
Administrator
Division of Financial Management
308 North 8th Street, 3rd Floor
Boise, ID 83720
P: (208) 334-3900
F: (208) 334-2438
E: jani.revier@dfm.idaho.gov

ILLINOIS
Mr. Scott Harry
Director
Governor's Office of Management & Budget
603 Stratton Building
Springfield, IL 62706
P: (217) 782-4520
F: (217) 524-4876
E: Scott.Harry@illinois.gov

INDIANA
Mr. Jason D. Dudich
Director
State Budget Agency
200 West Washington Street, Room 212
Indianapolis, IN 46204
P: (317) 232-5610
F: (317) 233-3323
E: jdudich@gov.in.gov

IOWA
Mr. David Roederer
Director
Department of Management
State Capitol Building, Room 12
Des Moines, IA 50319
P: (515) 281-3322
F: (515) 242-5897
E: david.roederer@iowa.gov

KANSAS
Mr. Shawn Sullivan
Director
Division of the Budget
900 Southwest Jackson, Suite 504
Topeka, KS 66612
P: (785) 296-2436
F: (785) 296-0231
E: shawn.sullivan@budget.ks.gov

KENTUCKY
Mr. John E. Chilton
State Budget Director
Office of the State Budget Director
702 Capitol Avenue
284 Capitol Annex Building
Frankfort, KY 40601
P: (502) 564-7300
F: (502) 564-6684

LOUISIANA
Mr. Barry Dusse
State Director of Planning & Budget
Division of Administration
1201 North Third Street, Suite 7-150
Baton Rouge, LA 70804
P: (225) 342-7005
F: (225) 342-7220
E: barry.dusse@la.gov

MAINE
Ms. Melissa Gott
State Budget Officer
Department of Administrative & Financial Services
58 State House Station
Augusta, ME 04333
P: (207) 624-7810
E: Melissa.L.Gott@maine.gov

MARYLAND
Mr. David R. Brinkley
Secretary
Department of Budget & Management
45 Calvert Street
Annapolis, MD 21401
P: (410) 260-7041
F: (410) 974-2585
E: David.Brinkley@maryland.gov

Budget

MASSACHUSETTS
Ms. Kristen Lepore
Secretary
Executive Office for Administration & Finance
State House, Room 373
Boston, MA 02133
P: (617) 727-2040
F: (617) 727-2779
E: kristen.lepore@state.ma.us

MICHIGAN
Mr. Alton L. Pscholka
State Budget Director
State Budget Office
111 South Capitol Avenue, 6th Floor
Lansing, MI 48913
P: (517) 373-7560
F: (517) 241-5428
E: Contact-SBO@michigan.gov

MINNESOTA
Mr. Myron Frans
Commissioner
Management & Budget
658 Cedar Street, Suite 400
St. Paul, MN 55155
P: (651) 201-8011
F: (651) 296-8685
E: myron.frans@state.mn.us

MISSISSIPPI
Ms. Pricilla Ware
Director
Office of Budget & Fund Management
501 North West Street, Suite 1301-E
Jackson, MS 39201
P: (601) 359-2872
F: (601) 359-6758
E: Priscilla.Ware@dfa.ms.gov

MISSOURI
Mr. Dan Haug
Acting Budget Director
Division of Budget & Planning
Room 124, State Capitol
Box 809
Jefferson City, MO 65102
P: (573) 751-2345
F: (573) 526-4811
E: dhaug@senate.mo.gov

MONTANA
Mr. Dan Villa
Budget Director
Office of Budget & Program Planning
State Capitol, Room 277
P.O. Box 200802
Helena, MT 59620
P: (406) 444-3616
F: (406) 444-4670
E: dvilla@mt.gov

NEBRASKA
Mr. Gerry A. Oligmueller
State Budget Administrator
Budget Division
Department of Administrative Services
State Capitol, Room 1320
Lincoln, NE 68509
P: (402) 471-2526
E: gerry.oligmueller@nebraska.gov

NEVADA
Mr. James Wells
Director
Budget Division
Governor's Finance Office
209 East Musser Street, Room 200
Carson City, NV 89701
P: (775) 684-0222
F: (775) 684-0260
E: jwells@finance.nv.gov

NEW HAMPSHIRE
Ms. Vicki Quiram
Commissioner
Department of Administrative Services
25 Capitol Street
State House Annex, Room 120
Concord, NH 03301
P: (603) 271-3201
F: (603) 271-6600
E: vicki.quiram@nh.gov

NEW JERSEY
Mr. David A. Ridolfino
Director
Office of Management & Budget
Department of Treasury
33 West State Street, P.O. Box 221
Trenton, NJ 08625
P: (609) 292-6746
F: (609) 633-8179
E: david.ridolfino@treas.state.nj.us

NEW YORK
Mr. Robert Mujica Jr.
Budget Director
Division of the Budget
State Capitol
Albany, NY 12224
P: (518) 474-0132

NORTH CAROLINA
Mr. Charles Perusse
State Budget Director
Office of State Budget & Management
20320 Mail Service Center
Raleigh, NC 27699
P: (919) 807-4717
E: charles.perusse@osbm.nc.gov

NORTH DAKOTA
Ms. Sheila Peterson
Director, Fiscal Management Division
Office of Management & Budget
600 East Boulevard Avenue
Department 110
Bismarck, ND 58505
P: (701) 328-2680
F: (701) 328-4230
E: omb@nd.gov

NORTHERN MARIANA ISLANDS
Mr. Matt Deleon Guerrero
Chief of Staff
Office of the Governor
Caller Box 10007, Capitol Hill
Saipan, MP 96950
P: (670) 237-2231
F: (670) 664-2211

OHIO
Mr. Timothy S. Keen
Director
Office of Budget & Management
30 East Broad Street, 34th Floor
Columbus, OH 43215
P: (614) 752-2579
F: (614) 485-1058
E: tim.keen@obm.state.oh.us

OKLAHOMA
Ms. Jill Geiger
Budget Director
Office of State Finance
2300 North Lincoln Boulevard, Room 122
Oklahoma City, OK 73105
P: (405) 521-2141
F: (405) 521-3902

PENNSYLVANIA
Mr. Randy Albright
Secretary of the Budget
Office of the Budget
19th Floor, Harristown 2
333 Market Street
Harrisburg, PA 17101
P: (717) 787-2542
F: (717) 783-3368
E: budget@pa.gov

PUERTO RICO
Mr. Luis F. Batista Cruz
Director
Office of Management & Budget
P.O. Box 9023228
San Juan, PR 00902
P: (787) 725-9420
F: (787) 722-0299

RHODE ISLAND
Mr. Thomas A. Mullaney
Executive Director/State Budget Officer
Budget Office
Office of Management & Budget
One Capitol Hill, 4th Floor
Providence, RI 02908
P: (401) 222-6300
F: (401) 222-6436
E: thomas.mullaney@budget.ri.gov

SOUTH CAROLINA
Mr. Brian J. Gaines
Director
Executive Budget Office
1205 Pendleton Street, Suite 529
Columbia, SC 29201
P: (803) 734-2280
F: (803) 734-0645
E: Brian.Gaines@admin.sc.gov

SOUTH DAKOTA
Ms. Liza Clark
Chief Financial Officer & Commissioner
Bureau of Finance & Management
500 East Capitol Avenue
Pierre, SD 57501
P: (605) 773-3411
F: (605) 773-4711
E: liza.clark@state.sd.us

TENNESSEE
Mr. Larry Martin
Commissioner
Department of Finance & Administration
312 Rosa Parks Avenue, 18th Floor
Nashville, TN 37243
P: (615) 741-4806
E: Larry.Martin@tn.gov

TEXAS
Mr. Steven Albright
Director
Office of the Governor
1100 San Jacinto, 4th Floor
Austin, TX 78711
P: (512) 463-1778
F: (512) 463-1975

U.S. VIRGIN ISLANDS
Mr. Nellon Bowry
Director
Office of Management & Budget
No. 5041 Norre Gade, Second Floor
Emancipation Garden Station
St. Thomas, VI 00802
P: (340) 774-0750 Ext. 227
F: (340) 776-0069
E: nellon.bowry@omb.vi.gov

UTAH
Ms. Kristen Cox
Executive Director
Governor's Office of Management & Budget
State Capitol, Suite 150
P.O. Box 132210
Salt Lake City, UT 84114
P: (801) 538-1705
F: (801) 538-1547
E: kristencox@utah.gov

VERMONT
Mr. Andrew Pallito
Commissioner
Department of Finance & Management
109 State Street
Montpelier, VT 05609
P: (802) 828-2376
F: (802) 828-2428
E: andy.pallito@vermont.gov

VIRGINIA
Mr. Daniel Timberlake
Director
Department of Planning & Budget
1111 East Broad Street, 5th Floor
Richmond, VA 23219
P: (804) 786-7455
F: (804) 225-3291
E: dan.timberlake@dpb.virginia.gov

WASHINGTON
Mr. David Schumacher
Director
Office of Financial Management
P.O. Box 43113
Olympia, WA 98504
P: (360) 902-0530
F: (360) 664-2832
E: ofm.administration@ofm.wa.gov

WEST VIRGINIA
Mr. Mike McKown
Director
State Budget Office
Department of Revenue
Building 1, Room W-310
Charleston, WV 25305
P: (304) 558-0040
F: (304) 558-1588
E: Mike.P.McKown@wv.gov

WISCONSIN
Mr. Waylon Hurlburt
Administrator
Division of Executive Budget & Finance
P.O. Box 7864
Madison, WI 53707
P: (608) 266-1035
E: WaylonR.Hurlburt@wisconsin.gov

WYOMING
Mr. Kevin Hibbard
Deputy Director
Budget Division
Administration & Information
2001 Capitol Avenue, Room 105
Cheyenne, WY 82002
P: (307) 777-7203
E: kevin.hibbard@wyo.gov

Building Codes

Establishes and enforces standards of construction, materials and occupancy for all buildings.

ALABAMA
Ms. Katherine Lynn
Director
Building Commission
770 Washington Avenue, Suite 470
P.O. Box 301150
Montgomery, AL 36130
P: (334) 242-4082
F: (334) 242-4182

ARIZONA
Ms. Debra Blake
Assistant Deputy Director
Manufactured Housing Division
Department of Housing
1110 West Washington, Suite 280
Phoenix, AZ 85007
P: (602) 364-1022
F: (602) 364-1052

ARKANSAS
Mr. Aaron Howard
Director
Manufactured Home Commission
101 East Capitol Avenue, Suite 210
Little Rock, AR 72201
P: (501) 324-9032
F: (501) 683-3538

CALIFORNIA
Mr. Richard Conrad
Manager
Division of the State Architect
Architectural Code & Building Systems
1102 Q Street, Suite 5100
Sacramento, CA 95814
P: (916) 324-7180
F: (916) 445-3521
E: Richard.Conrad@dgs.ca.gov

Mr. Chester Widom
State Architect
Division of the State Architect
1102 Q Street, Suite 5100
Sacramento, CA 95811
P: (916) 445-8100
F: (916) 445-3521
E: chester.widom@dgs.ca.gov

COLORADO
Ms. Alison George
Director
Division of Housing
Department of Local Affairs
1313 Sherman, Room 500
Denver, CO 80203
P: (303) 864-7818
F: (303) 864-7856
E: alison.george@state.co.us

CONNECTICUT
Mr. Joseph V. Cassidy
State Building Inspector
Office of State Building Inspector
Department of Administrative Services
450 Columbus Boulevard, Suite 1303
Hartford, CT 06103
P: (860) 713-5900
F: (860) 713-7410
E: joseph.cassidy@ct.gov

DELAWARE
Mr. Grover P. Ingle
State Fire Marshal
Office of the State Fire Marshal
1537 Chestnut Grove Road
Dover, DE 19904
P: (302) 739-5665
F: (302) 739-3696
E: fire.marshal@state.de.us

DISTRICT OF COLUMBIA
Ms. Melinda M. Bolling
Director
Department of Consumer & Regulatory Affairs
1100 4th Street, Southwest
Washington, DC 20024
P: (202) 442-4400
F: (202) 442-9445
E: dcra@dc.gov

FLORIDA
Ms. Julie Dennis
Director
Division of Community Development
Department of Economic Opportunity
Caldwell Building, 107 East Madison
Tallahassee, FL 32399
P: (850) 245-7105

GEORGIA
Mr. Theodore N. Miltiades
Director, Office of Construction Codes & Research
Planning & Environmental Management Division
Department of Community Affairs
60 Executive Park South, Northeast
Atlanta, GA 30329
P: (404) 679-3106
E: ted.miltiades@dca.ga.gov

HAWAII
Mr. Manuel P. Neves
Chair
State Fire Council
636 South Street
Honolulu, HI 96813
P: (808) 723-7101
F: (808) 723-7111

IDAHO
Mr. Chris Jensen
Administrator
Division of Building Safety
1090 East Watertower Street, Suite 150
Meridian, ID 83642
P: (208) 334-3950
F: (877) 810-2840
E: chris.jensen@dbs.idaho.gov

ILLINOIS
Mr. Ray Boosinger
Building Codes & Regulations
3rd Floor Stratton
401 South Spring Street
Springfield, IL 62706
P: (217) 557-6140
F: (217) 524-4208
E: Ray.Boosinger@illinois.gov

INDIANA
Mr. James L. Greeson
Division Director & State Fire Marshal
Division of Fire & Building Safety
Department of Homeland Security
302 West Washington Street, Room E241
Indianapolis, IN 46204
P: (317) 232-2226
E: jgreeson@dhs.in.gov

IOWA
Ms. Roxann M. Ryan
Commissioner
Department of Public Safety
215 East 7th Street
Des Moines, IA 50319
P: (515) 725-6182
E: dpsinfo@dps.state.ia.us

KANSAS
Mr. Douglas Jorgensen
State Fire Marshal
Office of the Fire Marshal
800 Southwest Jackson, Suite 104
Topeka, KS 66612
P: (785) 296-3401
F: (785) 296-0151

KENTUCKY
Mr. Steve Miller
Commissioner
Department of Housing, Buildings & Construction
101 Sea Hero Road, Suite 100
Frankfort, KY 40601
P: (502) 573-0365
F: (502) 573-1057
E: steve.milby@ky.gov

LOUISIANA
Mr. Mark A. Moses
Director
Office of Facility Planning & Control
Division of Administration
P.O. Box 94095
Baton Rouge, LA 70804
P: (225) 342-0820
F: (225) 342-7624
E: mark.moses@la.gov

MAINE
Mr. Robert V. LeClair
Executive Director
Manufactured Housing Board
Professional & Financial Regulation
35 State House Station
Augusta, ME 04333
P: (207) 624-8612
F: (207) 624-8637
E: manuhousing.board@maine.gov

MARYLAND
Mr. Norman C. Wang
Director, Building Codes Administration
Division of Credit Assurance
Housing & Community Development
7800 Harkins Road
Lanham, MD 20706
P: (301) 429-7666
E: norman.wang1@maryland.gov

MASSACHUSETTS
Mr. Thomas P. Hopkins
Director
Architectural Access Board
Consumer Affairs & Business Regulation
One Ashburton Place, Room 1310
Boston, MA 02108
P: (617) 727-0660
F: (617) 727-0665
E: Thomas.Hopkins@state.ma.us

MICHIGAN
Mr. Irvin Poke
Director
Bureau of Construction Codes
Licensing & Regulatory Affairs
P.O. Box 30254
Lansing, MI 48909
P: (517) 241-9313
F: (517) 241-9308
E: pokei@michigan.gov

MINNESOTA
Mr. Scott McLellan
Director & State Building Official
Construction Codes & Licensing Division
Department of Labor & Industry
443 Lafayette Road, North
St. Paul, MN 55155
P: (651) 284-5012
F: (651) 284-5749
E: Scott.McLellan@state.mn.us

MISSISSIPPI
Mr. Ricky Davis
Chief Deputy Fire Marshal
State Fire Marshal's Office
Insurance Department
660 North Street, Suite 100-B
Jackson, MS 39202
P: (601) 359-1061
F: (601) 359-1076
E: ricky.davis@mid.ms.gov

MISSOURI
Mr. Justin Smith
Manager
Manufactured Housing & Modular Unit Program
Public Service Commission
P.O. Box 360
Jefferson City, MO 65102
P: (573) 526-2833
F: (573) 522-2509
E: justin.smith@psc.mo.gov

MONTANA
Mr. Todd Younkin
Division Administrator
Business Standards Division
Department of Labor & Industry
P.O. Box 200513
Helena, MT 59620
P: (406) 841-2300
E: dlibsdhelp@mt.gov

NEBRASKA
Mr. Mark Luttich
Director
Housing & Recreational Vehicles
Public Service Commission
1200 N Street, Suite 300
Lincoln, NE 68508
P: (402) 471-3101
F: (402) 471-0254
E: mark.luttich@nebraska.gov

NEVADA
Mr. Bruce H. Breslow
Director
Department of Business & Industry
3300 West Sahara Avenue, Suite 425
Las Vegas, NV 89102
P: (702) 486-2750
F: (702) 486-2758
E: breslow@business.nv.gov

NEW HAMPSHIRE
Mr. J. William Degnan
State Fire Marshal/Director
Division of Fire Safety
Department of Safety
33 Hazen Drive
Concord, NH 03305
P: (603) 223-4289
F: (603) 223-4294
E: fmo@dos.nh.gov

NEW JERSEY
Mr. Edward Smith
Director
Division of Codes & Standards
Department of Community Affairs
101 South Broad Street, P.O. Box 802
Trenton, NJ 08625
P: (609) 292-7899
F: (609)-633-6729

NEW MEXICO
Mr. Pat McMurray
Director
Construction Industries & Manufactured Housing
Regulation & Licensing Department
2550 Cerrillos Road, 3rd Floor
Santa Fe, NM 87505
P: (505) 476-4689
F: (505) 476-4702

NEW YORK
Mr. John R. Addario
Acting Director & Assistant Director for Educational and Technical Support
Division of Building Standards & Codes
One Commerce Plaza
99 Washington Avenue, Suite 1160
Albany, NY 12231
P: (518) 474-4073
F: (518) 486-4487
E: codes@dos.state.ny.us

NORTH CAROLINA
Mr. Cliff Isaac
Deputy Commissioner of Engineering
Engineering & Codes, Office of State Fire Marshal
Department of Insurance
1202 Mail Service Center
Raleigh, NC 27699
P: (919) 715-0067
E: cliff.Isaac@ncdoi.gov

NORTHERN MARIANA ISLANDS
Mr. Donald Anderson
Building Safety Official
Building Safety Code Division
2nd Floor, Joeten Commercial Center
Gualo Rai
Saipan, MP 96950
P: (670) 235-5827
F: (670) 235-6346

OHIO
Ms. Regina Hanshaw
Executive Secretary
Board of Building Standards
6606 Tussing Road
P.O. Box 4009
Reynoldsburg, OH 43068
P: (614) 644-2613
F: (614) 644-3147
E: rhanshaw@com.state.oh.us

OKLAHOMA
Mr. Robert Doke
State Fire Marshal
Office of the State Fire Marshal
2401 Northwest 23rd, Suite 4
Oklahoma City, OK 73107
P: (405) 522-5005
F: (405) 522-5028
E: robert.doke@fire.ok.gov

OREGON
Mr. Mark S. Long
Administrator
Building Codes Division
1535 Edgewater Street, Northwest
P.O. Box 14470
Salem, OR 97309
P: (503) 373-7235
F: (503) 378-2322
E: Mark.Long@oregon.gov

RHODE ISLAND
Mr. John P. Leyden
State Building Code Commissioner
Building Code Commission
560 Jefferson Boulevard, 2nd Floor
Suite 204
Warwick, RI 02886
P: (401) 889-5487
F: (401) 889-5535
E: Jeanne.Enos@doa.ri.gov

SOUTH CAROLINA
Mr. Roger K. Lowe
Administrator
Building Codes Council
110 Centerview Drive
Columbia, SC 29210
P: (803) 896-4688
F: (803) 896-4814
E: roger.lowe@llr.sc.gov

SOUTH DAKOTA
Mr. Paul Merriman
State Fire Marshal
Department of Public Safety
118 West Capitol Avenue
Pierre, SD 57501
P: (605) 773-3562
F: (605) 773-6631
E: paul.merriman@state.sd.us

Building Codes

TENNESSEE
Mr. Gary L. West
Assistant Commissioner
Fire Prevention Division
Department of Commerce & Insurance
500 James Robertson Parkway
Nashville, TN 37243
P: (615) 741-2981
F: (615) 741-1583
E: Fire.Prevention@TN.Gov

UTAH
Mr. Mark B. Steinagel
Director
Department of Commerce, Division of Occupational & Professional Licensing
160 East 300 South, 4th Floor
P.O. Box 146741
Salt Lake City, UT 84114
P: (801) 530-6628
F: (801) 530-6511
E: msteinagel@utah.gov

VERMONT
Mr. Matthew Lindhiem
Fire Safety Building Engineer
Division of Fire Safety
Department of Public Safety
1311 U.S. Route 302, Suite 600
Barre, VT 05641
P: (802) 479-4273
F: (802) 479-7562
E: Matthew.Lindhiem@vermont.gov

VIRGINIA
Ms. Cindy L. Davis
Deputy Director of Building & Fire Regulation
Department of Housing & Community Development
Main Street Centre
600 East Main Street, Suite 300
Richmond, VA 23219
P: (804) 371-7000
F: (804) 371-7090
E: cindy.davis@dhcd.virginia.gov

WASHINGTON
Mr. Tim Nogler
Managing Director
State Building Code Council
1500 Jefferson Avenue, Southeast
P.O. Box 41449
Olympia, WA 98504
P: (360) 407-9277
F: (360) 586-9088
E: tim.nogler@des.wa.gov

WEST VIRGINIA
Mr. Kenneth E. Tyree
State Fire Marshal
Office of the State Fire Marshal
1207 Quarrier Street, 2nd Floor
Charleston, WV 25301
P: (304) 558-2191
F: (304) 558-2537
E: Kenneth.E.Tyree@wv.gov

WISCONSIN
Ms. Laura Gutierrez
Secretary
Department of Safety & Professional Services
P.O. Box 8935
Madison, WI 53708
P: (608) 266-2112
F: (608) 266-9946

WYOMING
Mr. J. Michael Reed
Director & State Fire Marshal
Department of Fire Prevention & Electrical Safety
Capitol Hill Building, 3rd Floor
320 West 25th Street
Cheyenne, WY 82002
P: (307) 777-7288
F: (307) 777-7119
E: mike.reed@wyo.gov

Campaign Finance Administration

Administers and enforces campaign finance laws.

ALABAMA
The Honorable John Merrill (R)
Secretary of State
Office of the Secretary of State
P.O. Box 5616
Montgomery, AL 36103
P: (334) 242-7200
F: (334) 242-4993
E: john.merrill@sos.alabama.gov

ALASKA
Ms. Heather Hebdon
Executive Director
Public Offices Commission
Department of Administration
2221 East Northern Lights, Room 128
Anchorage, AK 99508
P: (907) 276-4176
F: (907) 276-7018
E: heather.hebdon@alaska.gov

AMERICAN SAMOA
Dr. Uiagalelei Lealofi
Chief Election Officer
Territorial Election Office
P.O. Box 3790
Pago Pago, AS 96799
P: (684) 699-3570
F: (684) 699-3574
E: lealofi.uiagalelei@gmail.com

ARKANSAS
The Honorable Mark Martin (R)
Secretary of State
Office of the Secretary of State
256 State Capitol Building
Little Rock, AR 72201
P: (501) 682-1010
F: (501) 682-3510
E: info@sos.arkansas.gov

CALIFORNIA
Ms. Jana Lean
Chief of Elections
Elections Division
1500 11th Street, 5th Floor
Sacramento, CA 95814
P: (916) 657-2166
F: (916) 653-3214
E: jana.lean@sos.ca.gov

COLORADO
Mr. Judd Choate
Director of Elections
Elections Division
Department of State
1700 Broadway, Suite 200
Denver, CO 80290
P: (303) 894-2200
F: (303) 869-4861
E: judd.choate@sos.state.co.us

CONNECTICUT
The Honorable Denise W. Merrill (D)
Secretary of State
Office of the Secretary of State
Capitol Office
P.O. Box 150470
Hartford, CT 06115
P: (860) 509-6200
F: (860) 509-6209
E: denise.merrill@ct.gov

DELAWARE
Ms. M. Elaine Manlove
State Election Commissioner
Office of the State Election Commissioner
905 South Governors Avenue, Suite 170
Dover, DE 19904
P: (302) 739-4277
F: (302) 739-6794
E: coe_vote@state.de.us

DISTRICT OF COLUMBIA
Ms. Cecily E. Collier-Montgomery
Director
Office of Campaign Finance
Frank D. Reeves Municipal Building
2000 14th Street, Northwest, Suite 433
Washington, DC 20009
P: (202) 671-0547
F: (202) 671-0658
E: ocf@dc.gov

FLORIDA
The Honorable Kenneth Detzner (R)
Secretary of State
Office of the Secretary of State
R.A. Gray Building
500 South Bronough Street, Suite 100
Tallahassee, FL 32399
P: (850) 245-6000
F: (850) 245-6125
E: secretaryofstate@dos.myflorida.com

GUAM
Ms. Maria I.D. Pangelinan
Executive Director
Elections Commission
414 West Soledad Avenue
GCIC Building, Suite 200
Hagatna, GU 96910
P: (671) 477-9791
F: (671) 477-1895
E: vote@gec.guam.gov

HAWAII
Ms. Kristin E. Izumi-Nitao
Executive Director
Campaign Spending Commission
Leiopapa A. Kamehameha Building
235 South Beretania Street, Room 300
Honolulu, HI 96813
P: (808) 586-0285
F: (808) 586-0288

IDAHO
The Honorable Lawerence Denney (R)
Secretary of State
Office of the Secretary of State
P.O. Box 83720
Boise, ID 83720
P: (208) 334-2300
F: (208) 334-2282
E: ldenney@sos.idaho.gov

ILLINOIS
Mr. Steve Sandvoss
Executive Director
State Board of Elections
2329 South Macarthur Boulevard
Springfield, IL 62704
P: (217) 782-4141
F: (217) 782-5959
E: ssandvoss@elections.il.gov

INDIANA
Mr. J. Bradley King
Co-Director
Election Division
Office of the Secretary of State
302 West Washington Street, Room E-204
Indianapolis, IN 46204
P: (317) 233-0929
F: (317) 233-6793
E: bking@iec.in.gov

IOWA
Ms. Megan Tooker
Executive Director & Legal Counsel
Ethics & Campaign Disclosure Board
510 East 12th, Suite 1A
Des Moines, IA 50319
P: (515) 281-3489
F: (515) 281-4073
E: megan.tooker@iowa.gov

KANSAS
Ms. Carol E. Williams
Executive Director
Governmental Ethics Commission
901 South Kansas Avenue
Topeka, KS 66612
P: (785) 296-4219
F: (785) 296-2548
E: ethics@ethics.ks.gov

KENTUCKY
Mr. John R. Steffen
Executive Director
Registry of Election Finance
140 Walnut Street
Frankfort, KY 40601
P: (502) 564-2226
F: (502) 564-5622
E: john.steffen@ky.gov

LOUISIANA
Ms. Kathleen Allen
Ethics Administrator
Ethics Administration Program
617 North Third Street, Suite 10-36
P.O. Box 4368
Baton Rouge, LA 70821
P: (225) 219-5600
F: (225) 381-7271
E: kathleen.allen@la.gov

MAINE
Mr. Jonathan Wayne
Executive Director
Commission on Governmental Ethics & Election Practices
135 State House Station
Augusta, ME 04333
P: (207) 287-4179
F: (207) 287-6775
E: Jonathan.Wayne@maine.gov

Campaign Finance Administration

MARYLAND
Mr. Jared DeMarinis
Director
Division of Candidacy & Campaign Finance
State Board of Elections
P.O. Box 6486
Annapolis, MD 21401
P: (410) 269-2853
F: (410) 974-5415
E: Jared.DeMarinis@maryland.gov

MASSACHUSETTS
Mr. Michael J. Sullivan
Director
Office of Campaign & Political Finance
John W. McCormack Building
One Ashburton Place, Room 411
Boston, MA 02108
P: (617) 979-8300
F: (617) 727-6549
E: ocpf@cpf.state.ma.us

MICHIGAN
Mr. Christopher M. Thomas
Director
Bureau of Elections
Department of State
Lansing, MI 48918
P: (517) 335-2789
F: (517) 373-0941
E: ChristopherT@michigan.gov

MINNESOTA
Mr. Jeff Sigurdson
Executive Director
Campaign Finance & Public Disclosure Board
Centennial Office Building, Suite 190
658 Cedar Street
St. Paul, MN 55155
P: (651) 539-1190
F: (651) 539-1196
E: jeff.sigurdson@state.mn.us

MISSISSIPPI
Ms. Kimberly P. Turner
Assistant Secretary of State
Elections Division
Secretary of State's Office
401 Mississippi Street, P.O. Box 136
Jackson, MS 39205
P: (601) 359-5137
F: (601) 576-2545
E: Kim.Turner@sos.ms.gov

MISSOURI
Mr. James Klahr
Executive Director
Ethics Commission
3411A Knipp Drive
P.O. Box 1370
Jefferson City, MO 65102
P: (573) 751-2020
F: (573) 526-4506
E: helpdesk@mec.mo.gov

MONTANA
Mr. Jeff Mangan
Commissioner
Commissioner of Political Practices
1209 8th Avenue
P.O. Box 202401
Helena, MT 59620
P: (406) 444-2942
F: (406) 444-1643

NEBRASKA
Mr. Frank Daley
Executive Director
Accountability & Disclosure Commission
P.O. Box 95086
Lincoln, NE 68509
P: (402) 471-2522
F: (402) 471-6599
E: frank.daley@nebraska.gov

NEVADA
The Honorable Barbara Cegavske (R)
Secretary of State
Office of the Secretary of State
101 North Carson Street, Suite 3
Carson City, NV 89701
P: (775) 684-5708
F: (775) 684-5724
E: sosexec@sos.nv.gov

NEW HAMPSHIRE
The Honorable William M. Gardner (D)
Secretary of State
Office of the Secretary of State
State House, Room 204
Concord, NH 03301
P: (603) 271-3242
F: (603) 271-6316
E: kladd@sos.state.nh.us

NEW JERSEY
Mr. Jeffrey M. Brindle
Executive Director
Election Law Enforcement Commission
P.O. Box 185
Trenton, NJ 08625
P: (609) 292-8700
F: (609) 777-1448
E: jeff.brindle@elec.state.nj.us

NEW MEXICO
Ms. Kari Fresquez
Interim Elections Director
Bureau of Elections
Secretary of State's Office
325 Don Gaspar, Suite 300
Santa Fe, NM 87501
P: (505) 827-3600
F: (505) 827-8403
E: kari.fresquez@state.nm.us

NEW YORK
Mr. Robert A. Brehm
Co-Executive Director
State Board of Elections
40 North Pearl Street, Suite 5
Albany, NY 12207
P: (518) 474-8100
F: (518) 486-4068
E: Robert.Brehm@elections.ny.gov

Mr. Todd D. Valentine
Co-Executive Director
State Board of Elections
40 North Pearl Street, Suite 5
Albany, NY 12207
P: (518) 474-8100
F: (518) 486-4068
E: Todd.Valentine@elections.ny.gov

NORTH CAROLINA
Ms. Kim Westbrook Strach
Executive Director
State Board of Elections
441 North Harrington Street
P.O. Box 27255
Raleigh, NC 27611
P: (919) 733-7173
F: (919) 715-0135
E: kim.strach@ncsbe.gov

NORTH DAKOTA
Ms. LeeAnn Oliver
Elections Specialist
Office of the Secretary of State
600 East Boulevard Avenue
Department 108
Bismarck, ND 58505
P: (701) 328-4146
F: (701) 328-3413
E: soselect@nd.gov

NORTHERN MARIANA ISLANDS
Mr. Michael S. Pai
Public Auditor
Office of the Public Auditor
P.O. Box 501399
Saipan, MP 96950
P: (670) 322-6481
F: (670) 322-7812
E: mpai@opacnmi.com

OHIO
The Honorable Jon Husted (R)
Secretary of State
Office of the Secretary of State
180 East Broad Street, 16th Floor
Columbus, OH 43215
P: (614) 466-2655
F: (614) 644-0649
E: jhusted@ohiosecretaryofstate.gov

OREGON
Mr. Stephen Trout
Director of Elections
Office of the Secretary of State
255 Capitol Street, Northeast, Suite 501
Salem, OR 97310
P: (503) 986-1518
F: (503) 373-7414
E: steve.trout@state.or.us

PENNSYLVANIA
Mr. Jonathan M. Marks
Commissioner
Bureau of Commissions, Elections & Legislation
Department of State, 401 North Street
210 North Office Building
Harrisburg, PA 17120
P: (717) 787-5280
F: (717) 705-0721
E: RA-BCEL@pa.gov

PUERTO RICO
Mr. Angel A. Roman Gonzalez
Executive Director
State Election Commission
P.O. Box 195552
San Juan, PR 00919
P: (787) 777-8682
F: (787) 296-0173

RHODE ISLAND
Mr. Robert Rapoza
Acting Executive Director
Board of Elections
50 Branch Avenue
Providence, RI 02904
P: (401) 222-2345
F: (401) 222-3135
E: campaignfinance@elections.ri.gov

SOUTH CAROLINA
Mr. Steven W. Hamm
Interim Executive Director
State Ethics Commission
5000 Thurmond Mall, Suite 250
Columbia, SC 29201
P: (803) 253-4192
F: (803) 253-7539

TENNESSEE
Ms. Norma Lester
Chair
Registry of Election Finance
404 James Robertson Parkway, Suite 104
Nashville, TN 37243
P: (615) 741-7959
F: (615) 532-8905
E: registry.info@tn.gov

TEXAS
Ms. Seana Willing
Executive Director
Ethics Commission
201 East 14th Street, 10th Floor
P.O. Box 12070
Austin, TX 78711
P: (512) 463-5800
F: (512) 463-5777
E: seana.willing@ethics.state.tx.us

U.S. VIRGIN ISLANDS
Ms. Caroline Fawkes
Supervisor of Elections
Election System of the Virgin Islands
P.O. Box 1499, Kingshill
St. Croix, VI 00851
P: (340) 773-1021
F: (340) 773-4523
E: caroline.fawkes@vi.gov

UTAH
Mr. Mark Thomas
Director of Elections
Office of the Lieutenant Governor
Utah State Capitol Suite 220
P.O. Box 142325
Salt Lake City, UT 84114
P: (801) 538-1041
F: (801) 538-1133
E: mjthomas@utah.gov

VERMONT
The Honorable Jim Condos (D)
Secretary of State
Office of the Secretary of State
128 State Street
Montpelier, VT 05633
P: (802) 828-2148
F: (802) 828-2496
E: jim.condos@sec.state.vt.us

VIRGINIA
Mr. Edgardo Cortes
Commissioner
Department of Elections
Washington Building
1100 Bank Street, First Floor
Richmond, VA 23219
P: (804) 864-8901
F: (804) 371-0194
E: edgardo.cortes@elections.virginia.gov

WASHINGTON
B.G. Sandahl
Acting Executive Director
Public Disclosure Commission
711 Capitol Way, Room 206
P.O. Box 40908
Olympia, WA 98504
P: (360) 586-1042
F: (360) 753-1112
E: pdc@pdc.wa.gov

WISCONSIN
Mr. Michael Haas
Administrator
Elections Commission
212 East Washington Avenue, 3rd Floor
P.O. Box 7984
Madison, WI 53707
P: (608) 266-0136
F: (608) 267-0500
E: Michael.Haas@wi.gov

WYOMING
The Honorable Ed Murray (R)
Secretary of State
Office of the Secretary of State
2020 Carey Avenue, Suite 600 & 700
Cheyenne, WY 82002
P: (307) 777-7378
F: (307) 777-6217
E: secofstate@wyo.gov

Chief Information Officer

Oversees state information technology operations and develops, implements, and monitors state IT initiatives.

ALABAMA
Ms. Joanne Hale
Acting Secretary of Information Technology
Office of Information Technology
445 Dexter Avenue, Suite 9050
Montgomery, AL 36104
P: (334) 242-7360

ALASKA
Mr. Bill Vajda
Chief Information Officer
Division of Enterprise Technology Services
Department of Administration
333 Willoughby Avenue, 10th Floor
Juneau, AK 99801
P: (907) 465-8461
E: bill.vajda@alaska.gov

ARIZONA
Mr. Morgan Reed
Chief Information Officer
Strategic Enterprise Technology Agency
100 North 15th Avenue, Suite 400
Phoenix, AZ 85007
P: (602) 540-8831
F: (602) 542-4272

ARKANSAS
Ms. Yessica Jones
Director & Chief Technology Officer
Department of Information Systems
P.O. Box 3155
Little Rock, AR 72203
P: (501) 683-1620

CALIFORNIA
Ms. Amy Tong
Director & Chief Information Officer
Department of Technology
1325 J Street, Suite 1600
Sacramento, CA 95814
P: (916) 319-9223
F: (916) 324-1734
E: amy.tong@state.ca.gov

COLORADO
Ms. Suma Nallapati
Secretary of Technology & Chief Information Officer
Governor's Office of Information Technology
601 East 18th Avenue, Suite 250
Denver, CO 80203
P: (303) 764-7707
E: oit@state.co.us

CONNECTICUT
Mr. Mark D. Raymond
Chief Information Officer
Department of Administrative Services
55 Farmington Avenue
Hartford, CT 06105
P: (860) 622-2419
F: (860) 291-8665
E: mark.raymond@ct.gov

DELAWARE
Mr. James L. Collins
Chief Information Officer
Department of Technology & Information
801 Silver Lake Boulevard
Dover, DE 19904
P: (302) 739-9500
F: (302) 739-9686
E: james.collins@state.de.us

DISTRICT OF COLUMBIA
Ms. Archana Vemulapalli
Acting Chief Technology Officer
Office of the Chief Technology Officer
200 I Street, Southeast
5th Floor
Washington, DC 20003
P: (202) 727-7349
F: (202) 727-6857
E: octo@dc.gov

FLORIDA
Mr. Eric Larson
Acting Executive Director & Chief Information Officer & Chief Operations Officer
Agency for State Technology
4050 Esplanade Way, Suite 115
Tallahassee, FL 32399
P: (850) 717-9506

GEORGIA
Mr. Calvin Rhodes
Executive Director & Chief Information Officer
Technology Authority
47 Trinity Avenue, Southwest
Atlanta, GA 30334
P: (404) 463-2300
F: (404) 463-2380
E: calvn.rhodes@gta.ga.gov

GUAM
Mr. Frank Lujan
Chief Technology Officer
Office of Technology
P.O. Box 884
Hagatna, GU 96932
P: (671) 635-4500

HAWAII
Mr. Todd Nacapuy
Chief Information Officer
Office of Enterprise Technology Services
P.O. Box 119
Honolulu, HI 96810
P: (808) 586-1910

IDAHO
Mr. Greg Zickau
Chief Information Officer
Department of Administration
650 West State Street, Suite 100
Boise, ID 83720
P: (208) 332-1875
F: (208) 334-2307
E: greg.zickau@cio.idaho.gov

ILLINOIS
Mr. Hardik Bhatt
Chief Information Officer
Department of Innovation & Technology
100 West Randolph, 4th Floor
Chicago, IL 60601
P: (217) 785-1943

INDIANA
Mr. Dewand Neely
Chief Information Officer & Director
Office of Technology
1000 North Senate Avenue
IGCN, Room N551
Indianapolis, IN 46204
P: (317) 234-0835

IOWA
Mr. Bob Von Wolffradt
Director & Chief Information Officer
Office of the Chief Information Officer
1305 East Walnut Street
Hoover Building, Level B
Des Moines, IA 50319
P: (515) 281-3462
F: (515) 281-6137
E: robert.vonwolffradt@iowa.gov

KANSAS
Mr. Phil Wittmer
Chief Information Technology Officer
Office of Information Technology Services
900 Southwest Jackson, Room 804
Topeka, KS 66603
P: (785) 296-3463

KENTUCKY
Mr. Jim Barnhart
Deputy Commissioner & Acting Chief Information Officer
Commonwealth Office of Technology
Finance & Administration Cabinet
101 Cold Harbor Drive
Frankfort, KY 40601
P: (502) 564-7777

LOUISIANA
Mr. Richard Howze
State Chief Information Officer
Office of Technology Services
Division of Administration
Claiborne Building, Suite 2-130
Baton Rouge, LA 70804
P: (225) 342-7105
F: (225) 219-9465
E: cio@la.gov

MAINE
Mr. Jim Smith
Chief Information Officer
Office of Information Technology
Administrative & Financial Services
51 Commerce Drive
Augusta, ME 04330
P: (207) 624-7568

MARYLAND
Mr. Michael Leahy
Acting Secretary of Information Technology
Department of Information Technology
100 Community Place
Annapolis, MD 21032
P: (410) 697-9406

MASSACHUSETTS
Mr. Mark Nunnelly
Executive Director
Executive Office for Administration & Finance
MassIT
One Ashburton Place, Room 804
Boston, MA 02108
P: (617) 626-4671

MICHIGAN
Mr. David Behen
Director
Department of Technology, Management & Budget
320 South Walnut Street, 2nd Floor
P.O. Box 30026
Lansing, MI 48909
P: (517) 373-1004
E: behend@michigan.gov

MINNESOTA
Mr. Tom Baden
Commissioner & Chief Information Officer
Information Technology Services
658 Cedar Street
St. Paul, MN 55155
P: (651) 556-8007

MISSISSIPPI
Dr. Craig P. Orgeron
Chief Information Officer & Executive Director
Department of Information Technology Services
3771 Eastwood Drive
Jackson, MS 39211
P: (601) 432-8000
F: (601) 713-6380
E: craig.orgeron@its.ms.gov

MISSOURI
Mr. Rich Kliethermes
Chief Information Officer
Information Technology Services Division
Office of Administration
301 West High Street, Suite 270
Jefferson City, MO 65101
P: (573) 526-7742

MONTANA
Mr. Ron Baldwin
Chief Information Officer
Information Technology Services Division
Department of Administration
P.O. Box 200113
Helena, MT 59620
P: (406) 444-2777
F: (406) 444-2701

NEBRASKA
Mr. Ed Toner
Chief Information Officer
Office of the Chief Information Officer
501 South 14th Street
P.O. Box 95045
Lincoln, NE 68508
P: (402) 471-3717
E: ed.toner@nebraska.gov

NEVADA
Ms. Shannon Rahming
Administrator & Chief Information Officer
Enterprise Information Technology Services
100 North Stewart Street, Suite 100
Carson City, NV 89701
P: (775) 684-5800

NEW HAMPSHIRE
Mr. Denis Goulet
Commissioner
Department of Information Technology
27 Hazen Drive
Concord, NH 03301
P: (603) 223-5701
E: Denis.Goulet@Doit.nh.gov

NEW JERSEY
Mr. Dave Weinstein
Chief Information Officer
Office of Information Technology
300 Riverview Plaza
Trenton, NJ 08625
P: (609) 777-5865

NEW MEXICO
Mr. Darryl Ackley
Secretary & Chief Information Officer
Department of Information Technology
P.O. Box 22550
Santa Fe, NM 87505
P: (505) 476-3070
F: (505) 827-2948

NORTH CAROLINA
Mr. Danny Lineberry
Acting Chief Information Officer
Department of Information Technology
P.O. Box 17209
Raleigh, NC 27619
P: (919) 754-6576

NORTH DAKOTA
Mr. Shawn Riley
Chief Information Officer
Information Technology Department
4201 Normandy Street
Bismarck, ND 58503
P: (701) 328-1001
F: (701) 328-1075
E: sriley@nd.gov

OHIO
Mr. Stuart R. Davis
Chief Information Officer & Assistant Director
Office of Information Technology
Department of Administrative Services
30 East Broad Street, 39th Floor
Columbus, OH 43215
P: (614) 644-6446
F: (614) 728-5297
E: Stu.Davis@das.ohio.gov

OKLAHOMA
Mr. Bo Reese
Chief Information Officer
Office of Management & Enterprise Services
Information Services Division
3115 North Lincoln Boulevard
Oklahoma City, OK 73105
P: (405) 522-5722
F: (405) 521-3902

OREGON
Mr. Alex Pettit
Chief Information Officer
Department of Administrative Services
Executive Building
155 Cottage Street Northeast, 4th Floor
Salem, OR 97301
P: (503) 378-2128
F: (503) 378-3795
E: alex.pettit@das.state.or.us

PENNSYLVANIA
Mr. John MacMillan
Deputy Secretary for Information Technology & Chief Information Officer
Office for Information Technology
Governor's Office of Administration
613 North Street, Room 210
Harrisburg, PA 17109
P: (717) 787-5440
F: (717) 787-4523
E: cio@pa.gov

PUERTO RICO
Mr. Luis Arocho
Chief Information Officer
Commonwealth of Puerto Rico
La Fortaleza
P.O. Box 9020082
San Juan, PR 00901
P: (787) 725-9420

RHODE ISLAND
Mr. Christopher Antonellis
Chief Information Officer
Office of Information Technology
Department of Administration
50 Service Avenue
Warwick, RI 02886
P: (401) 462-2185

SOUTH CAROLINA
Mr. Keith Osman
Chief Information Officer
Division of Technology Operations
Department of Administration
4430 Broad River Road
Columbia, SC 29210
P: (803) 896-0222

SOUTH DAKOTA
Mr. David Zolnowsky
Commissioner
Bureau of Information & Telecommunications
Kneip Building
700 Governors Drive
Pierre, SD 57501
P: (605) 773-5110
F: (605) 773-6040

TENNESSEE
Mr. Mark Bengel
Chief Information Officer
Strategic Technology Solutions
Department of Finance & Administration
901 5th Avenue, North
Nashville, TN 37243
P: (615) 741-7951
F: (615) 532-0471

TEXAS
Mr. Todd Kimbriel
Chief Information Officer
Department of Information Resources
300 West 15th Street, Suite 1300
Austin, TX 78701
P: (512) 475-0579
F: (512) 475-4759

U.S. VIRGIN ISLANDS
Mr. Angelo Riddick
Director & Chief Information Officer
Bureau of Information Technology
9059 Estate Castle Coakley
Christiansted, VI 00820
P: (340) 713-0354
F: (340) 719-1623

Chief Information Officer

UTAH
Mr. Michael Hussey
Chief Information Officer
Department of Technology Services
1 State Office Buidling, Floor 6
Salt Lake City, UT 84114
P: (801) 538-3298
F: (801) 538-3622
E: mhussey@utah.gov

VERMONT
Ms. Darwin J. Thompson
Commissioner
Department of Information & Innovation
133 State Street, 5th Floor
Montpelier, VT 05633
P: (802) 828-1142
E: darwin.thompson@vermont.gov

VIRGINIA
Mr. Nelson Moe
Chief Information Officer
Information Technologies Agency
11751 Meadowville Lane
Chester, VA 23836
P: (804) 416-6004
F: (804) 416-6355
E: cio@vita.virginia.gov

WASHINGTON
Mr. Michael Cockrill
Director & Chief Information Officer
State Technology Solutions
1500 Jefferson Street, Southeast
Olympia, WA 98504
P: (360) 407-8675
F: (360) 664-0495
E: ocio@ofm.wa.gov

WEST VIRGINIA
Mr. John Dunlap
Chief Technology Officer
Office of Technology
Capitol Complex, Building 5, 10th Floor
Charleston, WV 25305
P: (304) 558-8100
F: (304) 558-0136
E: John.D.Dunlap@wv.gov

WISCONSIN
Mr. David Cagigal
Chief Information Officer
Division of Enterprise Technology
Department of Administration
101 East Wilson Street
Madison, WI 53707
P: (608) 264-9502
F: (608) 267-0626
E: David.Cagigal@wisconsin.gov

WYOMING
Mr. Tony Young
Chief Information Officer
Department of Enterprise Technology Services
Emerson Building, Room 237
2001 Capitol Avenue
Cheyenne, WY 82002
P: (307) 777-5840

Chief Justice

The chief justice or judge of the state court of last resort.

ALABAMA
The Honorable Lyn Stuart (R)
Chief Justice
Supreme Court
300 Dexter Avenue
Montgomery, AL 36104
P: (334) 242-4609

ALASKA
The Honorable Craig F. Stowers
Chief Justice
Supreme Court
303 K Street
Anchorage, AK 99501
P: (907) 264-0612

AMERICAN SAMOA
The Honorable F. Michael Kruse
Chief Justice
High Court
Courthouse, P.O. Box 309
Pago Pago, AS 96799
P: (684) 633-1410
F: (684) 633-1318

ARIZONA
The Honorable W. Scott Bales
Chief Justice
Supreme Court
1501 West Washington
Suite, 402
Phoenix, AZ 85007
P: (602) 542-9396

ARKANSAS
The Honorable Dan Kemp
Chief Justice
Supreme Court
Justice Building
625 Marshall
Little Rock, AR 72201
P: (501) 682-6849

CALIFORNIA
The Honorable Tani Cantil-Sakauye
Chief Justice
Supreme Court
350 McAllister Court
San Francisco, CA 94102
P: (415) 865-7015

COLORADO
The Honorable Nancy E. Rice
Chief Justice
Supreme Court
2 East 14th Avenue, Fourth Floor
Denver, CO 80203
P: (303) 867-1111 Ext. 266

CONNECTICUT
The Honorable Chase T. Rogers
Chief Justice
Supreme Court
231 Capitol Avenue
Hartford, CT 06106
P: (860) 757-2200
F: (860) 757-2217

DELAWARE
The Honorable Leo E. Strine Jr.
Chief Justice
Supreme Court
New Castle Courthouse
500 North King Street, Suite 11400
Wilmington, DE 19801
P: (302) 255-0511
F: (302) 255-2276

DISTRICT OF COLUMBIA
The Honorable Anna Blackburne-Rigsby
Chief Judge
Court of Appeals
Moultrie Courthouse
500 Indiana Avenue, Northwest, 6th Floor
Washington, DC 20001
P: (202) 879-2771

FLORIDA
The Honorable Jorge Labarga
Chief Justice
Supreme Court
500 South Duval Street
Tallahassee, FL 32399
P: (850) 488-2281
F: (850) 488-6130

GEORGIA
The Honorable P. Harris Hines
Chief Justice
Supreme Court
244 Washington Street, Southwest
Room 572, State Office Annex
Atlanta, GA 30334
P: (404) 656-3470
F: (404) 656-2253

GUAM
The Honorable Katherine A. Maraman
Chief Justice
Supreme Court
Suite 300, Guam Judicial Center
120 West O'Brien Drive
Hagatna, GU 96910

HAWAII
The Honorable Mark E. Recktenwald
Chief Justice
Supreme Court
Aliiolani Hale
417 South King Street
Honolulu, HI 96813
P: (808) 539-4919
F: (808) 539-4928

IDAHO
The Honorable Roger S. Burdick
Chief Justice
Supreme Court
P.O. Box 83720
451 West State Street
Boise, ID 83720
P: (208) 334-3464
F: (208) 947-7590

ILLINOIS
The Honorable Lloyd A. Karmeier (R)
Chief Justice
Supreme Court
Supreme Court Building
200 East Capitol Avenue
Springfield, IL 62701
P: (217) 782-2035

INDIANA
The Honorable Loretta H. Rush
Chief Justice
Supreme Court
315 State House
200 West Washington Street
Indianapolis, IN 46204
P: (317) 242-2540

IOWA
The Honorable Mark S. Cady
Chief Justice
Supreme Court
Iowa Judicial Branch Building
111 East Court Avenue
Des Moines, IA 50319
P: (515) 281-5174

KANSAS
The Honorable Lawton R. Nuss
Chief Justice
Supreme Court
Judicial Center
301 Southwest 10th Avenue
Topeka, KS 66612
P: (785) 296-3229
F: (785) 296-1028
E: nussl@kscourts.org

KENTUCKY
The Honorable John D. Minton Jr.
Chief Justice
Supreme Court
1001 Center Street, 2nd Floor
Room 204
Bowling Green, KY 42101
P: (270) 746-7867

LOUISIANA
The Honorable Bernette J. Johnson
Chief Justice
Supreme Court
400 Royal Street
New Orleans, LA 70130
P: (504) 310-2300

MAINE
The Honorable Leigh I. Saufley
Chief Justice
Supreme Judicial Court
142 Federal Street
P.O. Box 368
Portland, ME 04112
P: (207) 822-4286

MARYLAND
The Honorable Mary Ellen Barbera
Chief Judge
Court of Appeals
Judicial Center
50 Maryland Avenue
Rockville, MD 20850
P: (240) 777-9320

MASSACHUSETTS
The Honorable Ralph D. Gants
Chief Justice
Supreme Judicial Court
John Adams Courthouse, Suite 2500
One Pemberton Square
Boston, MA 02108
P: (617) 557-1000
F: (617) 557-1145

Chief Justice

MICHIGAN
The Honorable Stephen J. Markman
Chief Justice
Supreme Court
P.O. Box 30052
Lansing, MI 48909
P: (517) 373-0120

MINNESOTA
The Honorable Lorie S. Gildea
Chief Justice
Supreme Court
Minnesota Judicial Center
25 Rev. Martin Luther King Jr. Boulevard
St. Paul, MN 55155

MISSISSIPPI
The Honorable William L. Waller Jr.
Chief Justice
Supreme Court
Gartin Building, 3rd Floor
P.O. Box 249
Jackson, MS 39205
P: (601) 359-3694
F: (601) 359-2407

MISSOURI
The Honorable Patricia Breckenridge
Chief Justice
Supreme Court
P.O. Box 150
Jefferson City, MO 65102
P: (573) 751-4144
F: (573) 751-7514

MONTANA
The Honorable Mike McGrath (D)
Chief Justice
Supreme Court
215 North Sanders
P.O. Box 203001
Helena, MT 59620
P: (406) 444-5490
F: (404) 444-3274

NEBRASKA
The Honorable Michael G. Heavican
Chief Justice
Supreme Court
State Capitol, Room 2214
Lincoln, NE 68509
P: (402) 471-3738
F: (402) 471-2197
E: mike.heavican@nebraska.gov

NEVADA
The Honorable Michael A. Cherry
Chief Justice
Supreme Court
201 South Carson Street
Carson City, NV 89701
P: (775) 684-1600

NEW HAMPSHIRE
The Honorable Linda S. Dalianis
Chief Justice
Supreme Court
Supreme Court Building
One Charles Doe Drive
Concord, NH 03301
P: (603) 271-2646

NEW JERSEY
The Honorable Stuart Rabner (D)
Chief Justice
Supreme Court
Richard J. Hughes Justice Complex
P.O. Box 970
Trenton, NJ 08625
P: (609) 292-4837

NEW MEXICO
The Honorable Charles W. Daniels
Chief Justice
Supreme Court
P.O. Box 848
Santa Fe, NM 87504
P: (505) 827-4860

NEW YORK
The Honorable Janet DiFiore
Chief Judge
Court of Appeals
20 Eagle Street
Albany, NY 12207
P: (518) 455-7700
F: (518) 463-6869

NORTH CAROLINA
The Honorable Mark D. Martin
Chief Justice
Supreme Court
P.O. Box 2170
Raleigh, NC 27602
P: (919) 733-3723

NORTH DAKOTA
The Honorable Gerald W. VandeWalle
Chief Justice
Supreme Court
State Capitol Building
600 East Boulevard Avenue, Dept. 180
Bismark, ND 58505
P: (701) 328-2221
F: (701) 328-4480
E: GVandeWalle@ndcourts.gov

NORTHERN MARIANA ISLANDS
The Honorable Alexandro C. Castro
Chief Justice
Supreme Court
P.O. Box 502165
Saipan, MP 96950
P: (670) 236-9700
F: (670) 236-9702

OHIO
The Honorable Maureen O'Connor (R)
Chief Justice
Supreme Court
65 South Front Street, 9th Floor
Columbus, OH 43215
P: (614) 466-5201
F: (614) 752-4418

OKLAHOMA
The Honorable Doug Combs
Chief Justice
Supreme Court
P.O. Box 53126
Oklahoma City, OK 73152
P: (405) 521-2163

OREGON
The Honorable Thomas A. Balmer
Chief Justice
Supreme Court
1163 State Street
Salem, OR 97301
P: (503) 986-5717
F: (503) 986-5730

PENNSYLVANIA
The Honorable Thomas G. Saylor
Chief Justice
Supreme Court
434 Main Capitol
P.O. Box 624
Harrisburg, PA 17108
P: (717) 787-6181

PUERTO RICO
The Honorable Maite Oronoz Rodriguez
Chief Justice
Supreme Court
P.O. Box 9022392
San Juan, PR 00902
P: (787) 723-6033

RHODE ISLAND
The Honorable Paul A. Suttell
Chief Justice
Supreme Court
250 Benefit Street, 7th Floor
Providence, RI 02903
P: (401) 222-3272
F: (401) 222-3599

SOUTH CAROLINA
The Honorable Donald W. Beatty
Chief Justice
Supreme Court
P.O. Box 11330
Columbia, SC 29211
P: (803) 734-1080
F: (803) 734-1499

SOUTH DAKOTA
The Honorable David Gilbertson
Chief Justice
Supreme Court
500 East Capitol Avenue
Pierre, SD 57501
P: (605) 773-3511
F: (605) 773-6128

TENNESSEE
The Honorable Jeffrey Bivins
Chief Justice
Supreme Court
Supreme Court Building
401 7th Avenue, North
Nashville, TN 37219
P: (615) 741-2681

TEXAS
The Honorable Nathan L. Hecht
Chief Justice
Supreme Court
P.O. Box 12248
Austin, TX 78711
P: (512) 463-1312
F: (512) 463-1365

U.S. VIRGIN ISLANDS
The Honorable Rhys S. Hodge
Chief Justice
Supreme Court
P.O. Box 590
St. Thomas, VI 00804
P: (340) 774-2237
F: (340) 774-2258

UTAH
The Honorable Matthew B. Durrant
Chief Justice
Supreme Court
450 South State Street
P.O. Box 140210
Salt Lake City, UT 84114
P: (801) 238-7937
F: (801) 238-7980

VERMONT
The Honorable Paul L. Reiber
Chief Justice
Supreme Court
109 State Street
Montpelier, VT 05609
P: (802) 828-3278
F: (802) 828-4750

VIRGINIA
The Honorable Donald W. Lemons
Chief Justice
Supreme Court
100 North 9th Street
P.O. Box 1315
Richmond, VA 23218
P: (804) 786-2251
F: (804) 786-6249

WASHINGTON
The Honorable Mary E. Fairhurst
Chief Justice
Supreme Court
415 12th Avenue, Southwest
P.O. Box 40929
Olympia, WA 98504
P: (360) 357-2053
F: (360) 357-2102

WEST VIRGINIA
The Honorable Allen H. Loughry II
Chief Justice
Supreme Court
1900 Kanawha Boulevard, East
State Capitol, Room E-317
Charleston, WV 25305

WISCONSIN
The Honorable Patience D. Roggensack
Chief Justice
Supreme Court
16 East State Capitol
P.O. Box 1688
Madison, WI 53701
P: (608) 266-1888
F: (608) 261-8299

WYOMING
The Honorable E. James Burke
Chief Justice
Supreme Court
Supreme Court Building
2301 Capitol Avenue
Cheyenne, WY 82001
P: (307) 777-7316
F: (307) 777-6129

Child Support Enforcement

Processes child support cases and implements required provisions of child support enforcement program.

ALABAMA
Ms. Lathesia Saulsberry
Director
Child Support Enforcement Division
Department of Human Resources
P.O. Box 304000
Montgomery, AL 36130
P: (334) 242-9300
F: (334) 242-0606
E: lathesia.saulsberry@dhr.alabama.gov

ALASKA
Mr. Randall Hoffbeck
Commissioner
Department of Revenue
P.O. Box 110400
Juneau, AK 99811
P: (907) 465-2300
F: (907) 465-2389
E: randall.hoffbeck@alaska.gov

AMERICAN SAMOA
Dr. Taeaoafua Meki Solomona
Director
Department of Human & Social Services
P.O. Box 997534
Pago Pago, AS 96799
P: (684) 633-1664
F: (684) 633-7449
E: mtsolomona@dhss.as

ARIZONA
Ms. Heather Noble
Interim Director
Division of Child Support Services
Department of Economic Security
1789 West Jefferson Street
Phoenix, AZ 85007
P: (602) 542-4500

ARKANSAS
Mr. Alan McVey
Administrator
Office of Child Support Enforcement
Department of Finance & Administration
322 South Main Street
Little Rock, AR 72201
P: (501) 682-6169
E: Alan.McVey@ocse.arkansas.gov

COLORADO
Mr. Larry Desbian
Director
Division of Child Support Services
Department of Human Services
1575 Sherman Street, 5th Floor
Denver, CO 80203
P: (303) 866-4300
F: (303) 866-4360

CONNECTICUT
Asha Stead
Office of Child Support Services
Department of Social Services
55 Farmington Avenue
Hartford, CT 06105
P: (860) 424-5255
E: asha.stead@ct.gov

DELAWARE
Mr. Theodore G. Mermigos Jr.
Director
Division of Child Support Enforcement
Department of Health & Social Services
P.O. Box 11223
Wilmington, DE 19850
P: (302) 255-9040
F: (302) 255-4429

DISTRICT OF COLUMBIA
Ms. Benidia A. Rice
Deputy
Child Support Services Division
One Judiciary Square
441 4th Street, Northwest, N550
Washington, DC 20001
P: (202) 442-9900
E: cssd.oag@dc.gov

FLORIDA
Ms. Ann Coffin
Program Director
Child Support Enforcement Program
Department of Revenue
P.O. Box 8030
Tallahassee, FL 32314
P: (850) 717-7000
E: ann.coffin@floridarevenue.com

GEORGIA
Ms. Robyn A. Crittenden
Commissioner
Department of Human Services
2 Peachtree Street, Northwest
Suite 29-250
Atlanta, GA 30303
P: (404) 656-5680
F: (404) 651-8669

GUAM
Ms. Rebecca Perez
Deputy Attorney General
Child Support Enforcement Division
590 South Marine Corps Drive
ITC Building, Suite 902
Tamuning, GU 96913
P: (671) 475-3360
F: (671) 475-3203
E: rebecca.perez@guamag.org

HAWAII
Ms. Lynette Lau
Administrator
Child Support Enforcement Agency
Kakuhihewa Building
601 Kamokila Boulevard, Suite 251
Kapolei, HI 96707
P: (808) 692-8265
F: (808) 692-7060

IDAHO
Ms. Nicole McKay
Division Chief
Health & Human Services Division
Office of the Attorney General
P.O. Box 83720
Boise, ID 83720
P: (208) 334-5537
F: (208) 334-5548
E: nicole.mckay@dhw.idaho.gov

ILLINOIS
Ms. Pam Lowry
Administrator
Child Support Services
Healthcare & Family Services
509 South 6th Street
Springfield, IL 62701
P: (217) 782-2624
F: (217) 524-4608

INDIANA
Ms. Mary Beth Bonaventura
Director
Department of Child Services
302 West Washington Street
Indianapolis, IN 46204
P: (317) 234-3323
F: (317) 232-4490
E: MaryBeth.Bonaventura@dcs.IN.gov

IOWA
Mr. Charles M. Palmer
Director
Department of Human Services
Hoover State Office Building
1305 East Walnut Street
Des Moines, IA 50319
P: (515) 281-5452
F: (515) 281-4980
E: cpalmer1@dhs.state.ia.us

KANSAS
Ms. Trisha Thomas
Director
Child Support Services
Department for Children & Families
555 South Kansas Avenue
Topeka, KS 66603
P: (785) 296-3237
F: (785) 296-5206

KENTUCKY
Mr. Steven P. Veno
Deputy Commissioner
Division of Child Support
Department for Income Support
P.O. Box 2150
Frankfort, KY 40601
P: (502) 564-2285
F: (502) 564-5988
E: steven.veno@ky.gov

LOUISIANA
Ms. Lisa Andry
Executive Director
Child Support Enforcement
Department of Children & Family Services
P.O. Box 94065
Baton Rouge, LA 70802
P: (225) 342-4780
F: (225) 342-7397
E: lisa.Andry@la.gov

MAINE
Ms. Bethany Hamm
Director
Office for Family Independence
Department of Health & Human Services
11 State House Station, 19 Union Street
Augusta, ME 04333
P: (207) 624-4168
F: (207) 287-5096

MASSACHUSETTS
Ms. Michele Cristello
Deputy Commissioner
Child Support Enforcement Division
Department of Revenue
100 Cambridge Street
Boston, MA 02114
P: (617) 660-1234

MICHIGAN
Mr. Steve Yager
Executive Director
Children's Services Agency
Department of Health & Human Services
P.O. Box 30195
Lansing, MI 48909
P: (517) 373-3740
E: YagerS@michigan.gov

MINNESOTA
Mr. Jeff Jorgenson
Director
Child Support Enforcement Division
Department of Human Services
P.O. Box 64946
St. Paul, MN 55164
P: (651) 431-4276
F: (651) 431-7517
E: jeffrey.j.jorgenson@state.mn.us

MISSISSIPPI
Mr. Walley Naylor
Director
Division of Field Operations
Department of Human Services
750 North State Street
Jackson, MS 39202
P: (877) 882-4916

MISSOURI
Mr. Patrick Luebbering
Acting Director
Family Support Division
Department of Social Services
P.O. Box 2320
Jefferson City, MO
P: (573) 751-3221

MONTANA
Mr. Chad Dexter
Administrator
Child Support Enforcement Division
2401 Colonial Drive, 1st Floor
P.O. Box 202943
Helena, MT 59620
P: (406) 444-1846
F: (406) 444-1370

NEBRASKA
Mr. Douglas J. Weinberg
Director
Division of Children & Family Services
Department of Health & Human Services
P.O. Box 95026
Lincoln, NE 60509
P: (402) 471-1757
E: doug.weinberg@nebraska.gov

NEW HAMPSHIRE
Ms. Mary S. Weatherill
Director
Division of Child Support Services
Department of Health & Human Services
129 Pleasant Street
Concord, NH 03301
P: (603) 271-4427
F: (603) 271-4787
E: mary.weatherill@dhhs.nh.gov

NEW JERSEY
Ms. Natasha Johnson
Director
Division of Family Development
Department of Human Services
P.O. Box 716
Trenton, NJ 08625
P: (609) 588-2400
F: (609) 584-4404

NEW MEXICO
Ms. Laura Galindo
Director
Child Support Enforcement Division
Human Services Department
P.O. Box 2348
Santa Fe, NM 87504
P: (800) 585-7631
F: (505) 476-7045

NEW YORK
Ms. Eileen Stack
Assistant Deputy Commissioner
Child Support Services
40 North Pearl Street
Albany, NY 12243
P: (518) 474-1078

NORTH CAROLINA
Mr. Wayne E. Black
Director
Division of Social Services
Department of Health & Human Services
2401 Mail Service Center
Raleigh, NC 27699
P: (919) 527-6335
F: (919) 334-1018
E: wayne.black@dhhs.nc.gov

NORTH DAKOTA
Mr. James Fleming
Director
Child Support Enforcement Division
Department of Human Services
P.O. Box 7190
Bismarck, ND 58507
P: (701) 328-3582
F: (701) 328-5425
E: centralofficecse@nd.gov

OHIO
Mr. Michael McCreight
Assistant Director, Health & Human Services
Department of Job & Family Services
30 East Broad Street, 32nd Floor
Columbus, OH 43215
P: (614) 466-6283
F: (614) 466-2815

OKLAHOMA
Mr. Jim Hutchinson
Interim Director
Child Support Services
Department of Human Services
P.O. Box 248822
Oklahoma City, OK 73124
P: (405) 522-2273
E: OCSS.Director@OKDHS.org

RHODE ISLAND
Ms. Sharon A. Santilli
Associate Director
Office of Child Support
Department of Human Services
77 Dorrance Street
Providence, RI 02903
P: (401) 458-4400
F: (401) 458-4465
E: richildsupport@cse.state.ri.us

SOUTH CAROLINA
Ms. V. Susan Alford
Director
Department of Social Services
1535 Confederate Avenue
P.O. Box 1520
Columbia, SC 29202
P: (803) 898-7360
F: (803) 898-7277

SOUTH DAKOTA
Ms. Gail Stoltenburg
Director
Division of Child Support
Department of Social Services
700 Governors Drive
Pierre, SD 57501
P: (605) 773-3641
F: (605) 773-7295
E: DCS@state.sd.us

TENNESSEE
Ms. Danielle W. Barnes
Commissioner
Department of Human Services
400 Deaderick Street
Nashville, TN 37243
P: (615) 313-4700
F: (615) 741-4165
E: danielle.w.barnes@tn.gov

Mr. Charles Bryson
Assistant Commissioner
Division of Family Assistance & Child Support Services
Department of Human Services
400 Deaderick Street, 15th Floor
Nashville, TN 37243
P: (615) 313-4712
F: (615) 741-4165

TEXAS
Mr. Steve Roddy
Deputy Attorney General for Child Support
Office of the Attorney General
300 West 15th Street
P.O. Box 12548
Austin, TX 78711
P: (512) 460-6000
F: (512) 463-2063
E: child.support@texasattorneygeneral.gov

U.S. VIRGIN ISLANDS
Ms. Charlotte Poole-Davis
Executive Director
Paternity & Child Support Division
8000 Nisky Shopping Center, Suite 500
2nd Floor
St. Thomas, VI 00802
P: (340) 775-3070
F: (340) 775-3808

Child Support Enforcement

UTAH
Ms. Liesa Stockdale
Director
Office of Recovery Services
Department of Human Services
515 East 100 South
Salt Lake City, UT 84102
P: (801) 536-8901
F: (801) 536-8509
E: orsconstituentaffairs
@utah.gov

VERMONT
Ms. Robin Arnell
Director
Office of Child Support
Department for Children &
Families
280 State Drive, NOB 1
Waterbury, VT 05671
P: (802) 241-2319
F: (802) 769-6429

VIRGINIA
Mr. Craig Burshem
Deputy Commissioner
Division of Child Support
Enforcement
Department of Social Services
801 East Main Street
Richmond, VA 23219
P: (804) 726-7405
E: craig.burshem
@dss.virginia.gov

WASHINGTON
Mr. David Stillman
Assistant Secretary
Economic Services
Department of Social & Health
Services
1115 Washington Street,
Southeast
Olympia, WA 98504
P: (800) 737-0617
F: (360) 664-5303

WEST VIRGINIA
Mr. Garrett M. Jacobs
Commissioner
Bureau for Child Support
Enforcement
350 Capitol Street, Room 147
Charleston, WV 25301
P: (304) 356-4707
F: (304) 558-4092
E: garrett.m.jacobs@wv.gov

WISCONSIN
Ms. Eloise Anderson
Secretary
Department of Children &
Families
201 East Washington Avenue,
2nd Floor
P.O. Box 8916
Madison, WI 53708
P: (608) 267-3905
F: (608) 266-6836
E: dcfweb@wisconsin.gov

WYOMING
Ms. Kristie Langley
Administrator
Child Support Program
2300 Capitol Avenue, 3th Floor
Hathaway Building
Cheyenne, WY 82002
P: (307) 777-6948
F: (307) 777-5588

Children and Youth Services

Implements programs designed to protect children and youth against abuse, neglect and exploitation.

ALABAMA
Ms. Jeana Ross
Commissioner
Department of Early Childhood Education
135 South Union Street, Suite 215
P.O. Box 302755
Montgomery, AL 36130
P: (334) 353-2700
F: (334) 353-2701
E: jeana.ross@ece.alabama.gov

ALASKA
Ms. Christy Lawton
Director
Office of Children's Services
Department of Health & Social Services
P.O. Box 110630
Juneau, AK 99811
P: (907) 465-3170
F: (907) 465-3397
E: christy.lawton@alaska.gov

AMERICAN SAMOA
Dr. Taeaoafua Meki Solomona
Director
Department of Human & Social Services
P.O. Box 997534
Pago Pago, AS 96799
P: (684) 633-1664
F: (684) 633-7449
E: mtsolomona@dhss.as

ARIZONA
Ms. Debbie Moak
Director
Governor's Office for Children, Youth & Families
1700 West Washington, Suite 230
Phoenix, AZ 85007
P: (602) 542-1773
F: (602) 542-3423
E: dmoak@az.gov

ARKANSAS
Ms. Mischa Martin
Director
Division of Children & Family Services
Department of Human Services
Donaghey Plaza, P.O. Box 1437
Little Rock, AR 72203
P: (501) 682-8770
E: mischa.martin@dhs.arkansas.gov

CALIFORNIA
Mr. Will Lightbourne
Director
Department of Social Services
744 P Street
Sacramento, CA 95814
P: (916) 657-2598
F: (916) 651-6569

COLORADO
Ms. Ann Rosales
Director
Division of Child Welfare
Department of Human Services
1575 Sherman Street, 2nd Floor
Denver, CO 80203
P: (303) 866-3538
E: ann.rosales@state.co.us

CONNECTICUT
Ms. Joette Katz
Commissioner
Department of Children & Families
505 Hudson Street
Hartford, CT 06106
P: (860) 550-6300
E: commissioner.dcf@ct.gov

DELAWARE
Ms. Josette DelleDonne Manning
Cabinet Secretary
Department of Services for Children, Youth & Their Families
1825 Faulkland Road
Wilmington, DE 19805
P: (302) 633-2500
E: info.dscyf@state.de.us

FLORIDA
Mr. Mike Carroll
Secretary
Department of Children & Families
1317 Winewood Boulevard
Building 1, Room 202
Tallahassee, FL 32399
P: (850) 487-1111
F: (850) 922-2993
E: mike.carroll@myflfamilies.com

GEORGIA
Mr. Bobby Cagle
Division Director
Division of Family & Children Services
Department of Human Services
Two Peachtree Street, Northwest
Atlanta, GA 30303
P: (404) 657-8986
F: (404) 657-5105
E: bobby.cagle@dhs.ga.gov

HAWAII
Mr. Merton Chinen
Executive Director
Office of Youth Services
Department of Human Services
P.O. Box 339
Honolulu, HI 96809
P: (808) 587-5710
F: (808) 587-5734

IDAHO
Mr. Gary Moore
Administrator
Division of Family & Community Services
Department of Health & Welfare
450 West State Street
Boise, ID 83720
P: (208) 334-0641
F: (208) 332-7331
E: mooreg@dhw.idaho.gov

ILLINOIS
Mr. George H. Sheldon
Director
Department of Children & Family Services
406 East Monroe Street
Springfield, IL 62701
P: (217) 785-2509
F: (217) 785-1052

INDIANA
Ms. Adrienne Shields
Director of Family Resources
Family & Social Services Administration
402 West Washington Street, Room W392
P.O. Box 7083
Indianapolis, IN 46204
P: (317) 234-2373
F: (317) 232-4490
E: Adrienne.Shields@fssa.IN.gov

IOWA
Ms. Wendy Rickman
Administrator
Division of Adult, Children & Family Services
Department of Human Services
1305 East Walnut
Des Moines, IA 50319
P: (515) 281-5521
F: (515) 242-6036
E: wrickma@dhs.state.ia.us

KENTUCKY
Ms. Adria Johnson
Commissioner
Department for Community Based Services
275 East Main Street
Mail Stop 3W-A
Frankfort, KY 40621
P: (502) 564-3703
F: (502) 564-6907

LOUISIANA
Ms. Marketa Garner Walters
Secretary
Department of Children & Family Services
627 North Fourth Street
Baton Rouge, LA 70802
P: (225) 342-7475
F: (225) 342-8636
E: DCFS.Secretary@la.gov

MAINE
Mr. James Martin
Director
Office of Child & Family Services
Department of Health & Human Services
2 Anthony Avenue, 11 State House Station
Augusta, ME 04333
P: (207) 624-7900
F: (207) 287-5282
E: james.martin@maine.gov

MARYLAND
Ms. Arlene Lee
Executive Director
Governor's Office for Children
100 Community Place
Crownsville, MD 21032
P: (410) 697-9235
F: (410) 333-5248
E: arlene.lee@maryland.gov

Children and Youth Services

MASSACHUSETTS
Mr. Peter Forbes
Commissioner
Department of Youth Services
Office of Health & Human Services
600 Washington Street, 4th Floor
Boston, MA 02111
P: (617) 960-3304
F: (617) 727-0696

MICHIGAN
Mr. Steve Yager
Executive Director
Children's Services Agency
Department of Health & Human Services
P.O. Box 30195
Lansing, MI 48909
P: (517) 373-3740
E: YagerS@michigan.gov

MISSISSIPPI
Ms. Jill Dent
Director
Division of Early Childhood Care & Development
P.O. Box 352
Jackson, MS 39205
P: (601) 359-4555
F: (601) 359-4422

MISSOURI
Mr. Tim Decker
Director
Division of Youth Services
3418 Knipp, Suite A-1
P.O. Box 447
Jefferson City, MO 65102
P: (573) 751-3324
F: (573) 526-4494
E: tim.decker@dss.mo.gov

NEBRASKA
Mr. Douglas J. Weinberg
Director
Division of Children & Family Services
Department of Health & Human Services
P.O. Box 95026
Lincoln, NE 60509
P: (402) 471-1757
E: doug.weinberg@nebraska.gov

NEVADA
Ms. Kelly Wooldridge
Administrator
Division of Child & Family Services
Department of Health & Human Services
4126 Technology Way, 3rd Floor
Carson City, NV 89706
P: (775) 684-4400
F: (775) 684-4455

NEW HAMPSHIRE
Ms. Maggie L. Bishop
Director
Division for Children, Youth & Families
Department of Health & Human Services
97 Pleasant Street
Concord, NH 03301
P: (603) 271-4440
F: (603) 271-4729
E: mbishop@dhhs.state.nh.us

NEW JERSEY
Dr. Allison Blake
Commissioner
Department of Children & Families
50 East State Street, 2nd Floor
P.O. Box 729
Trenton, NJ 08625
P: (609) 888-7900
E: dcf_commissioner@dcf.state.nj.us

NEW MEXICO
Ms. Monique Jacobson
Cabinet Secretary
Children, Youth & Families Department
P.O. Drawer 5160
Santa Fe, NM 87502
P: (505) 827-7602
F: (505) 827-4053
E: monique.jacobson@state.nm.us

NEW YORK
Ms. Sheila Poole
Acting Commissioner
Office of Children & Family Services
Capitol View Office Park
52 Washington Street
Rensselaer, NY 12144
P: (518) 473-7793
F: (518) 486-7550

NORTH CAROLINA
Mr. Wayne E. Black
Director
Division of Social Services
Department of Health & Human Services
2401 Mail Service Center
Raleigh, NC 27699
P: (919) 527-6335
F: (919) 334-1018
E: wayne.black@dhhs.nc.gov

NORTH DAKOTA
Ms. Shari Doe
Director
Children & Family Services
600 East Boulevard Avenue
Department 325
Bismarck, ND 58505
P: (701) 328-2316
F: (701) 328-3538
E: dhscfs@nd.gov

NORTHERN MARIANA ISLANDS
Mr. Robert H. Hunter
Secretary
Department of Community & Cultural Affairs
Caller Box 10007
Ascension Court, Capital Hill
Saipan, MP 96950
P: (670) 664-2577
F: (670) 664-2571
E: roberthhunter@gmail.com

OHIO
Ms. Cynthia C. Dungey
Director
Department of Job & Family Services
30 East Broad Street, 32nd Floor
Columbus, OH 43215
P: (614) 466-6283
F: (614) 466-2815

Mr. Michael McCreight
Assistant Director, Health & Human Services
Department of Job & Family Services
30 East Broad Street, 32nd Floor
Columbus, OH 43215
P: (614) 466-6283
F: (614) 466-2815

OKLAHOMA
Ms. Jami Ledoux
Director
Child Welfare Services
Department of Human Services
P.O. Box 25352
Oklahoma City, OK 73125
P: (405) 521-3777
F: (405) 521-4373

OREGON
Mr. Clyde Saiki
Director
Department of Human Services
500 Summer Street, Northeast
Salem, OR 97301
P: (503) 945-7001
F: (503) 581-6198
E: clyde.saiki@oregon.gov

PENNSYLVANIA
Ms. Cathy Utz
Deputy Secretary
Office of Children, Youth & Families
Department of Human Services
P.O. Box 2675
Harrisburg, PA 17110
P: (717) 787-4756
F: (717) 787-0414

PUERTO RICO
Ms. Glorimar Andujar Matos
Secretary
Department of the Family
P.O. Box 11398
Hato Rey, PR 00917
P: (787) 294-4900
F: (787) 297-0732

RHODE ISLAND
Dr. Trista Piccola
Director
Department of Children, Youth & Families
101 Friendship Street
Providence, RI 02903
P: (401) 528-3502

SOUTH CAROLINA
Ms. V. Susan Alford
Director
Department of Social Services
1535 Confederate Avenue
P.O. Box 1520
Columbia, SC 29202
P: (803) 898-7360
F: (803) 898-7277

SOUTH DAKOTA
Ms. Virgena Wieseler
Division Director
Department of Social Services
Division of Child Protection Services
700 Governors Drive
Pierre, SD 57501
P: (605) 773-3227
F: (605) 773-6834
E: CPS@state.sd.us

TENNESSEE
Ms. Bonnie Hommrich
Commissioner
Department of Childrens Services
UBS Tower, 315 Deaderick, 10th Floor
Nashville, TN 37243
P: (615) 741-9701
E: DCS.Custsrv@tn.gov

TEXAS
Mr. Hank Whitman Jr.
Commissioner
Department of Family & Protective Services
701 West 51st Street
P.O. Box 149030
Austin, TX 78714
P: (512) 438-4870

U.S. VIRGIN ISLANDS
Mr. Felicia Blyden
Commissioner
Department of Human Services
3011 Golden Rock
Christiansted
St. Croix, VI 00802
P: (340) 718-2980

UTAH
Mr. Brent Platt
Director
Division of Child & Family Services
Department of Human Services
195 North 1950 West
Salt Lake City, UT 84116
P: (801) 538-4100
F: (801) 538-3993
E: bplatt@utah.gov

VERMONT
Mr. Ken Schatz
Commissioner
Department for Children & Families
280 State Drive, HC 1 North
Waterbury, VT 05671
P: (802) 241-0929
E: ken.schatz@vermont.gov

VIRGINIA
Ms. Margaret Ross Schultze
Commissioner
Department of Social Services
801 East Main Street
Richmond, VA 23219
P: (804) 726-7011
E: margaret.schultze@dss.virginia.gov

WASHINGTON
Ms. Jennifer Strus
Assistant Secretary
Children's Administration
Department of Social & Health Services
1115 Washington Street, Southeast
Olympia, WA 98504
P: (800) 737-0617
E: Jennifer.Strus@dshs.wa.gov

WEST VIRGINIA
Ms. Nancy Exline
Commissioner
Bureau for Children & Families
Department of Health & Human Resources
350 Capitol Street, Room 730
Charleston, WV 25301
P: (304) 558-0628
F: (304) 558-4194

WISCONSIN
Ms. Eloise Anderson
Secretary
Department of Children & Families
201 East Washington Avenue, 2nd Floor
P.O. Box 8916
Madison, WI 53708
P: (608) 267-3905
F: (608) 266-6836
E: dcfweb@wisconsin.gov

WYOMING
Dr. Steve Corsi
Director
Department of Family Services
Hathaway Building, 3rd Floor
2300 Capitol Avenue
Cheyenne, WY 82002
P: (307) 777-6597
F: (307) 777-7747
E: steve.corsi@wyo.gov

Civil Rights

Overall responsibility for preventing and redressing discrimination in employment, education, housing, public accommodations and credit (because of race, color, sex, age, national origin, religion or disability.)

ALABAMA
Ms. Desiree Jackson
Director
Equal Employment/Civil Rights Division
Gordon Persons Building, Suite 2104
50 North Ripley Street
Montgomery, AL 36130
P: (334) 242-1550
E: oeecr@dhr.alabama.gov

ALASKA
Ms. Marti Buscaglia
Division Director
Commission for Human Rights
Office of the Governor
800 A Street, Suite 204
Anchorage, AK 99501
P: (907) 792-7241
E: marti.buscaglia@alaska.gov

ARIZONA
Ms. Theresa Rassas
Section Chief Counsel
Civil Rights Division
Office of the Attorney General
1275 West Washington Street
Phoenix, AZ 85007
P: (602) 542-8628
F: (602) 542-8885
E: civilrightsinfo@azag.gov

Mr. Paul Watkins
Division Chief Counsel
Civil Litigation Division
Office of the Attorney General
1275 West Washington Street
Phoenix, AZ 85007
P: (602) 542-8323
F: (602) 542-8885

CALIFORNIA
Mr. Kevin Kish
Director
Department of Fair Employment & Housing
2218 Kausen Drive, Suite 100
Elk Grove, CA 95758
P: (800) 884-1684
F: (916) 651-8866
E: tom.lee@dss.ca.gov

COLORADO
Ms. Aubrey Elenis
Director
Civil Rights Division
1560 Broadway, Suite 1050
Denver, CO 80202
P: (303) 894-2997

CONNECTICUT
Ms. Tanya Hughes
Executive Director
Commission on Human Rights & Opportunities
450 Columbus Boulevard
Hartford, CT 06103
P: (860) 541-3421
F: (860) 241-4875
E: tanya.hughes@ct.gov

DELAWARE
Ms. Romona S. Fullman
Director
Division of Human Relations
Department of State
820 North French Street, 4th Floor
Wilmington, DE 19801
P: (302) 577-5287
F: (302) 577-3486

DISTRICT OF COLUMBIA
Ms. Monica Palacio
Director
Office of Human Rights
441 4th Street, Northwest
Suite 570 North
Washington, DC 20001
P: (202) 727-4559
F: (202) 727-9589
E: ohr@dc.gov

FLORIDA
The Honorable Pam Bondi (R)
Attorney General
Office of the Attorney General
The Capitol, PL 01
Tallahassee, FL 32399
P: (850) 414-3300
F: (954) 712-4826

GEORGIA
Mr. Melvin J. Everson
Executive Director & Administrator
Commission on Equal Opportunity
7 Martin Luther King Jr. Drive Southeast
3rd Floor, Suite 351
Atlanta, GA 30334
P: (404) 232-1776
F: (404) 656-4399
E: meverson@gceo.state.ga.us

GUAM
Mr. Manuel Q. Cruz
Director
Department of Labor
Government of Guam
P.O. Box 9970
Tamuning, GU 96931
P: (671) 475-7044
F: (671) 674-6517

Mr. Tony A. Lamorena V
Director
Civil Service Commission
P.O. Box 3156
Hagatna, GU 96932
P: (671) 647-1855
F: (671) 647-1867

HAWAII
Mr. William D. Hoshijo
Executive Director
Civil Rights Commission
Labor & Industrial Relations Department
830 Punchbowl Street, Room 411
Honolulu, HI 96813
P: (808) 586-8636
F: (808) 586-8655
E: dlir.hcrc.infor@hawaii.gov

IDAHO
Ms. Linda L. Goodman
Administrator
Human Rights Commission
317 West Main Street, Second Floor
Boise, ID 83735
P: (208) 334-2873
F: (208) 334-2664
E: Linda.Goodman@labor.idaho.gov

ILLINOIS
Ms. Janice Glenn
Acting Director
Department of Human Rights
100 West Randolph Street, 10th Floor
Intake Unit
Chicago, IL 60601
P: (312) 814-6200
F: (312) 814-1436

IOWA
Ms. Kristin H. Johnson
Executive Director
Civil Rights Commission
Grimes State Office Building
400 East 14th Street
Des Moines, IA 50319
P: (515) 281-4576
F: (515) 242-5840
E: Kristin.Johnson2@iowa.gov

KANSAS
Ms. Ruth Glover
Executive Director
Human Rights Commission
900 Southwest Jackson Street
Suite 568-South
Topeka, KS 66612
P: (785) 296-3206
F: (785) 296-0589

KENTUCKY
Mr. John J. Johnson
Executive Director
Commission on Human Rights
332 West Broadway, 7th Floor
Louisville, KY 40202
P: (502) 595-4024
F: (502) 595-4801
E: john.johnson@ky.gov

LOUISIANA
The Honorable Jeffrey Landry (R)
Attorney General
Office of the Attorney General
P.O. Box 94095
Baton Rouge, LA 70804
P: (225) 326-6000
F: (225) 326-6797

MAINE
Ms. Amy Sneirson
Executive Director
Human Rights Commission
51 State House Station
Augusta, ME 04333
P: (207) 624-6290
F: (207) 624-8729
E: amy.sneirson@mhrc.maine.gov

MARYLAND
Mr. Alvin O. Gillard
Executive Director
Commission on Civil Rights
William Donald Schaefer Tower
6 Saint Paul Street, Suite 900
Baltimore, MD 21202
P: (410) 767-8585
F: (410) 333-1841
E: alvin.gillard@maryland.gov

MASSACHUSETTS
Ms. Sheila A. Hubbard
Commissioner
Commission Against Discrimination
One Ashburton Place, Suite 601
Boston, MA 02108
P: (617) 994-6000
F: (617) 994-6024
E: assistanttochairman@state.ma.us

Ms. Sunila Thomas-George
Commissioner
Commission Against Discrimination
One Ashburton Place, Suite 601
Boston, MA 02108
P: (617) 994-6000
F: (617) 994-6024
E: assistanttochairman@state.ma.us

Ms. Jamie R. Williamson
Chair
Commission Against Discrimination
One Ashburton Place, Suite 601
Boston, MA 02108
P: (617) 994-6000
F: (617) 994-6024
E: assistanttochairman@state.ma.us

MINNESOTA
Mr. Kevin Lindsey
Commissioner
Department of Human Rights
Freeman Building
625 Robert Street, North
St. Paul, MN 55155
P: (651) 539-1100
F: (651) 296-9042
E: Kevin.Lindsey@state.mn.us

MISSISSIPPI
The Honorable Jim Hood (D)
Attorney General
Office of the Attorney General
Department of Justice
P.O. Box 220
Jackson, MS 39205
P: (601) 359-3680
E: msag05@ago.state.ms.us

MISSOURI
Dr. Alisa Warren
Executive Director
Commission on Human Rights
3315 West Truman Boulevard, Room 212
P.O. Box 1129
Jefferson City, MO 65102
P: (573) 751-3325
F: (573) 751-2905
E: mchr@labor.mo.gov

MONTANA
Marieke Beck
Bureau Chief
Human Rights Bureau
P.O. Box 1728
Helena, MT 59624
P: (406) 444-4344
F: (406) 443-3234
E: kcobos@mt.gov

NEBRASKA
Mr. Stan Odenthal
Executive Director
Equal Opportunity Commission
301 Centennial Mall South, 5th Floor
P.O. Box 94934
Lincoln, NE 68509
P: (402) 471-2024
F: (402) 471-4059
E: stan.odenthal@nebraska.gov

NEVADA
Ms. Kara Jenkins
Commission Administrator
Equal Rights Commission
Employment, Training & Rehabilitation
1820 East Sahara Avenue, Suite 314
Las Vegas, NV 89104
P: (702) 486-7161
F: (702) 486-7054

NEW HAMPSHIRE
Ms. Joni N. Esperian
Executive Director
Commission for Human Rights
2 Industrial Park Drive
Concord, NH 03301
P: (603) 271-2767
F: (603) 271-6339
E: humanrights@nh.gov

NEW JERSEY
Mr. Craig Sashihara
Director
Division on Civil Rights
Office of the Attorney General
P.O. Box 090
Trenton, NJ 08625
P: (609) 292-4605
F: (609) 984-3812

NEW MEXICO
Ms. Patricia Wolf
Investigation, Compliance, & Alternative Dispute Resolution Staff Manager
Human Rights Bureau
Department of Workforce Solutions
1596 Pacheco Street, Suite103
Santa Fe, NM 87505
P: (505) 827-6856

NEW YORK
Ms. Helen Diane Foster
Commissioner
Division of Human Rights
One Fordham Plaza, 4th Floor
Bronx, NY 10458
P: (718) 741-8400

NORTH DAKOTA
Ms. Michelle Kommer
Commissioner of Labor
Department of Labor & Human Rights
600 East Boulevard Avenue
Department 406
Bismarck, ND 58505
P: (701) 328-2660
F: (701) 328-2031
E: mkommer@nd.gov

OHIO
Mr. G. Michael Payton
Executive Director
Civil Rights Commission
Rhodes State Office Tower
30 East Broad Street, 5th Floor
Columbus, OH 43215
P: (614) 466-2785
F: (614) 644-8776
E: paytonm@ocrc.state.oh.us

OREGON
Ms. Amy K. Klare
Administrator
Civil Rights Division
Bureau of Labor & Industries
800 Northeast Oregon Street, Suite 1045
Portland, OR 97232
P: (971) 673-0792
F: (971) 673-0765
E: Amy.K.Klare@state.or.us

PENNSYLVANIA
Ms. JoAnn L. Edwards
Executive Director
Human Relations Commission
333 Market Street, 8th Floor
Harrisburg, PA 17126
P: (717) 787-9780
E: phrc@pa.gov

PUERTO RICO
Ever Padilla-Ruiz
Executive Director
Civil Rights Commission
P.O. Box 192338
San Juan, PR 00919
P: (787) 764-8686
F: (787) 250-1756
E: director@cdc.pr.gov

RHODE ISLAND
Mr. Michael D. Evora
Executive Director
Commission for Human Rights
180 Westminster Street, 3rd Floor
Providence, RI 02903
P: (401) 222-2661
F: (401) 222-2616

SOUTH CAROLINA
Mr. Raymond Buxton II
Commissioner
Human Affairs Commission
1026 Sumter Street
Columbia, SC 29201
P: (803) 737-7800
E: rbuxton@schac.sc.gov

SOUTH DAKOTA
Ms. Marcia Hultman
Cabinet Secretary
Department of Labor & Regulation
123 West Missouri Avenue
Pierre, SD 57501
P: (605) 773-5395
F: (605) 773-6184
E: marcia.hultman@state.sd.us

Mr. James E. Marsh
Director
Division of Labor & Management
Department of Labor & Regulation
700 Governors Drive
Pierre, SD 57501
P: (605) 773-3681
F: (605) 773-4211
E: james.marsh@state.sd.us

TENNESSEE
Ms. Beverly L. Watts
Executive Director
Human Rights Commission
312 Rosa L. Parks Avenue, 23rd Floor
Nashville, TN 37243
P: (615) 741-5825
F: (615) 253-1886
E: ask.thrc@tn.gov

TEXAS
Mr. Kim Vickers
Executive Director
Commission on Law Enforcement
6330 East Highway 290, Suite 200
Austin, TX 78723
P: (512) 936-7700 Ext. 7713
F: (512) 936-7766
E: kim.vickers@tcole.texas.gov

Civil Rights

U.S. VIRGIN ISLANDS
Ms. Grethelyn Piper
Executive Director, Civil Rights Commission
Department of Justice
34-38 Kronprindsens Gade
GERS Building, 2nd Floor
St. Thomas, VI 00802
P: (340) 774-5666
F: (340) 776-3494

UTAH
Ms. Heather Gunnarson
Director
Antidiscrimination & Labor Division
160 East 300 South, 3rd Floor
P.O. Box 146600
Salt Lake City, UT 84114
P: (801) 536-7928
E: hgunnarson@utah.gov

VERMONT
Ms. Karen Richards
Executive Director
Human Rights Commission
14-16 Baldwin Street
Montpelier, VT 05633
P: (802) 828-2482
F: (802) 828-2481
E: karen.richards@vermont.gov

VIRGINIA
The Honorable Mark R. Herring (D)
Attorney General
Office of the Attorney General
202 North Ninth Street
Richmond, VA 23219
P: (804) 786-2071

WEST VIRGINIA
Dr. Darrell Cummings
Chair
Human Rights Commission
1321 Plaza East, Room 108A
Charleston, WV 25301
P: (304) 558-2616
F: (304) 558-0085

WISCONSIN
Mr. Robert A. Rodriguez
Administrator
Division of Equal Rights
201 East Washington Avenue
P.O. Box 8928
Madison, WI 53708
P: (608) 266-3345
F: (608) 267-4592
E: erinfo@dwd.wisconsin.gov

Clerk of the State's Highest Court

Individual who keeps records of the state's highest court.

ALABAMA
Ms. Julia Jordan Weller
Clerk
Supreme Court
300 Dexter Avenue
Montgomery, AL 36104
P: (334) 229-0700

ALASKA
Ms. Marilyn May
Clerk of the Appellate Courts
Appellate Courts
303 K Street
Anchorage, AK 99501
P: (907) 264-0612
F: (907) 264-0878
E: mmay
@appellate.courts.state.ak.us

AMERICAN SAMOA
Mr. Robert Gorniak
Chief Clerk
High Court of American Samoa
American Samoa Government
Pago Pago, AS 96799
P: (684) 633-4131
F: (684) 633-1318

ARIZONA
Ms. Janet Johnson
Clerk of the Court
Supreme Court
1501 West Washington, Suite 402
Phoenix, AZ 85007
P: (602) 452-3396
E: scclerk@courts.az.gov

ARKANSAS
Ms. Stacey Pectol
Clerk of the Courts
Supreme Court
1320 Justice Building
625 Marshall Street
Little Rock, AR 72201
P: (501) 682-6849
E: stacey.pectol
@arcourts.gov

CALIFORNIA
Mr. Frank A. McGuire
Clerk of the Court
Supreme Court
350 McAllister Street
San Francisco, CA 94102
P: (415) 865-7000

COLORADO
Mr. Christopher T. Ryan
Clerk of the Supreme Court
Supreme Court
2 East 14th Avenue
Denver, CO 80203
P: (720) 625-5150
E: Christopher.Ryan
@judicial.state.co.us

CONNECTICUT
Major Paul Hartan
Chief Clerk
Supreme Court
231 Capitol Avenue
Hartford, CT 06106
P: (860) 757-2200
F: (860) 757-2217

DELAWARE
Ms. Cathy L. Howard
Clerk of the Court
Supreme Court
Carvel State Office Building
820 North French Street, 11th Floor
Wilmington, DE 19801
P: (302) 739-4187
F: (302) 577-3702

DISTRICT OF COLUMBIA
Mr. Julio A. Castillo
Clerk of the Court of Appeals
Court of Appeals
Historic Courthouse
430 E Street, Northwest
Washington, DC 20001
P: (202) 879-2700

FLORIDA
Mr. John A. Tomasino
Clerk
Supreme Court
500 South Duval Street
Tallahassee, FL 32399
P: (850) 488-0125
E: supremecourt
@flcourts.org

GEORGIA
Ms. Therese S. Barnes
Clerk
Supreme Court
244 Washington Street
Room 572, State Office Annex Building
Atlanta, GA 30334
P: (404) 656-3470
F: (404) 656-2253

GUAM
Ms. Hannah M. Gutierrez-Arroyo
Clerk of Court
Supreme Court
Guam Judicial Center
120 West O'Brien Drive
Hagatna, GU 96910
P: (671) 475-3162
E: hgutierrezarroyo
@guamsupremecourt.com

HAWAII
Ms. Rochelle Hasuko
Chief Clerk
Supreme Court
Aliiolani Hale
417 South King Street
Honolulu, HI 96813
P: (808) 539-4919
F: (808) 539-4928

IDAHO
Mr. Stephen W. Kenyon
Clerk of the Supreme Court
Supreme Court
P.O. Box 83720
Boise, ID 83720
P: (208) 334-2210
F: (208) 947-7590

ILLINOIS
Ms. Carolyn Taft Grosboll
Clerk of the Supreme Court
Supreme Court
Supreme Court Building
200 East Capitol
Springfield, IL 62701
P: (217) 782-2035

INDIANA
Mr. Kevin Smith
Clerk/Administrator
State Courts
200 West Washington Street
315 State House
Indianapolis, IN 46204
P: (317) 232-2540
F: (317) 232-8372
E: Kevin.Smith
@courts.in.gov

IOWA
Ms. Donna Humpal
Clerk
Supreme Court
Iowa Judicial Branch Building
1111 East Court Avenue
Des Moines, IA 50319
P: (515) 281-5911
E: Donna.Humpal
@iowacourts.gov

KANSAS
Ms. Heather L. Smith
Clerk of the Appellate Courts
Supreme Court
Judicial Center
301 Southwest 10th Avenue, Room 374
Topeka, KS 66612
P: (785) 296-3229
F: (785) 296-1028
E: appellateclerk
@kscourts.org

KENTUCKY
Ms. Susan Stokley Clary
Clerk of the Supreme Court
Supreme Court
State Capitol
700 Capitol Avenue, Room 235
Frankfort, KY 40601
P: (502) 564-5444
F: (502) 564-2665

LOUISIANA
Mr. John Tarlton Olivier
Clerk of Court
Supreme Court
400 Royal Street, Suite 4200
New Orleans, LA 70130
P: (504) 310-2300

MAINE
Mr. Matthew Pollack
Clerk of the Law Court
Supreme Judicial Court
205 Newbury Street, Room 139
Portland, ME 04101
P: (207) 822-4146

MARYLAND
Ms. Bessie M. Decker
Clerk of Court of Appeals
Judiciary of Maryland
Robert Murphy Courts of Appeal Building
361 Rowe Boulevard
Annapolis, MD 21401
P: (410) 260-1500

MASSACHUSETTS
Mr. Francis V. Kenneally
Clerk
Supreme Judicial Court
John Adams Courthouse, Suite 1-400
One Pemberton Square
Boston, MA 02108
P: (617) 557-1020
F: (617) 557-1145
E: SJCCommClerk
@sjc.state.ma.us

Clerk of the State's Highest Court

MICHIGAN
Mr. Larry Royster
Clerk
Supreme Court
P.O. Box 30052
Lansing, MI 48909
P: (517) 373-0120
E: MSC_Clerk@courts.mi.gov

MINNESOTA
Ms. AnnMarie O'Neill
Clerk of Appellate Courts
Supreme Court
305 Minnesota Judicial Center
25 Martin Luther King Jr. Boulevard
St. Paul, MN 55155
P: (651) 296-2581

MISSISSIPPI
Ms. Muriel B. Ellis
Clerk
Supreme Court
450 High Street
P.O. Box 117
Jackson, MS 39201
P: (601) 359-3694
F: (601) 359-2407
E: sctclerk@mssc.state.ms.us

MISSOURI
Ms. Betsy AuBuchon
Supreme Court Clerk
Supreme Court
P.O. Box 150
Jefferson City, MO 65102
P: (573) 751-4144

MONTANA
Mr. Ed Smith
Clerk
Supreme Court
215 North Sanders, Room 323
P.O. Box 203003
Helena, MT 59620
P: (406) 444-3858
F: (406) 444-5705

NEBRASKA
Ms. Teresa Brown
Clerk
Supreme Court
2413 State Capitol
P.O. Box 98910
Lincoln, NE 68509
P: (402) 471-3731
F: (402) 471-3480
E: terri.a.brown@nebraska.gov

NEVADA
Ms. Elizabeth Brown
Chief Clerk
Supreme Court
201 South Carson Street
Carson City, NV 89701
P: (775) 684-1600
F: (775) 684-1601
E: nvscclerk@nvcourts.nv.gov

NEW HAMPSHIRE
Ms. Eileen Fox
Clerk of Court
Supreme Court
Supreme Court Building
One Charles Doe Drive
Concord, NH 03301
P: (603) 271-2646
F: (603) 271-6630

NEW JERSEY
Ms. Michelle Smith
Clerk
Supreme Court
Rihcard J. Hughes Justice Complex
P.O. Box 970
Trenton, NJ 08625
P: (609) 292-4837

NEW MEXICO
Mr. Joey D. Moya
Chief Clerk
Supreme Court
237 Don Gaspar Avenue, Room 104
P.O. Box 848
Santa Fe, NM 87504
P: (505) 827-4860
F: (505) 827-4837

NEW YORK
Mr. John P. Asiello
Clerk of the Court
Court of Appeals
20 Eagle Street
Albany, NY 12207
P: (518) 455-7700
F: (518) 463-6869

NORTH CAROLINA
Mr. J. Bryan Boyd
Clerk
Supreme Court
2 East Morgan Street
P.O. Box 2170
Raleigh, NC 27602
P: (919) 831-5700

NORTH DAKOTA
Ms. Penny Miller
Clerk of Supreme Court
Supreme Court
Judicial Wing, 1st Floor
600 East Boulevard Avenue
Bismarck, ND 58505
P: (701) 328-2221
F: (701) 328-4480
E: PMiller@ndcourts.gov

NORTHERN MARIANA ISLANDS
Ms. Deanna Ogo
Clerk
Supreme Court
P.O. Box 502165
Saipan, MP 96950
P: (670) 236-9800
F: (670) 236-9702
E: supreme.court@saipan.com

OHIO
Ms. Sandra Huth Grosko
Clerk of Court
Supreme Court
65 South Front Street, 8th Floor
Columbus, OH 43215
P: (614) 387-9530

OKLAHOMA
Mr. Michael S. Richie
Supreme Court Clerk
Supreme Court
P.O. Box 53126
Oklahoma City, OK 73152
P: (405) 521-2163

OREGON
Ms. Kingsley W. Click
State Court Administrator
Judicial Department
Supreme Court Building
1163 State Street
Salem, OR 97301
P: (503) 986-5500
F: (503) 986-5503
E: kingsley.w.click@state.or.us

PENNSYLVANIA
Ms. Patricia Johnson
Chief Clerk
Supreme Court
468 City Hall
Philadelphia, PA 19107
P: (215) 560-6370

Ms. Patricia A. Nicola
Chief Clerk
Supreme Court
801 City-County Building
Pittsburgh, PA 15219
P: (412) 565-2816

Ms. Elizabeth Zisk
Chief Clerk
Supreme Court
601 Commonwealth Avenue, Suite 4500
P.O. Box 62575
Harrisburg, PA 17106
P: (717) 787-6181

PUERTO RICO
Ms. Patricia Oton Oliveri
Secretary of Supreme Court
Supreme Court
P.O. Box 9022392
San Juan, PR 00902
P: (787) 723-6033
F: (787) 723-9199

RHODE ISLAND
Ms. Debra A. Saunders
Supreme Court Clerk
Supreme Court
Frank Licht Judicial Complex
250 Benefit Street
Providence, RI 02903
P: (401) 222-3272
E: dsaunders@courts.ri.gov

SOUTH CAROLINA
Mr. Daniel E. Shearouse
Clerk of Court
Supreme Court
1231 Gervais Street
P.O. Box 11330
Columbia, SC 29211
P: (803) 734-1080
F: (803) 734-1499

SOUTH DAKOTA
Ms. Shirley A. Jameson-Fergel
Clerk
Supreme Court
500 East Capitol Avenue
Pierre, SD 57501
P: (605) 773-3511
F: (605) 773-6128

TENNESSEE
Mr. James Hivner
Appellate Court Clerk
Supreme Court
Supreme Court Building
401 7th Avenue, North
Nashville, TN 37219
P: (615) 741-2681
F: (615) 532-8757

TEXAS
Mr. Blake A. Hawthorne
Clerk of the Court
Supreme Court
201 West 14th Street, Room 104
P.O. Box 12248
Austin, TX 78711
P: (512) 463-1312
F: (512) 463-1365

U.S. VIRGIN ISLANDS
Ms. Veronica J. Handy
Clerk of the Court
Supreme Court
P.O. Box 590
St. Thomas, VI 00804
P: (340) 774-2237
F: (340) 774-2258

UTAH
Ms. Nicole Gray
Clerk of the Court
Supreme Court
450 South State Street, 5th Floor
P.O. Box 140210
Salt Lake City, UT 84114
P: (801) 238-7974
E: nicoleg@utcourts.gov

VERMONT
Ms. Patricia Gabel
Court Administrator & Clerk
Supreme Court
109 State Street
Montpelier, VT 05609
P: (802) 828-3278
F: (802) 828-4750

VIRGINIA
Ms. Patricia L. Harrington
Clerk
Supreme Court
100 North 9th Street, 5th Floor
P.O. Box 1315
Richmond, VA 23219
P: (804) 786-2251

WASHINGTON
Ms. Susan Carlson
Clerk
Supreme Court
415 12th Avenue, Southwest
P.O. Box 40929
Olympia, WA 98504
P: (360) 357-2077

WEST VIRGINIA
Mr. Rory L. Perry II
Clerk of Court
Supreme Court of Appeals
State Capitol, Room E-317
1900 Kanawha Boulevard, East
Charleston, WV 25305
P: (304) 558-2601
F: (304) 558-3815

WISCONSIN
Ms. Diane M. Fremgen
Clerk of the Supreme Court
Supreme Court
100 East Main Street, Suite 215
P.O. Box 1688
Madison, WI 53701
P: (608) 261-4300
F: (608) 267-0640
E: Diane.Fremgen
@courts.state.wi.us

WYOMING
Ms. Carol Thompson
Clerk of Court
Supreme Court
2301 Capitol Avenue
Cheyenne, WY 82002
P: (307) 777-7316
F: (307) 777-6129
E: cthompson
@courts.state.wy.us

Commerce

Umbrella agency of commerce responsible for the overall regulation and growth of the state's economy.

ALABAMA
Mr. Greg Canfield
Secretary
Department of Commerce
401 Adams Avenue
P.O. Box 304106
Montgomery, AL 36130
P: (334) 242-0421
F: (334) 242-0415
E: greg.canfield@commerce.alabama.gov

ALASKA
Mr. Chris Hladick
Commissioner
Department of Commerce, Community & Economic Development
P.O. Box 110804
Juneau, AK 99811
P: (907) 465-2500
F: (907) 269-8125
E: chris.hladick@alaska.gov

AMERICAN SAMOA
Mr. Keniseli Lafaele
Director
Department of Commerce
American Samoa Government
Executive Office Building, Utulei
Pago Pago, AS 96799
P: (684) 633-5155 Ext. 222
F: (684) 633-4195
E: keniseli.lafaele@doc.as

ARIZONA
Ms. Sandra Watson
President & CEO
Commerce Authority
118 North 7th Avenue, Suite 400
Phoenix, AZ 85007
P: (602) 845-1215
F: (602) 845-1201
E: commerce@azcommerce.com

ARKANSAS
Mr. Mike Preston
Exeuctive Director
Economic Development Commission
900 West Capitol Avenue, Suite 400
Little Rock, AR 72201
P: (501) 682-7351
F: (501) 682-7394
E: mpreston@arkansasedc.com

CALIFORNIA
Ms. Panorea Avdis
Director
Governor's Office of Business & Economic Development
1325 J Street, Suite 1800
Sacramento, CA 95814
P: (877) 345-4633

COLORADO
Ms. Stephanie Copeland
Executive Director
Office of Economic Development & International Trade
1625 Broadway, Suite 2700
Denver, CO 80202
P: (303) 892-3840
F: (303) 892-3848
E: stephanie.copeland@state.co.us

CONNECTICUT
Ms. Catherine H. Smith
Commissioner
Department of Economic & Community Development
505 Hudson Street
Hartford, CT 06106
P: (860) 270-8000
E: catherine.smith@ct.gov

DELAWARE
Mr. Cerron Cade
Acting Cabinet Secretary
Economic Development Office
99 Kings Highway
Dover, DE 19901
P: (302) 672-6809
F: (302) 739-5749
E: cerron.cade@state.de.us

DISTRICT OF COLUMBIA
Mr. Brian Kenner
Deputy Mayor for Planning & Economic Development
Office of the Deputy Mayor for Planning & Economic Development
John A. Wilson Building, Suite 317
1350 Pennsylvania Avenue, Northwest
Washington, DC 20004
P: (202) 727-6365
F: (202) 727-6703
E: brian.kenner@dc.gov

FLORIDA
Mr. Karl Blischke
Director
Division of Strategic Business Development
Department of Economic Opportunity
107 East Madison St., Caldwell Building
Tallahassee, FL 32399
P: (850) 245-7105
F: (850) 921-3223
E: karl.blischke@deo.myflorida.com

GEORGIA
Mr. Pat Wilson
Commissioner
Department of Economic Development
75 5th Street Northwest
Suite 1200
Atlanta, GA 30308
P: (404) 962-4003
F: (404) 962-4009
E: ccarr@georgia.org

GUAM
Mr. Jay Rojas
Administrator
Economic Development Authority
590 South Marine Corps Drive
Suite 511, ITC Building
Tamuning, GU 96913
P: (671) 647-4332
F: (671) 649-4146

HAWAII
Ms. Catherine P. Awakuni Colon
Director
Department of Commerce & Consumer Affairs
King Kalakaua Building
335 Merchant Street
Honolulu, HI 96813
P: (808) 586-2850
F: (808) 586-2856
E: dcca@dcca.hawaii.gov

IDAHO
Ms. Megan Ronk
Director
Department of Commerce
700 West State Street
P.O. Box 83720
Boise, ID 83720
P: (208) 334-2470
F: (208) 334-2631
E: megan.ronk@commerce.idaho.gov

ILLINOIS
Mr. Sean McCarthy
Director
Department of Commerce & Economic Opportunity
100 West Randolph Street, Suite 3-400
Chicago, IL 60601
P: (312) 814-2811

INDIANA
Mr. Jim Schellinger
Secretary of Commerce
Economic Development Corporation
One North Capitol, Suite 700
Indianapolis, IN 46204
P: (317) 234-1359
F: (317) 232-4146
E: JSchellinger@iedc.IN.gov

IOWA
Mr. Ronald L. Hansen
Superintendent
Division of Banking
200 East Grand Avenue, Suite 300
Des Moines, IA 50309
P: (515) 281-4014
F: (515) 281-4862
E: rhansen@idob.state.ia.us

KANSAS
Mr. Antonio J. Soave
Secretary
Department of Commerce
1000 Southwest Jackson Street, Suite 100
Topeka, KS 66612
P: (785) 296-2994
F: (785) 296-5055
E: asoave@kansascommerce.com

KENTUCKY
Mr. Don Parkinson
Secretary
Tourism, Arts & Heritage Cabinet
100 Airport Road, Second Floor
Frankfort, KY 40601
P: (502) 564-4270
F: (502) 564-1512
E: Don.Parkinson@ky.gov

LOUISIANA
Mr. Donald Pierson Jr.
Secretary of Economic Development
Louisiana Economic Development
617 North Third Street
Baton Rouge, LA 70802
P: (225) 342-5388
E: don.pierson@la.gov

MAINE
Mr. George C. Gervais
Commissioner
Department of Economic & Community Development
59 State House Station
Augusta, ME 04333
P: (207) 624-9800

MARYLAND
Mr. R. Michael Gill
Secretary
Department of Commerce
Office of the Secretary
401 East Pratt Street
Baltimore, MD 21202
P: (410) 767-6301
F: (410) 333-8628
E: Mike.Gill@maryland.gov

MASSACHUSETTS
Mr. Jay Ash
Secretary
Executive Office of Housing & Economic Development
One Ashburton Place, Room 2101
Boston, MA 02108
P: (617) 788-3610
F: (617) 788-3605

MINNESOTA
Mr. Mike Rothman
Commissioner
Department of Commerce
85 7th Place East, Suite 280
St. Paul, MN 55101
P: (651) 539-1441
F: (651) 539-1547
E: commerce.commissioner@state.mn.us

MISSISSIPPI
The Honorable Cindy Hyde-Smith (R)
Commissioner
Department of Agriculture & Commerce
121 North Jefferson Street
Jackson, MS 39201
P: (601) 359-1100
F: (601) 354-7710

MISSOURI
Mr. Mike Downing
Acting Director
Department of Economic Development
P.O. Box 1157
Jefferson City, MO 65102
P: (573) 751-4770
F: (573) 526-7700
E: ecodev@ded.mo.gov

NEBRASKA
Ms. Courtney Dentlinger
Director
Department of Economic Development
301 Centennial Mall South
P.O. Box 94666
Lincoln, NE 68509
P: (402) 471-3746
F: (402) 471-3778
E: courtney.dentlinger@nebraska.gov

NEVADA
Mr. Bruce H. Breslow
Director
Department of Business & Industry
3300 West Sahara Avenue, Suite 425
Las Vegas, NV 89102
P: (702) 486-2750
F: (702) 486-2758
E: breslow@business.nv.gov

NEW HAMPSHIRE
Mr. Christopher Way
Acting Director
Division of Economic Development
72 Pembroke Road
Concord, NH 03301
P: (603) 271-2341
F: (603) 271-6784
E: Christopher.Way@dred.nh.gov

NEW JERSEY
Ms. Melissa Orsen
Chief Executive Officer
Economic Development Authority
36 West State Street
P.O. Box 990
Trenton, NJ 08625
P: (609) 858-6700
F: (609) 292-0885
E: CustomerCare@njeda.com

NEW MEXICO
Mr. Matthew Geisel
Secretary
Economic Development Department
1100 South Saint Francis Drive
P.O. Box 20003
Santa Fe, NM 87504
P: (505) 827-0305
F: (505) 827-0328
E: Matthew.Geisel@state.nm.us

NEW YORK
Mr. Howard Zemsky
President & CEO
Empire State Development
633 Third Avenue, Floor 37
New York, NY 10017
P: (212) 803-3100
F: (212) 803-3715

NORTH CAROLINA
Mr. Tony Copeland
Secretary
Department of Commerce
301 North Wilimington Street
4301 Mail Service Center
Raleigh, NC 27699
P: (919) 814-4603
E: acopeland@nccommerce.com

NORTH DAKOTA
Mr. Jay Schuler
Commissioner
Department of Commerce
1600 East Century Avenue, Suite 2
P.O. Box 2057
Bismarck, ND 58503
P: (701) 328-5300
F: (701) 328-5320
E: commerce@nd.gov

OHIO
Ms. Jacqueline Williams
Director
Department of Commerce
77 South High Street, 23rd Floor
Columbus, OH 43215
P: (614) 644-7047
E: director.office@com.state.oh.us

OKLAHOMA
Mr. Deby Snodgrass
Executive Director & Secretary
Department of Commerce
900 North Stiles Avenue
Oklahoma City, OK 73104
P: (405) 815-5306
E: deby.snodgrass@okcommerce.gov

OREGON
Mr. Chris Harder
Director
Business Oregon
775 Summer Street, Northeast, Suite 200
Salem, OR 97301
P: (503) 229-5009
F: (503) 581-5115
E: chris.harder@state.or.us

PENNSYLVANIA
Mr. Dennis Davin
Secretary
Department of Community & Economic Development
Commonwealth Keystone Building
400 North Street, 4th Floor
Harrisburg, PA 17120
P: (866) 787-3003
F: (717) 787-6866

PUERTO RICO
Mr. Manuel Laboy Rivera
Executive Director
Industrial Development Company
P.O. Box 362350
San Juan, PR 00936
P: (787) 758-4747
E: secretario@ddec.pr.gov

RHODE ISLAND
Mr. Darin Early
President
Commerce Corporation
315 Iron Horse Way, Suite 101
Providence, RI 02908
P: (401) 278-9100
F: (401) 273-8270
E: darin.early@commerceri.com

SOUTH CAROLINA
Mr. Robert M. Hitt III
Secretary
Department of Commerce
1201 Main Street, Suite 1600
Columbia, SC 29201
P: (803) 737-1800
F: (803) 737-0894

SOUTH DAKOTA
Mr. Scott Stern
Commissioner
Governor's Office of Economic Development
711 East Wells Avenue
Pierre, SD 57501
P: (800) 872-6190
F: (605) 773-3256
E: goedinfo@state.sd.us

TENNESSEE
Ms. Julie Mix McPeak
Commissioner
Department of Commerce & Insurance
Davy Crockett Tower
500 James Robertson Parkway
Nashville, TN 37243
P: (615) 741-2241
F: (615) 532-6934
E: ask.tdci@tn.gov

Commerce

U.S. VIRGIN ISLANDS
Ms. Beverly Nicholson Doty
Commissioner
Department of Tourism
Elainco Building
78 Contant 1-2-3
St. Thomas, VI 00802
P: (340) 774-8784
F: (340) 773-0495

UTAH
Ms. Francine A. Giani
Executive Director
Department of Commerce
160 East 300 South, 2nd Floor
P.O. Box 146701
Salt Lake City, UT 84114
P: (801) 530-6431
F: (801) 530-6446
E: fgiani@utah.gov

VERMONT
Mr. Michael Schirling
Secretary
Agency of Commerce & Community Development
One National Life Drive
Deane C. Davis Building, 6th Floor
Montpelier, VT 05620
P: (802) 828-3080
E: Michael.Schirling@vermont.gov

VIRGINIA
Mr. Todd Haymore
Secretary of Commerce & Trade
Office of Commerce & Trade
1111 East Broad Street
P.O. Box 1475
Richmond, VA 23218
P: (804) 786-7831
F: (804) 371-0250
E: Todd.Haymore@governor.virginia.gov

WASHINGTON
Mr. Brian Bonlender
Director
Department of Commerce
1011 Plum Street, Southeast
P.O. Box 42525
Olympia, WA 98504
P: (360) 725-4000
E: brian.bonlender@commerce.wa.gov

WEST VIRGINIA
Mr. H. Wood Thrasher
Cabinet Secretary
Department of Commerce
Capitol Complex Building 6, Room 525
1900 Kanawha Boulevard East
Charleston, WV 25305
P: (304) 558-2234
F: (304) 558-1189
E: W.Thrasher@wv.gov

WISCONSIN
Mr. Mark Hogan
Chief Executive Officer
Economic Development Corporation
201 West Washington Avenue
P.O. Box 1687
Madison, WI 53701
P: (608) 210-6701
E: Mark.Hogan@wedc.org

WYOMING
Mr. Shawn Reese
Chief Executive Officer
Business Council
214 West 15th Street
Cheyenne, WY 82002
P: (307) 777-2862
F: (307) 777-2837
E: shawn.reese@wyo.gov

Comptroller

The principal accounting and dispersing officer of the state.

Information provided by:

National Association of State Auditors, Comptrollers & Treasurers
Kinney Poynter
Executive Director
449 Lewis Hargett Circle
Suite 290
Lexington, KY 40503
P: (859) 276-1147
F: (859) 278-0507
kpoynter@nasact.org
www.nasact.org

ALABAMA
Ms. Kathleen Baxter
State Comptroller
Office of the State Comptroller
100 North Union Street, Suite 220
Montgomery, AL 36104
P: (334) 242-7063
F: (334) 242-2440

ALASKA
Mr. Scot Arehart
Director
Division of Finance
Department of Administration
P.O. Box 110204
Juneau, AK 99811
P: (907) 465-3435
F: (907) 465-2169
E: scot.arehart@alaska.gov

ARIZONA
Mr. D. Clark Partridge
State Comptroller
General Accounting Office
100 North 15th Avenue, Suite 302
Phoenix, AZ 85007
P: (602) 542-5405
F: (602) 542-5749
E: gaowebmr@azdoa.gov

ARKANSAS
The Honorable Andrea Lea (R)
Auditor of State
Office of the State Auditor
State Capitol Building, Room 230
Little Rock, AR 72201
P: (501) 682-6030
F: (501) 682-2521

Mr. Larry Walther
Director
Department of Finance & Administration
1509 West 7th Street
DFA Building, Room 401
Little Rock, AR 72201
P: (501) 682-2242
F: (501) 682-1029
E: larry.walther@dfa.arkansas.gov

CALIFORNIA
Mr. Todd Jerue
Chief Operating Officer
Department of Finance
State Capitol, Room 1145
915 L Street
Sacramento, CA 95814
P: (916) 445-4923
F: (916) 445-7997

The Honorable Betty T. Yee (D)
State Controller
Office of the State Controller
300 Capitol Mall, Suite 1850
P.O. Box 942805
Sacramento, CA 94250
P: (916) 445-2636
F: (916) 445-6379

COLORADO
Mr. Bob Jaros
State Controller
Department of Personnel & Administration
1525 Sherman Street, 5th Floor
Denver, CO 80203
P: (303) 866-6200
F: (303) 866-3569
E: bob.jaros@state.co.us

CONNECTICUT
Mr. Kevin Lembo
State Comptroller
Office of the Comptroller
55 Elm Street, Suite 307
Hartford, CT 06106
P: (860) 702-3301
F: (860) 702-3319
E: Kevin.Lembo@ct.gov

DELAWARE
Ms. Jane Cole
Director
Division of Accounting
820 Silver Lake Boulevard, Suite 200
Dover, DE 19904
P: (302) 672-5500
F: (302) 736-7969

DISTRICT OF COLUMBIA
Mr. Bill Slack (appointed)
Deputy Chief Financial Officer
Office of Financial Operations & Systems
1100 4th Street, Southwest
8th Floor
Washington, DC 20024
P: (202) 442-8200
F: (202) 442-8201

FLORIDA
The Honorable Jeffrey H. Atwater (R)
Chief Financial Officer
Department of Financial Services
200 East Gaines Street
Tallahassee, FL 32399
P: (850) 413-2850
F: (850) 413-2950
E: allison@jeffatwater.com

GEORGIA
Mr. Alan Skelton
State Accounting Officer
State Accounting Office
200 Piedmont Avenue
Suite 1604, West Tower
Atlanta, GA 30334
P: (404) 656-2133
F: (404) 463-5089

GUAM
Ms. Christine Baleto
Director
Department of Adminsitration
P.O. Box 884
Hagatna, GU 96928
P: (671) 475-1101
F: (671) 477-6788

HAWAII
Mr. Roderick Becker
Comptroller
Department of Accounting & General Services
1151 Punchbowl Street, Room 412
Honolulu, HI 96813
P: (808) 586-0400
F: (808) 586-0775
E: roderick.k.becker@hawaii.gov

IDAHO
The Honorable Brandon Woolf
State Controller
Office of the State Controller
700 West State Street
P.O. Box 83720
Boise, ID 83720
P: (208) 334-3100
F: (208) 334-3338
E: bwoolf@sco.idaho.gov

ILLINOIS
The Honorable Susana A. Mendoza (D)
State Comptroller
Office of the State Comptroller
201 State Capitol Building
Springfield, IL 62706
P: (217) 782-6000
F: (217) 782-7561

INDIANA
Ms. Tera Klutz
State Auditor
Office of the Auditor of State
State House, Room 240
200 West Washington Street
Indianapolis, IN 46204
P: (317) 232-3300
F: (317) 234-1916
E: comments@auditor.in.gov

IOWA
Mr. Calvin McKelvogue
Chief Operating Officer
Department of Administrative Services
State Accounting Enterprise
Hoover State Office Building, 3rd Floor
Des Moines, IA 50319
P: (515) 281-4877
F: (515) 281-5255
E: calvin.mckelvogue@iowa.gov

KANSAS
Ms. DeAnn Hill
Chief Financial Officer
Office of the Chief Financial Officer
700 Southwest Harrison Street
Suite 300
Topeka, KS 66603
P: (785) 368-7390
F: (785) 296-6841

KENTUCKY
Mr. Edgar C. Ross
Controller
Office of the Controller
Capitol Annex, Room 484
702 Capitol Avenue
Frankfort, KY 40601
P: (502) 564-2998
F: (502) 564-6597
E: edc.ross@ky.gov

Comptroller

LOUISIANA
Mr. Afranie Adomako
Director
Office of Statewide Reporting & Accounting Policy
Division of Administration
P.O. Box 94095
Baton Rouge, LA 70804
P: (225) 342-0708
F: (225) 342-1053
E: afranie.adomako@la.gov

MAINE
Mr. Douglas Cotnoir
State Controller
Office of the State Controller
Cross Office Building, 4th Floor
14 State House Station
Augusta, ME 04333
P: (207) 626-8420
F: (207) 626-8422
E: douglas.cotnoir@maine.gov

MARYLAND
The Honorable Peter Franchot (D)
Comptroller
Office of the Comptroller
L.L. Goldstein Treasury Building
80 Calvert Street, P.O. Box 466
Annapolis, MD 21404
P: (410) 260-7801
F: (410) 974-3808
E: mdcomptroller@comp.state.md.us

MASSACHUSETTS
Mr. Thomas Shack III
Comptroller
Office of the State Comptroller
One Ashburton Place, 9th Floor
Boston, MA 02108
P: (617) 973-2315
F: (617) 727-2163

MICHIGAN
Mr. Michael J. Moody
Director
Office of Financial Management
State Budget Office
111 South Capitol Avenue
Lansing, MI 48933
P: (517) 335-1942
F: (517) 373-6458
E: moodym1@michigan.gov

MINNESOTA
Mr. Myron Frans
Commissioner
Management & Budget
658 Cedar Street, Suite 400
St. Paul, MN 55155
P: (651) 201-8011
F: (651) 296-8685
E: myron.frans@state.mn.us

MISSISSIPPI
Ms. Laura Jackson
Executive Director
Department of Finance & Administration
501 North West, 701 Woolfolk Building
P.O. Box 267
Jackson, MS 39205
P: (601) 359-3402
F: (601) 359-5525
E: laura.jackson@dfa.ms.gov

MISSOURI
Ms. Stacy Neal
Director of Accounting
Office of Administration, Division of Accounting
Truman State Office Building, Room 570
P.O. Box 809
Jefferson City, MO 65102
P: (573) 751-4013
F: (573) 526-9810

MONTANA
Ms. Cheryl Grey
State Accountant & Bureau Chief
Financial Services Division
125 North Roberts Street
P.O. Box 200102
Helena, MT 59620
P: (406) 444-4609
F: (406) 444-2812
E: chgrey@mt.gov

NEBRASKA
Mr. Jerry Broz
State Accounting Administrator
Department of Administrative Services
1526 K Street, Suite 240
P.O. Box 94664
Lincoln, NE 68509
P: (402) 471-2581
F: (402) 471-2583

NEVADA
The Honorable Ron Knecht (R)
State Controller
Office of the State Controller
State Capitol Building
101 North Carson Street, Suite 5
Carson City, NV 89701
P: (775) 684-5632
F: (775) 684-5696

NEW HAMPSHIRE
Ms. Dana Call
State Comptroller
Department of Administrative Services
25 Capitol Street
State House Annex, Room 310
Concord, NH 03301
P: (603) 271-3190
F: (603) 271-6666

NEW JERSEY
Mr. David A. Ridolfino
Director
Office of Management & Budget
Department of Treasury
33 West State Street, P.O. Box 221
Trenton, NJ 08625
P: (609) 292-6746
F: (609) 633-8179
E: david.ridolfino@treas.state.nj.us

NEW MEXICO
Mr. Ronald Spilman
State Controller & Director
Department of Finance & Administration
Bataan Memorial Building, Suite 166
407 Galisteo Street
Santa Fe, NM 87501
P: (505) 827-3934
F: (505) 827-3692

NEW YORK
The Honorable Thomas P. DiNapoli (D)
Comptroller
Office of the State Comptroller
110 State Street
Albany, NY 12236
P: (518) 474-4040
F: (518) 474-3004
E: tdinapoli@osc.state.ny.us

Mr. Pete Grannis
First Deputy Comptroller
Office of the State Comptroller - Operations
110 State Street
Albany, NY 12236
P: (518) 474-2909
F: (518) 474-5220

NORTH CAROLINA
Ms. Linda Combs
State Controller
Office of the State Controller
3512 Bush Street
1410 Mail Service Center
Raleigh, NC 27699
P: (919) 707-0471
F: (919) 981-5567

NORTH DAKOTA
Ms. Pam Sharp
Director
Office of Management & Budget
600 East Boulevard Avenue
Department 110
Bismarck, ND 58505
P: (701) 328-4606
F: (701) 328-3230
E: psharp@nd.gov

NORTHERN MARIANA ISLANDS
Ms. Larrsa Larson
Secretary
Department of Finance
P.O. Box 5234, CHRB
Saipan, MP 96950
P: (670) 664-1100
F: (670) 664-1115
E: revtax@gtepacifica.net

OHIO
Mr. Timothy S. Keen
Director
Office of Budget & Management
30 East Broad Street, 34th Floor
Columbus, OH 43215
P: (614) 752-2579
F: (614) 485-1058
E: tim.keen@obm.state.oh.us

OKLAHOMA
Ms. Lynne Bajema
State Comptroller
Office of Management & Enterprise Services
5005 North Lincoln Boulevard, Suite 100
Oklahoma City, OK 73105
P: (405) 522-5577
F: (405) 521-3902
E: lynne.bajema@osf.ok.gov

OREGON
Mr. Robert Hamilton
Manager of Statewide Accounting
Department of Administrative Services
155 Cottage Street, Northeast, U-50
Salem, OR 97301
P: (503) 373-0265
F: (503) 378-3514

PENNSYLVANIA
Ms. Anna Maria Kiehl
State Comptroller/Chief Accounting Officer
Office of the Budget/Comptroller Operations
9th Floor Forum Place
555 Walnut Street
Harrisburg, PA 17101
P: (717) 787-6497
F: (717) 787-3376
E: akiehl@state.pa.us

RHODE ISLAND
Mr. Peter Keenan
State Controller
Office of Accounts & Control
Department of Administration
One Capitol Hill
Providence, RI 02908
P: (401) 222-2271
F: (401) 222-6437

SOUTH CAROLINA
The Honorable Richard Eckstrom (R)
Comptroller General
Office of the Comptroller General
305 Wade Hampton Office Building
1200 Senate Street
Columbia, SC 29201
P: (803) 734-2588
F: (803) 734-1765
E: reckstrom@cg.sc.gov

SOUTH DAKOTA
Mr. Steve Barnett
State Auditor
Office of the State Auditor
500 East Capitol Avenue
Pierre, SD 57501
P: (605) 773-3341
F: (605) 773-5929
E: steve.barnett@state.sd.us

Ms. Liza Clark
Chief Financial Officer & Commissioner
Bureau of Finance & Management
500 East Capitol Avenue
Pierre, SD 57501
P: (605) 773-3411
F: (605) 773-4711
E: liza.clark@state.sd.us

TENNESSEE
Mr. Mike Corricelli
Chief of Accounts
Department of Finance & Administration
W.R.S. Tennessee Tower, 21st Floor
312 Rosa L. Parks Avenue
Nashville, TN 37243
P: (615) 253-3048
F: (615) 782-6633

TEXAS
The Honorable Glenn Hegar (R)
Comptroller of Public Accounts
Office of the Comptroller of Public Accounts
LBJ State Office Building, 1st Floor
111 East 17th Street
Austin, TX 78774
P: (512) 463-4444
F: (512) 463-4902
E: glenn.hegar@cpa.state.tx.us

U.S. VIRGIN ISLANDS
Mr. Nellon Bowry (appointed)
Director
Office of Management & Budget
No. 5041 Norre Gade, Second Floor
Emancipation Garden Station
St. Thomas, VI 00802
P: (340) 774-0750 Ext. 227
F: (340) 776-0069
E: nellon.bowry@omb.vi.gov

UTAH
Mr. John C. Reidhead
Director
Division of Finance
2110 State Office Building
Salt Lake City, UT 84114
P: (801) 538-3095
F: (801) 538-3244
E: jreidhead@utah.gov

VERMONT
Mr. Andrew Pallito
Commissioner
Department of Finance & Management
109 State Street
Montpelier, VT 05609
P: (802) 828-2376
F: (802) 828-2428
E: andy.pallito@vermont.gov

VIRGINIA
Mr. David A. Von Moll
State Comptroller
Department of Accounts
101 North 14th Street
P.O. Box 1971
Richmond, VA 23219
P: (804) 225-2109
F: (804) 786-8587
E: david.vonmoll@doa.virginia.gov

WASHINGTON
Mr. David Schumacher
Director
Office of Financial Management
P.O. Box 43113
Olympia, WA 98504
P: (360) 902-0530
F: (360) 664-2832
E: ofm.administration@ofm.wa.gov

WEST VIRGINIA
The Honorable John McCuskey (R)
State Auditor
Office of the State Auditor
1900 Kanawha Boulevard East
Building 1, Suite W-100
Charleston, WV 25301
P: (304) 558-2251 Ext. 116
F: (304) 558-5200

Mr. Dave Mullins
Finance Division, Department of Administration
2101 Washington Street East, Building 17
Charleston, WV 25305
P: (304) 558-6181 Ext. 105
F: (304) 558-1950

WISCONSIN
Mr. Jeffrey Anderson
State Controller
Department of Administration
101 East Wilson Street, 5th Floor
P.O. Box 7932
Madison, WI 53593
P: (608) 266-8158
F: (608) 266-7734

WYOMING
The Honorable Cynthia I. Cloud (R)
State Auditor
Office of the State Auditor
State Capitol, Suite 114
200 West 24th Street
Cheyenne, WY 82002
P: (307) 777-7831
F: (307) 777-6983
E: SAOAdmin@wyo.gov

Consumer Protection

Investigates consumer complaints, develops consumer education programs and alerts citizens to current consumer concerns within the state.

ALABAMA
The Honorable Steve Marshall (R)
Attorney General
Office of the Attorney General
501 Washington Avenue
P.O. Box 300152
Montgomery, AL 36130
P: (334) 242-7300

ALASKA
Ms. Signe Andersen
Chief Assistant Attorney General, Section Supervisor
Commercial & Fair Business Practices
Department of Law
1031 West 4th Avenue, Suite 200
Anchorage, AK 99501
P: (907) 269-5200
F: (907) 276-8554
E: signe.andersen@alaska.gov

AMERICAN SAMOA
The Honorable Talauega V. Ale
Attorney General
Office of the Attorney General
American Samoa Government
Executive Office Building, Utulei
Pago Pago, AS 96799
P: (684) 633-4163

Mr. Keniseli Lafaele
Director
Department of Commerce
American Samoa Government
Executive Office Building, Utulei
Pago Pago, AS 96799
P: (684) 633-5155 Ext. 222
F: (684) 633-4195
E: keniseli.lafaele@doc.as

ARIZONA
Ms. Rebecca Eggleston
Section Chief
Consumer Protection & Advocacy Section
Office of the Attorney General
1275 West Washington Street
Phoenix, AZ 85007
P: (602) 542-7717
F: (602) 542-4579
E: consumerinfo@azag.gov

ARKANSAS
The Honorable Leslie Rutledge (R)
Attorney General
Office of the Attorney General
323 Center Street, Suite 200
Little Rock, AR 72201
P: (800) 482-8982
F: (501) 682-8084

CALIFORNIA
Ms. Melissa Wiekel
Manager
Public Inquiry Unit
Office Of The Attorney General
P.O. Box 944255
Sacramento, CA 94244
P: (916) 322-3360
F: (916) 323-5341

COLORADO
Ms. Janet Zavislan
Director
Consumer Protection Section, Office of the Attorney General
Ralph L. Carr Judicial Center
1300 Broadway, 7th Floor
Denver, CO 80203
P: (720) 508-6000
F: (720) 508-6030
E: jan.zavislan@coag.gov

CONNECTICUT
Ms. Michelle Seagull
Commissioner
Department of Consumer Protection
450 Columbus Boulevard, Suite 901
Hartford, CT 06103
P: (860) 713-6050
F: (860) 706-1203
E: michelle.seagull@ct.gov

DELAWARE
Mr. Timothy M. Mullaney Sr.
Director
Fraud & Consumer Protection Division
Carvel State Office Building
820 North French Street
Wilmington, DE 19801
P: (302) 577-8600
F: (302) 577-6499
E: consumer.protection@state.de.us

DISTRICT OF COLUMBIA
Ms. Melinda M. Bolling
Director
Department of Consumer & Regulatory Affairs
1100 4th Street, Southwest
Washington, DC 20024
P: (202) 442-4400
F: (202) 442-9445
E: dcra@dc.gov

FLORIDA
The Honorable Pam Bondi (R)
Attorney General
Office of the Attorney General
The Capitol, PL 01
Tallahassee, FL 32399
P: (850) 414-3300
F: (954) 712-4826

GEORGIA
Mr. John Sours
Administrator
Governor's Office of Consumer Protection
2 Martin Luther King Jr. Drive
Suite 356
Atlanta, GA 30334
P: (404) 651-8600
F: (404) 651-9018
E: john.sours@ocp.ga.gov

GUAM
Mr. Fred Nishihira
Deputy Attorney General
Consumer Protection Division
590 South Marine Corps Drive
ITC Building, Suite 210
Tamuning, GU 96913
P: (671) 475-3324
F: (671) 472-2493
E: fnishihira@guamag.org

HAWAII
Mr. Stephen H. Levins
Executive Director
Office of Consumer Protection
Leiopapa A. Kamehameha Building
235 South Beretania Street, Suite 801
Honolulu, HI 96813
P: (808) 586-2636
F: (808) 586-2640
E: ocp@dcca.hawaii.gov

IDAHO
The Honorable Lawrence Wasden (R)
Attorney General
Office of the Attorney General
Statehouse
Boise, ID 83720
P: (208) 334-2400
F: (208) 854-8071

ILLINOIS
Ms. Deborah Hagan
Chief
Division of Consumer Protection
Office of the Attorney General
500 South Second Street
Springfield, IL 62701
P: (217) 782-9021

IOWA
The Honorable Tom Miller (D)
Attorney General
Office of the Attorney General
Hoover State Office Building
1305 East Walnut
Des Moines, IA 50319
P: (515) 281-5164
F: (515) 281-4209

KANSAS
The Honorable Derek Schmidt (R)
Attorney General
Office of the Attorney General
120 Southwest 10th Avenue, 2nd Floor
Topeka, KS 66612
P: (785) 296-2215
F: (785) 296-6296

KENTUCKY
Mr. Benjamin Long
Executive Director
Office of Consumer Protection
1024 Capital Center Drive, Suite 200
Frankfort, KY 40601
P: (502) 696-5389
F: (502) 564-2894
E: consumer.protection@ag.ky.gov

LOUISIANA
The Honorable Jeffrey Landry (R)
Attorney General
Office of the Attorney General
P.O. Box 94095
Baton Rouge, LA 70804
P: (225) 326-6000
F: (225) 326-6797

MARYLAND
Mr. William D. Gruhn
Chief
Consumer Protection Division
Office of the Attorney General
200 Saint Paul Place
Baltimore, MD 21202
P: (410) 576-6558
F: (410) 576-6566
E: bgruhn@oag.state.md.us

MASSACHUSETTS
Mr. John Chapman
Undersecretary
Office of Consumer Affairs & Business Regulation
Ten Park Plaza, Suite 5170
Boston, MA 02116
P: (617) 973-8700
F: (617) 973-8799

MICHIGAN
Ms. Shelly Edgerton
Director
Department of Licensing & Regulatory Affairs
P.O. Box 30004
Lansing, MI 48909
P: (517) 373-1820
F: (517) 241-3683
E: EdgertonS1@michigan.gov

The Honorable Bill Schuette (R)
Attorney General
Office of the Attorney General
525 West Ottawa Street
P.O. Box 30212
Lansing, MI 48909
P: (517) 373-1110

MINNESOTA
The Honorable Lori Swanson (DFL)
Attorney General
Office of the Attorney General
Suite 102, State Capital
75 Dr. Martin Luther King, Jr. Boulevard
St. Paul, MN 55155
P: (651) 296-3353
F: (651) 297-4193
E: Attorney.General@ag.state.mn.us

MISSISSIPPI
Ms. Meredith Aldridge
Special Assistant Attorney
Consumer Protection Division
Office of the Attorney General
P.O. Box 22947
Jackson, MS 39225
P: (601) 359-4230
F: (601) 359-4231

MONTANA
Mr. Matthew Dale
Executive Director
Office of Victim Services
555 Fuller Avenue
P.O. Box 201410
Helena, MT 59601
P: (406) 442-2174
F: (406) 444-9680
E: dojovs@mt.gov

NEBRASKA
The Honorable Doug Peterson (R)
Attorney General
Office of the Attorney General
State Capitol
P.O. Box 98920
Lincoln, NE 68509
P: (402) 471-2682
F: (402) 471-3297

NEVADA
Mr. Eric P. Witkoski
Chief Deputy Attorney General
Bureau of Consumer Protection
Office of the Attorney General
100 North Carson Street
Carson City, NV 89701
P: (702) 486-3129
F: (775) 684-1108
E: ewitkoski@ag.nv.gov

NEW HAMPSHIRE
The Honorable Gordon MacDonald
Attorney General
Office of the Attorney General
33 Capitol Street
Concord, NH 03301
P: (603) 271-3658
F: (603) 271-2110

NEW JERSEY
Mr. Steve C. Lee
Director
Division of Consumer Affairs
Office of the Attorney General
124 Halsey Street
Newark, NJ 07102
P: (973) 504-6200
F: (973) 273-8035
E: askconsumeraffairs@lps.state.nj.us

NEW MEXICO
The Honorable Hector H. Balderas (D)
Attorney General
Office of the Attorney General
P.O. Drawer 1508
Santa Fe, NM 87504
P: (505) 490-4060
F: (505) 827-5826

NEW YORK
The Honorable Cesar A. Perales
Secretary of State
Office of the Secretary of State
One Commerce Plaza
99 Washington Avenue, Suite 1100
Albany, NY 12231
P: (518) 486-9846
F: (518) 474-4797
E: info@dos.ny.gov

NORTH CAROLINA
The Honorable Josh Stein (D)
Attorney General
Office of the Attorney General
Department of Justice
P.O. Box 629
Raleigh, NC 27602
P: (919) 716-6400
F: (919) 716-6750
E: jstein@ncdoj.gov

NORTH DAKOTA
Mr. Parrell Grossman
Director
Consumer Protection & Antitrust Division
Gateway Professional Center
1050 East Interstate Avenue, Suite 200
Bismarck, ND 58503
P: (701) 328-3404
F: (701) 328-3535
E: pgrossman@nd.gov

OHIO
The Honorable Mike DeWine (R)
Attorney General
Office of the Attorney General
State Office Tower
30 East Broad Street
Columbus, OH 43266
P: (614) 466-4320

OKLAHOMA
Mr. Scott Lesher
Administrator
Department of Consumer Credit
3613 Northwest 56th Street, Suite 240
Oklahoma City, OK 73112
P: (405) 521-3653
F: (405) 601-7639
E: slesher@okdocc.ok.gov

PENNSYLVANIA
Ms. Merenda Basil
Director & Chief Deputy Attorney General
Bureau of Consumer Protection
Office of the Attorney General
15th Floor, Strawberry Square
Harrisburg, PA 17120
P: (717) 787-9707
F: (717) 705-3795

PUERTO RICO
Adames Enoch Nery Soto
Secretary
Department of Consumer Affairs
P.O. Box 41059
Minillas Station
San Juan, PR 00940
P: (787) 722-7555
F: (787) 726-0077

RHODE ISLAND
The Honorable Peter F. Kilmartin (D)
Attorney General
Office of the Attorney General
150 South Main Street
Providence, RI 02903
P: (401) 274-4400

SOUTH CAROLINA
Ms. Carri Grube Lybarker
Administrator
Department of Consumer Affairs
2221 Devine Street, Suite 200
P.O. Box 5757
Columbia, SC 29250
P: (803) 734-4233
F: (803) 734-4060

SOUTH DAKOTA
Mr. Ray Klinger
Director
Division of Consumer Protection
Office of the Attorney General
1302 East Highway 14, Suite 3
Pierre, SD 57501
P: (605) 773-4400
F: (605) 773-7163
E: consumerhelp@state.sd.us

Consumer Protection

TENNESSEE
Ms. Cynthia Weil
Director
Division of Consumer Affairs
Department of Commerce & Insurance
500 James Robertson Parkway, 12th Floor
Nashville, TN 37243
P: (615) 741-4737
F: (615) 532-4994

TEXAS
Mr. Rudy Aguilar
Consumer Protection Director
Office of Consumer Credit Commissioner
2601 North Lamar Boulevard
Austin, TX 78705
P: (512) 936-7627
F: (512) 936-7610
E: rudy.aguilar@occc.state.tx.us

U.S. VIRGIN ISLANDS
Mr. Devin Carrington
Commissioner
Department of Licensing & Consumer Affairs
Golden Rock Shopping Center
3000 Estate Golden Rock, Suite 9
St. Croix, VI 00820
P: (340) 718-8250
F: (340) 718-6982

UTAH
Mr. Daniel O'Bannon
Director
Department of Commerce, Division of Consumer Protection
160 East 300 South, 2nd Floor
P.O. Box 146704
Salt Lake City, UT 84114
P: (801) 530-6601
F: (801) 530-6001
E: dobannon@utah.gov

WASHINGTON
The Honorable Bob Ferguson (D)
Attorney General
Office of the Attorney General
1125 Washington Street, Southeast
P.O. Box 40100
Olympia, WA 98504
P: (360) 753-6200
F: (360) 664-0228
E: bob.ferguson@atg.wa.gov

WEST VIRGINIA
Mr. Doug Davis
Assistant Attorney General
Consumer Protection & Antitrust Division
Office of the Attorney General
P.O. Box 1789
Charleston, WV 25326
P: (304) 558-8986
F: (304) 558-0184
E: douglas.l.davis@wvago.gov

WISCONSIN
Mr. Frank Frassetto
Administrator, Trade & Consumer Protection
Department of Agriculture, Trade & Consumer Protection
2811 Agriculture Drive
P.O. Box 8911
Madison, WI 53708
P: (608) 224-4949
F: (608) 224-4939
E: Frank.Frassetto@wisconsin.gov

Corporate Records

Maintains a variety of corporate filings, records and documents.

ALABAMA
Ms. Elaine Swearengin
Division Director
Business Services Division
11 South Union Street, Suite 119
P.O. Box 5616
Montgomery, AL 36130
P: (334) 242-7221
F: (334) 240-3138
E: Elaine.Swearengin@sos.alabama.gov

ALASKA
Ms. Janey Hovenden
Division Director
Division of Corporations, Business & Professional Licensing
P.O. Box 110806
Juneau, AK 99811
P: (907) 465-2550
F: (907) 465-2974
E: janey.hovenden@alaska.gov

AMERICAN SAMOA
The Honorable Talauega V. Ale
Attorney General
Office of the Attorney General
American Samoa Government
Executive Office Building, Utulei
Pago Pago, AS 96799
P: (684) 633-4163

Mr. Keniseli Lafaele
Director
Department of Commerce
American Samoa Government
Executive Office Building, Utulei
Pago Pago, AS 96799
P: (684) 633-5155 Ext. 222
F: (684) 633-4195
E: keniseli.lafaele@doc.as

ARIZONA
Ms. Patricia L. Barfield
Director
Corporations Division
Corporation Commission
1300 West Washington Street
Phoenix, AZ 85007
P: (602) 542-3521
F: (602) 542-0900
E: director.corp@azcc.gov

ARKANSAS
The Honorable Mark Martin (R)
Secretary of State
Office of the Secretary of State
256 State Capitol Building
Little Rock, AR 72201
P: (501) 682-1010
F: (501) 682-3510
E: info@sos.arkansas.gov

The Honorable Leslie Rutledge (R)
Attorney General
Office of the Attorney General
323 Center Street, Suite 200
Little Rock, AR 72201
P: (800) 482-8982
F: (501) 682-8084

CALIFORNIA
Ms. Betsy Bogart
Chief
Business Programs Division
Office of the Secretary of State
1500 11th Street, 3rd Floor
Sacramento, CA 95814
P: (916) 651-6973
E: bbogart@sos.ca.gov

COLORADO
Mr. Michael Hardin
Director of Business & Licensing
Department of State, Licensing Programs
1700 Broadway, Suite 200
Denver, CO 80290
P: (303) 894-2200
F: (303) 869-4864
E: mike.hardin@sos.state.co.us

CONNECTICUT
The Honorable Denise W. Merrill (D)
Secretary of State
Office of the Secretary of State
Capitol Office
P.O. Box 150470
Hartford, CT 06115
P: (860) 509-6200
F: (860) 509-6209
E: denise.merrill@ct.gov

DELAWARE
Ms. April Wright
Administrator
Division of Corporations
401 Federal Street, Suite 4
P.O. Box 898
Dover, DE 19903
P: (302) 739-3073
F: (302) 739-3812

DISTRICT OF COLUMBIA
Ms. Melinda M. Bolling
Director
Department of Consumer & Regulatory Affairs
1100 4th Street, Southwest
Washington, DC 20024
P: (202) 442-4400
F: (202) 442-9445
E: dcra@dc.gov

FLORIDA
Ms. Brenda Vorisek
Division Director, Corporations
Department of State
Clifton Building
2661 Executive Center Circle
Tallahassee, FL 32301
P: (850) 245-6000
E: Brenda.Vorisek@DOS.MyFlorida.com

GEORGIA
Ms. Shawnzia Thomas
Director of Corporations
Corporations Division
2 Martin Luther King Jr. Drive
Suite 313, Floyd West Tower
Atlanta, GA 30334
P: (404) 656-2817
E: sthomas@sos.ga.gov

GUAM
Ms. Maelinda B. Bayona
Supervisor, General Licensing & Registration
Department of Revenue & Taxation
Regulatory Division
P.O. Box 23607
GMF, GU 96921
F: (671) 633-2643

HAWAII
Ms. Catherine P. Awakuni Colon
Director
Department of Commerce & Consumer Affairs
King Kalakaua Building
335 Merchant Street
Honolulu, HI 96813
P: (808) 586-2850
F: (808) 586-2856
E: dcca@dcca.hawaii.gov

IDAHO
Kim Hunter
Director
Business Entity Division
450 North 4th Street
P.O. Box 83720
Boise, ID 83720
P: (208) 334-2301
F: (208) 334-2847
E: business@sos.idaho.gov

ILLINOIS
Mr. Ray Cachares
Director
Business Services
Office of the Secretary of State
501 South 2nd Street, Room 350
Springfield, IL 62756
P: (217) 782-6961

INDIANA
The Honorable Connie Lawson (R)
Secretary of State
Office of the Secretary of State
201 State House
Indianapolis, IN 46204
P: (317) 232-6536
F: (317) 233-3283
E: sos@sos.in.gov

IOWA
The Honorable Paul Pate (R)
Secretary of State
Office of the Secretary of State
Lucas Building, First Floor
321 East 12th Street
Des Moines, IA 50319
P: (515) 281-6230
F: (515) 242-5952
E: sos@sos.iowa.gov

KENTUCKY
The Honorable Alison L. Grimes (D)
Secretary of State
Office of the Secretary of State
700 Capital Avenue, Suite 152
Frankfort, KY 40601
P: (502) 564-3490
F: (502) 564-5687
E: sos.secretary@ky.gov

LOUISIANA
The Honorable Tom Schedler (R)
Secretary of State
Office of the Secretary of State
P.O. Box 94125
Baton Rouge, LA 70804
P: (225) 922-2880
F: (225) 922-2003
E: admin@sos.la.gov

MAINE
Ms. Julie L. Flynn
Deputy Secretary of State
Bureau of Corporation, Elections & Commissions
Office of the Secretary of State
101 State House Station
Augusta, ME 04333
P: (207) 624-7736
F: (207) 287-5428
E: Julie.Flynn@maine.gov

Corporate Records

MARYLAND
Mr. Michael L. Higgs Jr.
Acting Director
Department of Assessments & Taxation
Office of the Director, Suite 801
301 West Preston Street
Baltimore, MD 21201
P: (410) 767-1191
E: michael.higgs@maryland.gov

MASSACHUSETTS
The Honorable William F. Galvin (D)
Secretary of the Commonwealth
Office of the Secretary of the Commonwealth
220 Morrissey Blvd.
Boston, MA 02125
P: (617) 727-2816
F: (617) 288-8429
E: cis@sec.state.ma.us

MICHIGAN
Ms. Shelly Edgerton
Director
Department of Licensing & Regulatory Affairs
P.O. Box 30004
Lansing, MI 48909
P: (517) 373-1820
F: (517) 241-3683
E: EdgertonS1@michigan.gov

MINNESOTA
The Honorable Steve Simon (DFL)
Secretary of State
Office of the Secretary of State
180 State Office Building
100 Martin Luther King Jr. Boulevard
St. Paul, MN 55155
P: (651) 201-1324
F: (651) 269-9073
E: secretary.state@state.mn.us

MISSISSIPPI
Mr. Thomas H. Riley III
Assistant Secretary of State
Business Services Division
Office of the Secretary of State
125 South Congress Street, P.O. Box 136
Jackson, MS 39205
P: (601) 359-1633
F: (601) 359-1607

MISSOURI
Mr. Jon Barry
Deputy Director, Business Services
Office of the Secretary of State
Kirkpatrick State Information Center
P.O. Box 778
Jefferson City, MO 65102
P: (573) 751-4153
F: (573) 526-3124
E: corporations@sos.mo.gov

MONTANA
The Honorable Corey Stapleton (R)
Secretary of State
Office of the Secretary of State
P.O. Box 202801
Helena, MT 59620
P: (406) 444-2034
F: (406) 444-4249
E: sos@mt.gov

NEBRASKA
The Honorable John A. Gale (R)
Secretary of State
Office of the Secretary of State
P.O. Box 94608-4608
Lincoln, NE 68509
P: (402) 471-2554
F: (402) 471-3237
E: sos.info@nebraska.gov

NEVADA
The Honorable Barbara Cegavske (R)
Secretary of State
Office of the Secretary of State
101 North Carson Street, Suite 3
Carson City, NV 89701
P: (775) 684-5708
F: (775) 684-5724
E: sosexec@sos.nv.gov

NEW HAMPSHIRE
The Honorable William M. Gardner (D)
Secretary of State
Office of the Secretary of State
State House, Room 204
Concord, NH 03301
P: (603) 271-3242
F: (603) 271-6316
E: kladd@sos.state.nh.us

NEW MEXICO
The Honorable Dianna J. Duran (R)
Secretary of State
Office of the Secretary of State
325 Don Gaspar, Suite 300
Capitol Annex
Santa Fe, NM 87501
P: (505) 827-3600
F: (505) 827-8081
E: diannaj.duran@state.nm.us

Ms. Stacy Starr-Garcia
Bureau Chief
Corporations Bureau
Office of the Secretary of State
325 Don Gaspar, Suite 300
Santa Fe, NM 87501
P: (505) 827-4508
F: (505) 827-4387
E: stacy.starr-garcia@state.nm.us

NEW YORK
Mr. John Whalen
Acting Director
Division of Corporations, State Records & Uniform Commercial Code
99 Washington Avenue, 6th Floor
Albany, NY 12231
P: (518) 473-2492
F: (518) 474-5173
E: corporations@dos.ny.gov

NORTH CAROLINA
Ms. Cheri L. Myers
Director
Department of the Secretary of State
Corporations Division
P.O. Box 29622
Raleigh, NC 27626
P: (919) 807-2225
F: (919) 807-2039
E: cmyers@sosnc.com

NORTH DAKOTA
Ms. Jessica Trinneer
Director, Central Indexing
Office of the Secretary of State
600 East Boulevard Avenue
Department 108
Bismarck, ND 58505
P: (701) 328-3662
F: (701) 328-4214

OHIO
The Honorable Jon Husted (R)
Secretary of State
Office of the Secretary of State
180 East Broad Street, 16th Floor
Columbus, OH 43215
P: (614) 466-2655
F: (614) 644-0649
E: jhusted@ohiosecretaryofstate.gov

OREGON
Mr. Peter Threlkel
Director, Corporation Division
Office of the Secretary of State
Public Service Building
255 Capitol Street, Northeast, Suite 151
Salem, OR 97310
P: (503) 986-2200
F: (503) 986-1616
E: peter.threlkel@state.or.us

PENNSYLVANIA
Mr. Francisco Miranda
Director
Bureau of Corporations & Charitable Organizations
401 North Street
206 North Office Building
Harrisburg, PA 17120
P: (717) 783-9210
F: (717) 783-2244
E: RA-CORPS@pa.gov

RHODE ISLAND
The Honorable Nellie Gorbea (D)
Secretary of State
Office of the Secretary of State
82 Smith Street, Room 217
Providence, RI 02903
P: (401) 222-2357
F: (401) 222-1356
E: nmgorbea@sos.ri.gov

SOUTH CAROLINA
The Honorable Mark Hammond (R)
Secretary of State
Office of the Secretary of State
1205 Pendleton Street, Suite 525
Columbia, SC 29201
P: (803) 734-2170
F: (803) 734-1661
E: rdaggerhart@sos.sc.gov

TENNESSEE
Mr. Nathan Burton
Director
Division of Business Services
312 Rosa L. Parks Avenue
Snodgrass Tower, 6th Floor
Nashville, TN 37243
P: (615) 741-2286
F: (615) 741-7310
E: business.services
@state.tn.us

TEXAS
Ms. Carmen Flores
Division Director
Business & Public Filings Division
Office of the Secretary of State
P.O. Box 13697
Austin, TX 78711
P: (512) 463-5588
F: (512) 463-5709

UTAH
Ms. Kathy Berg
Director
Department of Commerce, Division of Corporations & UCC
160 East 300 South, 2nd Floor
P.O. Box 146705
Salt Lake City, UT 84114
P: (801) 530-4849
F: (801) 530-6438
E: kberg@utah.gov

VERMONT
Ms. Marlene Betit
Director
Corporations Division
Office of the Secretary of State
128 State Street
Montpelier, VT 05633
P: (802) 828-2477
F: (802) 828-2853
E: marlene.betit
@sec.state.vt.us

VIRGINIA
Mr. Joel Peck
Clerk
State Corporation Commission
Tyler Building, 1300 East Main Street
P.O. Box 1197
Richmond, VA 23218
P: (804) 371-9733
F: (804) 371-9521
E: joel.peck
@scc.virginia.gov

WASHINGTON
The Honorable Kim Wyman (R)
Secretary of State
Office of the Secretary of State
P.O. Box 40220
Olympia, WA 98503
P: (360) 902-4151
F: (360) 586-5629
E: kim.wyman@sos.wa.gov

WYOMING
The Honorable Ed Murray (R)
Secretary of State
Office of the Secretary of State
2020 Carey Avenue, Suite 600 & 700
Cheyenne, WY 82002
P: (307) 777-7378
F: (307) 777-6217
E: secofstate@wyo.gov

Corrections

Manages the state's corrections systems.

ALABAMA
Mr. Jefferson Dunn
Commissioner
Department of Corrections
P.O. Box 301501
101 South Union Street
Montgomery, AL 36130
P: (334) 353-3883

ALASKA
Mr. Dean Williams
Commissioner
Department of Corrections
550 West 7th Avenue, Suite 1800
Anchorage, AK 99501
P: (907) 269-7397
E: dean.williams@alaska.gov

AMERICAN SAMOA
Mr. Save Liuato Tuitele
Commissioner
Public Safety
American Samoa Government
P.O. Box 1086
Pato Pato, AS 96799
P: (684) 633-1111
F: (684) 633-7296
E: commissioner@dps.as.gov

ARIZONA
Mr. Charles L. Ryan
Director
Department of Corrections
1601 West Jefferson, MC 445
Phoenix, AZ 85007
P: (602) 542-5497
F: (602) 364-0159

ARKANSAS
Ms. Wendy Kelley
Director
Department of Correction
P.O. Box 8707
Pine Bluff, AR 71611
P: (870) 267-6999
F: (870) 267-6244

CALIFORNIA
Mr. Scott Kernan
Secretary
Department of Corrections & Rehabilitation
1515 S Street, Suite 502 South
P.O. Box 942883
Sacramento, CA 95811
P: (916) 323-6001

COLORADO
Mr. Rick Raemisch
Executive Director
Department of Corrections
2862 South Circle Drive, Suite 455
Colorado Springs, CO 80906
P: (719) 579-9580

CONNECTICUT
Mr. Scott Semple
Commissioner
Department of Correction
24 Wolcott Hill Road
Wethersfield, CT 06109
P: (860) 692-7480

DELAWARE
Mr. Perry Phelps
Cabinet Secretary
Department of Corrections
245 McKee Road
Dover, DE 19904
P: (302) 739-5601
F: (302) 739-4874

DISTRICT OF COLUMBIA
Mr. Quincy Booth
Director
Department of Corrections
2000 14th Street, Northwest
Washington, DC 20009
P: (202) 673-7316
F: (202) 332-1470

FLORIDA
Ms. Julie Jones
Secretary
Department of Corrections
501 South Calhoun Street
Tallahassee, FL 32399
P: (850) 488-5021

GEORGIA
Mr. Greg Dozier
Commissioner
Department of Corrections
7 Martin Luther King Jr. Boulevard
Atlanta, GA 30334
P: (478) 992-5211
F: (478) 992-5259
E: gdccommish@dcor.state.ga.us

GUAM
Mr. Jose San Agustin
Director
Department of Corrections
P.O. Box 3236
Agana, GU 96932
P: (671) 734-3981

HAWAII
Mr. Nolan Espinda
Director
Department of Public Safety
919 Ala Moana Boulevard, 4th Floor
Honolulu, HI 96814
P: (808) 587-1288
F: (808) 587-1282
E: psd.office.of.the.director@hawaii.gov

IDAHO
Mr. Henry Atencio
Director
Department of Corrections
1299 North Orchard Street, Suite 110
Boise, ID 83706
P: (208) 658-2140
E: hatencio@idoc.idaho.gov

ILLINOIS
Mr. John Baldwin
Director
Department of Corrections
1301 Concordia Court
P.O. Box 19277
Springfield, IL 62794
P: (217) 558-2200

INDIANA
Mr. Robert E. Carter Jr.
Commissioner
Department of Corrections
Government Center South, Room E334
302 West Washington Street
Indianapolis, IN 46204
P: (317) 232-5711
F: (317) 232-6798

IOWA
Mr. Jerry Bartruff
Director
Department of Corrections
510 East 12th Street
Des Moines, IA 50319
P: (515) 725-5701

KANSAS
Mr. Joe Norwood
Secretary
Department of Corrections
714 Southwest Jackson Street, Suite 300
Topeka, KS 66603
P: (785) 296-3317

KENTUCKY
Mr. Rodney Ballard
Commissioner
Department of Corrections
P.O. Box 2400
Frankfort, KY 40602
P: (502) 564-4726
F: (502) 564-5037
E: rodney.ballard@ky.gov

LOUISIANA
Mr. James M. LeBlanc
Secretary
Department of Public Safety & Corrections
Capitol Station
P.O. Box 94304
Baton Rouge, LA 70804
P: (225) 342-6740
F: (225) 342-3095
E: jleblanc@asca.net

MAINE
Dr. Joseph Fitzpatrick
Commissioner
Department of Corrections
State House Station 111
Augusta, ME 04333
P: (207) 287-2711
F: (207) 287-4370
E: joseph.fitzpatrick@maine.gov

MARYLAND
Mr. Stephen Moyer
Secretary
Department of Public Safety & Correctional Services
300 East Joppa Road, Suite 1000
10th Floor
Towson, MD 21286
P: (410) 339-5000

MASSACHUSETTS
Mr. Thomas Turco
Commissioner
Department of Correction
50 Maple Street, Suite 3
Milford, MA 01757
P: (508) 422-3300

MICHIGAN
Ms. Heidi Washington
Director
Department of Corrections
P.O. Box 30003
Lansing, MI 48909
P: (517) 373-0720

MINNESOTA
Mr. Tom Roy
Commissioner
Department of Corrections
1450 Energy Park Drive, Suite 200
St. Paul, MN 55108
P: (651) 361-7200
F: (651) 642-0414
E: tom.roy@state.mn.us

MISSISSIPPI
Ms. Pelicia Hall
Commissioner
Department of Corrections
633 North State Street
Jackson, MS 39202
P: (601) 359-5600
F: (601) 359-5680

MISSOURI
Mr. Anne L. Precythe
Director
Department of Corrections
2729 Plaza Drive
P.O. Box 236
Jefferson City, MO 65102
P: (573) 751-2389
F: (573) 751-4099

MONTANA
Ms. Loraine Wodnik
Interim Director
Department of Corrections
5 South Last Chance Gulch
P.O. Box 201301
Helena, MT 59620
P: (406) 444-3930
F: (406) 444-4920

NEBRASKA
Mr. Scott Frakes
Director
Department of Correctional Services
Folsom & Prospector Place, Building 1
Lincoln, NE 68509
P: (402) 471-2654

NEVADA
Mr. Jim Dzurenda
Director
Department of Corrections
5500 Snyder Avenue, Building 17
P.O. Box 7011
Carson City, NV 89702
P: (775) 887-3285

NEW HAMPSHIRE
Mr. William Wrenn
Commissioner
Department of Corrections
P.O. Box 1806
Concord, NH 03302
P: (603) 271-5600
F: (603) 271-5643
E: wwrenn@nhdoc.state.nh.us

NEW JERSEY
Mr. Gary M. Lanigan
Commissioner
Department of Corrections
Whittlesey Road
P.O. Box 863
Trenton, NJ 08625
P: (609) 292-4036
F: (609) 777-0445

NEW MEXICO
Mr. David Jablonski
Secretary
Corrections Department
P.O. Box 27116
Santa Fe, NM 87502
P: (505) 827-8645
F: (505) 827-8533

NEW YORK
Mr. Anthony Annucci
Commissioner
Department of Corrections & Community Supervision
1220 Washington Avenue, Building 2
Albany, NY 12226
P: (518) 457-8126

Mr. Joseph Ponte
Commissioner
New York City Department of Correction
7520 Astoria Boulevard
East Elmhurst, NY 11370
P: (718) 546-0896

NORTH CAROLINA
Mr. W. David Guice
Commissioner
Adult Correction
Department of Public Safety
512 North Salisbury Street
Raleigh, NC 27604
P: (919) 716-3700
E: David.Guice@ncdps.gov

NORTH DAKOTA
Ms. Leann Bertsch
Director
Department of Corrections & Rehabilitation
3100 Railroad Avenue
P.O. Box 1898
Bismarck, ND 58502
P: (701) 328-6390
F: (701) 328-6651
E: lbertsch@asca.net

OHIO
Mr. Gary C. Mohr
Director
Department of Rehabilitation & Correction
770 West Broad Street
Columbus, OH 43222
P: (614) 387-0588
F: (614) 752-1171

OKLAHOMA
Mr. Joe M. Allbaugh
Director
Department of Corrections
3400 North Martin Luther King Avenue
P.O. Box 11400
Oklahoma City, OK 73136
P: (405) 425-2500

OREGON
Ms. Colette S. Peters
Director
Department of Corrections
2575 Center Street, Northeast
Salem, OR 97301
P: (503) 945-9090
F: (503) 373-1173
E: colette.peters@state.or.us

PENNSYLVANIA
Mr. Michael Resnick
Commissioner
Philadelphia Prison System
7901 State Road
Philadelphia, PA 19136
P: (215) 685-8201

Mr. John E. Wetzel
Secretary
Department of Corrections
1920 Technology Parkway
Mechanicsburg, PA 17050
P: (717) 728-4109
F: (717) 731-0486
E: ra-crpadocsecretary@pa.gov

PUERTO RICO
Mr. Eric Rolon Suarez
Secretary
Department of Correction & Rehabilitation
P.O. Box 71308
San Juan, PR 00936
P: (787) 674-6067

RHODE ISLAND
Mr. Ashbel T. Wall II
Director
Department of Corrections
40 Howard Avenue
Cranston, RI 02920
P: (401) 462-1000
F: (401) 462-2630
E: at.wall@doc.ri.gov

SOUTH CAROLINA
Mr. Bryan Stirling
Director
Department of Corrections
4444 Broad River Road, Room 300
P.O. Box 21787
Columbia, SC 29221
P: (803) 896-8500

SOUTH DAKOTA
Mr. Denny Kaemingk
Secretary
Department of Corrections
3200 East Highway #34
Pierre, SD 57501
P: (605) 773-3478
F: (605) 773-3194

TENNESSEE
Mr. Tony Parker
Commissioner
Department of Correction
Rachel Jackson State Office Building
320 6th Avenue North, 6th Floor
Nashville, TN 37243
P: (615) 741-1000

TEXAS
Mr. Bryan Collier
Executive Director
Department of Criminal Justice
Capitol Station
P.O. Box 13084
Austin, TX 78711
P: (512) 463-9988

U.S. VIRGIN ISLANDS
Mr. Rick Mullgrav
Director
Bureau of Corrections
6040 Castle Coakley
Christiansted, VI 00820
P: (340) 715-7550

Corrections

UTAH
Mr. Rollin Cook
Executive Director
Department of Corrections
14717 South Minuteman Drive
Draper, UT 84020
P: (801) 545-5500

VERMONT
Ms. Lisa Menard
Commissioner
Department of Corrections
103 South Main Street
Waterbury, VT 05671
P: (802) 241-2276

VIRGINIA
Mr. Harold Clarke
Director
Department of Corrections
6900 Atmore Drive
Richmond, VA 23225
P: (804) 674-3000
F: (804) 674-3509
E: harold.clarke
@vadoc.virginia.gov

WASHINGTON
Mr. Stephen Sinclair
Secretary
Department of Corrections
P.O. Box 41101
Olympia, WA 98504
P: (360) 725-8213

WEST VIRGINIA
Ms. Loita Butcher
Acting Commissioner
Division of Corrections
112 California Avenue, Room
302
Charleston, WV 25305
P: (304) 558-2036
F: (304) 558-5367

WISCONSIN
Mr. Jon Litscher
Secretary
Department of Corrections
3099 East Washington Avenue
P. O. Box 7925
Madison, WI 53707
P: (608) 240-5000

WYOMING
Mr. Bob Lampert
Director
Department of Corrections
1934 Wyott Drive, Suite 100
Cheyenne, WY 82002
P: (307) 777-7208
F: (307) 777-7479
E: rlampert@asca.net

Crime Victims Compensation

Provides compensation to victims of crime.

ALABAMA
Dr. Cassie T. Jones
Executive Director
Crime Victims Compensation Commission
5845 Carmichael Road
P.O. Box 231267
Montgomery, AL 36123
P: (334) 290-4420
F: (334) 290-4455
E: cassie.jones@acvcc.alabama.gov

ALASKA
Ms. Kate Hudson
Executive Director
Violent Crimes Compensation Board
Department of Administration
P.O. Box 110230
Juneau, AK 99811
P: (907) 465-3040
F: (907) 465-2379
E: kate.hudson@alaska.gov

AMERICAN SAMOA
The Honorable Talauega V. Ale
Attorney General
Office of the Attorney General
American Samoa Government
Executive Office Building, Utulei
Pago Pago, AS 96799
P: (684) 633-4163

ARIZONA
The Honorable Mark Brnovich (R)
Attorney General
Office of the Attorney General
1275 West Washington Street
Phoenix, AZ 85007
P: (602) 542-4266
F: (602) 542-4085

ARKANSAS
The Honorable Leslie Rutledge (R)
Attorney General
Office of the Attorney General
323 Center Street, Suite 200
Little Rock, AR 72201
P: (800) 482-8982
F: (501) 682-8084

CALIFORNIA
Ms. Deborah Bain
Deputy Attorney General
Victims' Services Unit
P.O. Box 944255
Sacramento, CA 94244
P: (877) 433-9069

COLORADO
Ms. Kelly Kissell
Programs Manager
Office for Victims Programs
Division of Criminal Justice
700 Kipling Street, Suite 1000
Denver, CO 80215
P: (303) 239-4437
F: (303) 239-5743
E: Kelly.Kissell@state.co.us

DELAWARE
Ms. Lisa Borin Ogden
Executive Director
Victims Compensation Assistance Program
900 North King Street, Suite 4
Wilmington, DE 19801
P: (302) 255-1770
F: (302) 577-1326
E: Lisa.Ogden@state.de.us

DISTRICT OF COLUMBIA
Ms. Laura B. Reed
Program Director
Crime Victims Compensation Program
Court Building A
515 5th Street, Northwest, Room 109
Washington, DC 20001
P: (202) 879-4216
F: (202) 879-4230

FLORIDA
The Honorable Pam Bondi (R)
Attorney General
Office of the Attorney General
The Capitol, PL 01
Tallahassee, FL 32399
P: (850) 414-3300
F: (954) 712-4826

Ms. Michelle Crum
Chief
Bureau of Victim Compensation
Office of the Attorney General
The Capitol PL-01
Tallahassee, FL 32399
P: (850) 414-3300
F: (850) 487-1595

GUAM
The Honorable Elizabeth Barrett-Anderson
Attorney General
Office of the Attorney General
590 South Marine Corps Drive
ITC Building, Suite 706
Tamuning, GU 96913
P: (671) 475-3324
F: (671) 472-2493
E: law@guamag.org

HAWAII
Ms. Pamela Ferguson-Brey
Executive Director
Crime Victims Compensation Commission
Department of Public Safety
1136 Union Mall, Room 600
Honolulu, HI 96813
P: (808) 587-1143
F: (808) 587-1146
E: cvcc@hawaii.rr.com

IDAHO
Ms. Kristi Abel
Crime Victims Bureau Chief
Crime Victims Compensation Program
Industrial Commission, P.O. Box 83720
700 South Clearwater Lane
Boise, ID 83720
P: (208) 334-6025
F: (208) 332-7559
E: kristi.abel@iic.idaho.gov

ILLINOIS
Ms. Erica Katava
Director
Court of Claims
Office of the Secretary of State
630 South College Street
Springfield, IL 62756
P: (217) 782-7101

INDIANA
Ms. Jade Palin
Division Director, Victim Services
Criminal Justice Institute
101 West Washington Street
Suite 1170, East Tower
Indianapolis, IN 46204
P: (317) 232-1233
F: (317) 232-4979
E: JPalin@cji.IN.gov

IOWA
Ms. Julie Schulenberg
Victim Advocate
Crime Victim Assistance Division
Lucas State Office Building
321 East 12th Street
Des Moines, IA 50319
P: (515) 281-5044
F: (515) 281-8199
E: julie.schulenberg@iowa.gov

KANSAS
Mr. Jeff Wagaman
Executive Director
Division of Crime Victims Compensation
Office of the Attorney General
120 Southwest 10th Avenue, 2nd Floor
Topeka, KS 66612
P: (785) 296-2539
F: (785) 296-0652

KENTUCKY
Mr. Brian Richmond
Executive Director
Crime Victims Compensation Board
130 Brighton Park Boulevard
Frankfort, KY 40601
P: (502) 573-2290
F: (502) 573-4817
E: brian.richmond@ky.gov

LOUISIANA
Mr. Jim Craft
Executive Director
Commission on Law Enforcement & Administration of Criminal Justice
602 North Fifth Street
P.O. Box 3133
Baton Rouge, LA 70821
P: (225) 342-1500
F: (225) 342-1847
E: Jim.Craft@lcle.la.gov

MAINE
Ms. Tessa Mosher
Director of Victims Services
Department of Corrections
25 Tyson Drive, 3rd Floor
State House Station 111
Augusta, ME 04333
P: (207) 287-2711
F: (207) 287-4370
E: Tessa.Mosher@maine.gov

Crime Victims Compensation

MARYLAND
Mr. D. Scott Beard
Executive Director
Criminal Injuries Compensation Board
Public Safety & Correctional Services
6776 Reisterstown Road, Suite 312
Baltimore, MD 21215
P: (410) 585-3042
E: david.beard@maryland.gov

MASSACHUSETTS
The Honorable Maura Healey (D)
Attorney General
Office of the Attorney General
1 Ashburton Place
Boston, MA 02108
P: (617) 727-2200

Mr. Liam Lowney
Executive Director
Office for Victim Assistance
One Ashburton Place, Suite 1101
Boston, MA 02108
P: (617) 586-1340
F: (617) 727-6552
E: mova@state.ma.us

MINNESOTA
Raeone Magnuson
Executive Director
Crime Victims Services
Bremer Tower, Suite 2300
445 Minnesota Street
St. Paul, MN 55101
P: (651) 201-7305
F: (651) 296-5787
E: raeone.magnuson@state.mn.us

MISSISSIPPI
Ms. Amy Walker
Director
Crime Victims Compensation Program
Office of the Attorney General
P.O. Box 220
Jackson, MS 39205
P: (601) 359-6766
F: (601) 576-4445

MISSOURI
Ms. Lisa Harrison-Lineback
Program Manager
Crime Victims Services Unit
Department of Public Safety
P.O. Box 749
Jefferson City, MO 65102
P: (573) 526-1464
E: lisa.harrison-lineback@dps.mo.gov

MONTANA
Ms. Loraine Wodnik
Interim Director
Department of Corrections
5 South Last Chance Gulch
P.O. Box 201301
Helena, MT 59620
P: (406) 444-3930
F: (406) 444-4920

NEBRASKA
Ms. Lisa Stamm
Chief, Grants Division
Commission on Law Enforcement & Criminal Justice
301 Centennial Mall South
P.O. Box 94946
Lincoln, NE 68509
P: (402) 471-3687
F: (402) 471-2837
E: lisa.stamm@nebraska.gov

NEVADA
Ms. Rebecca Salazar
Program Manager
Victims of Crime Program
Department of Administration
2200 South Rancho Drive, Suite 210-A
Las Vegas, NV 89102
P: (702) 486-2740
F: (888) 941-7890
E: salazar@admin.nv.gov

NEW HAMPSHIRE
Ms. Lynda Ruel
Office of Victim/Witness Assistance
Office of the Attorney General
33 Capitol Street
Concord, NH 03301
P: (603) 271-3671
F: (603) 271-2110
E: lynda.ruel@doj.nh.gov

NEW JERSEY
Mr. Alvin Ricardo Little
Director
Crime Victims Compensation Office
Office of the Attorney General
50 Park Place
Newark, NJ 07102
P: (877) 658-2221

NEW MEXICO
Mr. Frank Zubia
Director
Crime Victims Reparation Commission
6200 Uptown Northeast, Suite 210
Albuquerque, NM 87110
P: (505) 222-6449
F: (505) 841-9437
E: Frank.Zubia@state.nm.us

NEW YORK
Ms. Elizabeth Cronin
Director
Office of Victim Services
Alfred E. Smith Building
80 South Swan Street, 2nd Floor
Albany, NY 12210
P: (518) 485-5719
F: (518) 457-8658

NORTH CAROLINA
Ms. Janice Carmichael
Section Chief
Victims Compensation Services
Department of Public Safety
4232 Mail Service Center
Raleigh, NC 27699
P: (919) 733-7974
F: (919) 715-4209
E: jcarmichael@nccrimecontrol.org

NORTH DAKOTA
Ms. Lori Steele
Administrator, Crime Victims Compensation
Department of Corrections & Rehabilitation, Division of Adult Services
Crime Victims Compensation
P.O. Box 1898
Bismarck, ND 58502
P: (701) 328-6195
F: (701) 328-6651
E: loristeele@nd.gov

NORTHERN MARIANA ISLANDS
Mr. Robert A. Guerrero
Commissioner
Department of Public Safety
Jose M. Sablan Building
Caller Box 10007
Saipan, MP 96950
P: (670) 664-9022
F: (670) 664-9027

OHIO
The Honorable Mike DeWine (R)
Attorney General
Office of the Attorney General
State Office Tower
30 East Broad Street
Columbus, OH 43266
P: (614) 466-4320

OKLAHOMA
Ms. Suzanne Breedlove
Director of Victims Services
Crime Victims' Compensation Board
District Attorneys Council
421 Northwest 13th, Suite 290
Oklahoma City, OK 73103
P: (405) 264-5006
E: victimsservices@dac.state.ok.us

OREGON
Ms. Shannon Sivell
Director
Crime Victims Services Division
1162 Court Street, Northeast
Salem, OR 97301
P: (503) 378-5348
F: (503) 378-5738
E: shannon.l.sivell@doj.state.or.us

PENNSYLVANIA
Derin Myers
Acting Executive Director
Commission on Crime & Delinquency
3101 North Front Street
P.O. Box 1167
Harrisburg, PA 17108
P: (717) 705-0888
F: (717) 705-0891

PUERTO RICO
Dr. Marilu Cintron Casado
Director
Office of Compensation & Services to Victims & Witnesses of Crime
Department of Justice
P.O. Box 9020192
San Juan, PR 00902
P: (787) 721-3997
E: marcintron@justicia.pr.gov

SOUTH CAROLINA
Dr. Larry Barker
Director
State Office of Victim Assistance
Edgar A. Brown Building, Room 401
1205 Pendleton Street
Columbia, SC 29201
P: (803) 734-1900
F: (803) 734-1708
E: sova@admin.sc.gov

SOUTH DAKOTA
Ms. Shannon Schweitzer
Program Manager
Department of Social Services
Victims Services Program
700 Governors Drive
Pierre, SD 57501
P: (605) 773-5884
F: (605) 773-2955
E: Shannon.Schweitzer@state.sd.us

TENNESSEE
The Honorable David H. Lillard Jr.
State Treasurer
Department of Treasury
State Capitol, First Floor
600 Charlotte Avenue
Nashville, TN 37243
P: (615) 741-2956
F: (615) 253-1591
E: david.lillard@tn.gov

TEXAS
Ms. Angie McCown
Director
Victim Services Division
Department of Criminal Justice
8712 Shoal Creek Boulevard, Suite 265
Austin, TX 78757
P: (512) 406-5917
F: (512) 452-0825
E: angie.mccown@tdcj.texas.gov

U.S. VIRGIN ISLANDS
Mr. Felicia Blyden
Commissioner
Department of Human Services
3011 Golden Rock
Christiansted
St. Croix, VI 00802
P: (340) 718-2980

UTAH
Ms. Connie Wettlaufer
Director
Office for Victims of Crime
Criminal & Juvenile Justice Commission
350 East 500 South, Suite 200
Salt Lake City, UT 84111
P: (801) 238-2360
F: (801) 533-4127
E: cwettlaufer@utah.gov

VERMONT
Mr. Chris Fenno
Executive Director
Center for Crime Victim Services
58 South Main Street, Suite 1
Waterbury, VT 05676
P: (802) 241-1250 Ext. 106
F: (802) 241-4337

VIRGINIA
Ms. Francine Ecker
Director
Department of Criminal Justice Services
1100 Bank Street, 12th Floor
Richmond, VA 23219
P: (804) 786-8718
F: (804) 371-8981
E: francine.ecker@dcjs.virginia.gov

WASHINGTON
Ms. Rena Shawver
Crime Victims Compensation Program
Department of Labor & Industries
P.O. Box 44520
Olympia, WA 98504
P: (800) 762-3716
F: (360) 902-5333
E: CrimeVictimsProgramM@Lni.wa.gov

WEST VIRGINIA
The Honorable Patrick Morrisey (R)
Attorney General
Office of the Attorney General
State Capitol
1900 Kanawha Boulevard, East
Charleston, WV 25305
P: (304) 558-2021
F: (304) 558-0140

WISCONSIN
Ms. Jill Karofsky
Director
Office of Crime Victims Services
P.O. Box 7951
Madison, WI 53707
P: (608) 264-9497
F: (608) 264-6368
E: karofskyjj@doj.state.wi.us

Criminal Justice

Oversees the administration of justice by providing public safety, assisting victims of crime, analyzing criminal data, administering funds, and providing training and guidance to law enforcement officials.

ALABAMA
Mr. William Babington
Division Chief
Law Enforcement & Traffic Safety Division
Economic & Community Affairs
P.O. Box 5690
Montgomery, AL 36103
P: (334) 242-5897
F: (334) 242-5099
E: bill.babington@adeca.alabama.gov

ALASKA
Mr. Walt Monegan
Commissioner
Department of Public Safety
5700 East Tudor Road
Anchorage, AK 99507
P: (907) 269-5086
F: (907) 269-4543
E: walt.monegan@alaska.gov

AMERICAN SAMOA
Mr. Lesei'au T. Laumoli
Director
Criminal Justice Planning Agency
Executive Office Building, Utulei
Territory of American Samoa
Pago Pago, AS 96799
P: (684) 633-5221
F: (684) 633-7552
E: laumoli33@gmail.com

ARIZONA
Mr. Andrew T. Lefevre
Executive Director
Criminal Justice Commission
1110 West Washington, Suite 230
Phoenix, AZ 85007
P: (602) 364-1156
E: alefevre@azcjc.gov

ARKANSAS
Colonel Bill Bryant
Director
State Police
1 State Police Plaza Drive
Little Rock, AR 72209
P: (501) 618-8299
F: (501) 618-8222
E: info@asp.arkansas.gov

COLORADO
Ms. Jeanne Smith
Director
Division of Criminal Justice
Department of Public Safety
700 Kipling Street, #1000
Denver, CO 80215
P: (303) 239-4442
F: (303) 239-4670
E: jeanne.smith@state.co.us

CONNECTICUT
Mr. Kevin T. Kane
Chief State's Attorney
Division of Criminal Justice
300 Corporate Place
Rocky Hill, CT 06067
P: (860) 258-5800
F: (860) 258-5858
E: conndcj@ct.gov

DELAWARE
Mr. Christian Kervick
Executive Director
Criminal Justice Council
Carvel State Office Building
820 North French Street, 10th Floor
Wilmington, DE 19801
P: (302) 577-8699
F: (302) 577-7056
E: Christian.Kervick@state.de.us

DISTRICT OF COLUMBIA
Mr. Peter Newsham
Chief of Police
Metropolitan Police Department
300 Indiana Avenue, Northwest
Room 5059
Washington, DC 20001
P: (202) 727-9099
F: (202) 727-4106
E: mpd@dc.gov

FLORIDA
Mr. Rick Swearingen
Commissioner
Department of Law Enforcement
2331 Phillips Road
P.O. Box 1489
Tallahassee, FL 32302
P: (850) 410-7011
E: RickSwearingen@fdle.state.fl.us

GEORGIA
Mr. Jay Neal
Executive Director
Criminal Justice Coordinating Council
104 Marietta Street, Suite 440
Atlanta, GA 30303
P: (404) 657-1956
F: (404) 657-1957
E: general.info@cjcc.ga.gov

GUAM
Mr. Joseph I. Cruz
Chief of Police
Police Department
#13-16A Mariner Avenue
P.O. Box 23909
Tiyan, GU 96913
P: (671) 475-8508
F: (671) 472-4036
E: chief@gpd.guam.gov

HAWAII
The Honorable Doug Chin (D)
Attorney General
Office of the Attorney General
425 Queen Street
Honolulu, HI 96813
P: (808) 586-1500

INDIANA
Mr. David R. Murtaugh
Executive Director
Criminal Justice Institute
101 West Washington Street
Suite 1170, East Tower
Indianapolis, IN 46204
P: (317) 232-1233
F: (317) 232-4979
E: dmurtaugh@cji.in.gov

IOWA
Mr. Steve Lukan
Director
Governor's Office of Drug Control Policy
215 East 7th Street
Des Moines, IA 50319
P: (515) 725-0305
F: (515) 242-6390
E: steven.lukan@iowa.gov

KANSAS
The Honorable Derek Schmidt (R)
Attorney General
Office of the Attorney General
120 Southwest 10th Avenue, 2nd Floor
Topeka, KS 66612
P: (785) 296-2215
F: (785) 296-6296

KENTUCKY
Mr. John Tilley
Secretary
Justice & Public Safety Cabinet
125 Holmes Street
Frankfort, KY 40601
P: (502) 564-7554
F: (502) 564-4840
E: john.tilley@ky.gov

LOUISIANA
Mr. Jim Craft
Executive Director
Commission on Law Enforcement & Administration of Criminal Justice
602 North Fifth Street
P.O. Box 3133
Baton Rouge, LA 70821
P: (225) 342-1500
F: (225) 342-1847
E: Jim.Craft@lcle.la.gov

MAINE
Mr. John E. Morris
Commissioner
Department of Public Safety
45 Commerce Drive, Suite 1
104 State House Station
Augusta, ME 04333
P: (207) 626-3800
F: (207) 287-3042
E: john.e.morris@maine.gov

MARYLAND
Mr. V. Glenn Fueston Jr.
Executive Director
Governor's Office of Crime Control & Prevention
100 Community Place
Crownsville, MD 21032
P: (410) 697-9338
F: (410) 321-3116
E: glenn.fueston@maryland.gov

MASSACHUSETTS
Mr. Daniel Bennett
Secretary
Executive Office of Public Safety & Security
One Ashburton Place, Suite 2133
Boston, MA 02108
P: (617) 727-7775
F: (617) 727-4764
E: eopsinfo@state.ma.us

MICHIGAN
Colonel Kriste Kibbey Etue
Director
State Police
P.O. Box 30634
Lansing, MI 48909
P: (517) 332-2521
F: (517) 241-0991
E: EtueK@michigan.gov

MINNESOTA
Ms. Ramona Dohman
Commissioner
Department of Public Safety
445 Minnesota Street, Suite 199
St. Paul, MN 55101
P: (651) 201-7160
F: (651) 297-5728
E: Mona.Dohman@state.mn.us

MISSISSIPPI
Ms. Joyce Word
Director
Office of Justice Programs
Department of Public Safety
P.O. Box 958
Jackson, MS 39205
P: (601) 977-3700
E: jword@dps.ms.gov

MISSOURI
Mr. Charles A. Juden
Director
Department of Public Safety
Office of the Director
P.O. Box 749
Jefferson City, MO 65102
P: (573) 751-4905
F: (573) 751-5399

MONTANA
Ms. Deb Matteucci
Executive Director
Board of Crime Control
5 South Last Chance Gulch
P.O. Box 201408
Helena, MT 59620
P: (406) 444-3615
F: (406) 444-4722
E: debMatteucci@mt.gov

NEBRASKA
Mr. Darrell Fischer
Executive Director
Commission on Law
Enforcement & Criminal Justice
301 Centennial Mall South
P.O. Box 94946
Lincoln, NE 68509
P: (402) 471-3847
F: (402) 471-2837
E: darrell.fisher
@nebraska.gov

NEVADA
Mr. James Wright
Director
Department of Public Safety
555 Wright Way
Carson City, NV 89711
P: (775) 684-4808
F: (775) 684-4809

NEW HAMPSHIRE
Ms. Rosemary Faretra
Director of Administration
Office of the Attorney General
Department of Justice
33 Capitol Street
Concord, NH 03301
P: (603) 271-3658
F: (603) 271-2110
E: rosemary.faretra
@doj.nh.gov

NEW JERSEY
Mr. Elie Honig
Director
Division of Criminal Justice
Richard J. Hughes Justice
Complex
25 Market Street, P.O. Box 80
Trenton, NJ 08625
P: (609) 984-6500
F: (609) 292-3508

NEW MEXICO
Mr. Scott Weaver
Cabinet Secretary
Department of Public Safety
4491 Cerrillos Road
P.O. Box 1628
Santa Fe, NM 87504
P: (505) 827-3370
F: (505) 827-3434

NEW YORK
Mr. Michael C. Green
Executive Deputy Commissioner
Division of Criminal Justice
Services
Alfred E. Smith Building
80 South Swan Street
Albany, NY 12210
P: (518) 457-5837
F: (518) 473-1271

NORTH CAROLINA
Ms. Gwen Burrell
Director
Governor's Crime Commission
1201 Front Street, Suite 200
4234 Mail Service Center
Raleigh, NC 27699
P: (919) 733-4564
F: (919) 733-4625
E: gwendolyn.burrell
@ncdps.gov

Ms. Caroline Valand
Executive Director
Governor's Crime Commission
512 North Salisbury Street
Raleigh, NC 27604
P: (919) 733-4564
E: caroline.valand
@ncdps.gov

NORTH DAKOTA
The Honorable Wayne
Stenehjem (R)
Attorney General
Office of the Attorney General
State Capitol
600 East Boulevard Avenue
Bismarck, ND 58505
P: (701) 328-2210
F: (701) 328-2226
E: wstenehjem@nd.gov

NORTHERN MARIANA ISLANDS
Mr. P. Paul Tenorio
Acting Executive Director
Criminal Justice Planning
Agency
P.O. Box 501133
Saipan, MP 96950
P: (670) 664-4550
F: (670) 664-4560

OHIO
Mr. Karhlton F. Moore
Executive Director
Office of Criminal Justice
Services
1970 West Broad Street
P.O. Box 182081
Columbus, OH 43218
P: (888) 448-4842
F: (614) 644-7731

OKLAHOMA
Mr. Trent H. Baggett
Executive Coordinator
District Attorneys Council
421 Northwest 13th, Suite 290
Oklahoma City, OK 73103
P: (405) 264-5000
F: (405) 264-5099

OREGON
Mr. Michael Schmidt
Executive Director
Criminal Justice Commission
885 Summer Street, Northeast
Salem, OR 97301
P: (503) 378-4858
F: (503) 378-4861
E: michael.schmidt
@oregon.gov

PENNSYLVANIA
Derin Myers
Acting Executive Director
Commission on Crime &
Delinquency
3101 North Front Street
P.O. Box 1167
Harrisburg, PA 17108
P: (717) 705-0888
F: (717) 705-0891

RHODE ISLAND
Mr. Michael J. Hogan
Administrative Manager
Public Safety Grant
Administration Office
311 Danielson Pike
Providence, RI 02857
P: (401) 764-5794
F: (401) 764-5834
E: Michael.Hogan@ripsga.gov

SOUTH CAROLINA
Mr. Lewis "Jackie" Swindler
Director
Criminal Justice Academy
5400 Broad River Road
Columbia, SC 29212
P: (803) 521-5368
F: (803) 896-7776
E: ljswindler@sccja.sc.gov

SOUTH DAKOTA
Mr. Trevor Jones
Secretary
Department of Public Safety
118 West Capitol Avenue
Pierre, SD 57501
P: (605) 773-3178
F: (605) 773-3018
E: DPSInfo@state.sd.us

TENNESSEE
Mr. Bill Scollon
Director
Office of Criminal Justice
Programs
William R. Snodgrass Tennessee
Tower
312 Rosa L. Parks Avenue, 18th
Floor
Nashville, TN 37243
P: (615) 532-2983
E: bill.scollon@tn.gov

TEXAS
Mr. Bryan Collier
Executive Director
Department of Criminal Justice
Capitol Station
P.O. Box 13084
Austin, TX 78711
P: (512) 463-9988

UTAH
Mr. Ronald Gordon
Executive Director
Commission on Criminal &
Juvenile Justice
Senate Building, Suite 330
P.O. Box 142330
Salt Lake City, UT 84114
P: (801) 538-1031
F: (801) 538-1024
E: rbgordon@utah.gov

Criminal Justice

VIRGINIA
Ms. Francine Ecker
Director
Department of Criminal Justice Services
1100 Bank Street, 12th Floor
Richmond, VA 23219
P: (804) 786-8718
F: (804) 371-8981
E: francine.ecker@dcjs.virginia.gov

WEST VIRGINIA
Mr. W. Richard Staton
Director
Division of Justice & Community Services
Military Affairs & Public Safety
1124 Smith Street, Suite 3100
Charleston, WV 25301
P: (304) 558-8814 Ext. 53335
F: (304) 558-0391
E: Rick.W.Staton@wv.gov

Debt Management

Responsible for structuring debt issues.

ALABAMA
Ms. Patricia Haigler
State Debt Manager
Division of Debt Management
Department of Finance
100 North Union Street, Room 224
Montgomery, AL 36130
P: (334) 353-3328
F: (334) 353-3466
E: patricia.haigler@finance.alabama.gov

AMERICAN SAMOA
The Honorable Ueli Tonumaipea
Treasurer
Department of Treasury
American Samoa Government
Pago Pago, AS 96799
P: (684) 633-4155
F: (684) 633-4100
E: ueli.tonumaipea@tr.as.gov

ARKANSAS
Mr. Aaron Burkes
President
Development Finance Authority
900 West Capitol, Suite 310
Little Rock, AR 72201
P: (501) 682-5900
F: (501) 682-5939
E: aaron.burkes@adfa.arkansas.gov

CALIFORNIA
Mr. Michael Cohen
Director
Department of Finance
915 L Street
Sacramento, CA 95814
P: (916) 445-3878
E: michael.cohen@dof.ca.gov

CONNECTICUT
The Honorable Denise L. Nappier (D)
State Treasurer
Office of State Treasurer
55 Elm Street, 7th Floor
Hartford, CT 06106
P: (860) 702-3010
F: (860) 702-3043
E: denise.nappier@ct.gov

FLORIDA
Mr. J. Ben Watkins III
Director
Division of Bond Finance
State Board of Administration
1801 Hermitage Centre, Suite 200
Tallahassee, FL 32308
P: (850) 488-4782
F: (850) 413-1315
E: watkins_ben@fsba.state.fl.us

IDAHO
The Honorable Ron G. Crane (R)
State Treasurer
State Treasurer's Office
700 West Jefferson Street, Suite E-126
P.O. Box 83720
Boise, ID 83720
P: (208) 334-3200
F: (208) 332-2959
E: idahotreasurer@sto.idaho.gov

ILLINOIS
Mr. Scott Harry
Director
Governor's Office of Management & Budget
603 Stratton Building
Springfield, IL 62706
P: (217) 782-4520
F: (217) 524-4876
E: Scott.Harry@illinois.gov

INDIANA
Mr. Tom Fite
Public Finance Director
Department of Financial Institutions
30 South Meridian Street
Suite 300
Indianapolis, IN 46204
P: (317) 453-2177
F: (317) 232-7655
E: tfite@dfi.IN.gov

IOWA
The Honorable Michael L. Fitzgerald (D)
State Treasurer
State Treasurer's Office
State Capitol Building
Des Moines, IA 50319
P: (515) 281-5368
F: (515) 281-7562
E: treasurer@iowa.gov

KENTUCKY
Mr. Ryan Barrow
Executive Director
Office of Financial Management
702 Capitol Avenue
Capitol Annex, Room 076
Frankfort, KY 40601
P: (502) 564-2924
F: (502) 564-7416

LOUISIANA
Ms. Lela M. Folse
Director
State Bond Commission
P.O. Box 44154
Baton Rouge, LA 70804
P: (225) 342-0040
F: (225) 342-0064
E: lfolse@treasury.state.la.us

MARYLAND
The Honorable Nancy K. Kopp (D)
State Treasurer
State Treasurer's Office
Goldstein Treasury Building
80 Calvert Street
Annapolis, MD 21401
P: (410) 260-7160
F: (410) 260-6056
E: nkopp@treasurer.state.md.us

MASSACHUSETTS
The Honorable Deborah B. Goldberg (D)
State Treasurer
Office of the State Treasurer
State House, Room 227
Boston, MA 02133
P: (617) 367-3900
F: (617) 248-0372

MINNESOTA
Mr. Myron Frans
Commissioner
Management & Budget
658 Cedar Street, Suite 400
St. Paul, MN 55155
P: (651) 201-8011
F: (651) 296-8685
E: myron.frans@state.mn.us

MISSISSIPPI
Ms. Mitzi Munroe Preziosi
Director
Investment & Cash Management Division
Office of the State Treasurer
P.O. Box 138
Jackson, MS 39205
P: (601) 359-3600
F: (601) 359-2001

MONTANA
Mr. Cody Pearce
State Accountant & Bureau Chief
State Accounting Bureau
125 North Roberts Street, Room 255
P.O. BOX 200102
Helena, MT 59620
P: (406) 444-4609
F: (406) 444-2812
E: CPearce@mt.gov

NEBRASKA
Mr. Byron L. Diamond
Director
Department of Administrative Services
1526 K Street, Suite 250
Lincoln, NE 68508
P: (402) 471-2331
E: byron.diamond@nebraska.gov

NEW HAMPSHIRE
The Honorable William Dwyer
State Treasurer
State Treasury
25 Capitol Street
Concord, NH 03301
P: (603) 271-2621
F: (603) 271-3922
E: bdwyer@treasury.state.nh.us

NEW MEXICO
Ms. Leila Burrows Kleats
Director
Board of Finance Division
181 Bataan Memorial Building
407 Galisteo Street
Santa Fe, NM 87501
P: (505) 827-4377
F: (505) 827-3985
E: LeilaK.Burrows@state.nm.us

NORTH DAKOTA
Ms. Pam Sharp
Director
Office of Management & Budget
600 East Boulevard Avenue
Department 110
Bismarck, ND 58505
P: (701) 328-4606
F: (701) 328-3230
E: psharp@nd.gov

Debt Management

OHIO
Mr. Kurt J. Kauffman
Debt Manager
Office of Budget & Management
30 East Broad Street, 34th Floor
Columbus, OH 43215
P: (614) 466-0691
F: (614) 466-3813
E: kurt.kauffman@obm.ohio.gov

OKLAHOMA
Mr. James C. Joseph
State Bond Advisor
State Bond Advisor's Office
9220 Noth Kelley Avenue
Oklahoma City, OK 73131
P: (405) 602-3100
F: (405) 848-3314
E: jjoseph@oksba.org

OREGON
Ms. Laura Lockwood-McCall
Director
Debt Management Division
Office of the State Treasurer
350 Winter Street, Northeast, Suite 100
Salem, OR 97301
P: (503) 378-4930
F: (503) 378-2237
E: laura.lockwood@state.or.us

PENNSYLVANIA
Mr. C. Daniel Hassell
Acting Secretary
Department of Revenue
Strawberry Square
Harrisburg, PA 17128
P: (717) 783-3683
F: (717) 787-3990

PUERTO RICO
Mr. Christian Sobrino-Vega
President
Government Development Bank for Puerto Rico
P.O. Box 42001
San Juan, PR 00940
P: (787) 722-2525 Ext. 5410
E: gdbcomm@bgf.gobierno.pr

SOUTH CAROLINA
Mr. Kevin Kibler
Senior Assistant State Treasurer, Debt Management
Office of the State Treasurer
116 Wade Hampton Building
Capitol Complex
Columbia, SC 29201
P: (803) 734-1391
F: (803) 734-2690
E: kevin.kibler@sto.sc.gov

TENNESSEE
Mr. Larry Martin
Commissioner
Department of Finance & Administration
312 Rosa Parks Avenue, 18th Floor
Nashville, TN 37243
P: (615) 741-4806
E: Larry.Martin@tn.gov

U.S. VIRGIN ISLANDS
Mr. Nellon Bowry
Director
Office of Management & Budget
No. 5041 Norre Gade, Second Floor
Emancipation Garden Station
St. Thomas, VI 00802
P: (340) 774-0750 Ext. 227
F: (340) 776-0069
E: nellon.bowry@omb.vi.gov

VERMONT
The Honorable Elizabeth Pearce
State Treasurer
Office of the State Treasurer
109 State Street
Montpelier, VT 05609
P: (802) 828-3322
F: (802) 828-2301
E: Beth.Pearce@state.vt.us

VIRGINIA
Ms. Janet A. Aylor
Director
Division of Bond Finance
Department of Treasury
101 North 14th Street
Richmond, VA 23219
P: (804) 371-6006
F: (804) 225-3187
E: janet.aylor@trs.virginia.gov

WASHINGTON
The Honorable Duane Davidson (R)
State Treasurer
Office of the State Treasurer
P.O. Box 40200
Olympia, WA 98504
P: (360) 902-9001
F: (360) 902-9044
E: Duane.Davidson@tre.wa.gov

WEST VIRGINIA
Mr. H. Craig Slaughter
Executive Director
Investment Management Board
500 Virginia Street, East, Suite 200
Charleston, WV 25301
P: (304) 345-2672
F: (304) 345-5939
E: info@wvimb.org

WYOMING
The Honorable Mark Gordon
State Treasurer
Office of the State Treasurer
200 West 24th Street
Cheyenne, WY 82002
P: (307) 777-7408
F: (307) 777-5411
E: treasurer@wyo.gov

Develop-mentally Disabled

Oversees the care, treatment and future service needs of the developmentally disabled.

ALABAMA
Ms. Courtney Tarver
Associate Commissioner
Division of Developmental Disabilities
Department of Mental Health
100 North Union Street, P.O. Box 301410
Montgomery, AL 36130
P: (334) 242-3701
E: courtney.tarver@mh.alabama.gov

ALASKA
Mr. Duane Mayes
Director
Senior & Disabilities Services
Department of Health & Social Services
550 West 8th Street
Anchorage, AK 99501
P: (907) 269-2083
F: (907) 269-3688
E: duane.mayes@alaska.gov

ARIZONA
Dr. Laura L. Love
Assistant Director
Division of Developmental Disabilities
Department of Economic Security
P.O. Box 6123, Site Code 791A
Phoenix, AZ 85005
P: (602) 542-0419
E: llove@azdes.gov

ARKANSAS
Ms. Melissa Stone
Director, Developmental Disabilities Services
Department of Human Services
Donaghey Plaza North
P.O. Box 1437, N505
Little Rock, AR 72203
P: (501) 682-8665
E: melissa.stone@dhs.arkansas.gov

CALIFORNIA
Ms. Nancy Bargmann
Director
Department of Developmental Services
P.O. Box 944202
Sacramento, CA 94244
P: (916) 654-1897
E: nancy.bargmann@dds.ca.gov

COLORADO
Ms. Barbara D. Ramsey
Deputy Director
Office of Community Living
1570 Grant Street
Denver, CO 80203
P: (303) 866-5140
E: barbara.ramsey@state.co.us

CONNECTICUT
Mr. Jordan Scheff
Acting Commissioner
Department of Developmental Services
460 Capitol Avenue
Hartford, CT 06106
P: (860) 418-6015
E: jordan.scheff@ct.gov

DELAWARE
Ms. Jill Rogers
Director
Developmental Disabilities Services
Woodbrook Professional Center, Suite 101
1056 South Governor's Avenue
Dover, DE 19904
P: (302) 744-9630
E: jill.rogers@state.de.us

DISTRICT OF COLUMBIA
Mr. Thomas Jared Morris
Deputy Director
Department of Disability Services
250 E Street, Southwest
Washington, DC 20024
P: (202) 730-1700
E: thomas.morris@dc.gov

FLORIDA
Ms. Barbara Palmer
Director
Agency for Persons with Disabilities
4030 Esplanade Way, Suite 380
Tallahassee, FL 32399
P: (850) 488-4257
E: barbara.palmer@apdcares.org

GEORGIA
Mr. Ronald Wakefield
Director
Department of Developmental Disabilities
Georgia DBHDD
Two Peachtree Street, Northwest, 22-210
Atlanta, GA 30303
P: (404) 657-2680
E: ronald.wakefield@dbhdd.ga.gov

HAWAII
Ms. Mary Brogan
Chief
Developmental Disabilities Division
Department of Health
P.O. Box 3378
Honolulu, HI 96801
P: (808) 586-5842
E: mary.brogan@doh.hawaii.gov

IDAHO
Mr. Cameron Gilliland
Deputy Administrator
Family & Community Services
Department of Health & Welfare
450 West State Street
Boise, ID 83720
P: (208) 334-5702
E: gillilac@dhw.idaho.gov

ILLINOIS
Mr. Gregory A. Fenton
Director
Division of Developmental Disabilities
Department of Human Services, Iles Park
600 East Ash, Building 400, 1st Floor
Springfield, IL 62703
P: (217) 524-7065
E: greg.fenton@illinois.gov

INDIANA
Ms. Kylee Hope
Director, Disability & Rehabilitative Services
Family & Social Services Administration
402 West Washington Street, W451
P.O. Box 7083
Indianapolis, IN 46207
P: (317) 232-1147
E: kylee.hope@fssa.in.gov

IOWA
Mr. Rick Shults
Division Administrator
Division of Mental Health & Disability Services
Department of Human Services
Hoover Building 5SE, 1305 East Walnut
Des Moines, IA 50319
P: (515) 281-8580
F: (515) 242-6036
E: rshults@dhs.state.ia.us

KANSAS
Mr. Tim Keck
Secretary
Aging & Disability Services
New England Building
503 South Kansas Avenue
Topeka, KS 66603
P: (785) 296-4986
F: (785) 296-0256
E: tim.keck@kdads.ks.gov

KENTUCKY
Ms. Claudia Johnson
Director
Developmental & Intellectual Disabilities
275 East Main Street, 4CF
Frankfort, KY 40621
P: (502) 782-6219
E: claudia.johnson@ky.gov

LOUISIANA
Mr. Mark Thomas
Assistant Secretary
Office for Citizens with Developmental Disabilities
Department of Health & Hospitals
628 North Fourth Street
Baton Rouge, LA 70821
P: (225) 342-0095
E: mark.thomas@la.gov

MAINE
Mr. Gary Wolcott
Director
Office of Aging & Disability Services
Department Health & Human Services
SHS#11, 41 Anthony Avenue
Augusta, ME 04333
P: (207) 287-4242
E: gary.wolcott@maine.gov

Developmentally Disabled

MARYLAND
Mr. Bernard Simons
Deputy Secretary
Developmental Disabilities Administration
Department of Health & Mental Hygiene
201 West Preston Street, 4th Floor
Baltimore, MD 21201
P: (410) 767-5600
E: bernard.simons@maryland.gov

MASSACHUSETTS
Ms. Elin Howe
Commissioner
Department of Developmental Services
500 Harrison Avenue
Boston, MA 02118
P: (617) 727-5608
E: elin.howe@state.ma.us

MICHIGAN
Ms. Lynda Zeller
Deputy Director
Behavioral Health & Developmental Disabilities Administration
Department of Community Health
320 South Walnut Street
Lansing, MI 48913
P: (517) 335-0196
F: (517) 335-4798
E: zellerl2@michigan.gov

MINNESOTA
Mr. Alex Bartolic
Director
Disability Services Division
Department of Human Services
P.O. Box 64967
St. Paul, MN 55164
P: (651) 431-2381
F: (651) 431-7412
E: alex.e.bartolic@state.mn.us

MISSISSIPPI
Ms. Renee Brett
Director
Bureau of Intellectual & Developmental Disabilities, Department of Mental Health
1101 Robert E. Lee Building
239 North Lamar Street
Jackson, MS 39201
P: (601) 359-1288
E: renee.brett@dmh.ms.gov

MISSOURI
Ms. Valerie Huhn
Director
Division of Developmental Disabilities
Department of Mental Health
1706 East Elm Street
Jefferson City, MO 65101
P: (573) 751-8676
E: valerie.huhn@dmh.mo.gov

MONTANA
Ms. Novelene Martin
Bureau Chief
Developmental Disabilities Program
Public Health & Human Services
P.O. Box 4210
Helena, MT 59604
P: (406) 444-5662
E: nomartin@mt.gov

NEBRASKA
Ms. Courtney Miller
Director
Division of Developmental Disabilities
Department of Health & Human Services
P.O. Box 95026
Lincoln, NE 68509
P: (402) 471-6038
E: courtney.miller@nebraska.gov

NEVADA
Mr. Eddie Ableser
Administrator
Aging & Disability Services Division
3416 Goni Road, Building D, Suite 132
Carson City, NV 89706
P: (775) 301-0904
F: (775) 687-4264
E: edwardableser@adsd.nv.gov

NEW HAMPSHIRE
Ms. Christine Santaniello
Bureau of Developmental Services
Department of Health & Human Services
105 Pleasant Street
Concord, NH 03301
P: (603) 271-5023
E: christine.santaniello@dhhs.nh.gov

NEW JERSEY
Ms. Elizabeth Shea
Assistant Commissioner
Division of Developmental Disabilities
Department of Human Services
P.O. Box 726
Trenton, NJ 08625
P: (609) 631-2217
E: liz.shea@dhs.state.nj.us

NEW MEXICO
Mr. Jim Copeland
Director
Developmental Disabilities Supports Division
Department of Health
P.O. Box 26110
Santa Fe, NM 87502
P: (505) 301-8419
E: james.copeland@state.nm.us

NEW YORK
Kerry A. Delaney
Acting Commissioner
Office for People With Developmental Disabilities
44 Holland Avenue
Albany, NY 12229
P: (518) 473-1997
E: kerry.a.delaney@opwdd.ny.gov

NORTH DAKOTA
Ms. Tina Bay
Director
Developmental Disabilities Division
Department of Human Services
1237 West Divide Avenue, Suite 1A
Bismarck, ND 58501
P: (701) 328-8966
E: tbay@nd.gov

OHIO
Mr. John L. Martin
Director
Department of Developmental Disabilities
30 East Broad Street, 12th Floor
Columbus, OH 43215
P: (614) 466-0129
F: (614) 644-5013
E: john.martin@dodd.ohio.gov

OKLAHOMA
Ms. Marie Moore
Interim Director
Developmental Disabilities Services
Department of Human Services
P.O. Box 25352
Oklahoma City, OK 73125
P: (405) 521-6267
E: marie.moore@okdhs.org

OREGON
Ms. Lilia Teninty
Director
Developmental Disability Services
Department of Human Services
500 Summer Street Northeast, E09
Salem, OR 97301
P: (503) 945-6918
E: lilia.teninty@state.or.us

PENNSYLVANIA
Ms. Nancy R. Thaler
Deputy Secretary
Office of Developmental Programs
Department of Human Services
625 Forster Street
Harrisburg, PA 17120
P: (717) 787-3700
E: nthaler@pa.gov

RHODE ISLAND
Ms. Kerri Zanchi
Director
Division of Developmental Disabilities
Barry Hall, 14 Harrington Road
Cranston, RI 02920
P: (401) 462-2721
E: kerri.zanchi@bhddh.ri.gov

SOUTH CAROLINA
Dr. Beverly A. H. Buscemi
Director
Department of Disabilities & Special Needs
P.O. Box 4706
Columbia, SC 29240
P: (803) 898-9769
F: (803) 898-9653
E: bbuscemi@ddsn.sc.gov

SOUTH DAKOTA
Mr. Darryl Millner
Director
Division of Developmental Disabilites, Department of Human Services
3800 East Highway 34, Hillsview Plaza
C/o 500 East Capitol Avenue
Pierre, SD 57501
P: (605) 773-3438
E: darryl.millner@state.sd.us

TENNESSEE
Ms. Debbie Payne
Commissioner
Department of Intellectual & Developmental Disabilities
Citizens Plaza, 10th Floor
400 Deaderick Street
Nashville, TN 37243
P: (615) 532-5970
E: debbie.payne@tn.gov

TEXAS
Ms. Sonja Gaines
Associate Commissioner
IDD & Behavioral Health Services
Health & Human Services
Brown-Heatly Building, 4900 North Lamar
Austin, TX 78751
P: (512) 437-3417
E: sonja.gaines@hhsc.state.tx.us

UTAH
Ms. Angela Pinna
Interim Director
Division of Services for People with Disabilities
Department of Human Services
195 North 1950 West
Salt Lake City, UT 84116
P: (801) 538-8299
E: apinna@utah.gov

VERMONT
Mr. Roy Gerstenberger
Director
Developmental Disabilities Services
Disabilities, Aging & Independent Living
280 State Drive, HC 2 South
Waterbury, VT 05671
P: (802) 241-0295
E: roy.gerstenberger@vermont.gov

VIRGINIA
Ms. Connie Cochran
Assistant Commissioner for Developmental Services
Department of Behavioral Health & Developmental Services
P.O. Box 1797
Richmond, VA 23218
P: (804) 663-7259
E: connie.cochran@dbhds.virginia.gov

WASHINGTON
Ms. Evelyn Perez
Assistant Secretary
Developmental Disabilities Services Administration
Social & Health Services
P.O. Box 45310
Olympia, WA 98504
P: (360) 725-3461
E: pereze@dshs.wa.gov

WEST VIRGINIA
Ms. Beth J. Morrison
Director, Mental Health Services
Behavioral Health & Health Facilities
350 Capitol Street, Room 350
Charleston, WV 25301
P: (304) 356-4976
E: beth.j.morrison@wv.gov

WISCONSIN
Mr. Curtis Cunningham
Deputy Administrator
Division of Long Term Care
Department of Health Services
1 West Wilson, Room 418
Madison, WI 53703
P: (608) 261-7810
E: curtis.cunningham@dhs.wisconsin.gov

WYOMING
Mr. Lee Grossman
Developmental Disabilities Section Director
Behavioral Health Division
Department of Health
6101 Yellowstone Road, Suite 220
Cheyenne, WY 82002
P: (307) 777-7460
E: lee.grossman1@wyo.gov

Economic Development

Responsible for efforts designed to encourage industry to locate, develop and expand in the state.

ALABAMA
Mr. Greg Canfield
Secretary
Department of Commerce
401 Adams Avenue
P.O. Box 304106
Montgomery, AL 36130
P: (334) 242-0421
F: (334) 242-0415
E: greg.canfield@commerce.alabama.gov

ALASKA
Ms. Britteny Cioni-Haywood
Division Director
Division of Economic Development
P.O. Box 110804
Juneau, AK 99811
P: (907) 465-2510
F: (907) 465-3767
E: britteny.cioni-haywood@alaska.gov

AMERICAN SAMOA
Mr. Keniseli Lafaele
Director
Department of Commerce
American Samoa Government
Executive Office Building, Utulei
Pago Pago, AS 96799
P: (684) 633-5155 Ext. 222
F: (684) 633-4195
E: keniseli.lafaele@doc.as

ARIZONA
Ms. Sandra Watson
President & CEO
Commerce Authority
118 North 7th Avenue, Suite 400
Phoenix, AZ 85007
P: (602) 845-1215
F: (602) 845-1201
E: commerce@azcommerce.com

ARKANSAS
Mr. Mike Preston
Exeuctive Director
Economic Development Commission
900 West Capitol Avenue, Suite 400
Little Rock, AR 72201
P: (501) 682-7351
F: (501) 682-7394
E: mpreston@arkansasedc.com

CALIFORNIA
Ms. Panorea Avdis
Director
Governor's Office of Business & Economic Development
1325 J Street, Suite 1800
Sacramento, CA 95814
P: (877) 345-4633

COLORADO
Ms. Stephanie Copeland
Executive Director
Office of Economic Development & International Trade
1625 Broadway, Suite 2700
Denver, CO 80202
P: (303) 892-3840
F: (303) 892-3848
E: stephanie.copeland@state.co.us

CONNECTICUT
Ms. Catherine H. Smith
Commissioner
Department of Economic & Community Development
505 Hudson Street
Hartford, CT 06106
P: (860) 270-8000
E: catherine.smith@ct.gov

DELAWARE
Mr. Cerron Cade
Acting Cabinet Secretary
Economic Development Office
99 Kings Highway
Dover, DE 19901
P: (302) 672-6809
F: (302) 739-5749
E: cerron.cade@state.de.us

DISTRICT OF COLUMBIA
Mr. Brian Kenner
Deputy Mayor for Planning & Economic Development
Office of the Deputy Mayor for Planning & Economic Development
John A. Wilson Building, Suite 317
1350 Pennsylvania Avenue, Northwest
Washington, DC 20004
P: (202) 727-6365
F: (202) 727-6703
E: brian.kenner@dc.gov

FLORIDA
Mr. Karl Blischke
Director
Division of Strategic Business Development
Department of Economic Opportunity
107 East Madison St., Caldwell Building
Tallahassee, FL 32399
P: (850) 245-7105
F: (850) 921-3223
E: karl.blischke@deo.myflorida.com

GEORGIA
Mr. Pat Wilson
Commissioner
Department of Economic Development
75 5th Street Northwest
Suite 1200
Atlanta, GA 30308
P: (404) 962-4003
F: (404) 962-4009
E: ccarr@georgia.org

GUAM
Mr. Jay Rojas
Administrator
Economic Development Authority
590 South Marine Corps Drive
Suite 511, ITC Building
Tamuning, GU 96913
P: (671) 647-4332
F: (671) 649-4146

HAWAII
Mr. Luis P. Salaveria
Director
Department of Business, Economic Development & Tourism
250 South Hotel Street, 5th Floor
Honolulu, HI 96813
P: (808) 586-2355
F: (808) 586-2377
E: director@dbedt.hawaii.gov

IDAHO
Ms. Megan Ronk
Director
Department of Commerce
700 West State Street
P.O. Box 83720
Boise, ID 83720
P: (208) 334-2470
F: (208) 334-2631
E: megan.ronk@commerce.idaho.gov

ILLINOIS
Mr. Sean McCarthy
Director
Department of Commerce & Economic Opportunity
100 West Randolph Street, Suite 3-400
Chicago, IL 60601
P: (312) 814-2811

INDIANA
Mr. Jim Schellinger
Secretary of Commerce
Economic Development Corporation
One North Capitol, Suite 700
Indianapolis, IN 46204
P: (317) 234-1359
F: (317) 232-4146
E: JSchellinger@iedc.IN.gov

IOWA
Ms. Debi Durham
Director
Economic Development Authority
200 East Grand Avenue
Des Moines, IA 50309
P: (515) 725-3022
F: (515) 725-3010
E: director@iowaeda.com

KANSAS
Mr. Antonio J. Soave
Secretary
Department of Commerce
1000 Southwest Jackson Street, Suite 100
Topeka, KS 66612
P: (785) 296-2994
F: (785) 296-5055
E: asoave@kansascommerce.com

KENTUCKY
Mr. Terry Gill
Cabinet Secretary
Cabinet for Economic Development
Old Capitol Annex
300 West Broadway Street, Floor 2
Frankfort, KY 40601
P: (502) 564-7670
F: (502) 564-3256
E: terry.gill@ky.gov

LOUISIANA
Mr. Donald Pierson Jr.
Secretary of Economic Development
Louisiana Economic Development
617 North Third Street
Baton Rouge, LA 70802
P: (225) 342-5388
E: don.pierson@la.gov

MAINE
Mr. George C. Gervais
Commissioner
Department of Economic & Community Development
59 State House Station
Augusta, ME 04333
P: (207) 624-9800

MARYLAND
Mr. R. Michael Gill
Secretary
Department of Commerce
Office of the Secretary
401 East Pratt Street
Baltimore, MD 21202
P: (410) 767-6301
F: (410) 333-8628
E: Mike.Gill@maryland.gov

MASSACHUSETTS
Mr. Jay Ash
Secretary
Executive Office of Housing & Economic Development
One Ashburton Place, Room 2101
Boston, MA 02108
P: (617) 788-3610
F: (617) 788-3605

MICHIGAN
Mr. Steve Arwood
CEO
Economic Development Corporation
300 North Washington Square
Lansing, MI 48913
P: (517) 241-1400
F: (517) 241-3683
E: arwoods1@michigan.org

MINNESOTA
Ms. Shawntera Hardy
Commissioner
Department of Employment & Economic Development
1st National Bank Building
332 Minnesota Street, Suite E-200
St. Paul, MN 55101
P: (651) 259-7119
F: (651) 296-4772
E: shawntera.hardy@state.mn.us

MISSISSIPPI
Mr. Glenn L. McCullough Jr.
Chief Executive Officer
Development Authority
501 North West Street
P.O. Box 849
Jackson, MS 39205
P: (601) 359-3449
F: (601) 359-3832
E: gmccullough@mississippi.org

MISSOURI
Mr. Mike Downing
Acting Director
Department of Economic Development
P.O. Box 1157
Jefferson City, MO 65102
P: (573) 751-4770
F: (573) 526-7700
E: ecodev@ded.mo.gov

MONTANA
Mr. Ken Fichtler
Chief Business Officer
Governor's Office of Economic Development
State Capitol
Helena, MT 59620
P: (406) 444-5470
F: (406) 444-3674
E: Ken.Fichtler@mt.gov

NEBRASKA
Ms. Courtney Dentlinger
Director
Department of Economic Development
301 Centennial Mall South
P.O. Box 94666
Lincoln, NE 68509
P: (402) 471-3746
F: (402) 471-3778
E: courtney.dentlinger@nebraska.gov

NEVADA
Mr. Steve Hill
Executive Director
Governor's Office of Economic Development
555 East Washington Avenue, Suite 5400
Las Vegas, NV 89101
P: (702) 486-2700
F: (702) 486-2701
E: ltaylor@diversifynevada.com

NEW HAMPSHIRE
Mr. Christopher Way
Acting Director
Division of Economic Development
72 Pembroke Road
Concord, NH 03301
P: (603) 271-2341
F: (603) 271-6784
E: Christopher.Way@dred.nh.gov

NEW JERSEY
Ms. Melissa Orsen
Chief Executive Officer
Economic Development Authority
36 West State Street
P.O. Box 990
Trenton, NJ 08625
P: (609) 858-6700
F: (609) 292-0885
E: CustomerCare@njeda.com

NEW MEXICO
Mr. Matthew Geisel
Secretary
Economic Development Department
1100 South Saint Francis Drive
P.O. Box 20003
Santa Fe, NM 87504
P: (505) 827-0305
F: (505) 827-0328
E: Matthew.Geisel@state.nm.us

NEW YORK
Mr. Howard Zemsky
President & CEO
Empire State Development
633 Third Avenue, Floor 37
New York, NY 10017
P: (212) 803-3100
F: (212) 803-3715

NORTH CAROLINA
Mr. Tony Copeland
Secretary
Department of Commerce
301 North Wilimington Street
4301 Mail Service Center
Raleigh, NC 27699
P: (919) 814-4603
E: acopeland@nccommerce.com

NORTH DAKOTA
Mr. John F. Schneider
Interim Director
Economic Development & Finance Division
Department of Commerce
1600 East Century Avenue, Suite 2
Bismark, ND 58503
P: (701) 328-5350
F: (701) 328-5320
E: jfschneider@nd.gov

NORTHERN MARIANA ISLANDS
Mr. Manuel A. Sablan
Executive Director
Commonwealth Development Authority
P.O. Box 502149
Saipan, MP 96950
P: (670) 234-6245
F: (670) 235-7147
E: administration@cda.gov.mp

OKLAHOMA
Mr. Deby Snodgrass
Executive Director & Secretary
Department of Commerce
900 North Stiles Avenue
Oklahoma City, OK 73104
P: (405) 815-5306
E: deby.snodgrass@okcommerce.gov

OREGON
Mr. Chris Harder
Director
Business Oregon
775 Summer Street, Northeast, Suite 200
Salem, OR 97301
P: (503) 229-5009
F: (503) 581-5115
E: chris.harder@state.or.us

PENNSYLVANIA
Mr. Dennis Davin
Secretary
Department of Community & Economic Development
Commonwealth Keystone Building
400 North Street, 4th Floor
Harrisburg, PA 17120
P: (866) 787-3003
F: (717) 787-6866

Economic Development

PUERTO RICO
Mr. Manuel Laboy Rivera
Executive Director
Industrial Development Company
P.O. Box 362350
San Juan, PR 00936
P: (787) 758-4747
E: secretario@ddec.pr.gov

RHODE ISLAND
Mr. Darin Early
President
Commerce Corporation
315 Iron Horse Way, Suite 101
Providence, RI 02908
P: (401) 278-9100
F: (401) 273-8270
E: darin.early@commerceri.com

SOUTH CAROLINA
Mr. Robert M. Hitt III
Secretary
Department of Commerce
1201 Main Street, Suite 1600
Columbia, SC 29201
P: (803) 737-1800
F: (803) 737-0894

SOUTH DAKOTA
Mr. Scott Stern
Commissioner
Governor's Office of Economic Development
711 East Wells Avenue
Pierre, SD 57501
P: (800) 872-6190
F: (605) 773-3256
E: goedinfo@state.sd.us

TENNESSEE
Mr. Bob Rolfe
Commissioner
Department of Economic & Community Development
312 Rosa L. Parks Avenue, 11th Floor
Nashville, TN 37243
P: (615) 741-1888
F: (615) 741-7306
E: Bob.Rolfe@tn.gov

TEXAS
Mr. Robert Allen
Executive Director
Economic Development Corporation
P.O. Box 12428
Austin, TX 78711
P: (512) 936-0101
F: (512) 936-0303

U.S. VIRGIN ISLANDS
Mr. Wayne L. Biggs Jr.
Acting Chief Executive Officer
Economic Development Authority
8000 Nisky Shopping Center, Suite 620
P.O. Box 305038
St. Thomas, VI 00802
P: (340) 714-1700
F: (340) 773-6499

UTAH
Mr. Q. Vale Hale
Executive Director
Governor's Office of Economic Development
60 East South Temple, 3rd Floor
Salt Lake City, UT 84111
P: (801) 538-8769
F: (801) 538-8888

VERMONT
Ms. Joan Goldstein
Commissioner
Department of Economic Development
1 National Life Drive, 6th Floor
Montpelier, VT 05620
P: (802) 727-2399
E: joan.goldstein@state.vt.us

VIRGINIA
Mr. Stephen Moret
President & CEO
Economic Development Partnership
901 East Byrd Street
P.O. Box 798
Richmond, VA 23218
P: (804) 545-5612
F: (804) 371-6524
E: Moret@yesvirginia.org

WASHINGTON
Mr. Brian Bonlender
Director
Department of Commerce
1011 Plum Street, Southeast
P.O. Box 42525
Olympia, WA 98504
P: (360) 725-4000
E: brian.bonlender@commerce.wa.gov

WEST VIRGINIA
Mr. H. Wood Thrasher
Cabinet Secretary
Department of Commerce
Capitol Complex Building 6, Room 525
1900 Kanawha Boulevard East
Charleston, WV 25305
P: (304) 558-2234
F: (304) 558-1189
E: W.Thrasher@wv.gov

WISCONSIN
Mr. Mark Hogan
Chief Executive Officer
Economic Development Corporation
201 West Washington Avenue
P.O. Box 1687
Madison, WI 53701
P: (608) 210-6701
E: Mark.Hogan@wedc.org

WYOMING
Mr. Shawn Reese
Chief Executive Officer
Business Council
214 West 15th Street
Cheyenne, WY 82002
P: (307) 777-2862
F: (307) 777-2837
E: shawn.reese@wyo.gov

Education (Chief State School Officer)

Overall responsibility for public elementary and secondary school systems.

ALABAMA
Mr. Michael Sentence
State Superintendent of Education
Department of Education
50 North Ripley Street
Montgomery, AL 36104
P: (334) 242-9700
E: msentance@alsde.edu

ALASKA
Dr. Michael Johnson
Commissioner
Department of Education & Early Development
801 West 10th Street, Suite 200
Juneau, AK 99811
P: (907) 465-2800
E: michael.johnson2@alaska.gov

AMERICAN SAMOA
Dr. Ruth S. Matagi-Tofiga
Director of Education
Department of Education
P.O. Box DOE
Pago Pago, AS 96799
P: (684) 633-5237

ARIZONA
The Honorable Diane Douglas (R)
Superintendent of Public Instruction
Department of Education
1535 West Jefferson Street
Phoenix, AZ 85007
P: (602) 542-5393
E: adeinbox@azed.gov

ARKANSAS
Mr. Johnny Key
Commissioner
Department of Education
Four Capitol Mall
Little Rock, AR 72201
P: (501) 682-4203
E: Johnny.Key@arkansas.gov

CALIFORNIA
The Honorable Tom Torlakson (D)
State Superintendent of Public Instruction
Department of Education
1430 N Street
Sacramento, CA 95814
P: (916) 319-0800
F: (916) 319-0175
E: superintendent@cde.ca.gov

COLORADO
Ms. Katy Anthes
Commissioner of Education
Department of Education
201 East Colfax Avenue
Denver, CO 80203
P: (303) 866-6646
E: anthes_k@cde.state.co.us

CONNECTICUT
Dr. Dianna R. Wentzell
Commissioner
Department of Education
165 Capitol Avenue
Hartford, CT 06106
P: (860) 713-6500
F: (860) 713-7001
E: dianna.roberge-wentzell@ct.gov

DELAWARE
Dr. Susan Bunting
Secretary of Education
Department of Education
John G. Townsend Building
Dover, DE 19901
P: (302) 735-4000
E: Susan.Bunting@doe.k12.de.us

DISTRICT OF COLUMBIA
Ms. Hanseul Kang
Superintendent of Education
Office of the State Superintendent of Education
810 First Street Northeast, 9th Floor
Washington, DC 20002
P: (202) 727-6436
E: osse@dc.gov

FLORIDA
Ms. Pam Stewart
Commissioner of Education
Department of Education
Turlington Building, Suite 1514
Tallahassee, FL 32399
P: (850) 245-0505
F: (850) 245-9667
E: Commissioner@fldoe.org

GEORGIA
The Honorable Richard L. Woods (R)
State School Superintendent
Department of Education
2066 Twin Towers East
Atlanta, GA 30334
P: (404) 657-1175
F: (404) 651-8737
E: state.superintendent@doe.k12.ga.us

GUAM
Mr. Jon Fernandez
Superintendent of Education
Department of Education
P.O. Box DE
Hagatna, GU 96932
P: (671) 475-0457
F: (671) 472-5001

HAWAII
Ms. Kathryn Matayoshi
Superintendent of Education
Department of Education
P.O. Box 2360
Honolulu, HI 96804
P: (808) 586-3230
F: (808) 586-3314
E: doe_info@hawaiidoe.org

IDAHO
The Honorable Sherri Ybarra (R)
Superintendent of Public Instruction
State Department of Educaiton
650 West State Street
Boise, ID 83720
P: (208) 332-6800
F: (208) 334-2228
E: info@sde.idaho.gov

ILLINOIS
Dr. Tony Smith
Superintendent of Education
State Board of Education
100 North First Street
Springfield, IL 62777
P: (866) 262-6663

INDIANA
The Honorable Jennifer McCormick (R)
Superintendent of Public Instruction
Department of Education
151 West Ohio Street
Indianapolis, IN 46204
P: (317) 232-6613
F: (317) 232-8004
E: superintendent@doe.in.gov

IOWA
Dr. Ryan Wise
Education Director
Department of Education
Grimes State Office Building
Des Moines, IA 50319
P: (515) 281-3436
F: (515) 242-5988
E: ryan.wise@iowa.gov

KANSAS
Dr. Randy Watson
Commissioner of Education
State Department of Education
900 Southwest Jackson Street, Room 600
Topeka, KS 66612
P: (785) 296-3202
E: rwatson@ksde.org

KENTUCKY
Dr. Stephen L. Pruitt
Commissioner of Education
Department of Education
300 Sower Boulevard, 5th Floor
Frankfort, KY 40601
P: (502) 564-3141

LOUISIANA
Mr. John White
State Superintendent of Education
Department of Education
P.O. Box 94064
Baton Rouge, LA 70804
P: (877) 453-2721
F: (225) 342-0193

MAINE
Mr. Robert G. Hasson Jr.
Commissioner
Department of Education
23 State House Station
Augusta, ME 04333
P: (207) 624-6620
E: commish.doe@maine.gov

MARYLAND
Dr. Karen B. Salmon
State Superintendent of Education
Department of Education
200 West Baltimore Street
Baltimore, MD 21201
P: (410) 767-0462

MASSACHUSETTS
Mr. Mitchell D. Chester
Commissioner of Education
Department of Elementary & Secondary Education
75 Pleasant Street
Malden, MA 02148
P: (781) 338-3100
F: (781) 338-3770
E: www@doe.mass.edu

Education (Chief State School Officer)

MICHIGAN
Mr. Brian Whiston
Superindendent of Public Instruction
Department of Education
608 West Allegan Street
Lansing, MI 48909
P: (517) 373-3324

MINNESOTA
Ms. Brenda Cassellius
Commissioner
Department of Education
1500 Highway 36 West
Roseville, MN 55113
P: (651) 582-8204
F: (651) 582-8724
E: Brenda.Cassellius@state.mn.us

MISSISSIPPI
Dr. Carey Wright
Superintendent of Education
Department of Education
P.O. Box 771
Jackson, MS 39205
P: (601) 359-3513

MISSOURI
Dr. Margie Vandeven
Commissioner
Department of Elementary & Secondary Education
P.O. Box 480
Jefferson City, MO 65102
P: (573) 751-4446
F: (573) 751-8613
E: commissioner@dese.mo.gov

MONTANA
The Honorable Elsie Arntzen (R)
Superintendent of Public Instruction
Office of Public Instruction
P.O. Box 202501
Helena, MT 59620
P: (406) 444-5658
F: (406) 444-9299
E: opisupt@mt.gov

NEBRASKA
Dr. Matthew Blomstedt
Commissioner of Education
Department of Education
301 Centennial Mall South
Lincoln, NE 68509
P: (402) 471-2295
F: (402) 471-0117

NEVADA
Mr. Steve Canavero
Superintendent of Public Instruction
Department of Education
700 East Fifth Street
Carson City, NV 89701
P: (775) 687-9200
F: (775) 687-9101

NEW HAMPSHIRE
Mr. Frank Edelblut
Commissioner of Education
Department of Education
101 Pleasant Street
Concord, NH 03301
P: (603) 271-3144
E: Frank.Edelblut@doe.nh.gov

NEW JERSEY
Ms. Kimberly Harrington
Acting Commissioner
Department of Education
P.O. Box 500
Trenton, NJ 08625
P: (609) 292-4450

NEW MEXICO
Ms. Hanna Skandera
Secretary of Education
Public Education Department
Jerry Apodaca Education Building
Santa Fe, NM 87501
P: (505) 827-5800
F: (505) 827-6520

NEW YORK
Ms. MaryEllen Elia
Commissioner
State Education Department
89 Washington Avenue
Albany, NY 12234
P: (518) 474-3852

NORTH CAROLINA
The Honorable Mark Johnson (R)
Superintendent of Public Instruction
Department of Public Instruction
Education Building
301 North Wilmington Street
Raleigh, NC 27699
P: (919) 807-3300
F: (919) 807-3445

NORTH DAKOTA
The Honorable Kirsten Baesler
Superintendent of Public Instruction
Department of Public Instruction
600 East Boulevard Avenue
Department 201
Bismarck, ND 58505
P: (701) 328-4570
F: (701) 328-2461
E: kbaesler@nd.gov

NORTHERN MARIANA ISLANDS
Ms. Rita Sablan
Commissioner of Education
CNMI Public School System
P.O. Box 501882
Saipan, MP 96950
P: (670) 237-3001
F: (670) 664-3798

OHIO
Mr. Paolo DeMaria
Superintendent of Public Instruction
Department of Education
25 South Front Street
Columbus, OH 43215
P: (614) 752-9059

OKLAHOMA
The Honorable Joy Hofmeister (R)
Superintendent of Public Instruction
State Department of Education
2500 North Lincoln Boulevard
Oklahoma City, OK 73105
P: (405) 521-3301
F: (405) 521-6205
E: Joy.Hofmeister@sde.ok.gov

OREGON
Dr. Salam Noor
Deputy Superintendent of Public Instruction
Department of Education
255 Capitol Street Northeast
Salem, OR 97310
P: (503) 947-5740
E: salam.noor@state.or.us

PENNSYLVANIA
Mr. Pedro A. Rivera
Secretary of Education
Department of Education
333 Market Street
Harrisburg, PA 17126
P: (717) 783-9780
E: parivera@pa.gov

PUERTO RICO
Ms. Julia Keleher
Secretary of Education
Department of Education
P.O. Box 190759
San Juan, PR 00919
P: (787) 766-2911
E: romanmr@de.pr.gov

RHODE ISLAND
Dr. Ken Wagner
Commissioner of Education
Department of Education
255 Westminster Street
Providence, RI 02903
P: (401) 222-8700
E: info@ride.ri.gov

SOUTH CAROLINA
The Honorable Molly M. Spearman (R)
Superintendent of Education
Department of Education
1429 Senate Street
Columbia, SC 29201
P: (803) 734-8500
F: (803) 734-3389
E: SCSuptEd@ed.sc.gov

SOUTH DAKOTA
Dr. Melody Schopp
Secretary of Education
Department of Education
800 Governors Drive
Pierre, SD 57501
P: (605) 773-5669
F: (605) 773-6139
E: melody.schopp@state.sd.us

TENNESSEE
Dr. Candice McQueen
Commissioner of Education
Department of Education
710 James Robertson Parkway
Nashville, TN 37243
P: (615) 741-8457
F: (615) 532-4791
E: Candice.McQueen@tn.gov

TEXAS
Mr. Mike Morath
Commissioner of Education
State Education Agency
William B. Travis Building
Austin, TX 78701
P: (512) 463-9734
E: commissioner@tea.texas.gov

U.S. VIRGIN ISLANDS
Dr. Sharon Ann McCollum
Commissioner
Department of Education
1834 Kongens Gade
St. Thomas, VI 00802
P: (340) 774-0100
F: (340) 779-7153

UTAH
Dr. Sydnee Dickson
Acting Superintendent
State Office of Education
250 East 500, South
P.O. Box 144200
Salt Lake City, UT 84114
P: (801) 538 7500

VERMONT
Ms. Rebecca Holcombe
Secretary of Education
Agency of Education
219 North Main Street, Suite 402
Barre, VT 05641
P: (802) 479-1030
E: rebecca.holcombe@vermont.gov

VIRGINIA
Dr. Steven Staples
Superintendent of Public Instruction
Department of Education
P.O. Box 2120
Richmond, VA 23218
P: (804) 225-2023
F: (804) 371-2099
E: steven.staples@doe.virginia.gov

WASHINGTON
The Honorable Chris Reykdal
Superintendent of Public Instruction
Office of Superintendent of Public Instruction
Old Capitol Building
Olympia, WA 98504
P: (360) 725-6115
F: (360) 753-6712

WEST VIRGINIA
Dr. Steve Paine
State Superintendent
Department of Education
1900 Kanawha Boulevard, East
Charleston, WV 25305
P: (304) 558-2681
E: superintendent@wvde.state.wv.us

WISCONSIN
The Honorable Anthony Evers
Superintendent of Public Instruction
Department of Public Instruction
125 South Webster Street
Madison, WI 53707
P: (608) 266-3390
E: anthony.evers@dpi.wi.gov

WYOMING
The Honorable Jillian Balow (R)
Superintendent of Public Instruction
Department of Education
2300 Capitol Avenue
Cheyenne, WY 82002
P: (307) 777-7675
F: (307) 777-6234
E: superintendent@wyo.gov

Elections Administration

Administers state election laws and supervises the printing and distribution of ballots.

ALABAMA
Mr. Ed Packard
Director of Elections
Office of the Secretary of State
P.O. Box 5616
Montgomery, AL 36103
P: (334) 242-4845
F: (334) 244-2444
E: ed.packard@sos.alabama.gov

ALASKA
Ms. Josephine Bahnke
Director
Division of Elections
P.O. Box 110017
Juneau, AK 99811
P: (907) 465-4611
F: (907) 465-3203
E: josie.bahnke@alaska.gov

AMERICAN SAMOA
Mr. Soliai T. Fuimaono
Chief Election Officer
Territorial Election Office
P.O. Box 3790
Pago Pago, AS 96799
P: (684) 699-3570
F: (684) 699-3574
E: Asgelect@samoatelco.com

ARIZONA
Mr. Eric Spencer
Election Director
Secretary of State's Office
1700 West Washington, 7th Floor
Phoenix, AZ 85007
P: (602) 542-8683
F: (602) 542-6172
E: espencer@azsos.gov

ARKANSAS
Ms. Leslie Bellamy
Director of Elections
Office of the Secretary of State
State Capitol, Room 062
Little Rock, AR 72201
P: (501) 683-3733
E: Leslie.Bellamy@sos.arkansas.gov

CALIFORNIA
Ms. Jana Lean
Chief of Elections
Elections Division
1500 11th Street, 5th Floor
Sacramento, CA 95814
P: (916) 657-2166
F: (916) 653-3214
E: jana.lean@sos.ca.gov

COLORADO
Mr. Judd Choate
Director of Elections
Secretary of State's Office
Department of State
1700 Broadway, Suite 200
Denver, CO 80290
P: (303) 894-2200
F: (303) 869-4861
E: judd.choate@sos.state.co.us

CONNECTICUT
Ms. Peggy Reeves
Director of Elections
Office of the Secretary of State
30 Trinity Street
Hartford, CT 06106
P: (860) 509-6123
F: (860) 509-6127
E: peggy.reeves@ct.gov

DELAWARE
Ms. M. Elaine Manlove
State Election Commissioner
Office of the State Election Commissioner
905 South Governors Avenue, Suite 170
Dover, DE 19904
P: (302) 739-4277
F: (302) 739-6794
E: coe_vote@state.de.us

DISTRICT OF COLUMBIA
Ms. Alice P. Miller
Executive Director
Board of Elections & Ethics
441 Fourth Street, Northwest
Suite 250N
Washington, DC 20001
P: (202) 727-6511
E: apmiller@dcboee.org

FLORIDA
Mr. Gary J. Holland
Assistant Director, Division of Elections
Department of State
R.A. Gray Building, Room 316
500 South Bronough Street
Tallahassee, FL 32399
P: (850) 245-6268
F: (850) 245-6217
E: Gary.Holland@DOS.MyFlorida.com

Ms. Maria Matthews
Director, Division of Elections
Department of State
R.A. Gray Building, Room 316
500 South Bronough Street
Tallahassee, FL 32399
P: (850) 245-6268
F: (850) 245-6217
E: Maria.Matthews@DOS.MyFlorida.com

GEORGIA
Mr. Chris Harvey
Director of Elections
Office of the Secretary of State
2 Martin Luther King Jr. Drive Southeast
Suite 802, West Tower
Atlanta, GA 30334
P: (404) 656-2871
F: (404) 651-9531
E: wharvey@sos.ga.gov

GUAM
Ms. Maria I.D. Pangelinan
Executive Director
Election Commission
414 West Soledad Avenue
GCIC Building, Suite 200
Hagatna, GU 96910
P: (671) 477-9791
F: (671) 477-1895
E: vote@gec.guam.gov

HAWAII
Mr. Scott Nago
Chief Election Officer
Office of Elections
802 Lehua Avenue
Pearl City, HI 96782
P: (808) 453-8683
F: (808) 453-6006
E: elections@hawaii.gov

IDAHO
Ms. Betsie Kimbrough
Election Director
Office of the Secretary of State
304 North 8th, Suite 149
P.O. Box 83720
Boise, ID 83720
P: (208) 334-2852
F: (208) 334-2282
E: bkimbrough@sos.idaho.gov

ILLINOIS
Mr. Steve Sandvoss
Executive Director
State Board of Elections
2329 South Macarthur Boulevard
Springfield, IL 62704
P: (217) 782-4141
F: (217) 782-5959
E: ssandvoss@elections.il.gov

INDIANA
Mr. J. Bradley King
Co-Director
Election Division
Office of the Secretary of State
302 West Washington Street, Room E-204
Indianapolis, IN 46204
P: (317) 233-0929
F: (317) 233-6793
E: bking@iec.in.gov

Ms. Angela M. Nussmeyer
Co-Director
Elections Division
Office of the Secretary of State
302 West Washington Street, Room E-204
Indianapolis, IN 46204
P: (317) 232-3940
F: (317) 233-6793
E: anussmeyer@iec.in.gov

IOWA
Ms. Carol Olson
Deputy Secretary of State
Secretary of State Office
Lucas Building
321 East 12th Street
Des Moines, IA 50319
P: (515) 242-5071
F: (515) 242-5953
E: carol.olson@sos.state.ia.us

KANSAS
Mr. Bryan Caskey
Election Director
Office of the Secretary of State
120 Southwest 10th Avenue
Memorial Hall, 1st Floor
Topeka, KS 66612
P: (785) 296-4561
F: (785) 291-3051
E: election@sos.ks.gov

KENTUCKY
Ms. Maryellen Allen
Executive Director
State Board of Elections
140 Walnut Street
Frankfort, KY 40601
P: (502) 573-7100
F: (502) 573-4369
E: maryellen.allen@ky.gov

LOUISIANA
Ms. Angie Rogers
Commissioner of Elections
Secretary of State's Office
8549 United Plaza Boulevard
P.O. Box 94125
Baton Rouge, LA 70802
P: (225) 922-0900
F: (225) 922-0945
E: Angie.rogers@sos.louisiana.gov

MAINE
Ms. Julie L. Flynn
Deputy Secretary of State
Office of the Secretary of State
Office of the Secretary of State
101 State House Station
Augusta, ME 04333
P: (207) 624-7736
F: (207) 287-5428
E: Julie.Flynn@maine.gov

MARYLAND
Ms. Linda H. Lamone
Administrator of Elections
State Board of Elections
P.O. Box 6486
Annapolis, MD 21401
P: (410) 269-2840
F: (410) 974-2019
E: Linda.Lamone@Maryland.gov

MASSACHUSETTS
Ms. Michelle Tassinari
Director of Elections & Legal Counsel
Election Division
One Ashburton Place, Room 1705
Boston, MA 02108
P: (617) 727-2828
F: (617) 742-3238
E: Michelle.Tassinari@sec.state.ma.us

MICHIGAN
Mr. Christopher M. Thomas
Director
Bureau of Elections
Department of State
Lansing, MI 48918
P: (517) 335-2789
F: (517) 373-0941
E: ChristopherT@michigan.gov

MINNESOTA
Mr. Gary Poser
Director of Elections
Office of the Secretary of State
174 State Office Building
100 Martin Luther King Jr. Boulevard
St. Paul, MN 55155
P: (651) 556-0612
F: (651) 296-9073
E: Gary.Poser@state.mn.us

MISSISSIPPI
Ms. Kimberly P. Turner
Assistant Secretary of State
Elections Division
Secretary of State's Office
401 Mississippi Street, P.O. Box 136
Jackson, MS 39205
P: (601) 359-5137
F: (601) 576-2545
E: Kim.Turner@sos.ms.gov

MISSOURI
Mr. Brandon Alexander
Co-Director of Elections
Secretary of State's Office
P.O. Box 1767
Jefferson City, MO 65102
P: (573) 751-2301
E: brandon.alexander@sos.mo.gov

Ms. Chrissy Peters
Co-Director of Elections
Secretary of State's Office
P.O. Box 1767
Jefferson City, MO 65102
P: (573) 751-2301
E: chrissy.peters@sos.mo.gov

MONTANA
Mr. Derek Oestreicher
Elections Director
Office of the Secretary of State
P.O. Box 202801
Helena, MT 59620
P: (406) 444-4275
E: derek.oestreicher@mt.gov

NEVADA
Mr. Wayne Thorley
Deputy Secretary for Elections
Office of the Secretary of State
101 North Carson Street, Suite 3
Carson City, NV 89701
P: (775) 684-5705
E: wthorley@sos.nv.gov

NEW HAMPSHIRE
Mr. Anthony B. Stevens
Assistant Secretary of State
Office of the Secretary of State
State House, Room 204
Concord, NH 03301
P: (603) 271-8238
F: (603) 271-7933
E: Anthony.Stevens@sos.nh.gov

NEW JERSEY
Mr. Robert F. Giles
Director
Division of Elections
225 West State Street, 3rd Floor
P.O. Box 304
Trenton, NJ 08625
P: (609) 292-3760
F: (609) 777-1280
E: Robert.Giles@sos.state.nj.us

NEW MEXICO
Ms. Kari Fresquez
Interim Elections Director
Bureau of Elections
Secretary of State's Office
325 Don Gaspar, Suite 300
Santa Fe, NM 87501
P: (505) 827-3600
F: (505) 827-8403
E: kari.fresquez@state.nm.us

NEW YORK
Mr. Robert A. Brehm
Co-Executive Director
State Board of Elections
40 North Pearl Street, Suite 5
Albany, NY 12207
P: (518) 474-8100
F: (518) 486-4068
E: Robert.Brehm@elections.ny.gov

Mr. Todd D. Valentine
Co-Executive Director
State Board of Elections
40 North Pearl Street, Suite 5
Albany, NY 12207
P: (518) 474-8100
F: (518) 486-4068
E: Todd.Valentine@elections.ny.gov

NORTH CAROLINA
Ms. Kim Westbrook Strach
Executive Director
Board of Elections
441 North Harrington Street
P.O. Box 27255
Raleigh, NC 27611
P: (919) 733-7173
F: (919) 715-0135
E: kim.strach@ncsbe.gov

NORTH DAKOTA
Mr. John Arnold
Director of Elections
Office of the Secretary of State
600 East Boulevard Avenue
Department 108
Bismarck, ND 58505
P: (701) 328-3721
F: (701) 328-1690
E: jarnold@nd.gov

Mr. Jim Silrum
Deputy Secretary of State
Office of the Secretary of State
600 East Boulevard Avenue
Department 108
Bismarck, ND 58505
P: (701) 328-3660
F: (701) 328-1690
E: jsilrum@nd.gov

OHIO
Mr. Matthew Damschroder
Deputy Assistant Secretary of State
Office of the Secretary of State
180 East Broad Street, 15th Floor
Columbus, OH 43215
P: (614) 466-5515
F: (614) 485-7526
E: mdamschroder@ohiosecretaryofstate.gov

OKLAHOMA
Mr. Paul Ziriax
Secretary
State Election Board
Room 6, State Capitol
Oklahoma City, OK 73105
P: (405) 522-6615
F: (405) 521-6457
E: pziriax@elections.ok.gov

OREGON
Mr. Stephen Trout
Director of Elections
Office of the Secretary of State
255 Capitol Street, Northeast, Suite 501
Salem, OR 97310
P: (503) 986-1518
F: (503) 373-7414
E: steve.trout@state.or.us

Elections Administration

PENNSYLVANIA
Mr. Jonathan M. Marks
Commissioner
Bureau of Commissions, Elections & Legislation
Department of State, 401 North Street
210 North Office Building
Harrisburg, PA 17120
P: (717) 787-5280
F: (717) 705-0721
E: RA-BCEL@pa.gov

PUERTO RICO
Ms. Liza Garcia Velez
Election Commission
P.O. Box 195552
San Juan, PR 00919
P: (787) 777-8675
E: lgarcia@cee.gobierno.pr

RHODE ISLAND
Mr. Rob Rock
Director of Elections
Office of the Secretary of State
148 West River Street
Providence, RI 02904
P: (401) 222-2340
E: rrock@sos.ri.gov

SOUTH CAROLINA
Ms. Marci Andino
Executive Director
State Election Commission
1122 Lady Street
Suite 500
Columbia, SC 29201
P: (803) 530-8350
E: marci@elections.sc.gov

SOUTH DAKOTA
Ms. Kea Warner
Deputy Secretary of State, Elections Division
Office of the Secretary of State
500 East Capitol Avenue, Suite 204
Pierre, SD 57501
P: (605) 773-5003
F: (605) 773-6580
E: Kea.Warner@state.sd.us

TENNESSEE
Mr. Mark K. Goins
Coordinator of Elections
Secretary of State's Office
312 Rosa L. Parks Avenue
Snodgrass Tower, 9th Floor
Nashville, TN 37243
P: (615) 741-7956
F: (615) 741-1278
E: Mark.Goins@tn.gov

TEXAS
Mr. Keith Ingram
Director of Elections
Elections Division
Office of the Secretary of State
P.O. Box 12060
Austin, TX 78711
P: (512) 463-5650
F: (512) 475-2811
E: elections@sos.texas.gov

U.S. VIRGIN ISLANDS
Ms. Caroline Fawkes
Supervisor of Elections
Election System
P.O. Box 1499, Kingshill
St. Croix, VI 00851
P: (340) 773-1021
F: (340) 773-4523
E: caroline.fawkes@vi.gov

UTAH
Mr. Mark Thomas
Director of Elections
Office of the Lieutenant Governor
Utah State Capitol Suite 220
P.O. Box 142325
Salt Lake City, UT 84114
P: (801) 538-1041
F: (801) 538-1133
E: mjthomas@utah.gov

VERMONT
Mr. Will Senning
Director of Elections & Campaign Finance
Office of the Secretary of State
26 Terrace Street, Drawer 09
Montpelier, VT 05609
P: (802) 828-2363
F: (802) 828-5171
E: will.senning@sec.state.vt.us

VIRGINIA
Mr. Edgardo Cortes
Commissioner
Department of Elections
Washington Building
1100 Bank Street, First Floor
Richmond, VA 23219
P: (804) 864-8901
F: (804) 371-0194
E: edgardo.cortes@elections.virginia.gov

WASHINGTON
Ms. Lori Augino
Director of Elections
Elections Division
Office of Secretary of State
Legislative Building, P.O. Box 40220
Olympia, WA 98504
P: (360) 725-5771
F: (360) 664-4619
E: lori.augino@sos.wa.gov

WEST VIRGINIA
Mr. Donald Kersey II
Elections Director
Office of the Secretary of State
State Capitol, Room 157-K
1900 Kanawha Boulevard, East
Charleston, WV 25305
P: (304) 558-6000
E: dkersey@wvsos.com

WISCONSIN
Mr. Michael Haas
Administrator
Government Accountability Board
212 East Washington Avenue, 3rd Floor
P.O. Box 7984
Madison, WI 53707
P: (608) 266-0136
F: (608) 267-0500
E: Michael.Haas@wi.gov

WYOMING
Mr. Kai Schon
State Election Director
Office of the Secretary of State
2020 Carey Avenue, Suite 600
Cheyenne, WY 82002
P: (307) 777-3416
E: kai.schon@wyo.gov

Emergency Management

Prepares, maintains and/or implements state disasters plans and coordinates emergency activities.

Information provided by:

National Emergency Management Association
Trina Sheets
Executive Director
1776 Avenue of the States
Lexington, KY 40511
P: (859) 244-8000
F: (859) 244-8239
tsheets@csg.org
www.nemaweb.org

ALABAMA
Mr. Art Faulkner
Director
Emergency Management Agency
5898 County Road 41
P.O. Box 2160
Clanton, AL 35046
P: (205) 280-2201
F: (334) 224-9142
E: art.faulkner@ema.alabama.gov

ALASKA
Mr. Mike O'Hare
Director
Division of Homeland Security & Emergency Management
Military & Veterans Affairs
P.O. Box 5750
Joint Base Elemendorf
Richardson, AK 99505
P: (907) 428-7066
E: mike.ohare@alaska.gov

AMERICAN SAMOA
Semo Ve'ave'e
Director
Department of Homeland Security
P.O. Box 4567
Pago Pago, AS 96799
P: (684) 699-0411
F: (684) 258-1774
E: s.veavea@asdhs.as.gov

ARIZONA
Ms. Wendy Smith-Reeve
Director
Department of Emergency & Military Affairs
5636 East McDowell Road
Phoenix, AZ 85008
P: (602) 464-6203
F: (602) 319-2330
E: wendy.smith-reeve@azdema.gov

ARKANSAS
A.J. Gary
Director & State Homeland Security Advisor
Department of Emergency Management
Building 9501, Camp Joseph T. Robinson
North Little Rock, AR 72199
P: (501) 683-7834
F: (501) 680-7961
E: AJ.Gary@adem.arkansas.gov

CALIFORNIA
Mr. Mark Ghilarducci
Director
Governor's Office of Emergency Services
3650 Schriever Avenue
Mather, CA 95655
P: (916) 845-8506
F: (916) 662-3155
E: mark.ghilarducci@caloes.ca.gov

COLORADO
Ms. Marilyn Gally
Director
Office of Emergency Management
9195 East Mineral Avenue, Suite 200
Centennial, CO 80112
P: (720) 852-6694
F: (720) 852-6768
E: marilyn.gally@state.co.us

CONNECTICUT
Mr. William J. Hackett
Director
State Division of Emergency Management & Homeland Security
1111 Country Club Road, 3rd Floor
Middletown, CT 06457
P: (860) 256-0801
F: (860) 250-6947
E: william.j.hackett@ct.gov

DELAWARE
A.J. Schall
Director
State Emergency Management Agency
165 Brick Store Landing Road
Smyrna, DE 19977
P: (302) 659-2320
F: (302) 893-2512
E: a.j.schall@state.de.us

DISTRICT OF COLUMBIA
Mr. Brian Baker
Interim Director
Homeland Security & Emergency Management Agency
2720 Martin Luther King Jr. Avenue
Southeast, 2nd Floor
Washington, DC 20032
P: (202) 481-3088
F: (202) 525-0564
E: Brian.Baker@dc.gov

FLORIDA
Mr. Bryan Koon
Director
Division of Emergency Management
2555 Shumard Oak Boulevard
Tallahassee, FL 32399
P: (850) 413-9930
F: (850) 519-7966
E: bryan.koon@em.myflorida.com

GEORGIA
Mr. Homer Bryson
Director
Emergency Management Agency/Office of Homeland Security
935 East Confederate Avenue, Southeast
Building 2
Atlanta, GA 30316
P: (404) 635-7008
F: (404) 276-4950
E: homer.bryson@gema.ga.gov

GUAM
Mr. Charles Esteves
Administrator
Homeland Security/Office of Civil Defense
221-B Chalan Palaso
Agana Heights, GU 96910
P: (671) 475-9600
E: charles.esteves@ghs.guam.gov

HAWAII
Mr. Vern Miyagi
Administrator
State Emergency Management Agency
3949 Diamond Head Road
Honolulu, HI 96816
P: (808) 733-4300 Ext. 501
F: (808) 294-0807
E: vern.t.miyagi@hawaii.gov

IDAHO
Colonel Brad Richy
Director
State Bureau of Homeland Security
4040 West Guard Street, Building 600
Boise, ID 83705
P: (208) 258-6591
F: (208) 841-8974
E: brichy@bhs.idaho.gov

ILLINOIS
Mr. James Joseph
Director
State Emergency Management Agency
2200 South Dirksen Parkway
Springfield, IL 62703
P: (217) 782-2700
F: (217) 670-4206
E: james.joseph@illinois.gov

INDIANA
Mr. Bryan Langley
Executive Director
Department of Homeland Security
302 West Washington Street, Room E-208
Indianapolis, IN 46204
P: (317) 232-3980
F: (317) 452-5326
E: blangley@dhs.in.gov

IOWA
Mr. Mark J. Schouten
Director
Homeland Security & Emergency Management Department
7900 Hickmand Road, Suite 500
Windsor Heights, IA 50324
P: (515) 725-3223
F: (515) 975-4382
E: mark.schouten@iowa.gov

Emergency Management

KANSAS
Ms. Angee Morgan
Deputy Director
Division of Emergency Management
2800 Southwest Topeka Boulevard
Topeka, KS 66611
P: (785) 274-1403
F: (785) 207-1546
E: angelynn.t.morgan.nfg@mail.mil

KENTUCKY
Mr. Michael Dossett
Director
State Emergency Management
100 Minuteman Parkway, Room 106
Boone National Guard Center
Frankfort, KY 40601
P: (502) 607-1682
F: (502) 352-8054
E: michael.e.dossett.nfg@mail.mil

LOUISIANA
Mr. James Waskom
Director
Governor's Office of Homeland Security & Emergency Preparedness
7667 Independence Boulevard
Baton Rouge, LA 70608
P: (225) 925-7345
F: (337) 780-5383
E: james.waskom@la.gov

MAINE
Mr. Bruce Fitzgerald
Director
State Emergency Management Agency
45 Commerce Drive, Suite #2
Augusta, ME 04333
P: (207) 624-4400
F: (207) 287-3178
E: bruce.fitzgerald@maine.gov

MARYLAND
Mr. Russell Strickland
Executive Director
State Emergency Management Agency
5401 Rue Saint Lo Drive
Reisterstown, MD 21136
P: (410) 517-3625
F: (240) 477-9299
E: russell.strickland@maryland.gov

MASSACHUSETTS
Mr. Kurt Schwartz
Director
State Emergency Management Agency
400 Worcester Road
Framingham, MA 01702
P: (508) 820-2014
F: (508) 820-2010
E: kurt.schwartz@state.ma.us

MICHIGAN
Captain Chris A. Kelenske
Deputy State Director
State Police, Emergency Management & Homeland Security
7150 Harris Drive
Dimondale, MI 48821
P: (517) 284-3966
F: (517) 719-1194
E: kelenskec@michigan.gov

MINNESOTA
Mr. Joseph Kelly
Director
State Division of Homeland Security & Emergency Management
445 Minnesota Street, Suite 223
St. Paul, MN 55101
P: (651) 201-7404
F: (651) 775-0233
E: joseph.kelly@state.mn.us

MISSISSIPPI
Mr. Lee Smithson
Executive Director
Emergency Management Agency
#1 MEMA Drive
P.O. Box 5644
Pearl, MS 39288
P: (601) 933-6882
F: (601) 850-6362
E: lsmithson@mema.ms.gov

MISSOURI
Mr. Ernie Rhodes
Director
Emergency Management Agency
P.O. Box 116
Jefferson City, MO 65102
P: (573) 526-9101
F: (573) 301-6090
E: Ernie.Rhodes@sema.dps.mo.gov

MONTANA
Ms. Delila Bruno
Administrator/Director
State Disaster & Emergency Services
1956 Mount Majo Street
P.O. Box 4789
Fort Harrison, MT 59636
P: (406) 324-4766
F: (406) 459-4606
E: dbruno@mt.gov

NEBRASKA
Mr. Bryan Tuma
Assistant Director
State Emergency Management Agency
2433 Northwest 24th Street
Lincoln, NE 68524
P: (402) 471-7410
F: (402) 540-2238
E: Bryan.Tuma@nebraska.gov

NEVADA
Mr. Caleb Cage
Chief
Division of Emergency Management/Homeland Security
2478 Fairview Drive
Carson City, NV 89701
P: (775) 687-0300
F: (775) 443-8814
E: cscage@dps.state.nv.us

NEW HAMPSHIRE
Mr. Perry Plummer
Director
Homeland Security & Emergency Management
33 Hazen Drive
Concord, NH 03305
P: (603) 271-2231
F: (603) 419-0255
E: perry.plummer@dos.nh.gov

NEW JERSEY
Mr. Jeffrey Mottley
LTC
State Office of Emergency Management
P.O. Box 7068
West Trenton, NJ 08628
P: (609) 882-2000 Ext. 6161
F: (609) 468-5117
E: lpp5300@gw.njsp.org

NEW MEXICO
Mr. Jay Mitchell
Secretary
State Department of Homeland Security & Emergency Management
13 Bataan Boulevard
P.O. Box 27111
Santa Fe, NM 87502
P: (505) 476-9655
E: jay.mitchell@state.nm.us

NEW YORK
Mr. Kevin Wisely
Director
State Office of Emergency Management
1220 Washington Avenue
Building 22, Suite 101
Albany, NY 12226
P: (518) 292-2301
F: (518) 669-8984
E: kevin.wisely@dhses.ny.gov

NORTH CAROLINA
Mr. Michael Sprayberry
Director
State Division of Emergency Management
1636 Gold Star Drive
4236 Mail Service Center
Raleigh, NC 27607
P: (919) 825-2291
F: (919) 369-4174
E: mike.sprayberry@ncdps.gov

NORTH DAKOTA
Mr. Greg Wilz
Director, Division of Homeland Security
Department of Emergency Services
Fraine Barracks Lane, Building 35
P.O. Box 5511
Bismarck, ND 58506
P: (701) 328-8100 Ext. 8101
F: (701) 995-0446
E: gwilz@nd.gov

NORTHERN MARIANA ISLANDS
Mr. Gerald Deleon Guerrero
Special Assistant for Homeland Security & Emergency Management
Homeland Security & Emergency Management
Office of the Governor
Caller Box 1007, 1313 Anatahan Drive
Saipan, MP 96950
P: (670) 664-2216
F: (670) 287-7166
E: gerald.guerrero@cnmihsem.gov.mp

OHIO
Ms. Sima Merick
Executive Director
State Emergency Management Agency
2855 West Dublin-Granville Road
Columbus, OH 43235
P: (614) 799-3674
F: (614) 561-6298
E: smerick@dps.ohio.gov

OKLAHOMA
Mr. Albert Ashwood
Director
Department of Emergency Management
P.O. Box 53365
Oklahoma City, OK 73105
P: (405) 521-2481
F: (405) 590-0110
E: albert.ashwood@oem.ok.gov

OREGON
Mr. Andrew Phelps
Director, Office of Emergency Management
State Military Department
P.O. Box 14370
Salem, OR 97309
P: (503) 378-3933
F: (971) 283-4258
E: andrew.phelps@state.or.us

PENNSYLVANIA
Mr. Richard Flinn Jr.
Director
State Emergency Management Agency
2605 Interstate Drive
Harrisburg, PA 17110
P: (717) 651-2007
F: (717) 317-1741
E: rflinn@pa.gov

PUERTO RICO
Mr. Abner Gomez-Cortes
Executive Director
State Emergency Management Agency
P.O. Box 194140
San Juan, PR 00919
P: (787) 724-0124 Ext. 40075
F: (787) 399-5063
E: agomez@prema.pr.gov

RHODE ISLAND
Mr. Peter Gaynor
Director
State Emergency Management Agency
645 New London Avenue
Cranston, RI 02920
P: (401) 946-9996
E: peter.gaynor@ema.ri.gov

SOUTH CAROLINA
Mr. Kim Stenson
Director
State Emergency Management Division
2779 Fish Hatchery Road
West Columbia, SC 29172
P: (803) 737-8566
F: (803) 413-4669
E: kstenson@emd.sc.gov

SOUTH DAKOTA
Ms. Tina Titze
Director
State Office of Emergency Management
118 West Capitol Avenue
Pierre, SD 57501
P: (605) 773-3231
E: tina.titze@state.sd.us

TENNESSEE
Mr. Patrick Sheehan
Director
Emergency Management Agency
3041 Sidco Drive
Nashville, TN 37204
P: (615) 741-0001
F: (615) 852-0040
E: Patrick.Sheehan@tn.gov

TEXAS
Mr. Nim Kidd
Chief
State Division of Emergency Management
5805 North Lamar Boulevard
P.O. Box 4087
Austin, TX 78752
P: (512) 424-2443
F: (512) 468-8288
E: nim.kidd@dps.texas.gov

U.S. VIRGIN ISLANDS
Ms. Mona Barnes
Territorial Emergency Management Agency
8221 Estate Nisky
St. Thomas, VI 00802
P: (340) 773-2244
F: (340) 244-3515
E: Mona.Barnes@vitema.vi.gov

UTAH
Mr. Kris J. Hamlet
Director
Division of Emergency Management
Department of Public Safety
1110 State Office Building
Salt Lake City, UT 84114
P: (801) 538-9553
F: (801) 243-0147
E: krishamlet@utah.gov

VERMONT
Ms. Erica Bornemann
Director
Division of Emergency Management & Homeland Security
45 State Drive
Waterbury, VT 05671
P: (802) 241-5450
F: (802) 233-4299
E: erica.bornemann@vermont.gov

VIRGINIA
Mr. Jeffrey Stern
State Coordinator
State Department of Emergency Management
10501 Trade Court
North Chesterfield, VA 23236
P: (804) 897-6501
F: (804) 896-6263
E: jeff.stern@vdem.virginia.gov

WASHINGTON
Mr. Robert Ezelle
Director
State Emergency Management Division
20 Aviation Drive
Building 20, MS: TA-20
Camp Murray, WA 98430
P: (253) 512-7003
F: (253) 324-8020
E: Robert.ezelle@mil.wa.gov

WEST VIRGINIA
Mr. James (Jimmy) Gianato
Director
Division of Homeland Security & Emergency Management
1900 Kanawha Boulevard, East
Building 1, Room EB-80
Charleston, WV 25305
P: (304) 558-5380
F: (304) 541-9990
E: jimmy.j.gianato@wv.gov

WISCONSIN
Mr. Brian M. Satula
Administrator
State Division of Emergency Management
2400 Wright Street
P.O. Box 7865
Madison, WI 53704
P: (608) 242-3210
F: (608) 514-3461
E: brian.satula@wisconsin.gov

WYOMING
Mr. Guy Cameron
Director
Office of Homeland Security
5500 Bishop Boulevard
Cheyenne, WY 82002
P: (307) 777-8511
F: (307) 630-0566
E: guy.cameron@wyo.gov

Employment Services

Provides job counseling, testing and placement services in the state.

ALABAMA
Mr. Fitzgerald Washington
Secretary
Department of Labor
649 Monroe Street
Montgomery, AL 36131
P: (334) 242-8055
E: fwashington@labor.alabama.gov

ALASKA
Mr. Mike Andrews
Director
Division of Employment & Training Services
Labor & Workforce Development
P.O. Box 115509
Juneau, AK 99811
P: (907) 465-2712
F: (907) 465-4537
E: mike.andrews@alaska.gov

Mr. Ed Flanagan
Director
Division of Employment & Training Services
Labor & Workforce Development
P.O. Box 115509
Juneau, AK 99811
P: (907) 465-2712
F: (907) 465-4537
E: ed.flanagan@alaska.gov

AMERICAN SAMOA
Mr. Esenaeiaso J. Liu
Director
Department of Human Resources
Executive Office Building
AP Lutali, 2nd Floor
Pago Pago, AS 96799
P: (684) 644-4485
F: (684) 633-1139
E: eseneiaso.liu@hr.as.gov

ARIZONA
Mr. Michael Wisehart
Director
Division of Employment & Rehabilitation Services
Department of Economic Security
1789 West Jefferson Street
Phoenix, AZ 85007
P: (602) 542-3596

ARKANSAS
Mr. Daryl Bassett
Director
Department of Workforce Services
#2 Capitol Mall
Little Rock, AR 72201
P: (501) 682-3394
F: (501) 682-8845
E: daryl.bassett@arkansas.gov

COLORADO
Ms. Ellen Golombek
Executive Director
Department of Labor & Employment
633 17th Street, Suite 201
Denver, CO 80202
P: (303) 318-8017
F: (303) 318-8047
E: Ellen.Golombek@state.co.us

CONNECTICUT
Mr. Scott D. Jackson
Commissioner
Department of Labor
200 Folly Brook Boulevard
Westerfield, CT 06109
P: (860) 263-6000
F: (850) 263-6529
E: scott.jackson@ct.gov

DELAWARE
Ms. Lori Reeder
Director
Department of Labor
Division of Employment & Training
4425 North Market Street
Wilmington, DE 19802
P: (302) 761-8085
E: lori.reeder@state.de.us

DISTRICT OF COLUMBIA
Mr. Odie Donald II
Director
Department of Employment Services
4058 Minnesota Avenue, Northeast
Washington, DC 20019
P: (202) 724-7000
F: (202) 673-6993
E: does@dc.gov

GEORGIA
The Honorable Mark Butler (R)
Commissioner
Department of Labor
148 International Boulevard Northeast
Atlanta, GA 30303
P: (404) 232-7300
F: (404) 656-2683
E: commissioner@gdol.ga.gov

GUAM
Mr. Manuel Q. Cruz
Director
Department of Labor
Government of Guam
P.O. Box 9970
Tamuning, GU 96931
P: (671) 475-7044
F: (671) 674-6517

HAWAII
Ms. Elaine Young
Administrator
Workforce Development Division
Labor & Industrial Relations Department
830 Punchbowl Street, Room 329
Honolulu, HI 96813
P: (808) 586-8812
F: (808) 586-8822
E: dlir.workforce.develop@hawaii.gov

IDAHO
Mr. Kenneth D. Edmunds
Director
Department of Labor
317 West Main Street
Boise, ID 83735
P: (208) 332-3570
F: (208) 334-6430
E: kenneth.edmunds@labor.idaho.gov

INDIANA
Mr. Steve Braun
Commissioner
Department of Workforce Development
Government Center South
10 North Senate Avenue
Indianapolis, IN 46204
P: (317) 232-7676
E: SBraun@dwd.IN.gov

IOWA
Ms. Beth Townsend
Executive Director
Workforce Development
1000 East Grand Avenue
Des Moines, IA 50319
P: (515) 281-5364
E: beth.townsend@iwd.iowa.gov

KANSAS
Mr. Antonio J. Soave
Secretary
Department of Commerce
1000 Southwest Jackson Street, Suite 100
Topeka, KS 66612
P: (785) 296-2994
F: (785) 296-5055
E: asoave@kansascommerce.com

LOUISIANA
Mr. Byron Decoteau Jr.
Director
Department of State Civil Service
1201 North Third Street
P.O. Box 94111
Baton Rouge, LA 70804
P: (225) 342-8272
F: (225) 342-0966
E: bryon.decoteau@la.gov

MAINE
Ms. Jeanne Paquette
Commissioner
Department of Labor
54 State House Station
Augusta, ME 04333
P: (207) 623-7900
F: (207) 623-7934
E: jeanne.paquette@maine.gov

MARYLAND
Ms. Cynthia Kollner
Executive Director
Office of Personnel Services & Benefits
Department of Budget & Management
301 West Preston Street, Room 609
Baltimore, MD 21201
P: (410) 767-4715
F: (410) 333-5262
E: cindy.kollner@maryland.gov

MASSACHUSETTS
Mr. Ronald L. Walker II
Secretary
Executive Office of Labor & Workforce Development
One Ashburton Place, Suite 2112
Boston, MA 02108
P: (617) 626-7122

MINNESOTA
Ms. Shawntera Hardy
Commissioner
Department of Employment & Economic Development
1st National Bank Building
332 Minnesota Street, Suite E-200
St. Paul, MN 55101
P: (651) 259-7119
F: (651) 296-4772
E: shawntera.hardy@state.mn.us

MISSISSIPPI
Mr. Mark Henry
Executive Director
Department of Employment Security
1235 Echelon Parkway
P.O. Box 1699
Jackson, MS 39215
P: (601) 321-6000
F: (601) 321-6104
E: mhenry@mdes.ms.gov

MISSOURI
Mr. Mike Downing
Acting Director
Department of Economic Development
P.O. Box 1157
Jefferson City, MO 65102
P: (573) 751-4770
F: (573) 526-7700
E: ecodev@ded.mo.gov

MONTANA
Ms. Pam Bucy
Commissioner
Department of Labor & Industry
P.O. Box 1728
Helena, MT 59624
P: (406) 444-2840
F: (406) 444-1419
E: dliquestions@mt.gov

NEBRASKA
Ms. Courtney Dentlinger
Director
Department of Economic Development
301 Centennial Mall South
P.O. Box 94666
Lincoln, NE 68509
P: (402) 471-3746
F: (402) 471-3778
E: courtney.dentlinger@nebraska.gov

NEVADA
Ms. Renee Olson
Administrator
Department of Employment, Training & Rehabilitation
Employment Security Division
500 East Third Street
Carson City, NV 89701
P: (775) 684-3909
F: (775) 684-3850
E: rlolson@nvdetr.org

NEW JERSEY
Dr. Aaron R. Fichtner
Acting Commissioner
Department of Labor & Workforce Development
1 John Fitch Plaza
P.O. Box 110
Trenton, NJ 08625
P: (609) 292-1070
E: aaron.fichtner@dol.state.nj.us

NEW MEXICO
Ms. Celina Bussey
Secretary
Department of Workforce Solutions
401 Broadway, Northeast
P.O. Box 1928
Albuquerque, NM 87103
P: (505) 841-8405
F: (505) 841-8491
E: celina.bussey@state.nm.us

NEW YORK
Ms. Roberta Reardon
Commissioner
Department of Labor
W. Averell Harriman State Office Campus
Building 12
Albany, NY 12240
P: (518) 457-9000
F: (518) 485-6297
E: roberta.reardon@labor.state.ny.us

NORTH CAROLINA
W.T. Brinn Jr.
Assistant Secretary
Division of Employment Security
700 Wade Avenue
P.O. Box 25903
Raleigh, NC 27611
P: (919) 707-1600
E: assistantsecretary@nccommerce.com

NORTH DAKOTA
Ms. Cheri Giesen
Executive Director
Job Service North Dakota
P.O. Box 5507
Bismarck, ND 58506
P: (701) 328-2825
F: (701) 328-4000

OHIO
Mr. Bruce Madson
Assistant Director, Employment Services
Department of Job & Family Services
30 East Broad Street, 32nd Floor
Columbus, OH 43215
P: (614) 466-6283
F: (614) 466-2815

OKLAHOMA
Mr. Richard McPherson
Executive Director
Employment Security Commission
P.O. Box 52003
Oklahoma City, OK 73152
P: (405) 557-7201
E: richard.mcpherson@oesc.state.ok.us

Ms. Lucinda Meltabarger
Administrator
Human Capital Management Division
2101 North Lincoln Boulevard
Room G-80
Oklahoma City, OK 73105
P: (405) 521-3928
F: (405) 524-6942
E: lucinda.meltabarger@omes.ok.gov

OREGON
Ms. Kay Erickson
Director
Employment Department
875 Union Street, Northeast
Salem, OR 97311
P: (503) 947-1394
F: (503) 947-1472

PENNSYLVANIA
Ms. Sharon Minnich
Secretary
Governor's Office of Administration
207 Finance Building
Harrisburg, PA 17102
P: (717) 783-0247
E: sminnich@pa.gov

PUERTO RICO
Mr. Carlos J. Saavedra Gutierrez
Secretary
Department of Labor & Human Resources
P.O. Box 195540
San Juan, PR 00919
P: (787) 754-5353
F: (787) 753-9550

RHODE ISLAND
Mr. Scott Jensen
Director
Department of Labor & Training
Center General Complex
1511 Pontiac Avenue
Cranston, RI 02920
P: (401) 462-8000
F: (401) 462-8872
E: director-dlt@dlt.ri.gov

SOUTH CAROLINA
Ms. Cheryl M. Stanton
Executive Director
Department of Employment & Workforce
1550 Gadsden Street
P.O. Box 995
Columbia, SC 29202
P: (803) 737-2617
E: cstanton@dew.sc.gov

SOUTH DAKOTA
Ms. Marcia Hultman
Cabinet Secretary
Department of Labor & Regulation
123 West Missouri Avenue
Pierre, SD 57501
P: (605) 773-5395
F: (605) 773-6184
E: marcia.hultman@state.sd.us

TENNESSEE
Mr. Burns Phillips
Commissioner
Department of Labor & Workforce Development
220 French Landing Drive
Nashville, TN 37243
P: (844) 224-5818
F: (615) 741-5078
E: burns.phillips@tn.gov

Employment Services

TEXAS
Mr. Larry E. Temple
Executive Director
Workforce Commission
101 East 15th Street
Austin, TX 78778
P: (512) 463-0735
F: (512) 475-2321
E: larry.temple
@twc.state.tx.us

U.S. VIRGIN ISLANDS
Ms. Catherine Ann Hendry
Commissioner of Labor
Department of Labor
4401 Sion Farm, Suite 1
Christiansted, VI 00820
P: (340) 773-1994
F: (340) 713-3415
E: chendry@vidol.gov

UTAH
Mr. Jon S. Pierpont
Executive Director
Department of Workforce
Services
P.O. Box 45249
Salt Lake City, UT 84145
P: (801) 526-9210
F: (801) 526-9211
E: jpierpo@utah.gov

VERMONT
Ms. Lindsay H. Kurrle
Commissioner
Department of Labor
5 Green Mountain Drive
P.O. Box 488
Montpelier, VT 05601
P: (802) 828-4301
F: (802) 828-4022
E: Labor.WebInput
@vermont.gov

VIRGINIA
Ms. Ellen Marie Hess
Commissioner
Employment Commission
703 East Main Street
P.O. Box 1358
Richmond, VA 23219
P: (866) 832-2363
E: ellenmarie.hess
@vec.virginia.gov

WASHINGTON
Mr. Dale Peinecke
Commissioner
Employment Security
Department
212 Maple Park Avenue,
Southeast
P.O. Box 9046
Olympia, WA 98507
P: (360) 902-9500
E: dpeinecke@esd.wa.gov

Mr. Franklin Plaistowe
Assistant Director
State Human Resources
128th 10th Avenue
P.O. Box 47500
Olympia, WA 98504
P: (360) 407-4104
E: StateHR@ofm.wa.gov

WEST VIRGINIA
Mr. H. Wood Thrasher
Cabinet Secretary
Department of Commerce
Capitol Complex Building 6,
Room 525
1900 Kanawha Boulevard East
Charleston, WV 25305
P: (304) 558-2234
F: (304) 558-1189
E: W.Thrasher@wv.gov

WYOMING
Mr. John F. Cox
Director
Department of Workforce
Services
614 South Greeley Highway
Cheyenne, WY 82002
P: (307) 777-8728
F: (307) 777-5857
E: john.cox@wyo.gov

Energy

Develops and administers programs relating to energy conservation, alternative energy research and development, and energy information.

ALASKA
Mr. Michael Lamb
Executive Director
Energy Authority
813 West Northern Lights Boulevard
Anchorage, AK 99503
P: (907) 771-3000
F: (907) 771-3044
E: mlamb@aidea.org

AMERICAN SAMOA
Aliitama Sotoa
Director
Territorial Energy Office
American Samoa Government
Executive Office Building
Pago Pago, AS 96799
P: (684) 633-4116
F: (684) 633-2269
E: info@as.gov

ARKANSAS
Mr. Mitchell Simpson
Director
State Energy Office
900 West Capitol Avenue, Suite 400
Little Rock, AR 72201
P: (501) 682-1060
F: (501) 682-7499
E: simpson@adeq.state.ar.us

CALIFORNIA
Mr. Rob Oglesby
Executive Director
State Energy Commission
1516 Ninth Street, MS-29
Sacramento, CA 95814
P: (916) 654-4996
F: (916) 654-4423
E: rob.oglesby@energy.ca.gov

COLORADO
Ms. Kathleen Staks
Executive Director
State Energy Office
1580 Logan Street, Suite 100
Denver, CO 80203
P: (303) 866-2462

CONNECTICUT
Ms. Katie Scharf Dykes
Chair
Public Utilities Regulatory Authority
Energy & Environmental Protection
10 Franklin Square
New Britain, CT 06051
P: (860) 827-1553
F: (860) 418-6495
E: katie.dykes@ct.gov

DELAWARE
Mr. Philip J. Cherry
Division Director
Division of Energy & Climate
100 West Water Street, Suite 5A
Dover, DE 19904
P: (302) 735-3480
F: (302) 739-1840
E: philip.cherry@state.de.us

DISTRICT OF COLUMBIA
Mr. Tommy Wells
Director
Department of Energy & Environment
1200 First Street, Northeast
Washington, DC 20002
P: (202) 535-2600
F: (202) 535-1359
E: tommy.wells@dc.gov

FLORIDA
Ms. Kelley Smith Burk
Acting Director
Office of Energy
Agriculture & Consumer Services
600 South Calhoun Street, Suite B04
Tallahassee, FL 32399
P: (850) 617-7470
F: (850) 617-7471
E: Energy@FreshFromFlorida.com

GEORGIA
Mr. David Gipson
Director, Energy Resources Division
State Environmental Finance Authority
233 Peachtree Street, Northeast
Harris Tower, Suite 900
Atlanta, GA 30303
P: (404) 584-1007
F: (404) 584-1069
E: dgipson@gefa.ga.gov

GUAM
Ms. Lorilee T. Crisostomo
Administrator
Energy Office
548 North Marine Corps Drive
Tamuning, GU 96913
P: (671) 646-4361
F: (671) 649-1215
E: lorilee.crisostomo@epa.guam.gov

HAWAII
Mr. Terrence G. Surles
Acting Energy Program Administrator
State Energy Office
Business, Economic Development & Tourism
P.O. Box 2359
Honolulu, HI 96804
P: (808) 587-3807
F: (808) 586-2536
E: dbedt.energyoffice@hawaii.gov

IDAHO
Mr. John Chatburn
Administrator
Governor's Office of Energy & Mineral Resources
304 North 8th Street, Suite 250
P.O. Box 83720
Boise, ID 83720
P: (208) 332-1660
F: (208) 332-1661
E: John.Chatburn@oer.idaho.gov

ILLINOIS
Ms. Molly Lunn
Assistant Deputy Director
Energy & Recycling Office
Commerce & Economic Opportunity
100 West Randolph Street, Suite 3-400
Chicago, IL 60601
P: (312) 814-2354
F: (217) 558-2647
E: marion.lunn@illinois.gov

INDIANA
Mr. Tristan Vance
Director
State Office of Energy Development
1 North Capitol, Suite 900
Indianapolis, IN 46204
P: (317) 232-8939
F: (317) 233-6887
E: TVance1@oed.IN.gov

IOWA
Mr. Brian Selinger
Team Lead
Energy Office
Economic Development Authority
200 East Grand Avenue
Des Moines, IA 50309
P: (515) 725-0434
F: (515) 725-3010
E: brian.selinger@iowa.gov

KANSAS
Ms. Lynn Retz
Energy Program Executive
Energy Division
State Corporation Commission
1500 Southwest Arrowhead Road
Topeka, KS 66604
P: (785) 271-3170
E: l.retz@kcc.ks.gov

KENTUCKY
Mr. John Bender
Executive Advisor
Department for Energy Development & Independence
Energy & Environment Cabinet
300 Sower Boulevard, 3rd Floor
Frankfort, KY 40601
P: (502) 564-7192
F: (502) 564-7484
E: John.Bender@ky.gov

LOUISIANA
Mr. Paul Miller
Division Director
Technology Assessment Division
617 North Third Street
P.O. Box 94396
Baton Rouge, LA 70804
P: (225) 342-2133
F: (225) 342-1397
E: paul.miller@la.gov

MAINE
Mr. Michael Stoddard
Executive Director
Efficiency Maine
168 Capitol Street, Suite 1
Augusta, ME 04330
P: (207) 213-4150
F: (207) 287-1039
E: Michael.stoddard@efficiencymaine.com

Energy

MARYLAND
Ms. Mary Beth Tung
Director
Energy Administration
1800 Washington Boulevard, Suite 755
Baltimore, MD 21230
P: (410) 537-4000
E: marybeth.tung@maryland.gov

MASSACHUSETTS
Ms. Judith F. Judson
Commissioner
Department of Energy Resources
Office of Energy & Environmental Affairs
100 Cambridge Street, Suite 1020
Boston, MA 02114
P: (617) 626-7332
F: (617) 727-0030
E: jane.may@state.ma.us

MICHIGAN
Ms. Valerie J.M. Brader
Executive Director
State Agency for Energy
7109 West Saginaw Highway
P.O. Box 30221
Lansing, MI 48909
P: (517) 284-8335
F: (517) 284-8334

MINNESOTA
Mr. Bill Grant
Deputy Commissioner
Division of Energy Resources
Department of Commerce
85 7th Place East, Suite 280
St. Paul, MN 55101
P: (651) 539-1801
E: bill.grant@state.mn.us

MISSISSIPPI
Mr. Blake Kelly
Project Manager, Energy Policy, Planning, & Research
Energy & Natural Resources Division
State Development Authority
501 North West Street, P.O. Box 849
Jackson, MS 39205
P: (601) 359-3449
F: (601) 359-6642
E: bkelly@mississippi.org

MISSOURI
Ms. Kristy Manning
Director
Division of Energy
Department of Economic Development
P.O. Box 1766
Jefferson City, MO 65102
P: (573) 751-2254
F: (573) 526-7553
E: energy@ded.mo.gov

MONTANA
Ms. Laura Andersen
Energy Bureau Chief
Department of Environmental Quality
1520 East Sixth Avenue
P.O. Box 200901
Helena, MT 59620
P: (406) 444-6588
F: (406) 444-6836
E: landersen3@mt.gov

NEBRASKA
Mr. David Bracht
Director
State Energy Office
P.O. Box 95085
Lincoln, NE 68509
P: (402) 471-2867
F: (402) 471-3064
E: david.bracht@nebraska.gov

NEVADA
Ms. Angie Dykema
Director
State Office of Energy
755 North Roop Street, Suite 202
Carson City, NV 89701
P: (775) 687-1850
F: (775) 687-1869
E: info@energy.nv.gov

NEW HAMPSHIRE
Mr. Myles Matteson
Director
Office of Energy & Planning
Johnson Hall, 3rd Floor
107 Pleasant Street
Concord, NH 03301
P: (603) 271-2705
E: myles.matteson@nh.gov

NEW JERSEY
Mr. Thomas Walker
Director
Division of Energy
Board of Public Utilities
44 South Clinton Avenue
Trenton, NJ 08625
P: (609) 292-2453
F: (609) 341-5781
E: bill.grant@state.mn.us

NEW MEXICO
Ms. Louise Martinez
Director, Energy Conservation and Management Division
State Energy, Minerals & Natural Resources Department
Wendell Chino Building, First Floor
1220 South St. Francis Drive
Santa Fe, NM 87505
P: (505) 476-3315
F: (505) 476-3322
E: Louise.n.martinez@state.nm.us

NEW YORK
Mr. John B. Rhodes
President & CEO
State Energy Research & Development Authority
17 Columbia Circle
Albany, NY 12203
P: (518) 862-1090
F: (518) 862-1091
E: info@nyserda.ny.gov

NORTH CAROLINA
Tracy E. Davis
Director
Division of Energy, Mineral & Land Resources
Department of Environmental Quality
217 West Jones Street
Raleigh, NC 27603
P: (919) 707-9201
E: tracy.davis@ncdenr.gov

NORTH DAKOTA
Ms. Bonnie Malo
Director, Division of Community Services
Department of Commerce
1600 East Century Avenue, Suite 2
P.O. Box 2057
Bismarck, ND 58503
P: (701) 328-2476
F: (701) 328-2308
E: bmalo@nd.gov

NORTHERN MARIANA ISLANDS
Ms. Thelma B. Inos
Energy Director
Commonwealth of the Northern Mariana Islands
Energy Division
P.O. Box 500340
Saipan, MP 96950
P: (670) 664-4480
F: (670) 664-4483
E: cnmienergy@gmail.com

OHIO
Mr. David Goodman
Director
State Development Services Agency
77 South High Street, 29th Floor
P.O. Box 1001
Columbus, OH 43216
P: (614) 466-3379
F: (614) 466-1864
E: david.goodman@development.ohio.gov

OKLAHOMA
Mr. Vaughn Clark
Director, Community Development
Department of Commerce
Department of Commerce
900 North Stiles Street
Oklahoma City, OK 73104
P: (405) 815-5370
F: (405) 605-2870
E: vaughn.clark@okcommerce.gov

OREGON
Mr. Michael Kaplan
Director
Department of Energy
550 Capitol Street Northeast, 1st Floor
Salem, OR 97301
P: (503) 373-7563
F: (503) 373-7806
E: mike.kaplan@oregon.gov

PENNSYLVANIA
Mr. Dave A. Althoff Jr.
Alternative Energy & Transportation Programs
Office of Pollution Prevention & Energy Assistance
400 Market Street, 2nd Floor
P.O. Box 8772
Harrisburg, PA 17105
P: (717) 783-0542
F: (717) 783-2703
E: dalthoff@pa.gov

RHODE ISLAND
Ms. Carol Grant
Commissioner
State Office of Energy Resources
One Capitol Hill
Providence, RI 02908
P: (401) 574-9100
F: (401) 574-9125
E: carol.grant@energy.ri.gov

SOUTH CAROLINA
Mr. M. Anthony James
Director of Energy Policy
State Energy Office
1401 Main Street, Suite 900
Columbia, SC 29201
P: (803) 737-2090
F: (803) 737-0842
E: majames@regstaff.sc.gov

SOUTH DAKOTA
Ms. Michele Farris
Statewide Energy Manager
Energy Management Office
Bureau of Administration
821 North Capitol Street
Mitchell, SD 57301
P: (605) 995-8254
F: (605) 773-5980
E: Michele.Farris@state.sd.us

TENNESSEE
Ms. Molly Cripps
Director
Office of Energy Programs
Department of Environment & Conservation
312 Rosa L. Parks Avenue, 2nd Floor
Nashville, TN 37243
P: (615) 253-1945
F: (615) 741-5070
E: molly.cripps@tn.gov

TEXAS
Mr. William E. Taylor
Director
State Energy Conservation Office
Comptroller of Public Accounts
111 East 17th Street, #314
Austin, TX 78774
P: (512) 463-8352
F: (512) 475-2569
E: dub.taylor@cpa.state.tx.us

UTAH
Dr. Laura Nelson
Executive Director
State Office of Energy Development
P.O. Box 144845
Salt Lake City, UT 84114
P: (801) 538-8732
F: (855) 271-4373
E: lnelson@utah.gov

VERMONT
Mr. Ed McNamara
Director
Planning & Energy Resources Division
Department of Public Service
112 State Street, Third Floor
Montpelier, VT 05620
P: (802) 828-4007
F: (802) 828-2342

VIRGINIA
Mr. John Warren
Director
Division of Energy
Department of Mines, Minerals and Energy
1100 Bank Street, 8th Floor
Richmond, VA 23219
P: (804) 692-3200
F: (804) 692-3237
E: john.warren@dmme.virginia.gov

WASHINGTON
Mr. Michael Furze
Assistant Director, State Energy Office
Department of Commerce
1011 Plum Street, Southeast
P.O. Box 42525
Olympia, WA 98504
P: (360) 725-2950
F: (360) 586-0489
E: michael.furze@commerce.wa.gov

WEST VIRGINIA
Ms. Bonnie J. Shumate
Executive Secretary
State Division of Energy
1900 Kanawha Boulevard, East
Capitol Complex, Building 6, Room 645
Charleston, WV 25305
P: (304) 558-2234
F: (304) 558-0362
E: Bonnie.J.Shumate@wv.gov

WISCONSIN
Ms. Maria Redmond
Director, Office of Energy Innovation
State Energy Office
610 North Whitney Way, 2nd Floor
Madison, WI 53707
P: (608) 266-1521
F: (608) 266-3957
E: maria.redmond@wisconsin.gov

WYOMING
Ms. Sherry Hughes
Energy Efficiency Program Manager
State Energy Office
State Business Council
214 West 15th Street
Cheyenne, WY 82002
P: (307) 777-2824
F: (307) 777-2837
E: sherry.hughes@wyo.gov

Environmental Protection

Oversees the overall quality of the environment by coordinating and managing the state's pollution control programs and planning, permit granting and regulation of standards.

ALABAMA
Mr. Lance R. LeFleur
Director
Department of Environmental Management
P.O. Box 301463
Montgomery, AL 36130
P: (334) 271-7710
F: (334) 279-3043

ALASKA
Mr. Larry Hartig
Commissioner
Department of Environmental Conservation
410 Willoughby Avenue, Suite 303
P.O. Box 111800
Juneau, AK 99811
P: (907) 465-5065
F: (907) 465-5070
E: dec.commissioner@alaska.gov

ARIZONA
Mr. Misael Cabrera
Director
Deaprtment of Environmental Quality
1110 West Washington Street
Phoenix, AZ 85007
P: (602) 771-2203
F: (602) 771-2218
E: cabrera.misael@azdeq.gov

ARKANSAS
Ms. Becky Keogh
Director
Department of Environmental Quality
5301 Northshore Drive
North Little Rock, AR 72118
P: (501) 682-0959
F: (501) 682-0798
E: keogh@adeq.state.ar.us

CALIFORNIA
Mr. Matthew Rodriquez
Secretary
Environmental Protection Agency
1001 I Street
P.O. Box 2815
Sacramento, CA 95812
P: (916) 323-2514
F: (916) 445-6401

COLORADO
Ms. Martha Rudolph
Director of Environmental Programs
Department of Public Health & Environment
4300 Cherry Creek Drive, South
Denver, CO 80246
P: (303) 692-2000
F: (303) 691-7702
E: martha.rudolph@state.co.us

DELAWARE
Mr. Shawn Garvin
Secretary
Department of Natural Resources & Environmental Control
89 Kings Highway
Dover, DE 19901
P: (302) 739-9000

Mr. Robert J. Zimmerman
Chief Operating Officer
Department of Natural Resources & Environmental Control
89 Kings Highway
Dover, DE 19901
P: (302) 739-9000
F: (302) 739-6242

DISTRICT OF COLUMBIA
Mr. Tommy Wells
Director
Department of the Environment
1200 First Street, Northeast
Washington, DC 20002
P: (202) 535-2600
F: (202) 535-1359
E: tommy.wells@dc.gov

FLORIDA
Mr. Ryan Matthews
Interim Secretary
Department of Environmental Protection
3900 Commonwealth Boulevard, M.S. 49
Tallahassee, FL 32399
P: (850) 245-2011

GEORGIA
Ms. Lauren Curry
Deputy Director, Environmental Protection Division
Department of Natural Resources
2 Martin Luther King Jr. Drive Southeast
Suite 1152
Atlanta, GA 30334
P: (404) 656-4713

Mr. Richard Dunn
Director, Environmental Protection Division
Department of Natural Resources
2 Martin Luther King Jr. Drive Southeast
Suite 1152
Atlanta, GA 30334
P: (404) 656-4713

HAWAII
Mr. Keith Kawaoka
Deputy Director
Department of Health
Department of Health
1250 Punchbowl Street
Honolulu, HI 96813
P: (808) 586-4424
F: (808) 586-4368

IDAHO
Mr. Jess Byrne
Deputy Director
Department of Environmental Quality
1410 North Hilton
Boise, ID 83706
P: (208) 373-0240
E: jess.byrne@deq.idaho.gov

Mr. John Tippets
Director
Department of Environmental Quality
1410 North Hilton
Boise, ID 83706
P: (208) 373-0240
F: (208) 373-0417
E: john.tippets@deq.idaho.gov

ILLINOIS
Mr. Gerald Keenan
Chairman
Pollution Control Board
1021 North Grand Avenue, East
P.O. Box 19274
Springfield, IL 62794
P: (217) 524-8500

Mr. Alec Messina
Director
Environmental Protection Agency
1021 North Grand Avenue, East
P.O. Box 19276
Springfield, IL 62794
P: (217) 782-3397

INDIANA
Mr. Bruno Pigott
Commissioner
Department of Environmental Management
Government Center North
100 North Senate Avenue
Indianapolis, IN 46204
P: (317) 232-8603

IOWA
Mr. Bill Ehm
Division Administrator of DNR
Department of Natural Resources
4th Floor, Wallace Building
502 East 9th Street
Des Moines, IA 50319
P: (515) 725-8200
F: (515) 725-8201
E: william.ehm@dnr.iowa.gov

KANSAS
Mr. John Mitchell
Director
Department of Health & Environment
Curtis State Office Building
1000 Southwest Jackson
Topeka, KS 66612
P: (785) 296-1500
F: (785) 296-8464
E: jmitchell@kdheks.gov

KENTUCKY
Mr. Aaron Keatley
Commissioner
Department of Environmental Protection
300 Sower Boulevard, 2nd Floor
Frankfort, KY 40601
P: (502) 564-0323
E: envhelp@ky.gov

LOUISIANA
Dr. Chuck Carr Brown
Secretary
Department of Environmental Quality
602 North Fifth Street
Baton Rouge, LA 70802
P: (225) 219-5337
F: (225) 219-3970
E: Chuck.Brown@la.gov

MAINE
Mr. Paul Mercer
Commissioner
Department of Environmental Protection
17 State House Station
28 Tyson Drive
Augusta, ME 04333
P: (207) 287-7688
F: (207) 287-2814
E: paul.mercer@maine.gov

MARYLAND
Mr. Ben Grumbles
Secretary
Department of the Environment
1800 Washington Boulevard
Baltimore, MD 21230
P: (410) 537-3000
F: (410) 537-3888

MASSACHUSETTS
Mr. Martin Suuberg
Commissioner
Department of Environmental Protection
One Winter Street
Boston, MA 02108
P: (617) 292-5500
F: (617) 574-6880

MICHIGAN
Ms. Heidi Grether
Director
Department of Environmental Quality
P.O. Box 30473
Lansing, MI 48909
P: (517) 284-6700
F: (517) 241-7401
E: GretherH@michigan.gov

MINNESOTA
Mr. John Linc Stine
Commissioner
Pollution Control Agency
520 Lafayette Road, North
St. Paul, MN 55155
P: (651) 757-2014
F: (651) 296-6334
E: john.stine@state.mn.us

MISSISSIPPI
Mr. Gary Rikard
Executive Director
Department of Environmental Quality
P. O. Box 2261
Jackson, MS 39225
P: (601) 961-5000
F: (601) 961-5093
E: gary_rikard@deq.state.ms.us

MISSOURI
Ms. Carol S. Comer
Director
Department of Natural Resources
1101 Riverside Drive
P.O. Box 176
Jefferson City, MO 65102
P: (573) 751-4732
F: (573) 751-7627
E: carol.comer@ded.mo.gov

MONTANA
Mr. Tom Livers
Director
Department of Environmental Quality
1520 East 6th Avenue
Helena, MT 59620
P: (406) 444-6815
F: (406) 444-4386
E: tlivers@mt.gov

NEBRASKA
Mr. Jim Macy
Director
Department of Environmental Quality
1200 N Street, Suite 400
P.O. Box 98922
Lincoln, NE 68509
P: (402) 471-2186
F: (402) 471-2909
E: Jim.Macy@nebraska.gov

NEVADA
Mr. Bradley Crowell
Director
Division of Environmental Protection
901 South Stewart Street, Suite 1003
Carson City, NV 89701
P: (775) 684-2700
F: (775) 684-2715
E: bcrowell@dcnr.nv.gov

Mr. Greg Lovato
Administrator
Division of Environmental Protection
901 South Stewart Street, Suite 4001
Carson City, NV 89701
P: (775) 687–4670

NEW HAMPSHIRE
Mr. Clark Freise
Assistant Commissioner
Department of Environmental Services
29 Hazen Drive
P.O. Box 95
Concord, NH 03302
P: (603) 271-3503

NEW JERSEY
Mr. Bob Martin
Commissioner & State Historic Preservation Officer
Department of Environmental Protection
401 East State Street, Mail Code 401-07
P.O. Box 402
Trenton, NJ 08625
P: (609) 292-2885
F: (609) 292-7695

NEW MEXICO
Mr. Butch Tongate
Acting Cabinet Secretary
Environment Department
Harold L. Runnels Building
1190 St. Francis Drive, Suite N4050
Santa Fe, NM 87505
P: (505) 827-2855
F: (505) 827-4422

NEW YORK
Mr. Basil Seggos
Commissioner
Department of Environmental Conservation
625 Broadway
Albany, NY 12233
P: (518) 402-8545
F: (518) 402-8541

NORTH CAROLINA
Ms. Sheila Holman
Assistant Secretary
Department of Environment & Natural Resources
217 West Jones Street
Raleigh, NC 27603
P: (919) 707-8600
E: sheila.holman@ncdenr.gov

Mr. Michael Regan
Secretary
Department of Environment & Natural Resources
217 West Jones Street
Raleigh, NC 27603
P: (919) 707-8600

NORTH DAKOTA
Mr. L. David Glatt
Chief
Environmental Health Section
Department of Health
918 East Divide Avenue
Bismarck, ND 58501
P: (701) 328-5151
F: (701) 328-5200
E: dglatt@nd.gov

OKLAHOMA
Mr. Michael Teague
Secretary of Energy & Environment
Department of Environmental Quality
204 North Robinson, Suite 1010
Oklahoma City, OK 73102
P: (405) 522-7099
F: (405) 530-8999
E: ee@ee.ok.gov

Mr. Scott Thompson
Executive Director
Department of Environmental Quality
707 North Robinson
P.O. Box 1677
Oklahoma City, OK 73101
P: (405) 702-0100
F: (405) 702-7101

OREGON
Mr. Richard Whitman
Interim Director
Department of Environmental Quality
700 Northeast Multnomah Street
Suite 600
Portland, OR 97232
P: (503) 229-5696
F: (503) 229-5850

PENNSYLVANIA
Mr. Patrick McDonnell
Secretary
Department of Environmental Protection
Rachel Carson State Office Building
400 Market Street
Harrisburg, PA 17101
P: (717) 783-2300

PUERTO RICO
Mr. Weldin Fernando Ortiz Franco
Chairman
Environmental Quality Board
Apartado 11488
San Juan, PR 00910
P: (787) 767-8181

RHODE ISLAND
Ms. Janet Coit
Director
Department of Environmental Management
235 Promenade Street
Providence, RI 02908
P: (401) 222-6800
F: (401) 222-6802
E: janet.coit@dem.ri.gov

Environmental Protection

SOUTH CAROLINA
Ms. Myra Reece
Director of Environmental Affairs
Department of Health & Environmental Control
2600 Bull Street
Columbia, SC 29201
P: (803) 898-3432
F: (803) 896-4001
E: info@dhec.sc.gov

SOUTH DAKOTA
Mr. Steven M. Pirner
Secretary
Department of Environment & Natural Resources
Joe Foss Building
523 East Capital Avenue
Pierre, SD 57501
P: (605) 773-5559
F: (605) 773-6035
E: denrinternet@state.sd.us

TENNESSEE
Mr. Robert J. Martineau Jr.
Commissioner
Department of Environment & Conservation
William R. Snodgrass Tennessee Tower
312 Rosa L. Parks Avenue, 2nd Floor
Nashville, TN 37243
P: (615) 532-0109
F: (615) 532-0120

Ms. Shari Meghreblian
Deputy Commissioner of Environment
Department of Environment & Conservation
William R. Snodgrass Tennessee Tower
312 Rosa L. Parks Avenue, 2nd Floor
Nashville, TN 37243
P: (615) 532-0109
F: (615) 532-0120

TEXAS
Mr. Toby Baker
Commissioner
Commission on Environmental Quality
12100 Park 35 Circle
P.O. Box 13087
Austin, TX 78711
P: (512) 239-5510
F: (512) 239-5533

Dr. Bryan W. Shaw
Chair
Commission on Environmental Quality
12100 Park 35 Circle
P.O. Box 13087
Austin, TX 78711
P: (512) 239-5510
F: (512) 239-5533
E: bryan.shaw@tceq.texas.gov

UTAH
Mr. Bradley T. Johnson
Deputy Director
Department of Environmental Quality
195 North 1950 West
Salt Lake City, UT 84114
P: (801) 536-4404

Mr. Alan Matheson
Executive Director
Department of Environmental Quality
195 North 1950 West
Salt Lake City, UT 84114
P: (801) 536-4404
F: (801) 536-0061
E: amatheson@utah.gov

VERMONT
Ms. Emily Boedecker
Commissioner
Department of Environmental Conservation
Main Building - 2nd Floor
One National Life Drive
Montpelier, VT 05620
P: (802) 828-1556

Ms. Julie Moore
Secretary
Agency of Natural Resources
103 South Main Street, Center Building
Waterbury, VT 05671
P: (802) 828-1294
F: (802) 244-1102
E: julie.moore@vermont.gov

VIRGINIA
Mr. David K. Paylor
Director
Department of Environmental Quality
629 East Main Street
P.O. Box 1105
Richmond, VA 23219
P: (804) 698-4000
F: (804) 698-4019
E: david.paylor@deq.virginia.gov

WASHINGTON
Ms. Maia Bellon
Ecology Director
Department of Ecology
300 Desmond Drive, Southeast
Lacey, WA 98503
P: (360) 407-6000
F: (360) 407-6989
E: maib461@ecy.wa.gov

WEST VIRGINIA
Mr. Austin Caperton
Cabinet Secretary
Department of Environmental Protection
601 57th Street, Southeast
Charleston, WV 25304
P: (304) 926-0440

WISCONSIN
Ms. Cathy Stepp
Secretary
Department of Natural Resources
101 South Webster Street
P.O. Box 7921
Madison, WI 53707
P: (608) 266-2121
F: (608) 266-6983
E: DNRSecretary@Wisconsin.gov

Mr. Patrick Stevens
Deputy Administrator
Department of Natural Resources
101 South Webster Street
P.O. Box 7921
Madison, WI 53707
P: (608) 264-9210
E: Patrick.Stevens@Wisconsin.gov

WYOMING
Mr. Todd Parfitt
Director
Department of Environmental Quality
200 West 17th Street
Cheyenne, WY 82002
P: (307) 777-7937
F: (307) 635-1784
E: todd.parfitt@wyo.gov

Equal Employment Opportunity

Enforces laws promoting equal employment opportunity in the state.

ALABAMA
Mr. Fitzgerald Washington
Secretary
Department of Labor
649 Monroe Street
Montgomery, AL 36131
P: (334) 242-8055
E: fwashington@labor.alabama.gov

ALASKA
Ms. Camille Brill
EEO Program Manager
Department of Administration
550 West 7th Avenue, Suite 1960
Anchorage, AK 99501
P: (907) 375-7705
F: (907) 375-7719
E: camille.brill@alaska.gov

AMERICAN SAMOA
Mr. Esenaeiaso J. Liu
Director
Department of Human Resources
Executive Office Building
AP Lutali, 2nd Floor
Pago Pago, AS 96799
P: (684) 644-4485
F: (684) 633-1139
E: eseneiaso.liu@hr.as.gov

ARIZONA
Ms. LoValerie Mullins
Equal Opportunity Program Manager
Governor's Office of Equal Opportunity
100 North Fifteenth Avenue, Suite 261
Phoenix, AZ 85007
P: (602) 542-3711
F: (602) 542-3712
E: EqualOpportunity@az.gov

ARKANSAS
Ms. Gloria Johnson
Equal Opportunity Manager
Department of Workforce Services
#2 Capitol Mall
Little Rock, AR 72201
P: (501) 682-2389
F: (501) 682-3748
E: gloria.johnson@arkansas.gov

CALIFORNIA
Mr. Kevin Kish
Director
Department of Fair Employment & Housing
2218 Kausen Drive, Suite 100
Elk Grove, CA 95758
P: (800) 884-1684
F: (916) 651-8866
E: tom.lee@dss.ca.gov

COLORADO
Ms. Aubrey Elenis
Director
Civil Rights Division
1560 Broadway, Suite 1050
Denver, CO 80202
P: (303) 894-2997

CONNECTICUT
Ms. Tanya Hughes
Executive Director
Commission on Human Rights & Opportunities
450 Columbus Boulevard
Hartford, CT 06103
P: (860) 541-3421
F: (860) 241-4875
E: tanya.hughes@ct.gov

DELAWARE
Ms. Sandy Reyes
Human Resource Administrator
Human Resource Management
Office of Management and Budget
122 Martin Luther King Jr. Blvd., South
Dover, DE 19901
P: (302) 739-4195
F: (302) 739-3000
E: sandy.reyes@state.de.us

DISTRICT OF COLUMBIA
Ms. Monica Palacio
Director
Office of Human Rights
441 4th Street, Northwest
Suite 570 North
Washington, DC 20001
P: (202) 727-4559
F: (202) 727-9589
E: ohr@dc.gov

FLORIDA
Mr. Peter De Haan
EO Officer
Office for Civil Rights
Office of Attorney General
The Capitol PL-01
Tallahassee, FL 32399
P: (850) 414-3300
F: (850) 921-7671
E: peter.dehaan@awi.state.fl.us

GEORGIA
Mr. Melvin J. Everson
Executive Director & Administrator
Commission on Equal Opportunity
7 Martin Luther King Jr. Drive Southeast
3rd Floor, Suite 351
Atlanta, GA 30334
P: (404) 232-1776
F: (404) 656-4399
E: meverson@gceo.state.ga.us

GUAM
Mr. Manuel Q. Cruz
Director
Department of Labor
Government of Guam
P.O. Box 9970
Tamuning, GU 96931
P: (671) 475-7044
F: (671) 674-6517

HAWAII
Mr. William D. Hoshijo
Executive Director
Civil Rights Commission
Labor & Industrial Relations Department
830 Punchbowl Street, Room 411
Honolulu, HI 96813
P: (808) 586-8636
F: (808) 586-8655
E: dlir.hcrc.infor@hawaii.gov

IDAHO
Ms. Linda L. Goodman
Administrator
Human Rights Commission
317 West Main Street, Second Floor
Boise, ID 83735
P: (208) 334-2873
F: (208) 334-2664
E: Linda.Goodman@labor.idaho.gov

ILLINOIS
Ms. Janice Glenn
Acting Director
Department of Human Rights
100 West Randolph Street, 10th Floor
Intake Unit
Chicago, IL 60601
P: (312) 814-6200
F: (312) 814-1436

INDIANA
Ms. Lavenia Haskett
Program Director
Employee Relations
State Personnel Department
402 West Washington, Room W161
Indianapolis, IN 46204
P: (317) 232-4555
F: (317) 232-3089
E: lhaskett@spd.in.gov

IOWA
Ms. Kristin H. Johnson
Executive Director
Civil Rights Commission
Grimes State Office Building
400 East 14th Street
Des Moines, IA 50319
P: (515) 281-4576
F: (515) 242-5840
E: Kristin.Johnson2@iowa.gov

KANSAS
Ms. Ruth Glover
Executive Director
Human Rights Commission
900 Southwest Jackson Street
Suite 568-South
Topeka, KS 66612
P: (785) 296-3206
F: (785) 296-0589

Ms. Lana Gordon
Secretary of Labor
Department of Labor
401 Southwest Topeka Boulevard
Topeka, KS 66603
P: (785) 296-5000
F: (785) 368-5289
E: lana.gordon@dol.ks.gov

KENTUCKY
Mr. Chris Johnson
Executive Director
Office of Diversity & Equality
Personnel Cabinet
501 High Street, 3rd Floor
Frankfort, KY 40601
P: (502) 564-8000
F: (502) 564-0182

Equal Employment Opportunity

LOUISIANA
Ms. Ava Dejoie
Executive Director
Workforce Commission
1001 North 23rd Street
P.O. Box 94094
Baton Rouge, LA 70804
P: (225) 342-3111
F: (225) 342-3778
E: owd@lwc.la.gov

MAINE
Ms. Joyce Oreskovich
Director
Bureau of Human Resources
#4 State House Station
Burton M. Cross Building, 4th Floor
Augusta, ME 04333
P: (207) 624-7761
F: (207) 287-4414
E: joyce.a.oreskovich@maine.gov

MARYLAND
Mr. Alvin O. Gillard
Executive Director
Commission on Civil Rights
William Donald Schaefer Tower
6 Saint Paul Street, Suite 900
Baltimore, MD 21202
P: (410) 767-8585
F: (410) 333-1841
E: alvin.gillard@maryland.gov

MASSACHUSETTS
Ms. Sandra E. Borders
Director
Office of Diversity & Equal Opportunity
One Ashburton Place, Room 213
Boston, MA 02108
P: (617) 727-7441
F: (617) 878-9830

Ms. Linda Spears
Commissioner
Department of Children & Families
Office of Health & Human Services
600 Washington Street
Boston, MA 02111
P: (617) 748-2000
F: (617) 261-7435
E: dcfcommissioner@state.ma.us

MINNESOTA
Mr. Kevin Lindsey
Commissioner
Department of Human Rights
Freeman Building
625 Robert Street, North
St. Paul, MN 55155
P: (651) 539-1100
F: (651) 296-9042
E: Kevin.Lindsey@state.mn.us

MISSOURI
Dr. Alisa Warren
Executive Director
Commission on Human Rights
3315 West Truman Boulevard, Room 212
P.O. Box 1129
Jefferson City, MO 65102
P: (573) 751-3325
F: (573) 751-2905
E: mchr@labor.mo.gov

MONTANA
Ms. Anjenette Schafer
Administrator
Human Resources Division
Department of Administration
P.O. Box 200127
Helena, MT 59620
P: (406) 444-3885
F: (406) 444-0703
E: aschafer2@mt.gov

NEBRASKA
Mr. Stan Odenthal
Executive Director
Equal Opportunity Commission
301 Centennial Mall South, 5th Floor
P.O. Box 94934
Lincoln, NE 68509
P: (402) 471-2024
F: (402) 471-4059
E: stan.odenthal@nebraska.gov

NEVADA
Ms. Kara Jenkins
Commission Administrator
Equal Rights Commission
Employment, Training & Rehabilitation
1820 East Sahara Avenue, Suite 314
Las Vegas, NV 89104
P: (702) 486-7161
F: (702) 486-7054

NEW HAMPSHIRE
Ms. Joni N. Esperian
Executive Director
Commission for Human Rights
2 Industrial Park Drive
Concord, NH 03301
P: (603) 271-2767
F: (603) 271-6339
E: humanrights@nh.gov

NEW JERSEY
Ms. Mamta Patel
Director
Division of Equal Employment Opportunity & Affirmative Action
44 South Clinton Avenue
P.O. Box 315
Trenton, NJ 08625
P: (609) 984-1096
F: (609) 292-7067

NEW MEXICO
Ms. Patricia Wolf
Investigation, Compliance, & Alternative Dispute Resolution Staff Manager
Human Rights Bureau
Department of Workforce Solutions
1596 Pacheco Street, Suite103
Santa Fe, NM 87505
P: (505) 827-6856

NORTH CAROLINA
Ms. Nancy Astrike
Director, Diversity & Workforce Services
Office of State Human Resources
116 West Jones Street
1331 Mail Service Center
Raleigh, NC 27699
P: (919) 807-4814
E: nancy.astrike@nc.gov

NORTH DAKOTA
Ms. Michelle Kommer
Commissioner of Labor
Department of Labor & Human Rights
600 East Boulevard Avenue
Department 406
Bismarck, ND 58505
P: (701) 328-2660
F: (701) 328-2031
E: mkommer@nd.gov

NORTHERN MARIANA ISLANDS
Mr. Isidro Seman
Director of Personnel
Office of Personnel Management
P.O. Box 5153 CHRB
Saipan, MP 96950
P: (670) 234-6925 Ext. 101
F: (670) 234-1013

OHIO
Mr. Robert Blair
Director
Department of Administrative Services
30 East Broad Street, 40th Floor
Columbus, OH 43215
P: (614) 466-6511
F: (614) 644-8151
E: jackie.murray@das.ohio.gov

OKLAHOMA
Mr. Ross Tripp
Workforce Services Director
Workforce Diversity & Certified Discrimination Complaint Investigator
Human Capital Management Division
2101 North Lincoln Boulevard, Room G-80
Oklahoma City, OK 73105
P: (405) 521-6376
F: (405) 524-6942

OREGON
The Honorable Brad Avakian (D)
Commissioner
Bureau of Labor & Industries
800 Northeast Oregon Street
Suite 1045
Portland, OR 97232
P: (971) 673-0781
F: (971) 673-0762
E: brad.avakian@state.or.us

PENNSYLVANIA
Ms. Kathy M. Manderino
Secretary
Department of Labor & Industry
651 Boas Street
Harrisburg, PA 17121
P: (717) 787-5279
F: (717) 787-8826

PUERTO RICO
Mr. Carlos J. Saavedra Gutierrez
Secretary
Department of Labor & Human Resources
P.O. Box 195540
San Juan, PR 00919
P: (787) 754-5353
F: (787) 753-9550

RHODE ISLAND
Ms. Cheryl A. Burrell
Associate Director
Office of Diversity, Equity & Opportunity
Department of Administration
One Capitol Hill
Providence, RI 02908
P: (401) 222-6397
F: (401) 222-1453
E: Cheryl.Burrell@doa.ri.gov

SOUTH CAROLINA
Mr. Raymond Buxton II
Commissioner
Human Affairs Commission
1026 Sumter Street
Columbia, SC 29201
P: (803) 737-7800
E: rbuxton@schac.sc.gov

SOUTH DAKOTA
Ms. Laurie R. Gill
Commissioner
Bureau of Human Resources
500 East Capitol Avenue
Pierre, SD 57501
P: (605) 773-4918
F: (605) 773-6947
E: laurie.gill@state.sd.us

TENNESSEE
Ms. Rebecca R. Hunter
Commissioner
Department of Human Resources
James K. Polk Building, 1st Floor
505 Deaderick Street
Nashville, TN 37243
P: (615) 741-2958
F: (615) 741-7880
E: rebecca.hunter@tn.gov

TEXAS
Mr. Lowell A. Keig
Division Director
Civil Rights Division
Texas Workforce Commission
101 East 15th Street
Austin, TX 78778
P: (512) 463-4432
E: lowell.keig@twc.state.tx.us

U.S. VIRGIN ISLANDS
Ms. Catherine Ann Hendry
Commissioner of Labor
Department of Labor
4401 Sion Farm, Suite 1
Christiansted, VI 00820
P: (340) 773-1994
F: (340) 713-3415
E: chendry@vidol.gov

UTAH
Ms. Heather Gunnarson
Director
Antidiscrimination & Labor Division
160 East 300 South, 3rd Floor
P.O. Box 146600
Salt Lake City, UT 84114
P: (801) 536-7928
E: hgunnarson@utah.gov

VIRGINIA
Mrs. Sara Redding Wilson
Director
Department of Human Resource Management
101 North 14th Street, 12th Floor
Richmond, VA 23219
P: (804) 225-2237
F: (804) 371-7401
E: sara.wilson@dhrm.virginia.gov

WASHINGTON
Mr. Franklin Plaistowe
Assistant Director
State Human Resources
128th 10th Avenue
P.O. Box 47500
Olympia, WA 98504
P: (360) 407-4104
E: StateHR@ofm.wa.gov

WEST VIRGINIA
Ms. Jann Hoke
Director
Equal Employment Opportunity Office
50 Dee Drive
Charleston, WV 25311
P: (304) 558-0400
F: (304) 558-3861
E: Jann.D.Hoke@wv.gov

WISCONSIN
Mr. Robert A. Rodriguez
Administrator
Division of Equal Rights
201 East Washington Avenue
P.O. Box 8928
Madison, WI 53708
P: (608) 266-3345
F: (608) 267-4592
E: erinfo@dwd.wisconsin.gov

WYOMING
Mr. John F. Cox
Director
Department of Workforce Services
614 South Greeley Highway
Cheyenne, WY 82002
P: (307) 777-8728
F: (307) 777-5857
E: john.cox@wyo.gov

Ethics

Administers and enforces the state ethics laws applying to public officials.

ALABAMA
Mr. Thomas B. Albritton
Executive Director
Ethics Commission
100 North Union Street, Suite 104
P.O. Box 4840
Montgomery, AL 36103
P: (334) 242-2997
F: (334) 242-0248
E: info@ethics.alabama.gov

ALASKA
Mr. Jerry D. Anderson
Administrator
Select Committee on Legislative Ethics
P.O. Box 190251
Anchorage, AK 99519
P: (907) 269-0150
F: (907) 269-0152
E: jerry.anderson@akleg.gov

ARKANSAS
Mr. Graham Sloan
Director
State Ethics Commission
501 Woodlane Street, Suite 301N
P.O. Box 1917
Little Rock, AR 72203
P: (501) 324-9600
F: (501) 324-9606
E: graham.sloan@arkansas.gov

CALIFORNIA
Ms. Erin Peth
Executive Director
Fair Political Practices Commission
428 J Street, Suite 620
Sacramento, CA 95814
P: (916) 327-2026
F: (916) 322-0886
E: executivedirector@fppc.ca.gov

COLORADO
Mr. Dino Ioannides
Executive Director
Independent Ethics Commission
1300 Broadway, Suite 240
Denver, CO 80203
P: (303) 625-5697
F: (303) 625-5696
E: dino.ioannides@state.co.us

CONNECTICUT
Ms. Carol Carson
Executive Director
Office of State Ethics
18-20 Trinity Street, Suite 205
Hartford, CT 06106
P: (860) 263-2384
F: (860) 263-2402
E: carol.carson@ct.gov

DELAWARE
Ms. Deborah Moreau
Commission's Legal Counsel
Public Integrity Commission
Margaret O'Neill Building
410 Federal Street, Suite 3
Dover, DE 19901
P: (302) 739-2399
F: (302) 739-2398
E: deborah.moreau@state.de.us

DISTRICT OF COLUMBIA
Ms. Alice P. Miller
Executive Director
Board of Elections & Ethics
441 Fourth Street, Northwest
Suite 250N
Washington, DC 20001
P: (202) 727-6511
E: apmiller@dcboee.org

FLORIDA
Ms. Virlindia Doss
Executive Director
Commission on Ethics
P.O. Drawer 15709
Tallahassee, FL 32317
P: (850) 488-7864
F: (904) 488-3077
E: doss.virlindia@leg.state.fl.us

GEORGIA
Mr. Stefan Ritter
Executive Director
Government Transparency & Campaign Finance Commission
200 Piedmont Avenue, Southeast
Suite 1402, West Tower
Atlanta, GA 30334
P: (404) 463-1980
F: (404) 463-1988
E: gaethics@ethics.ga.gov

HAWAII
Mr. Reynaldo D. Graulty
Chair
State Ethics Commission
1001 Bishop Street, Suite 970
Honolulu, HI 96813
P: (808) 587-0460
F: (808) 587-0470
E: ethics@hawaiiethics.org

IDAHO
The Honorable Lawrence Wasden (R)
Attorney General
Office of the Attorney General
Statehouse
Boise, ID 83720
P: (208) 334-2400
F: (208) 854-8071

ILLINOIS
Mr. Randy Erford
Executive Director
Legislative Ethics Commission
420 Stratton Building
Springfield, IL 62706
P: (217) 558-1561
F: (217) 557-0505
E: randye@ilga.gov

Mr. Chad Fornoff
Executive Director
Executive Ethics Commission
401 South Spring Street
513 William Stratton Building
Springfield, IL 62706
P: (217) 558-1393
F: (217) 558-1399
E: Chad.Fornoff@illinois.gov

INDIANA
Ms. Jennifer Cooper
State Ethics Director
Office of the Inspector General
315 West Ohio Street, Room 104
Indianapolis, IN 46202
P: (317) 234-4108
F: (317) 232-0707
E: JCooper@ig.IN.gov

IOWA
Ms. Megan Tooker
Executive Director & Legal Counsel
Ethics & Campaign Disclosure Board
510 East 12th, Suite 1A
Des Moines, IA 50319
P: (515) 281-3489
F: (515) 281-4073
E: megan.tooker@iowa.gov

KANSAS
Ms. Carol E. Williams
Executive Director
Governmental Ethics Commission
901 South Kansas Avenue
Topeka, KS 66612
P: (785) 296-4219
F: (785) 296-2548
E: ethics@ethics.ks.gov

KENTUCKY
Ms. Kathryn Gabhart
Executive Director
Executive Branch Ethics Commission
#3 Fountain Place
Frankfort, KY 40601
P: (502) 564-7954
E: kathryn.gabhart@ky.gov

Mr. John Schaaf
Executive Director
Legislative Ethics Commission
22 Mill Creek Park
Frankfort, KY 40601
P: (502) 573-2863
F: (502) 573-2929
E: john.schaaf@lrc.ky.gov

LOUISIANA
Ms. Kathleen Allen
Ethics Administrator
Ethics Administration Program
617 North Third Street, Suite 10-36
P.O. Box 4368
Baton Rouge, LA 70821
P: (225) 219-5600
F: (225) 381-7271
E: kathleen.allen@la.gov

MAINE
Mr. Jonathan Wayne
Executive Director
Commission on Governmental Ethics & Election Practices
135 State House Station
Augusta, ME 04333
P: (207) 287-4179
F: (207) 287-6775
E: Jonathan.Wayne@maine.gov

MARYLAND
Mr. Michael W. Lord
Executive Director
State Ethics Commission
45 Calvert Street, 3rd Floor
Annapolis, MD 21401
P: (410) 260-7770
F: (410) 260-7746
E: Michael.Lord@Maryland.gov

MASSACHUSETTS
Mr. David A. Wilson
Executive Director
Ethics Commission
One Ashburton Place, Room 619
Boston, MA 02108
P: (617) 371-9519
F: (617) 723-5851
E: David.A.Wilson@massmail.state.ma.us

MICHIGAN
Mr. John Gnodtke
Executive Secretary
State Board of Ethics
400 South Pine Street
P.O. Box 30002
Lansing, MI 48909
P: (517) 373-3644
F: (517) 373-7690
E: GnodtkeJ@michigan.gov

MINNESOTA
Mr. Jeff Sigurdson
Executive Director
Campaign Finance & Public Disclosure Board
Centennial Office Building, Suite 190
658 Cedar Street
St. Paul, MN 55155
P: (651) 539-1190
F: (651) 539-1196
E: jeff.sigurdson@state.mn.us

MISSISSIPPI
Mr. Tom Hood
Executive Director & Chief Counsel
Ethics Commission
660 North Street, Suite 100-C
P.O. Box 22746
Jackson, MS 39225
P: (601) 359-1285
F: (601) 359-1292
E: info@ethics.state.ms.us

MISSOURI
Mr. James Klahr
Executive Director
Ethics Commission
3411A Knipp Drive
P.O. Box 1370
Jefferson City, MO 65102
P: (573) 751-2020
F: (573) 526-4506
E: helpdesk@mec.mo.gov

MONTANA
Mr. Jeff Mangan
Commissioner
Commissioner of Political Practices
1209 8th Avenue
P.O. Box 202401
Helena, MT 59620
P: (406) 444-2942
F: (406) 444-1643

NEBRASKA
Mr. Frank Daley
Executive Director
Accountability & Disclosure Commission
P.O. Box 95086
Lincoln, NE 68509
P: (402) 471-2522
F: (402) 471-6599
E: frank.daley@nebraska.gov

NEVADA
Ms. Yvonne Navarez-Goodson
Executive Director
Commission on Ethics
704 West Nye Lane, Suite 204
Carson City, NV 89703
P: (775) 687-5469
F: (775) 687-1279
E: ynevarez@ethics.nv.gov

NEW HAMPSHIRE
Mr. Joseph DiBrigida Jr.
Chair
Executive Branch Ethics Committee
33 Capitol Street
Concord, NH 03301
P: (603) 271-3658
F: (603) 271-2110
E: ethics@doj.nh.gov

Mr. Richard M. Lambert
Executive Administrator
Legislative Ethics Committee
State House, Room 112
107 North Main Street
Concord, NH 03301
P: (603) 271-3435
F: (603) 271-6607
E: richard.lambert@leg.state.nh.us

NEW JERSEY
Ms. Susana E. Guerrero
Exeuctive Director
State Ethics Commission
28 West State Street, Room 1407
P.O. Box 082
Trenton, NJ 08625
P: (609) 292-1892
F: (609) 633-9252
E: ethics@ethics.nj.gov

NEW MEXICO
Ms. Kari Fresquez
Interim Elections Director
Bureau of Elections
Secretary of State's Office
325 Don Gaspar, Suite 300
Santa Fe, NM 87501
P: (505) 827-3600
F: (505) 827-8403
E: kari.fresquez@state.nm.us

NEW YORK
Ms. Lisa P. Reid
Executive Director/Counsel
Legislative Ethics Commission
Legislative Office Building
Box 75
Albany, NY 12247
P: (518) 432 7837
F: (518) 432-7838
E: lreid@nysenate.gov

Mr. Michael K. Rozen
Acting Chair
Joint Commission on Public Ethics
540 Broadway
Albany, NY 12207
P: (518) 408-3976
F: (518) 408-3975

NORTH CAROLINA
Mr. Perry Newson
Executive Director
State Ethics Commission
424 North Blount Street
1324 Mail Service Center
Raleigh, NC 27699
P: (919) 814-3600
F: (919) 715-1644
E: ethics.commission@doa.nc.gov

OHIO
Mr. Paul M. Nick
Executive Director
Ethics Commission
30 West Spring Street, L3
Columbus, OH 43215
P: (614) 466-7090
F: (614) 466-8368
E: paul.nick@ethics.ohio.gov

OKLAHOMA
Ms. Ashley Kemp
Executive Director
Ethics Commission
2300 North Lincoln Boulevard, Room B-5
Oklahoma City, OK 73105
P: (405) 521-3451
F: (405) 521-4905
E: ethics@ethics.ok.gov

OREGON
Mr. Ronald A. Bersin
Executive Director
Government Ethics Commission
3218 Pringle Road, Southeast, Suite 220
Salem, OR 97302
P: (503) 378-5105
F: (503) 373-1456
E: ron.a.bersin@oregon.gov

PENNSYLVANIA
Mr. Robert Caruso
Executive Director
State Ethics Commission
P.O. Box 11470
Room 309, Finance Building
Harrisburg, PA 17108
P: (717) 783-1610
F: (717) 787-0806

PUERTO RICO
Ms. Zulma L. Rosario Vega
Executive Director
Office of Governmental Ethics
P.O. Box 194200
San Juan, PR 00919
P: (787) 722-0305
F: (787) 754-0977

RHODE ISLAND
Mr. Kent A. Willever
Executive Director/Chief Prosecutor
Ethics Commission
40 Fountain Street, 8th Floor
Providence, RI 02903
P: (401) 222-3790 Ext. 10
F: (401) 222-3382

SOUTH CAROLINA
Mr. Steven W. Hamm
Interim Executive Director
State Ethics Commission
5000 Thurmond Mall, Suite 250
Columbia, SC 29201
P: (803) 253-4192
F: (803) 253-7539

TENNESSEE
Mr. Drew Rawlins
Executive Director
Ethics Commission
Registry of Election Finance
404 James Robertson Parkway, Suite 104
Nashville, TN 37243
P: (615) 741-7959
F: (615) 532-8905
E: registry.info@tn.gov

Ethics

TEXAS
Ms. Seana Willing
Executive Director
Ethics Commission
201 East 14th Street, 10th Floor
P.O. Box 12070
Austin, TX 78711
P: (512) 463-5800
F: (512) 463-5777
E: seana.willing@ethics.state.tx.us

U.S. VIRGIN ISLANDS
Ms. Pamela Tepper
Solicitor General
Department of Justice
34-38 Kronprindsens Gade
GERS Building, 2nd Floor
St. Thomas, VI 00802
P: (340) 774-5666 Ext. 118
F: (340) 776-3494

UTAH
Ms. Kim Jones Bouck
Executive Director
Independent Legislative Ethics Commission
P.O. Box 141175
Salt Lake City, UT 84114
P: (801) 326-1422
E: kbouck@le.utah.gov

VERMONT
The Honorable Jim Condos (D)
Secretary of State
Office of the Secretary of State
128 State Street
Montpelier, VT 05633
P: (802) 828-2148
F: (802) 828-2496
E: jim.condos@sec.state.vt.us

WASHINGTON
Mr. Keith Buchholz
Counsel
Legislative Ethics Board
P.O. Box 40482
Olympia, WA 98504
P: (360) 786-7343
E: Keith.Buchholz@leg.wa.gov

B.G. Sandahl
Acting Executive Director
Public Disclosure Commission
711 Capitol Way, Room 206
P.O. Box 40908
Olympia, WA 98504
P: (360) 586-1042
F: (360) 753-1112
E: pdc@pdc.wa.gov

WEST VIRGINIA
Ms. Rebecca L. Stepto
Executive Director
Ethics Commission
210 Brooks Street, Suite 300
Charleston, WV 25301
P: (304) 558-0664
F: (304) 558-2169
E: rebecca.l.stepto@wv.gov

WISCONSIN
Mr. Michael Haas
Administrator
Elections Commission
212 East Washington Avenue, 3rd Floor
P.O. Box 7984
Madison, WI 53707
P: (608) 266-0136
F: (608) 267-0500
E: Michael.Haas@wi.gov

WYOMING
The Honorable Ed Murray (R)
Secretary of State
Office of the Secretary of State
2020 Carey Avenue, Suite 600 & 700
Cheyenne, WY 82002
P: (307) 777-7378
F: (307) 777-6217
E: secofstate@wyo.gov

Facilities Management

Maintains, constructs, designs, renovates and delivers basic services to state-owned facilities.

Information provided by:

National Association of State Facilities Administrators
Marcia Stone
Association Manager
1776 Avenue of the States
Lexington, KY 40511
P: (859) 244-8181
F: (859) 244-8001
nasfa@nasfa.net
www.nasfa.net

ALABAMA
Mr. Sean Cassidy
Chief of Services
Services Division, Department of Finance
425 South Union Street
Montgomery, AL 36130
P: (334) 353-0371

ALASKA
Mr. Joel St. Aubin
Director
Statewide Public Facilities
Transportation & Public Facilities
2200 East 42nd Avenue
Anchorage, AK 99508
P: (907) 269-0619
F: (907) 269-0805
E: joel.st.aubin@alaska.gov

ARIZONA
Mr. Matt Halstead
General Manager
Facilities Operations & Maintenance
Department of Administration
100 North 15th Avenue, Suite 202
Phoenix, AZ 85007
P: (602) 542-1579
E: matt.halstead@azdoa.gov

ARKANSAS
Mr. Floyd Farmer
State Engineer
Design Review Section
Building Authority
501 Woodlane, Suite 600
Little Rock, AR 72201
P: (501) 682-5563
E: ffarmer@aba.state.ar.us

CALIFORNIA
Mr. Jemahl Amen
Deputy Director
Facilities Management Division
Department of General Services
707 3rd Street
West Sacramento, CA 95605
P: (916) 376-4700
E: Jemahl.Amen@dgs.ca.gov

COLORADO
Mr. Bradford T. Membel
Director
Division of Facilities Management
Department of Human Services
4112 South Knox Court
Denver, CO 80236
P: (303) 866-7290
F: (303) 866-7299
E: bradford.membel@state.co.us

CONNECTICUT
Mr. David Barkin
Chief Architect
Office of Design & Construction
165 Capitol Avenue, Room 477
Hartford, CT 06106
P: (860) 713-5631

Mr. Allen Herring
Chief Engineer
State of Connecticut
165 Capitol Avenue, Room 469
Hartford, CT 06106
P: (860) 713-5691

DELAWARE
Mr. Mark DeVore
Chief of Engineering & Operations
Division of Facilities Management
Office of Management & Budget
540 South Dupont Highway, Suite 1
Dover, DE 19901
P: (302) 739-5644
E: mark.devore@state.de.us

Mr. Michael M. Svaby
Director
Division of Facilities Management
540 South Dupont Highway, Suite 1
Dover, DE 19901
P: (302) 739-5644
E: michael.svaby@state.de.us

DISTRICT OF COLUMBIA
Ms. Greer Johnson Gillis
Director
Department of General Services
2000 14th Street, Northwest, 8th Floor
Washington, DC 20009
P: (202) 727-2800
E: dgs@dc.gov

FLORIDA
Mr. Tom Berger
Director
Real Estate Development & Management
Department of Management Services
4050 Esplanade Way, Suite 315
Tallahassee, FL 32399
P: (850) 487-9921
E: tom.berger@dms.myflorida.com

GEORGIA
Mr. Steve Fanczi
Deputy Executive Director
State Building Authority
1 Martin Luther King Jr. Drive
Atlanta, GA 30334
P: (404) 463-4683
F: (404) 651-9595
E: sfanczi@doas.ga.gov

Mr. Steve Stancil
State Property Officer
State Building Authority
47 Trinity Avenue Southwest, Suite G02
Atlanta, GA 30334
P: (404) 656-3253
F: (404) 656-6006
E: sstancil@gsfic.ga.gov

HAWAII
Mr. Roderick Becker
Comptroller
Department of Accounting & General Services
1151 Punchbowl Street, Room 412
Honolulu, HI 96813
P: (808) 586-0400
F: (808) 586-0775
E: roderick.k.becker@hawaii.gov

IDAHO
Ms. Jan Frew
Administrator
Division of Public Works
Department of Administration
502 North 4th Street
Boise, ID 83702
P: (208) 332-1912
F: (208) 334-4031
E: jan.frew@adm.idaho.gov

ILLINOIS
Ms. Kathryn Martin
Deputy Director of Operations
State Capital Development Board
W. G. Stratton Building
401 South Spring Street, Room 50
Springfield, IL 62706
P: (312) 814-4441

INDIANA
Mr. Brian Renner
Deputy Commissioner of Facilities/Public Works
Department of Administration
302 West Washington Street, Room E-024
Indianapolis, IN 46204
P: (317) 232-3125
E: brenner@idoa.in.gov

IOWA
Mr. Scott Gustafson
Facilities Engineer I
Support Services & Design
Department of Transportation
800 Lincoln Way
Ames, IA 50010
P: (515) 239-1443
E: scott.gustafson@dot.iowa.gov

KANSAS
Mr. Frank Burnam
Director
Office of Facilities & Property Management
Department of Administration
800 Southwest Jackson, Suite 600
Topeka, KS 66612
P: (785) 291-3989
E: Frank.Burnam@ks.gov

Facilities Management

KENTUCKY
Mr. Paul McPherson
Deputy Commissioner,
Department for Facilities & Support Services
Finance & Administration Cabinet
Finance & Administration Cabinet
403 Wapping Street
Frankfort, KY 40601
P: (502) 564-3590
F: (502) 564-0569

LOUISIANA
Mr. Mark A. Moses
Assistant Commissioner, Facility Planning & Control
State of Louisiana
Division of Administration
P.O. Box 94095
Baton Rouge, LA 70804
P: (225) 342-0820
E: mark.moses@la.gov

MAINE
Mr. Gilbert Bilodeau
Interim Director
Bureau of General Services
77 State House Station
Augusta, ME 04333
P: (207) 624-7314
E: gilbert.bilodeau@maine.gov

MARYLAND
Mr. Ellington E. Churchill Jr.
Cabinet Secretary
Department of General Services
301 West Preston Street, Room 1401
Baltimore, MD 21201
P: (410) 767-4960
E: ellington.churchill2@maryland.gov

MASSACHUSETTS
Ms. Carol Gladstone
Commissioner
Division of Capital Asset Management & Maintenance
Administration & Finance
One Ashburton Place, 15th Floor
Boston, MA 02108
P: (617) 727-4050
F: (617) 727-4050
E: carol.gladstone@state.ma.us

MICHIGAN
Mr. Alton L. Pscholka
State Budget Director
Department of Technology, Management & Budget
111 South Capitol Avenue, 6th Floor
Lansing, MI 48913
P: (517) 373-7560
F: (517) 241-5428
E: Contact-SBO@michigan.gov

MINNESOTA
Mr. Wayne Waslaski
Senior Director, Real Estate & Construction Services
Department of Administration
309 Administration Building
50 Sherburne Avenue
St. Paul, MN 55155
P: (651) 201-2548
E: Wayne.Waslaski@state.mn.us

MISSISSIPPI
Mr. Glenn Kornbrek
Director
Bureau of Buildings, Grounds & Real Property Management
Department of Finance & Administration
501 North West Street, Suite 1401 B
Jackson, MS 39201
P: (601) 359-3402
F: (601) 359-2470
E: Glenn.Kornbrek@dfa.ms.gov

MISSOURI
Mr. Gary Claspill
Design Development Survey Manager
State of Missouri
301 West High Street, Room 730
P.O. Box 809
Jefferson City, MO 65102
P: (573) 751-3740
F: (573) 751-7277
E: gary.claspill@oa.mo.gov

MONTANA
Mr. Thomas O'Connell
Administrator
Architecture & Engineering Division
Department of Administration
P.O. Box 200103
Helena, MT 59620
P: (406) 444-3104
F: (406) 444-3399
E: toconnell@mt.gov

NEBRASKA
Ms. Amber Brannigan
Administrator
State Building Division
Department of Administrative Services
521 South 14th Street, Suite 500
Lincoln, NE 68508
P: (402) 471-2662
E: amber.brannigan@nebraska.gov

NEVADA
Mr. Gustavo Nunez
Administrator
State Public Works Division
Department of Administration
515 East Musser Street, Room 102
Carson City, NV 89701
P: (775) 684-4141
E: gnunez@spwb.state.nv.us

NEW HAMPSHIRE
Ms. Michelle Juliano
Assistant Administrator
Public Works
Public Works, Design & Construction
7 Hazen Drive
Concord, NH 03302
P: (603) 271-1645
E: mjuliano@dot.state.nh.us

NEW JERSEY
Mr. Guy Bocage
Deputy Director
Division of Property Management & Construction
Department of the Treasury
33 West State Street, P.O. Box 230
Trenton, NJ 08625
P: (609) 292-5111
F: (609) 984-2575
E: guy.bocage@treas.state.nj.us

NEW MEXICO
Mr. Christopher Lee
Acting Division Director
Facilities Management Division
General Services Department
2542 Cerrilos Road, P.O. Box 6850
Santa Fe, NM 87502
P: (505) 216-8837
E: christopher.lee@state.nm.us

NEW YORK
Ms. Margaret Larkin
Director, Division of Design & Construction
Department of General Services
Corning Tower 32nd Floor
Empire State Plaza
Albany, NY 12242
P: (518) 474-0337

NORTH CAROLINA
Mr. Latif Kaid
Acting Director
State Construction Office
Department of Administration
1301 Mail Service Center, 116 West Jones
Raleigh, NC 27699
P: (919) 807-4100
F: (919) 807-4110
E: latif.kaid@doa.nc.gov

NORTH DAKOTA
Mr. John Boyle
Director, Facilities Management
Office of Management & Budget
State Capitol Building, 4th Floor
600 East Boulevard Avenue
Bismarck, ND 58505
P: (701) 328-4002
E: jaboyle@nd.gov

Mr. Joel Leapaldt
State Facility Planner, Division of Facility Management
Office of Management & Budget
State Capitol Building, 4th Floor
600 East Boulevard Avenue
Bismarck, ND 58505
P: (701) 328-1968
F: (701) 328-3230
E: jleapaldt@nd.gov

OHIO
Mr. Peter A.J. Gunnell
State Chief Facitilies Officer
General Services
Division/Office of Properties & Facilities
Department of Administrative Services
4200 Surface Road
Columbus, OH 43228
P: (614) 752-0455
E: pete.gunnell@das.state.oh.us

OKLAHOMA
Mr. Mark Sauchuk
Director
Office of Facilities Management
Department of Central Services
2222 North Walnut
Oklahoma City, OK 73105
P: (405) 522-0084
E: mark_sauchuk@dcs.state.ok.us

OREGON
Ms. Debbie Howard
Interim Operations Manager
Facilities Division
Department of Administrative Services
1240 Ferry Street, Southeast, U100
Salem, OR 97301
P: (503) 378-2381

PENNSYLVANIA
Mr. Julien Gaudion
Deputy Secretary for Property & Asset Management
Department of General Services
515 North Office Building
Harrisburg, PA 17125
P: (717) 783-5028
E: jgaudion@state.pa.us

RHODE ISLAND
Mr. Marco Schiappa
Associate Director
Facilities Management
Department of Administration
One Capitol Hill, 2nd Floor
Providence, RI 02908
P: (401) 222-5717
E: MSchiappa@gw.doa.state.ri.us

SOUTH CAROLINA
Ms. Ashlie Lancaster
Deputy Director
Division of Facilities Management & Property Services
Department of Administration
1200 Senate Street, Suite 408
Columbia, SC 29201
P: (803) 737-3880

SOUTH DAKOTA
Ms. Kristi Honeywell
State Engineer
Bureau of Administration
Joe Foss Building
523 East Capitol
Pierre, SD 57501
P: (605) 773-3466
E: Kristi.Honeywell@state.sd.us

TENNESSEE
Mr. Bob Oglesby
Commissioner
Department of General Services
22nd Floor, 312 8th Avenue, North
Nashville, TN 37243
P: (615) 741-2081
E: bob.oglesby@tn.gov

Mr. J. Alan Robertson
Assistant State Architect
State of Tennessee
312 Rosa L. Parks Avenue
Snodgrass Tennessee Tower
Nashville, TN 37243
P: (615) 741-3259
E: alan.robertson@tn.gov

TEXAS
Mr. Harvey Hilderbran
Executive Director
Facilities Commission
1711 San Jacinto
Austin, TX 78701
P: (512) 463-3446
E: Harvey.Hilderbran@tfc.state.tx.us

VERMONT
Mr. William Laferriere
Director of Property Management
Department of Buildings & Property Management
Four Governor Aiken Avenue
Montpelier, VT 05633
P: (802) 828-1115
F: (802) 828-6501
E: bill.laferriere@vermont.gov

VIRGINIA
Mr. Mike Coppa
Acting Director
Division of Engineering & Buildings
Department of General Services
1100 Bank Street, Suite 506
Richmond, VA 23219
P: (804) 786-3263
E: Mike.Coppa@dgs.virginia.gov

WASHINGTON
Mr. Scott Kibler
Assistant Director, Buildings & Grounds
Department of Enterprise Services
P.O. Box 41004
Olympia, WA 98504
P: (360) 407-8524
E: scott.kibler@des.wa.gov

WEST VIRGINIA
Mr. Micheal Q. Evans
Architecture & Engineering Manager
General Services Division
1900 Kanawha Boulevard, East
Charleston, WV 25305
P: (304) 957-7145
E: Micheal.Q.Evans@wv.gov

WISCONSIN
Mr. Keith Beck
Director of Facilities
Division of Facilities Management
101 East Wilson Street
P.O. Box 7866
Madison, WI 53703
P: (608) 266-2645
E: keith.beck@wisconsin.gov

Mr. John Klenke
Administrator, Division of Facilities Development
State Building Commission
131 West Wilson Street
P.O. Box 7866
Madison, WI 53707
P: (608) 266-1031
E: John.Klenke@wisconsin.gov

WYOMING
Mr. Raymond Vigil Jr.
Field Operations & Facilities Program Manager, Facilities Management
Department of Transportation
5300 Bishop Boulevard
Building 6101, Room B-25
Cheyenne, WY 82009
P: (307) 777-4474
F: (307) 777-3801
E: raymond.vigil@dot.state.wy.us

Finance

Responsible for multiple financial functions (budget, payroll, accounting, revenue estimation.)

ALABAMA
Mr. Clinton Carter
Director of Finance
Department of Finance
State Capitol
600 Dexter Avenue, Suite N-105
Montgomery, AL 36130
P: (334) 242-7160
F: (334) 353-3300
E: clinton.carter@finance.alabama.gov

ALASKA
Mr. Scot Arehart
Director
Division of Finance
Department of Administration
P.O. Box 110204
Juneau, AK 99811
P: (907) 465-3435
F: (907) 465-2169
E: scot.arehart@alaska.gov

AMERICAN SAMOA
The Honorable Ueli Tonumaipea
Treasurer
Department of Treasury
American Samoa Government
Pago Pago, AS 96799
P: (684) 633-4155
F: (684) 633-4100
E: ueli.tonumaipea@tr.as.gov

ARIZONA
Mr. D. Clark Partridge
State Comptroller
General Accounting Office
100 North 15th Avenue, Suite 302
Phoenix, AZ 85007
P: (602) 542-5405
F: (602) 542-5749
E: gaowebmr@azdoa.gov

ARKANSAS
Mr. Larry Walther
Director
Department of Finance & Administration
1509 West 7th Street
DFA Building, Room 401
Little Rock, AR 72201
P: (501) 682-2242
F: (501) 682-1029
E: larry.walther@dfa.arkansas.gov

CALIFORNIA
Mr. Michael Cohen
Director
Department of Finance
915 L Street
Sacramento, CA 95814
P: (916) 445-3878
E: michael.cohen@dof.ca.gov

CONNECTICUT
Mr. Benjamin Barnes
Secretary
Office of Policy & Management
450 Capitol Avenue
Hartford, CT 06106
P: (860) 418-6500
F: (860) 418-6487
E: Ben.Barnes@Ct.gov

DELAWARE
Mr. Richard J. Geisenberger
Secretary of Finance
Department of Finance
Carvel State Building, 8th Floor
820 North French Street
Wilmington, DE 19801
P: (302) 577-8987
F: (302) 577-8982

GUAM
Ms. Christine Baleto
Director
Department of Administration
P.O. Box 884
Hagatna, GU 96928
P: (671) 475-1101
F: (671) 477-6788

HAWAII
The Honorable Wesley Machida
Director of Finance
Department of Budget & Finance
P.O. Box 150
Honolulu, HI 96810
P: (808) 586-1518
F: (808) 586-1976
E: hi.budgetandfinance@hawaii.gov

IDAHO
Mr. Gavin M. Gee
Director
Department of Finance
800 Park Boulevard, Suite 200
P.O. Box 83720
Boise, ID 83720
P: (208) 332-8010
F: (208) 332-8097
E: gavin.gee@finance.idaho.gov

ILLINOIS
Mr. Scott Harry
Director
Governor's Office of Management & Budget
603 Stratton Building
Springfield, IL 62706
P: (217) 782-4520
F: (217) 524-4876
E: Scott.Harry@illinois.gov

INDIANA
Mr. Jason D. Dudich
Director
State Budget Agency
200 West Washington Street, Room 212
Indianapolis, IN 46204
P: (317) 232-5610
F: (317) 233-3323
E: jdudich@gov.in.gov

IOWA
Ms. Courtney M. Kay-Decker
Director
Department of Revenue
Hoover State Office Building
1305 East Walnut Street
Des Moines, IA 50319
P: (515) 281-3204
E: courtney.decker@iowa.gov

KANSAS
Ms. Colleen Becker
Director
Office of Financial Management
Eisenhower State Office Building
700 Southwest Harrison Street, Suite 101
Topeka, KS 66603
P: (785) 296-0534
E: colleen.becker@da.ks.gov

KENTUCKY
Mr. William Landrum III
Secretary
Finance & Administration Cabinet
383 Capitol Annex
Frankfort, KY 40601
P: (502) 564-4240
E: william.landrum@ky.gov

LOUISIANA
Ms. Marella Haughton
Deputy Undersecretary
Office of Finance & Support Services
Division of Administration
P.O. Box 94095
Baton Rouge, LA 70804
P: (225) 342-0700
F: (225) 342-2606
E: Marella.Houghton@la.gov

MAINE
Mr. Richard W. Rosen
Commissioner
Department of Administrative & Financial Services
78 State House Station
Augusta, ME 04333
P: (207) 624-7800
F: (207) 624-7804
E: richard.rosen@maine.gov

MARYLAND
Mr. David R. Brinkley
Secretary
Department of Budget & Management
45 Calvert Street
Annapolis, MD 21401
P: (410) 260-7041
F: (410) 974-2585
E: David.Brinkley@maryland.gov

MICHIGAN
Mr. Alton L. Pscholka
State Budget Director
State Budget Office
111 South Capitol Avenue, 6th Floor
Lansing, MI 48913
P: (517) 373-7560
F: (517) 241-5428
E: Contact-SBO@michigan.gov

MINNESOTA
Mr. Myron Frans
Commissioner
Management & Budget
658 Cedar Street, Suite 400
St. Paul, MN 55155
P: (651) 201-8011
F: (651) 296-8685
E: myron.frans@state.mn.us

MISSISSIPPI
Ms. Laura Jackson
Executive Director
Department of Finance & Administration
501 North West, 701 Woolfolk Building
P.O. Box 267
Jackson, MS 39205
P: (601) 359-3402
F: (601) 359-5525
E: laura.jackson@dfa.ms.gov

Finance

MISSOURI
Ms. Debbie Hardman
Commissioner of Finance
Division of Finance
Truman State Office Building, Room 630
P.O. Box 716
Jefferson City, MO 65102
P: (573) 751-3242
F: (573) 751-9192
E: finance@dof.mo.gov

MONTANA
Mr. Dan Villa
Budget Director
Office of Budget & Program Planning
State Capitol, Room 277
P.O. Box 200802
Helena, MT 59620
P: (406) 444-3616
F: (406) 444-4670
E: dvilla@mt.gov

NEBRASKA
Mr. Byron L. Diamond
Director
Department of Administrative Services
1526 K Street, Suite 250
Lincoln, NE 68508
P: (402) 471-2331
E: byron.diamond@nebraska.gov

NEVADA
Mr. Patrick Cates
Director
Department of Administration
515 East Musser Street
Room 300
Carson City, NV 89701
P: (775) 684-0294
F: (775) 684-0260
E: pcates@admin.nv.gov

NEW HAMPSHIRE
Ms. Vicki Quiram
Commissioner
Department of Administrative Services
25 Capitol Street
State House Annex, Room 120
Concord, NH 03301
P: (603) 271-3201
F: (603) 271-6600
E: vicki.quiram@nh.gov

NEW JERSEY
Mr. David A. Ridolfino
Director
Office of Management & Budget
Department of Treasury
33 West State Street, P.O. Box 221
Trenton, NJ 08625
P: (609) 292-6746
F: (609) 633-8179
E: david.ridolfino@treas.state.nj.us

NORTH CAROLINA
Mr. Charles Perusse
State Budget Director
Office of State Budget & Management
20320 Mail Service Center
Raleigh, NC 27699
P: (919) 807-4717
E: charles.perusse@osbm.nc.gov

NORTH DAKOTA
Ms. Sheila Peterson
Director, Fiscal Management Division
Office of Management & Budget
600 East Boulevard Avenue
Department 110
Bismarck, ND 58505
P: (701) 328-2680
F: (701) 328-4230
E: omb@nd.gov

Ms. Pam Sharp
Director
Office of Management & Budget
600 East Boulevard Avenue
Department 110
Bismarck, ND 58505
P: (701) 328-4606
F: (701) 328-3230
E: psharp@nd.gov

OKLAHOMA
Mr. Preston L. Doerflinger
Secretary & Director of Finance
Office of Management & Enterprise Services
2300 North Lincoln Boulevard, Room 122
Oklahoma City, OK 73105
P: (405) 521-2141
F: (405) 521-3902

OREGON
Mr. George M. Naughton
Chief Financial Officer
Chief Financial Office
Department of Administrative Services
155 Cottage Street, Northeast, U10
Salem, OR 97301
P: (503) 378-5460
F: (503) 373-7643
E: george.m.naughton@oregon.gov

PENNSYLVANIA
Mr. Randy Albright
Secretary of the Budget
Office of the Budget
19th Floor, Harristown 2
333 Market Street
Harrisburg, PA 17101
P: (717) 787-2542
F: (717) 783-3368
E: budget@pa.gov

PUERTO RICO
Mr. Luis F. Batista Cruz
Director
Office of Management & Budget
P.O. Box 9023228
San Juan, PR 00902
P: (787) 725-9420
F: (787) 722-0299

RHODE ISLAND
Mr. Thomas A. Mullaney
Executive Director/State Budget Officer
Budget Office
Office of Management & Budget
One Capitol Hill, 4th Floor
Providence, RI 02908
P: (401) 222-6300
F: (401) 222-6436
E: thomas.mullaney@budget.ri.gov

SOUTH DAKOTA
Ms. Liza Clark
Chief Financial Officer & Commissioner
Bureau of Finance & Management
500 East Capitol Avenue
Pierre, SD 57501
P: (605) 773-3411
F: (605) 773-4711
E: liza.clark@state.sd.us

TENNESSEE
Mr. Larry Martin
Commissioner
Department of Finance & Administration
312 Rosa Parks Avenue, 18th Floor
Nashville, TN 37243
P: (615) 741-4806
E: Larry.Martin@tn.gov

TEXAS
The Honorable Glenn Hegar (R)
Comptroller of Public Accounts
Office of the Comptroller of Public Accounts
LBJ State Office Building, 1st Floor
111 East 17th Street
Austin, TX 78774
P: (512) 463-4444
F: (512) 463-4902
E: glenn.hegar@cpa.state.tx.us

UTAH
Mr. John C. Reidhead
Director
Division of Finance
2110 State Office Building
Salt Lake City, UT 84114
P: (801) 538-3095
F: (801) 538-3244
E: jreidhead@utah.gov

VERMONT
Mr. Andrew Pallito
Commissioner
Department of Finance & Management
109 State Street
Montpelier, VT 05609
P: (802) 828-2376
F: (802) 828-2428
E: andy.pallito@vermont.gov

VIRGINIA
The Honorable Richard D. Brown
Secretary of Finance
Office of the Secretary of Finance
1111 East Broad Street
P.O. Box 1475
Richmond, VA 23218
P: (804) 786-1148
F: (804) 692-0676
E: Ric.Brown@governor.virginia.gov

WASHINGTON
Mr. David Schumacher
Director
Office of Financial Management
P.O. Box 43113
Olympia, WA 98504
P: (360) 902-0530
F: (360) 664-2832
E: ofm.administration
@ofm.wa.gov

WEST VIRGINIA
Mr. Dave Hardy
Cabinet Secretary
Department of Revenue
State Capitol
Building 1, W-300
Charleston, WV 25305
P: (304) 558-1017
F: (304) 558-2324

WISCONSIN
Mr. Waylon Hurlburt
Administrator
Division of Executive Budget &
Finance
P.O. Box 7864
Madison, WI 53707
P: (608) 266-1035
E: WaylonR.Hurlburt
@wisconsin.gov

WYOMING
The Honorable Cynthia I.
Cloud (R)
State Auditor
Office of the State Auditor
State Capitol, Suite 114
200 West 24th Street
Cheyenne, WY 82002
P: (307) 777-7831
F: (307) 777-6983
E: SAOAdmin@wyo.gov

Firearms

Conducts background checks for firearm purchases, issues weapon permits, regulates firearm sales, and oversees all other matters relating to the buying and selling of firearms within the state.

ALABAMA
The Honorable Steve Marshall (R)
Attorney General
Office of the Attorney General
501 Washington Avenue
P.O. Box 300152
Montgomery, AL 36130
P: (334) 242-7300

ALASKA
Mr. Walt Monegan
Commissioner
Department of Public Safety
5700 East Tudor Road
Anchorage, AK 99507
P: (907) 269-5086
F: (907) 269-4543
E: walt.monegan@alaska.gov

AMERICAN SAMOA
Mr. Le'i S. Thompson
Commissioner
Department of Public Safety
American Samoa Government
P.O. Box 1086
Pago Pago, AS 96799
P: (684) 633-1111
F: (684) 633-7296
E: lei.thompson@dps.as.gov

ARIZONA
Ms. Donna J. Street
Supervisor
Concealed Weapons Permit Unit
Department of Public Safety
P.O. Box 6488
Phoenix, AZ 85005
P: (602) 256-6280
F: (602) 223-2928

ARKANSAS
Colonel Bill Bryant
Director
State Police
1 State Police Plaza Drive
Little Rock, AR 72209
P: (501) 618-8299
F: (501) 618-8222
E: info@asp.arkansas.gov

CALIFORNIA
Mr. Stephen Lindley
Chief
Bureau of Firearms
P.O. Box 820200
Sacramento, CA 94203
P: (916) 227-7527
F: (916) 227-7480
E: stephen.lindley@doj.ca.gov

COLORADO
Mr. Michael Rankin
Director
Bureau of Investigation
690 Kipling Street, Suite 4000
Lakewood, CO 80215
P: (303) 239-4203
F: (303) 235-0568
E: michael.rankin@state.co.us

CONNECTICUT
Mr. Frank P. Blando
Chair
Board of Firearms Permit Examiners
Office of Governmental Accountability
20 Trinity Street, 5th Floor
Hartford, CT 06106
P: (860) 256-2947
F: (860) 256-2997
E: bfpe@ct.gov

DELAWARE
The Honorable Matthew Denn (D)
Attorney General
Office of the Attorney General
Carvel State Office Building
820 North French Street
Wilmington, DE 19801
P: (302) 577-8338
E: matthew.denn@state.de.us

DISTRICT OF COLUMBIA
Mr. Peter Newsham
Chief of Police
Metropolitan Police Department
300 Indiana Avenue, Northwest
Room 5059
Washington, DC 20001
P: (202) 727-9099
F: (202) 727-4106
E: mpd@dc.gov

FLORIDA
Mr. Rick Swearingen
Commissioner
Department of Law Enforcement
2331 Phillips Road
P.O. Box 1489
Tallahassee, FL 32302
P: (850) 410-7011
E: RickSwearingen@fdle.state.fl.us

GEORGIA
Mr. Vernon M. Keenan
Director
Bureau of Investigation
3121 Panthersville Road
Decatur, GA 30034
P: (404) 244-2501
F: (404) 270-8352
E: vernon.keenan@gbi.ga.gov

IDAHO
The Honorable Lawrence Wasden (R)
Attorney General
Office of the Attorney General
Statehouse
Boise, ID 83720
P: (208) 334-2400
F: (208) 854-8071

ILLINOIS
Mr. Leo P. Schmitz
Director
State Police
801 South 7th Street, Suite 1100 – S
Springfield, IL 62703
P: (217) 782-7263
E: askisp@isp.state.il.us

INDIANA
Mr. Douglas G. Carter
Superintendent
State Police
Indiana Government Center North
100 North Senate Avenue
Indianapolis, IN 46204
P: (317) 232-8248
E: ISP@isp.in.gov

KANSAS
The Honorable Derek Schmidt (R)
Attorney General
Office of the Attorney General
120 Southwest 10th Avenue, 2nd Floor
Topeka, KS 66612
P: (785) 296-2215
F: (785) 296-6296

Mr. Kirk D. Thompson
Director
Bureau of Investigation
1620 Southwest Tyler Street
Topeka, KS 66612
P: (785) 296-8200

KENTUCKY
Mr. Richard Sanders
Commissioner
State Police
919 Versailles Road
Frankfort, KY 40601
F: (502) 573-1479

LOUISIANA
Colonel Kevin W. Reeves
Superintendent
State Police
Public Safety Services
7919 Independence Boulevard
Baton Rouge, LA 70806
P: (225) 925-6118

MAINE
Colonel Robert A. Williams
Chief
State Police
42 State House Station
45 Commerce Drive
Augusta, ME 04333
P: (207) 624-7200
E: robert.a.williams@maine.gov

MARYLAND
Colonel William Pallozzi
Superintendent
Department of State Police
1201 Reisterstown Road
Pikesville, MD 21208
P: (410) 653-4219
E: msp.superintendent@maryland.gov

MASSACHUSETTS
Colonel Richard D. McKeon
Superintendent
State Police
Office of Public Safety & Security
470 Worcester Road
Framingham, MA 01702
P: (508) 820-2300
F: (617) 727-6874

MICHIGAN
Colonel Kriste Kibbey Etue
Director
State Police
P.O. Box 30634
Lansing, MI 48909
P: (517) 332-2521
F: (517) 241-0991
E: EtueK@michigan.gov

MINNESOTA
Ms. Ramona Dohman
Commissioner
Department of Public Safety
445 Minnesota Street, Suite 199
St. Paul, MN 55101
P: (651) 201-7160
F: (651) 297-5728
E: Mona.Dohman@state.mn.us

MISSISSIPPI
Lieutenant Odis Easterling
Director
Firearm Permits Unit
Department of Public Safety
P.O. Box 958
Jackson, MS 39205
P: (601) 987-1268
E: oeasterling@dps.ms.gov

MONTANA
The Honorable Tim Fox (R)
Attorney General
Department of Justice
Justice Building
215 North Sanders
Helena, MT 59620
P: (406) 444-2026
F: (406) 444-3549
E: contactdoj@mt.gov

NEBRASKA
Colonel Bradley Rice
Superintendent of Law
Enforcement & Public Safety
State Patrol
1600 Highway 2
Lincoln, NE 68502
P: (402) 471-4545
F: (402) 479-4002
E: Brad.Rice@nebraska.gov

NEW HAMPSHIRE
Mr. John J. Barthelmes
Commissioner
Department of Safety
James H. Hayes Safety Building
33 Hazen Drive
Concord, NH 03305
P: (603) 223-3889
F: (603) 271-3903
E: john.barthelmes
@dos.nh.gov

NEW JERSEY
Colonel Joseph R. Fuentes
Superintendent
State Police
P.O. Box 7068
West Trenton, NJ 08628
P: (609) 882-2000
F: (609) 530-4383

NEW MEXICO
Mr. Scott Weaver
Cabinet Secretary
Department of Public Safety
4491 Cerrillos Road
P.O. Box 1628
Santa Fe, NM 87504
P: (505) 827-3370
F: (505) 827-3434

NEW YORK
Mr. Joseph D'Amico
Superintendent
State Police
1220 Washington Avenue,
Building 22
Albany, NY 12226
P: (518) 457-6721
E: nyspmail@troopers.ny.gov

NORTHERN MARIANA ISLANDS
Mr. Robert A. Guerrero
Commissioner
Department of Public Safety
Jose M. Sablan Building
Caller Box 10007
Saipan, MP 96950
P: (670) 664-9022
F: (670) 664-9027

OHIO
Colonel John Born
Director
Department of Public Safety
1970 West Broad Street
P.O. Box 182081
Columbus, OH 43218
P: (614) 466-3383
F: (614) 466-0433

OKLAHOMA
Mr. Stan Florence
Director
State Bureau of Investigation
6600 North Harvey
Oklahoma City, OK 73116
P: (405) 848-6724

OREGON
Captain Alex Gardner
Director
Forensic Services Division
State Department of Police
3565 Trelstad Avenue
Salem, OR 97317
P: (503) 934-0237
F: (503) 363-5475
E: Alexander.Gardner
@state.or.us

PENNSYLVANIA
Colonel Tyree C. Blocker
Commissioner
State Police
1800 Elmerton Avenue
Harrisburg, PA 17110
P: (717) 783-5599
F: (717) 787-2948

SOUTH CAROLINA
Mr. Mark A. Keel
Chief
State Law Enforcement Division
4400 Broad River Road
Columbia, SC 29210
P: (803) 896-9223
F: (803) 896-7588

TENNESSEE
Ms. Lisa Knight
Program Director
Handgun Carry Permits
Department of Safety &
Homeland Security
P.O. Box 945
Nashville, TN 37243
P: (615) 251-8590
F: (615) 532-3056

TEXAS
Mr. Steve McCraw
Director
Department of Public Safety
5805 North Lamar Boulevard
P.O. Box 4087
Austin, TX 78773
P: (512) 424-2000
F: (512) 483-5708

U.S. VIRGIN ISLANDS
Mr. Delroy Richards Sr.
Commissioner
Police Department
Farrelly Criminal Justice Center
Charlotte Amalie
St. Thomas, VI 00802
P: (340) 774-2211
F: (340) 715-5517

UTAH
Ms. Alice Moffat
Bureau Chief
Bureau of Criminal
Indentification
Department of Public Safety
3888 West 5400 South
Taylorsville, UT 84129
P: (801) 965-4445
F: (801) 965-4749
E: AERICKSO@utah.gov

VIRGINIA
Colonel W. Steven Flaherty
Superintendent
Department of State Police
7700 Midlothian Turnpike
P.O. Box 27472
Richmond, VA 23261
P: (804) 674-2000
F: (804) 674-2936
E: steve.flaherty
@vsp.virginia.gov

WEST VIRGINIA
Colonel J. L. Cahill
Superintendent
State Police
725 Jefferson Road
South Charleston, WV 25309
P: (304) 746-2115

WYOMING
Mr. Steve Woodson
Director
Division of Criminal
Investigation
Combined Laboratories Building
208 South College Drive
Cheyenne, WY 82002
P: (307) 777-7181
F: (307) 777-7252

Fish and Wildlife

Protects and manages fish and wildlife resources and enforces the state's fish and game laws.

ALABAMA
Mr. Charles Sykes
Director
Division of Wildlife & Freshwater Fisheries
Conservation & Natural Resources
64 North Union Street
Montgomery, AL 36130
P: (334) 242-3465
F: (334) 242-3032
E: dcnr.wffdirector@dcnr.alabama.gov

ALASKA
Mr. Sam Cotten
Commissioner
Department of Fish & Game
P.O. Box 25526
Juneau, AK 99802
P: (907) 465-6141
F: (907) 465-2332
E: sam.cotten@alaska.gov

ARIZONA
Mr. Larry D. Voyles
Director
Game & Fish Department
5000 West Carefree Highway
Phoenix, AZ 85086
P: (623) 942-3000

ARKANSAS
Mr. Jeff Crow
Director
Game & Fish Commission
#2 Natural Resources Drive
Little Rock, AR 72205
P: (501) 978-7370
E: Jeffrey.Crow@agfc.ar.gov

CALIFORNIA
Mr. Charlton H. Bonham
Director
Department of Fish & Wildlife
1416 Ninth Street, 12th Floor
P.O. Box 944209
Sacramento, CA 94244
P: (916) 653-7667
F: (916) 653-7387
E: director@wildlife.ca.gov

COLORADO
Ms. Madeleine West
Director
Division of Parks & Wildlife
1313 Sherman Street, Room 718
Denver, CO 80203
P: (303) 866-3311
E: madeleine.west@state.co.us

CONNECTICUT
Mr. William Hyatt
Bureau Chief
Bureau of Natural Resources
79 Elm Street
Hartford, CT 06106
P: (860) 424-3010
F: (860) 424-4070
E: william.hyatt@ct.gov

DELAWARE
Mr. Dave Saveikis
Director
Division of Fish & Wildlife
89 Kings Highway
Dover, DE 19901
P: (302) 739-9910
F: (302) 739-6157
E: David.Saveikis@state.de.us

DISTRICT OF COLUMBIA
Mr. Bryan King
Associate Director
Fisheries & Wildlife Division
Department of the Environment
51 N Street, Northeast, 5th Floor
Washington, DC 20002
P: (202) 997-9607
F: (202) 535-1373
E: bryan.king@dc.gov

FLORIDA
Mr. Nick Wiley
Executive Director
Fish & Wildlife Conservation Commission
620 South Meridian Street
Tallahassee, FL 32399
P: (850) 487-3796
F: (850) 921-5786

GEORGIA
Mr. Rusty Garrison
Director
Wildlife Resources Division
2067 U.S. Highway 278, Southeast
Social Circle, GA 30025
P: (770) 918-6401
F: (706) 557-3030

GUAM
Mr. Matthew L.G. Sablan
Director
Division of Aquatic & Wildlife Resources
Department of Agriculture
163 Dairy Road
Mangilao, GU 96923
P: (671) 300-7965
F: (671) 734-6569

HAWAII
Ms. Suzanne D. Case
Chairperson
Department of Land & Natural Resources
Kalanimoku Building
1151 Punchbowl Street
Honolulu, HI 96813
P: (808) 587-0400
F: (808) 587-0390
E: dlnr@hawaii.gov

IDAHO
Mr. Virgil Moore
Director
Fish & Game Department
Box 25, 600 South Walnut
Boise, ID 83707
P: (208) 334-3772
F: (208) 334-2148
E: virgil.moore@idfg.idaho.gov

ILLINOIS
Mr. Wayne Rosenthal
Director
Department of Natural Resources
One Natural Resources Way
Springfield, IL 62702
P: (217) 782-6302
F: (217) 785-9236
E: wayne.rosenthal@illinois.gov

INDIANA
Mr. Mark Reiter
Director
Fish & Wildlife - Central Office
Department of Natural Resources
402 West Washington Street, Room W-273
Indianapolis, IN 46204
P: (317) 232-8129
F: (317) 232-8150
E: MREITER@dnr.IN.gov

IOWA
Mr. Chuck Gipp
Director
Department of Natural Resources
4th Floor, Wallace Building
502 East 9th Street
Des Moines, IA 50319
P: (515) 725-8282
F: (515) 281-8895
E: chuck.gipp@dnr.iowa.gov

KANSAS
Mr. Keith Sexson
Assistant Secretary, Wildlife Operations
Department of Wildlife & Parks
512 Southeast 25th Avenue
Pratt, KS 67124
P: (316) 672-5911
F: (316) 672-6020

KENTUCKY
Mr. Greg Johnson
Commissioner
Department of Fish & Wildlife Resources
One Sportsman's Lane
Frankfort, KY 40601
P: (502) 564-3400
F: (502) 564-0506

LOUISIANA
Mr. Charlie Melancon
Secretary
Department of Wildlife & Fisheries
2000 Quail Drive
P.O. Box 98000
Baton Rouge, LA 70898
P: (225) 765-2800
F: (225) 765-0948

MAINE
Mr. Chandler E. Woodcock
Commissioner
Department of Inland Fisheries & Wildlife
41 State House Station
Augusta, ME 04333
P: (207) 287-8000
F: (207) 287-6395
E: chandler.woodcock@maine.gov

MARYLAND
Mr. Paul Peditto
Director
Wildlife & Heritage Service
Department of Natural Resources
580 Taylor Avenue, E-1
Annapolis, MD 21401
P: (410) 260-8549
F: (410) 260-8595
E: ppeditto@dnr.state.md.us

MASSACHUSETTS
Mr. James Buckley
Director
Division of Fisheries & Wildlife
100 Hartwell Street, Suite 230
West Boylan, MA 01583
P: (508) 389-6300
E: masswildlife@state.ma.us

MICHIGAN
Mr. Keith Creagh
Director
Department of Natural Resources
Executive Division
P.O. Box 30028
Lansing, MI 48909
P: (517) 284-6367
E: DNR-Director@michigan.gov

MINNESOTA
Mr. Jim Leach
Director
Division of Fish & Wildlife
Department of Natural Resources
500 Lafayette Road
St. Paul, MN 55155
P: (651) 259-5180
F: (651) 297-7272
E: James.Leach@state.mn.us

MISSISSIPPI
Dr. Sam Polles
Executive Director
Department of Wildlife, Fisheries & Parks
2906 Building
P.O. Box 451
Jackson, MS 39205
P: (601) 432-2001
F: (601) 432-2024

MISSOURI
Ms. Sara Parker Pauley
Director
Department of Conservation
2901 West Truman Boulevard
P.O. Box 176
Jefferson City, MO 65102
P: (573) 751-4732
F: (573) 751-7627
E: sara.pauley@ded.mo.gov

MONTANA
Ms. Martha Williams
Director
Department of Fish, Wildlife & Parks
1420 East Sixth Avenue
P.O. Box 200701
Helena, MT 59620
P: (406) 444-3186
F: (406) 444-4952
E: fwpgen@mt.gov

NEBRASKA
Mr. James Douglas
Director
Game & Parks Commission
2200 North 33rd, Box 30370
Lincoln, NE 68510
P: (402) 471-5539
F: (402) 471-5528
E: jim.douglas@nebraska.gov

NEVADA
Mr. Tony Wasley
Director
Department of Wildlife
1100 Valley Road
Reno, NV 89512
P: (775) 688-1500
F: (775) 688-1207
E: twasley@ndow.org

NEW HAMPSHIRE
Mr. Glenn Normandeau
Executive Director
Fish & Game Department
11 Hazen Drive
Concord, NH 03301
P: (603) 271-3511
F: (603) 271-1438
E: glenn.normandeau@wildlife.nh.gov

NEW JERSEY
Mr. Larry Herrighty
Director
Division of Fish & Wildlife
Department of Environmental Protection
501 East State Street, 3rd Floor
Trenton, NJ 08625
P: (609) 292-9410
F: (609) 292-8207

NEW MEXICO
Ms. Alexa Sandoval
Director
Department of Game & Fish
One Wildlife Way
Santa Fe, NM 87507
P: (505) 476-8008
E: alexandra.sandoval@state.nm.us

NEW YORK
Mr. Anthony Wilkinson
Director
Division of Fish, Wildlife & Marine Resources
625 Broadway
Albany, NY 12233
P: (518) 402-8924
F: (518) 402-9027
E: fwinfo@gw.dec.state.ny.us

NORTH CAROLINA
Mr. Gordon Myers
Executive Director
Wildlife Resources Commission
1722 Mail Service Center
1751 Varsity Drive, Room 451
Raleigh, NC 27695
P: (919) 707-0151
F: (919) 707-0020
E: gordon.myers@ncwildlife.org

NORTH DAKOTA
Mr. Terry Steinwand
Director
Game & Fish Department
100 North Bismarck Expressway
Bismarck, ND 58501
P: (701) 328-6305
F: (701) 328-6352
E: tsteinwa@nd.gov

OHIO
Mr. Ray Petering
Chief
Division of Wildlife
2045 Morse Road, Building G
Columbus, OH 43229
P: (614) 265-6304
F: (614) 262-1143

OKLAHOMA
Mr. J.D. Strong
Director
Department of Wildlife Conservation
P.O. Box 53465
Oklahoma City, OK 73152
P: (405) 522-6279
F: (405) 521-6505

OREGON
Mr. Curt Melcher
Director
Department of Fish & Wildlife
4034 Fairview Industrial Drive Southeast
Salem, OR 97302
P: (503) 947-6044
F: (503) 947-6042

PENNSYLVANIA
Mr. John Arway
Executive Director
Fish & Boat Commission
P.O. Box 67000
Harrisburg, PA 17106
P: (717) 705-7801
F: (717) 705-7802

Mr. Bryan J. Burhans
Executive Director
Game Commission
2001 Elmerton Avenue
Harrisburg, PA 17110
P: (717) 787-3633
F: (717) 772-0502

PUERTO RICO
Mr. Miguel A. Garcia
Director, Terrestrial Resources Division
Department of Natural & Environmental Resources
Bureau of Fish & Wildlife
P.O. Box 366147
San Juan, PR 00936
P: (787) 723-3090
F: (787) 724-0365

Mr. Craig G. Lilyestrom
Director, Marine Resources Division
Department of Natural & Environmental Resources
P.O. Box 366147
San Juan, PR 00936
P: (787) 723-3090
F: (787) 724-0365

RHODE ISLAND
Ms. Catherine Sparks
Chief
Division of Fish & Wildlife
235 Promenade Street
Providence, RI 02908
P: (401) 222-4700
E: catherine.sparks@dem.ri.gov

SOUTH CAROLINA
Mr. Paul Johansen
Chief
Wildlife Resources Section
Division of Natural Resources
324 4th Avenue
South Charleston, SC 25303
P: (304) 558-2771
F: (304) 558-3147
E: Paul.R.Johansen@wv.gov

Fish and Wildlife

Mr. Alvin A. Taylor
Director
Department of Natural Resources
1000 Assembly Street
P.O. Box 167
Columbia, SC 29202
P: (803) 734-4007
F: (803) 734-9809
E: taylora@dnr.sc.gov

SOUTH DAKOTA
Ms. Kelly Helper
Secretary
Games, Fish & Parks Department
523 East Capitol Avenue
Pierre, SD 57501
P: (605) 773-3718
F: (605) 773-6245

TENNESSEE
Mr. Ed Carter
Executive Director
Wildlife Resources Agency
P.O. Box 40747
Nashville, TN 37204
P: (615) 781-6552
F: (615) 781-6551

TEXAS
Mr. Carter P. Smith
Executive Director
Parks & Wildlife Department
4200 Smith School Road
Austin, TX 78744
P: (512) 389-4800
F: (512) 389-4814

U.S. VIRGIN ISLANDS
Mr. Roy Pemberton
Director
Division of Fish & Wildlife
6291 Estate Nazareth 101
St. Thomas, VI 00802
P: (340) 775-6762
F: (340) 775-3972
E: roy.pemberton@dpnr.gov.vi

UTAH
Mr. Greg Sheehan
Director
Division of Wildlife Resources
1594 West North Temple, Suite 2110
P.O. Box 146301
Salt Lake City, UT 84114
P: (801) 538-4702
F: (801) 538-4709
E: gregsheehan@utah.gov

VERMONT
Mr. Louis Porter
Commissioner
Department of Fish & Wildlife
103 South Main Street, 10 South
Waterbury, VT 05671
P: (802) 241-3700
E: louis.porter@state.vt.us

VIRGINIA
Mr. Bob Duncan
Director
Department of Game & Inland Fisheries
4010 West Broad Street, Box 11104
Richmond, VA 23230
P: (804) 367-9231
F: (804) 367-0405
E: bob.duncan@dgif.virginia.gov

WASHINGTON
Mr. Jim Unsworth
Director
Department of Fish & Wildlife
600 Capitol Way North
Olympia, WA 98501
P: (360) 902-2200
F: (360) 902-2947
E: director@dfw.wa.gov

WISCONSIN
Ms. Cathy Stepp
Secretary
Department of Natural Resources
101 South Webster Street
P.O. Box 7921
Madison, WI 53707
P: (608) 266-2121
F: (608) 266-6983
E: DNRSecretary@Wisconsin.gov

WYOMING
Mr. Scott Talbott
Director
Game & Fish Department
5400 Bishop Boulevard
Cheyenne, WY 82006
P: (307) 777-4600
F: (307) 777-4699

Gaming Officials

Head of the entity that administers and regulates state gaming laws.

ALASKA
Mr. Ken Alper
Director
Tax Division
Department of Revenue
P.O. Box 110420
Juneau, AK 99811
P: (907) 465-8221
F: (907) 465-2375
E: ken.alper@alaska.gov

ARIZONA
Mr. Dan Bergin
Director
Department of Gaming
1110 West Washington Street, Suite 450
Phoenix, AZ 85007
P: (602) 771-4263
F: (602) 255-3883

ARKANSAS
Mr. Cecil Alexander
Chair
Racing Commission
1515 Building
1515 West 7th Street, Suite 505
Little Rock, AR 72201
P: (501) 682-1467
F: (501) 682-5273

COLORADO
Mr. Flavio Quintana
Director
Division of Gaming
Department of Revenue
17301 West Colfax Avenue, Suite 135
Golden, CO 80401
P: (303) 205-1300
F: (303) 205-1342
E: flavio.quintana@state.co.us

CONNECTICUT
Mr. William Ryan
Director
Division of Gaming
Department of Consumer Protection
450 Columbus Boulevard, Suite 901
Hartford, CT 06103
P: (860) 713-6301
F: (860) 707-1965
E: William.Ryan@ct.gov

DELAWARE
Mr. Vernon Kirk
Director
State Lottery
McKee Business Park
1575 McKee Road, Suite 102
Dover, DE 19904
P: (302) 739-5291
F: (302) 739-6706

FLORIDA
Ms. Matilde Miller
Interim Secretary
Department of Business & Professional Regulation
1940 North Monroe Street
Tallahassee, FL 32399
P: (850) 487-1395
F: (850) 488-1830
E: matilde.miller@myfloridalicense.com

GEORGIA
Mr. Vernon M. Keenan
Director
Bureau of Investigation
3121 Panthersville Road
Decatur, GA 30034
P: (404) 244-2501
F: (404) 270-8352
E: vernon.keenan@gbi.ga.gov

GUAM
Mr. Artemio B. Ilagan
Banking & Insurance Commissioner
Regulatory Division
Department of Revenue & Taxation
P.O. Box 23607
GMF Barrigada, GU 96921
P: (671) 635-1817
F: (671) 633-2643
E: art.ilagan@revtax.gov.gu

IDAHO
Mr. Jeffrey R. Anderson
Director
State Liquor Division
1199 Shoreline Lane, Suite 100
P.O. Box 6537
Boise, ID 83707
P: (208) 334-2600
F: (208) 947-9401
E: info@idaholottery.com

ILLINOIS
Mr. Mark Ostrowski
Administrator
Gaming Board
160 North LaSalle, Suite 300
Chicago, IL 60601
P: (312) 814-4700
F: (312) 814-4602

INDIANA
Ms. Sara Gonso Tait
Executive Director
Gaming Commission
East Tower, Suite 1600
101 West Washington Street
Indianapolis, IN 46204
P: (317) 233-0046
F: (317) 233-0047
E: STait@igc.IN.gov

IOWA
Mr. Brian J. Ohorilko
Administrator
Racing & Gaming Commission
DMACC Capitol Center
1300 Des Moines Street, Suite 100
Des Moines, IA 50309
P: (515) 281-7352
F: (515) 242-6560
E: brian.ohorilko@iowa.gov

KANSAS
Mr. Mark Dodd
Executive Director
State Gaming Agency
420 Southwest 6th Street, Suite 3000
Topeka, KS 66607
P: (785) 368-6202
F: (785) 291-3798
E: ksga@ksgaming.org

KENTUCKY
Ms. Margaret Gibbs
Acting President & CEO
State Lottery
1011 West Main Street
Louisville, KY 40202
P: (502) 560-1500
F: (502) 560-1532

Mr. Marc Guilfoil
Executive Director
Horse Racing Commission
4063 Ironworks Parkway, Building B
Lexington, KY 40511
P: (859) 246-2040
E: marc.guilfoil@ky.gov

LOUISIANA
Lieutenant Colonel Murphy Paul
Deputy Superintendent
Bureau of Investigations
State Police
7919 Independence Boulevard
Baton Rouge, LA 70806
P: (800) 434-8007

MAINE
Mr. John E. Morris
Commissioner
Department of Public Safety
45 Commerce Drive, Suite 1
104 State House Station
Augusta, ME 04333
P: (207) 626-3800
F: (207) 287-3042
E: john.e.morris@maine.gov

MARYLAND
Mr. Michael J. Frenz
Chief Executive Officer
Stadium Authority
333 West Camden Street, Suite 500
Baltimore, MD 21201
P: (410) 333-1560
F: (410) 333-1888
E: mfrenz@mdstad.com

MASSACHUSETTS
Mr. John Chapman
Undersecretary
Office of Consumer Affairs & Business Regulation
Ten Park Plaza, Suite 5170
Boston, MA 02116
P: (617) 973-8700
F: (617) 973-8799

MICHIGAN
Mr. Richard S. Kalm
Executive Director
Gaming Control Board
3062 West Grand Boulevard, Suite L-700
Detroit, MI 48202
P: (313) 456-4100
F: (313) 456-4200
E: KalmR@michigan.gov

MINNESOTA
Mr. Mike Vekich
Interim Executive Director
State Lottery
2645 Long Lake Road
Roseville, MN 55113
P: (651) 635-8100
E: lottery@mnlottery.com

MISSISSIPPI
Mr. Allen Godfrey
Executive Director
Gaming Commission
620 North Street, Suite 200
P.O. Box 23577
Jackson, MS 39225
P: (601) 576-3800
F: (601) 576-3929
E: info@mgc.state.ms.us

Gaming Officials

MISSOURI
Mr. William K. Seibert Jr.
Executive Director
Gaming Commission
3417 Knipp Dirve
P.O. Box 1847
Jefferson City, MO 65102
P: (573) 526-4080
F: (573) 526-1999

MONTANA
The Honorable Tim Fox (R)
Attorney General
Department of Justice
Justice Building
215 North Sanders
Helena, MT 59620
P: (406) 444-2026
F: (406) 444-3549
E: contactdoj@mt.gov

NEBRASKA
Mr. Tony Fulton
Tax Commissioner
Department of Revenue
P.O. Box 94818
Lincoln, NE 68509
P: (402) 471-5605
F: (402) 471-5608
E: tony.fulton@nebraska.gov

NEVADA
Mr. A.G. Burnett
Chair
Gaming Control Board
1919 College Parkway
P.O. Box 8003
Carson City, NV 89702
P: (775) 684-7700
F: (775) 687-5817

NEW JERSEY
Mr. David L. Rebuck
Director
Division of Gaming Enforcement
Office of the Attorney General
140 East Front Street, P.O. Box 047
Trenton, NJ 08625
P: (609) 292-9394
F: (609) 633-7355
E: info@njdge.org

NEW MEXICO
Mr. Donovan Lieurance
Acting Executive Director
Gaming Control Board
4900 Alameda Boulevard, Northeast
Albuquerque, NM 87113
P: (505) 417-1079
F: (505) 841-9725
E: donovan.lieurance@state.nm.us

NEW YORK
Mr. Robert T. Williams
Executive Director
Gaming Commission
One Broadway Center
P.O. Box 7500
Schenectady, NY 12301
P: (518) 388-3400
F: (518) 347-1250
E: info@gaming.ny.gov

NORTH CAROLINA
Ms. Alice Garland
Executive Director
Education Lottery
2100 Yonkers Road
Raleigh, NC 27604
P: (919) 301-3300
F: (919) 715-8833
E: playerinfo@lotterync.net

NORTH DAKOTA
The Honorable Wayne Stenehjem (R)
Attorney General
Office of the Attorney General
State Capitol
600 East Boulevard Avenue
Bismarck, ND 58505
P: (701) 328-2210
F: (701) 328-2226
E: wstenehjem@nd.gov

OHIO
Mr. William Crawford
Executive Director
Racing Commission
77 South High Street, 18th Floor
Columbus, OH 43215
P: (614) 466-2757
F: (614) 466-1900
E: bill.crawford@racing.ohio.gov

OKLAHOMA
Mr. A. Keith Burt
Director
Alcoholic Beverage Laws Enforcement Commission
3812 North Santa Fe
Suite 200
Oklahoma City, OK 73118
P: (405) 521-3484
F: (405) 521-6578
E: kburt@able.ok.gov

Ms. Kelly G. Cathey
Executive Director
State Horse Racing Commission
Shepherd Mall
2401 Northwest 23rd Street, Suite 78
Oklahoma City, OK 73107
P: (405) 943-6472
F: (405) 943-6474
E: ohrc@socket.net

OREGON
Major Joel Lujan
Director
Gaming & Employee Services Bureau
State Department of Police
255 Capitol Street Northeast, 4th Floor
Salem, OR 97310
P: (503) 378-3720

PENNSYLVANIA
Mr. David M. Barasch
Chair
Gaming Control Board
P.O. Box 69060
Harrisburg, PA 17106
P: (717) 346-8300
F: (717) 346-8350

PUERTO RICO
Mr. Guillermo J. Cabret
Director
Gaming Division
P.O. Box 9023960
San Juan, PR 00902
P: (787) 721-2400
F: (787) 724-3009
E: logarcia@prtourism.com

RHODE ISLAND
Major Dennis B. Fleming
Detective Commander
State Police
Department of Public Safety
311 Danielson Pike
North Scituate, RI 02857
P: (401) 444-1000
F: (401) 444-1105

SOUTH CAROLINA
Mr. Alvin A. Taylor
Director
Department of Natural Resources
1000 Assembly Street
P.O. Box 167
Columbia, SC 29202
P: (803) 734-4007
F: (803) 734-9809
E: taylora@dnr.sc.gov

TENNESSEE
Ms. Rebecca Paul Hargrove
President & CEO
Education Lottery Corporation
26 Century Boulevard, Suite 200
Nashville, TN 37214
P: (615) 324-6500
F: (615) 324-6512

TEXAS
Mr. Gary Grief
Executive Director
Lottery Commission
611 East Sixth Street
Austin, TX 78701
P: (512) 344-5000
F: (512) 478-3682
E: gary.grief@lottery.state.tx.us

Mr. Chuck Trout
Executive Director
State Racing Commission
8505 Cross Park Drive, Suite 110
P.O. Box 12080
Austin, TX 78711
P: (512) 833-6699
F: (512) 833-6907

U.S. VIRGIN ISLANDS
The Honorable Claude E. Walker
Attorney General
Office of the Attorney General
34-38 Kronprinsdens Gade
GERS Building, 2nd Floor
St. Thomas, VI 00802
P: (340) 774-5666 Ext. 107

WASHINGTON
Mr. David Trujillo
Director
Gambling Commission
P.O. Box 42400
Olympia, WA 98504
P: (360) 486-3440
F: (360) 486-3629

WEST VIRGINIA
Mr. Dave Hardy
Cabinet Secretary
Department of Revenue
State Capitol
Building 1, W-300
Charleston, WV 25305
P: (304) 558-1017
F: (304) 558-2324

WISCONSIN
Mr. John Dillett
Acting Administrator
Division of Gaming
3319 West Beltline Highway, #1
P.O. Box 8979
Madison, WI 53708
P: (608) 270-2560
F: (608) 270-2564
E: john.dillett
@wisconsin.gov

WYOMING
Mr. Charles Moore
Executive Director/Simulcast
Steward
State Pari-Mutuel Commission
Energy II Building, Suite 335
951 Werner Court
Casper, WY 82601
P: (307) 265-4015
F: (307) 265-4279
E: charles.moore@wyo.gov

Geographic Information Systems

Coordinates geographic information systems within state government.

ALABAMA
Mr. Phillip Henderson
Director
Geographic Information Program Office
201 South Union Street, Suite 300
Montgomery, AL 36130
P: (334) 517-2561
E: phillip.henderson@alacop.gov

ALASKA
Ms. Anne Johnson
Geospatial Information Officer
Department of Natural Resources
550 West 7th Avenue, Suite 706
Anchorage, AK 99501
P: (907) 269-0880
E: anne.johnson@alaska.gov

ARIZONA
Mr. Curtis Pulford
State Cartographer
State Land Department
1616 West Adams Street
Phoenix, AZ 85007
P: (602) 542-3190
F: (602) 542-2600
E: cpulford@azland.gov

ARKANSAS
Mr. Shelby Johnson
Geographic Information Coordinator
Geographic Information Office
1 Capitol Mall, Suite 2B900
Little Rock, AR 72201
P: (501) 682-2767
F: (501) 682-4310
E: shelby.johnson@arkansas.gov

CALIFORNIA
Mr. Scott Gregory
Geospatial Information Officer
Technology Agency
1325 J Street
Sacramento, CA 95814
P: (916) 431-5449
E: scott.gregory@state.ca.gov

COLORADO
Mr. Jon Gottsegen
State GIS Coordinator
Department of Local Affairs
601 East 18th Avenue, Suite 250
Denver, CO 80203
P: (303) 764-7712
F: (303) 764-7725
E: jon.gottsegen@state.co.us

DELAWARE
Ms. Miriam Pomilio
Principal Planner/GIS Coordination
Office of State Planning Coordination
Haslet Armory
122 Martin Luther King Jr. Blvd., South
Dover, DE 19901
P: (302) 739-3090
E: miriam.pomilio@state.de.us

DISTRICT OF COLUMBIA
Mr. Matt Crossett
Office of the Chief Information Officer
200 I Street Southeast, 5632-J
Washington, DC 20003
P: (202) 442-7100
F: (202) 727-5660
E: matthew.crossett@dc.gov

FLORIDA
Mr. Richard Butgereit
Director
Division of Emergency Management
2555 Shumard Oak
Tallahassee, FL 32399
P: (850) 413-9907
E: richard.butgereit@em.myflorida.com

GEORGIA
Mr. Eric McRae
Associate Director
University of Georgia
1180 East Broad Street, Suite 2058
Athens, GA 30602
P: (706) 542-5308
F: (706) 542-6535
E: mcrae@cviog.itos.uga.edu

Ms. Susan Miller
Geospatial Information Officer
State of Georgia
60 Executive Park South, Northeast
Atlanta, GA 30329
P: (470) 599-0631
E: susan.miller@gio.ga.gov

HAWAII
Mr. Arthur Buto
Program Manager
Statewide GIS Program
Office of Planning
235 South Beretania Street, 6th Floor
Honolulu, HI 96813
P: (808) 587-2895
F: (808) 587-2824
E: Arthur.J.Buto@hawaii.gov

IDAHO
Mr. Bill Farnsworth
Geographic Information Officer
Office of the CIO
650 West State Street
Boise, ID 83720
P: (208) 332-1878
F: (208) 332-1884
E: bill.farnsworth@cio.idaho.gov

ILLINOIS
Mr. Mark Yacucci
Geoscience Data Coordinator & Section Head
State Geological Survey
University of Illinois Urbana-Champaign
615 East Peabody Drive
Champaign, IL 61820
P: (217) 265-0747
E: yacucci@illinois.edu

INDIANA
Mr. Jim Sparks
Geographic Information Officer
Geographic Information Council
100 North Senate Avenue
N551 Government Center North
Indianapolis, IN 46204
P: (317) 234-5889
F: (317) 234-0917
E: jsparks@iot.in.gov

Mr. Phillip Worrall
Executive Director
Geographic Information Council, Inc.
777 Indiana Avenue, Suite 210
Indianapolis, IN 46202
P: (317) 504-4389
E: pworrall@igic.org

IOWA
Mr. Jonathan Paoli
Homeland Security & Emergency Management
Joint Forces Headquarters
6100 Northwest 78th Avenue
Johnston, IA 50131
P: (515) 323-4384
F: (515) 323-4208
E: jonathan.paoli@iowa.gov

Mr. Patrick Wilke-Brown
GIS Coordinator
Office of the Chief Information Officer
State of Iowa
1305 East Walnut Street
Des Moines, IA 50319
P: (515) 782-1053
E: Patrick.Wilke-Brown@Iowa.Gov

KANSAS
Mr. Kenneth A. Nelson
Data Access & Support Center
Geological Survey, University of Kansas
1930 Constant Avenue
Lawrence, KS 66047
P: (785) 864-2164
F: (785) 864-5317
E: nelson@kgs.ku.edu

KENTUCKY
Mr. Thomas J. Rossman
Acting Director
Division of Geographic Information
100 Fair Oaks Lane
Frankfort, KY 40601
P: (502) 564-6412
F: (502) 564-0427
E: thomas.rossman@ky.gov

LOUISIANA
Mr. Craig Johnson
Administrative & Programmatic Support Manager
School of the Coast & Environment
E-313 Howe-Russell Building
Louisiana State University
Baton Rouge, LA 70803
P: (225) 578-3479
F: (225) 578-7289
E: cjohnson@lsu.edu

MAINE
Mr. Joseph Young
Executive Director
State GeoLibrary
SHS 145
51 Commerce Drive
Augusta, ME 04333
P: (207) 624-2664
F: (207) 287-1131
E: Joseph.Young@maine.gov

MARYLAND
Ms. Julia Fischer
Geographic Information Officer
Department of Information Technology
45 Calvert Street
Annapolis, MD 21401
P: (443) 370-3008
E: Julia.Fischer@maryland.gov

MASSACHUSETTS
Mr. Neil MacGaffey
Director
MassGIS
One Ashburton Place, Room 1601
Boston, MA 02108
P: (617) 619-5641
E: Neil.macgaffey@state.ma.us

MICHIGAN
Mr. Rob Surber
Center for Geographic Information
111 South Capitol Avenue, Floor 10
Lansing, MI 48933
P: (517) 373-7910
F: (517) 373-2939
E: surberr@michigan.gov

MINNESOTA
Mr. Dan Ross
Geospatial Information Office
658 Cedar Street, Suite 300
St. Paul, MN 55155
E: dan.ross@state.mn.us

MISSISSIPPI
Mr. Paul Barnes
Director
Harrison County GIS Department
P.O. Drawer C.C.
Gulfport, MS 39502
P: (228) 865-4182
E: pbarnes@co.harrison.ms.us

Mr. Jim Steil
Director
Automated Resource Information System
State Institutions of Higher Learning
3825 Ridgewood Road
Jackson, MS 39211
P: (662) 418-7349
F: (601) 432-6893
E: Jsteil@ihl.state.ms.us

MISSOURI
Mr. Tony Spicci
Central Regional Office & Conservation Research Center
3500 East Grans Road
Columbia, MO 65201
P: (573) 882-8388
E: Tony.Spicci@mdc.mo.gov

MONTANA
Ms. Erin Fashoway
Geographic Information Officer
Montana State Library
P.O. Box 201800
Helena, MT 59620
P: (406) 444-9013
F: (406) 444-0266
E: efashoway@mt.gov

NEBRASKA
Mr. John Watermolen
GIS Council Coordinator
GIS Council/NITC
Office of the Chief Information Officer
P.O. Box 95045
Lincoln, NE 68509
P: (402) 471-3206
F: (402) 471-4864
E: john.watermolen@nebraska.gov

NEVADA
Ms. Rachel Micander
GIS Specialist
Bureau of Mines & Geology
Mail Stop 178
University of Nevada
Reno, NV 89557
P: (775) 682-6351
E: rmicander@unr.edu

NEW HAMPSHIRE
Mr. Sean Goodwin
GIS Administrator
Division of Emergency Services
33 Hazen Drive
Concord, NH 03305
P: (603) 271-6911
E: sgoodwin@e911.nh.gov

NEW JERSEY
Mr. Andrew Rowan
Geographic Information Officer
Office of Information Technology
200 Riverview Plaza
P.O. Box 212
Trenton, NJ 08625
P: (609) 633-0276
F: (609) 633-0200
E: andrew.rowan@oit.nj.gov

NEW MEXICO
Gar Clarke
Broadband Program Manager
Department of Information Technology
715 Alta Vista Street
Santa Fe, NM 87505
P: (505) 827-1663
E: george.clarke@state.nm.us

Mr. Leland Pierce
Department of Game & Fish
P.O. Box 25112
Santa Fe, NM 87505
P: (505) 476-8094
F: (505) 476-8128
E: leland.pierce@state.nm.us

NEW YORK
Mr. Frank Winters
Director, GIS Program Office
Office of Information Technology Services
1220 Washington Avenue
State Office Campus, Building 7A
Albany, NY 12242
P: (518) 242-5036
E: francis.winters@its.ny.gov

NORTH CAROLINA
Mr. Tim Johnson
Director
Center for Geographic Information & Analysis
20322 Mail Service Center
Raleigh, NC 27699
P: (919) 754-6588
F: (919) 715-8551
E: tim.johnson@its.nc.gov

NORTH DAKOTA
Mr. Bob Nutsch
GIS Coordinator
Information Technology Department
600 East Boulevard Avenue
Department 112
Bismarck, ND 58505
P: (701) 328-3212
F: (701) 328-3000
E: bnutsch@nd.gov

OHIO
Mr. Jeff Smith
Spatial Data Infrastructure Manager
Geographically Referenced Information Program
Office of Information Technology
77 South High Street, 19th Floor
Columbus, OH 43215
P: (614) 466-8862
E: Jeff.Smith@das.ohio.gov

OKLAHOMA
Mr. Mike Sharp
Director, State GIS Coordinator
Conservation Commission
2800 North Lincoln Boulevard
Suite 160
Oklahoma City, OK 73105
P: (405) 521-4813
F: (405) 521-6686
E: mike.sharp@conservation.ok.gov

OREGON
Mr. Cy Smith
Geospatial Information Officer
DAS/CIO Geospatial Enterprise Office
155 Cottage Street, Northeast
4th Floor
Salem, OR 97301
P: (503) 378-6066
F: (503) 378-3795
E: cy.smith@oregon.gov

PENNSYLVANIA
Ms. Mary Fulton
Manager, Geospatial Technology Operations
Office of Information Technology
Office of Administration
5 Technology Park
Harrisburg, PA 17110
P: (717) 787-7878
F: (717) 783-6955
E: mfulton@pa.gov

RHODE ISLAND
Mr. Vincent Flood
Supervising Planner
Division of Planning
Department of Administration
One Capitol Hill, 3rd Floor
Providence, RI 02908
P: (401) 222-1243
E: vincent.flood@doa.ri.gov

SOUTH CAROLINA
Dr. Timothy M. De Troye
State GIS Coordinator
State Geographic Information Systems
1000 Assembly Street, Suite 134
Columbia, SC 29201
P: (803) 734-3894
F: (803) 734-7001
E: detroyet@gic.sc.gov

Geographic Information Systems

SOUTH DAKOTA
Mr. Chris Marsh
Software Engineer
Bureau of Information & Telecommunications
700 East Broadway Avenue
Pierre, SD 57501
P: (605) 773-6701
E: chris.marsh@state.sd.us

TENNESSEE
Mr. Dennis Pedersen
Director of OIR-GIS Services
Office for Information Resources
312 8th Avenue, North
Floor 16
Nashville, TN 37243
P: (615) 741-9356
F: (615) 532-0471
E: dennis.pedersen@tn.gov

TEXAS
Mr. Richard Wade
Geographic Information Officer
State of Texas
P.O. Box 13231
Room B40
Austin, TX 78711
P: (512) 463-4010
E: Richard.Wade@twdb.texas.gov

U.S. VIRGIN ISLANDS
Mr. Stevie Henry
Data Manager
University of Virgin Islands - ECC
University of the Virgin Islands
#2 John Brewer's Bay
St. Thomas, VI 00802
P: (340) 693-1020
F: (340) 693-1025
E: shenry@uvi.edu

UTAH
Mr. Bert Granberg
Director
Automated Geographic Refererence Center
1 State Office Building, Room 5130
Salt Lake City, UT 84114
P: (801) 538-3072
F: (801) 538-3317
E: bgranberg@utah.gov

VERMONT
Mr. John Adams
Director
Center for Geographic Information
1 National Life Drive
Davis Building, 6th Floor
Montpelier, VT 05620
P: (802) 522-0172
F: (802) 828-3383
E: john.e.adams@vermont.gov

WASHINGTON
Ms. Joy Paulus
GIS Coordinator
Office of the Chief Information Officer
P.O. Box 43113
Olympia, WA 98504
P: (360) 902-3447
E: joy.paulus@ofm.wa.gov

WEST VIRGINIA
Mr. Tony Simental
State GIS Coordinator
GIS Coordinator's Office
1 Mont Chateau Road
Morgantown, WV 26508
P: (304) 594-2331
F: (304) 594-2575
E: Tony.A.Simental@wv.gov

WISCONSIN
Mr. Howard Veregin
University of Wisconsin-Madison
Room 384, Science Hall
550 North Park Street
Madison, WI 53706
P: (608) 262-6852
F: (608) 262-5205
E: veregin@wisc.edu

WYOMING
Mr. Anthony Witbrod
Enterprise Solutions Architect, Office of Enterprise Architecture
Department of Enterprise Technology Services
Emerson Building, Room #238
2001 Capitol Avenue
Cheyenne, WY 82002
P: (307) 214-6670
E: anthony.witbrod@wyo.gov

Geological Survey

Conducts research on the state's terrain, mineral resources, and possible geological hazards such as earthquakes, faults, etc.

ALABAMA
Mr. Berry H. Tew Jr.
State Geologist & Oil and Gas Supervisor
Geological Survey of Alabama
State Oil & Gas Board
P.O. Box 869999
Tuscaloosa, AL 35486
P: (205) 349-2852
F: (205) 247-3676
E: ntew@gsa.state.al.us

ALASKA
Mr. Steve Masterman
State Geologist/Director
Division of Geological & Geophysical Surveys
Department of Natural Resources
3354 College Road
Fairbanks, AK 99709
P: (907) 451-5000
F: (907) 451-5050
E: steve.masterman@alaska.gov

ARIZONA
Mr. Philip A. Pearthree
Director & State Geologist
Geological Survey
1955 East Sixth Street
P.O. Box 210184
Tucson, AZ 85721
P: (520) 621-2470
E: pearthre@email.arizona.edu

ARKANSAS
Ms. Bekki White
State Geologist & Director
Geological Survey
3815 West Roosevelt Road
Little Rock, AR 72204
P: (501) 296-1877
F: (501) 663-7360
E: bekki.white@arkansas.gov

CALIFORNIA
Dr. John Parrish
State Geologist
Geological Survey
Department of Conservation
801 K Street, MS 12-30
Sacramento, CA 95814
P: (916) 445-1825
F: (916) 445-5718
E: John.Parrish@conservation.ca.gov

COLORADO
Ms. Karen Berry
State Geologist & Director
Geological Survey
School of Mines
1801 19th Street
Golden, CO 80401
P: (303) 384-2655
F: (303) 866-2461
E: kaberry@mines.edu

CONNECTICUT
Ms. Margaret A. Thomas
State Geologist
Geological & Natural History Survey
Energy & Environmental Protection
79 Elm Street
Hartford, CT 06106
P: (860) 424-3583
F: (860) 424-4058
E: margaret.thomas@ct.gov

DELAWARE
Dr. David R. Wunsch
Director & State Geologist
Geological Survey
257 Academy Street
Newark, DE 19716
P: (302) 831-2833
F: (302) 831-3579
E: dwunsch@udel.edu

FLORIDA
Mr. Jonathan Arthur
State Geologist
Geological Survey
Department of Environmental Protection
3000 Commonwealth Boulevard, Suite 1
Tallahassee, FL 32303
P: (850) 617-0300
F: (850) 488-8086
E: jonathan.arthur@dep.state.fl.us

GEORGIA
Mr. Jim Kennedy
State Geologist
Geologic Survey, Department of Natural Resources
2 Martin Luther King Jr. Drive
Suite 1152 East Tower
Atlanta, GA 30334
P: (404) 657-5947
F: (404) 651-5778
E: jim_kennedy@dnr.state.ga.us

HAWAII
Mr. Jeffrey T. Pearson
Deputy Director
Commission on Water Resource Management
Department of Land & Water Resources
1151 Punchbowl Street, Room 227
Honolulu, HI 96813
P: (808) 587-0214
F: (808) 587-0219
E: dlnr.cwrm@hawaii.gov

IDAHO
Mr. Michael Ratchford
Director & State Geologist
Geological Survey
University of Idaho
875 Perimeter Drive, MS 3014
Moscow, ID 83844
P: (208) 885-7991
F: (208) 885-5826
E: edratchford@uidaho.edu

ILLINOIS
Dr. Richard C. Berg
Director
State Geological Survey
University of Illinois
615 East Peabody Drive
Champaign, IL 61820
P: (217) 333-4747
F: (217) 244-7004
E: rberg@illinois.edu

INDIANA
Dr. Todd Thompson
Director & State Geologist
Geological Survey
Indiana University
611 North Walnut Grove
Bloomington, IN 47405
P: (812) 855-2862
F: (812) 855-2862
E: tthomps@indiana.edu

IOWA
Mr. Robert L. Libra
State Geologist
Geological Survey
University of Iowa
300 Trowbridge Hall
Iowa City, IA 52242
P: (319) 335-1575
F: (319) 335-2754
E: robert.libra@dnr.iowa.gov

KANSAS
Mr. Rolfe Mandel
Interim Director
Geological Survey
University of Kansas
1930 Constant Avenue
Lawrence, KS 66047
P: (785) 864-3965
E: mandel@kgs.ku.edu

KENTUCKY
Mr. Bill Haneberg
State Geologist & Director
Geological Survey
University of Kentucky
228 Mining & Mineral Resources Building
Lexington, KY 40506
P: (859) 257-5500
E: bill.haneberg@uky.edu

LOUISIANA
Dr. Chacko J. John
Director & State Geologist
Geological Survey
Louisiana State University
3079 Energy, Coastal & Environment Bldg.
Baton Rouge, LA 70803
P: (225) 578-5320
F: (225) 578-3662
E: cjohn@lsu.edu

MARYLAND
Mr. Richard A. Ortt Jr.
Director
Geological Survey
Department of Natural Resources
2300 St. Paul Street
Baltimore, MD 21218
P: (410) 554-5500
F: (410) 554-5502
E: richard.ortt@maryland.gov

Geological Survey

MASSACHUSETTS
Mr. Stephen B. Mabee
State Geologist
Office of the State Geologist
611 North Pleasant Street
University of Massachusetts
Amherst, MA 01003
P: (413) 545-4814
F: (413) 545-1200
E: sbmabee@geo.umass.edu

MICHIGAN
Mr. John Yellich
Director
Geological Survey
Western Michigan University
Geosciences Department, 1184 Rood Hall
Kalamazoo, MI 49008
P: (269) 387-8649
E: john.a.yellich@wmich.edu

MINNESOTA
Dr. Harvey Thorleifson
Professor & Director
Geological Survey
University of Minnesota
2609 West Territorial Road
St. Paul, MN 55114
P: (612) 626-2969
F: (612) 627-4778
E: thorleif@umn.edu

MISSISSIPPI
Mr. Michael Bograd
State Geologist
Office of Geology
Department of Environmental Quality
700 North State Street, P.O. Box 2279
Jackson, MS 39202
P: (601) 961-5500
F: (601) 961-5521
E: Michael_Bograd@deq.state.ms.us

MISSOURI
Mr. Joe Gillman
State Geologist & Director
Geological Survey
Department of Natural Resources
P.O. Box 250
Rolla, MO 65402
P: (800) 361-4827
F: (573) 368-2111
E: joe.gillman@dnr.mo.gov

MONTANA
Mr. John J. Metesh
Director & State Geologist
Bureau of Mines & Geology
Montana Tech
1300 West Park Street
Butte, MT 59701
P: (406) 496-4180
F: (406) 496-4451
E: jmetesh@mtech.edu

NEBRASKA
Mr. R.M. Joeckel
State Geologist & Associate Director for Conservation and Survey
Conservation & Survey Division
University of Nebraska, Lincoln
101 Hardin Hall, 3310 Holdrege Street
Lincoln, NE 68583
P: (402) 472-3471
F: (402) 472-3610
E: rjoeckel3@unl.edu

NEVADA
Mr. James E. Faulds
Director & State Geologist
Bureau of Mines & Geology
University of Nevada, Reno
Mail Stop 178
Reno, NV 89557
P: (775) 784-6691
F: (775) 784-1709
E: jfaulds@unr.edu

NEW HAMPSHIRE
Mr. Rick Chormann
State Geologist & Director
Geological Survey
Department of Environmental Services
29 Hazen Drive, P.O. Box 95
Concord, NH 03302
P: (603) 271-3503
F: (603) 271-3305
E: frederick.chormann@des.nh.gov

NEW JERSEY
Mr. Jeffrey L. Hoffman
State Geologist
Geological & Water Survey
Department of Environmental Protection
P.O. Box 420, Mail Code 29-01
Trenton, NJ 08625
P: (609) 292-1185
F: (609) 633-1004
E: njgsweb@dep.nj.gov

NEW MEXICO
Dr. Nelia W. Dunbar
Director & State Geologist
Bureau of Geology & Mineral Resources
New Mexico Tech
801 Leroy Place
Socorro, NM 87801
P: (575) 835-5490
E: nelia@nmbg.nmt.edu

NEW YORK
Dr. Andrew Kozlowski
Curator of Quaternary Landscape Materials
Geology Research Centers
State Museum
3140 Cultural Education Center
Albany, NY 12230
P: (518) 474-5877
F: (518) 486-2034
E: andrew.kozlowski@nysed.gov

NORTH CAROLINA
Dr. Kenneth B. Taylor
State Geologist
Geological Survey
Department of Environmental Quality
1612 Mail Service Center
Raleigh, NC 27699
P: (919) 707-9211
F: (919) 733-0900
E: kenneth.b.taylor@ncdenr.gov

NORTH DAKOTA
Mr. Edward C. Murphy
State Geologist
Geological Survey
Department of Mineral Resources
600 East Boulevard Avenue
Bismarck, ND 58505
P: (701) 328-8000
F: (701) 328-8010
E: emurphy@nd.gov

OHIO
Dr. Thomas J. Serenko
State Geologist & Division Chief
Division of Geological Survey
Department of Natural Resources
2045 Morse Road, Building C
Columbus, OH 43229
P: (614) 265-6576
F: (614) 447-1918
E: thomas.serenko@dnr.state.oh.us

OKLAHOMA
Dr. Jeremy L. Boak
Director
Geological Survey
University of Oklahoma
100 East Boyd, Suite N-131
Norman, OK 73019
P: (405) 325-3031
F: (405) 325-7069
E: jboak@ou.edu

OREGON
Mr. Brad Avy
State Geologist
Department of Geology & Mineral Industries
800 Northeast Oregon Street, Suite 965
Portland, OR 97232
P: (971) 673-1555
F: (971) 673-1562
E: Brad.Avy@oregon.gov

PENNSYLVANIA
Ms. Gale C. Blackmer
Bureau Director & State Geologist
Department of Conservation & Natural Resources
Geologic Survey
3240 Schoolhouse Road
Middletown, PA 17057
P: (717) 702-2017
F: (717) 702-2065
E: gelove@state.pa.us

PUERTO RICO
Ms. Ruth H. Velez
State Geologist
Bureau of Geology
Natural & Environmental Resources
P.O. Box 366147
San Juan, PR 00936
P: (787) 722-2526
F: (787) 723-4255
E: rhvelez@dnra.gobierno.pr

RHODE ISLAND
Dr. Jon C. Boothroyd
State Geologist
Geological Survey
University of Rhode Island
9 East Alumni Avenue, 314 Woodward Hall
Kingston, RI 02881
P: (401) 874-2265
F: (401) 874-2190
E: jon_boothroyd@uri.edu

SOUTH CAROLINA
Mr. Charles William Clendenin Jr.
State Geologist
Geological Survey
Department of Natural Resources
5 Geology Road
Columbia, SC 29212
P: (803) 896-7931
F: (803) 896-7695
E: clendeninb@dnr.sc.gov

SOUTH DAKOTA
Mr. Derric L. Iles
State Geologist
Geological Survey
Environment & Natural Resources
414 East Clark Street
Vermillion, SD 57069
P: (605) 677-5227
F: (605) 677-5895
E: derric.iles@usd.edu

TENNESSEE
Mr. Ronald P. Zurawski
State Geologist
Geological Survey
William R. Snodgrass Tower
312 Rosa L. Parks Avenue, 12th Floor
Nashville, TN 37243
P: (615) 532-1502
F: (615) 532-1517
E: Ronald.Zurawski@tn.gov

TEXAS
Dr. Scott W. Tinker
Director
Bureau of Economic Geology
University of Texas At Austin
University Station, Box X
Austin, TX 78713
P: (512) 471-1534
F: (512) 471-0140
E: scott.tinker@beg.utexas.edu

UTAH
Mr. Rick Allis
Director
Geological Survey, Department of Natural Resources
1594 West North Temple
P.O. Box 146100
Salt Lake City, UT 84114
P: (801) 537-3300
F: (801) 537-3400
E: rickallis@utah.gov

VERMONT
Ms. Marjorie Gale
State Geologist & Director
Geological Survey
Department of Environmental Conservation
1 National Life Drive, Main 2
Montpelier, VT 05620
P: (802) 522-5210
F: (802) 241-4585
E: marjorie.gale@vermont.gov

VIRGINIA
Mr. David Spears
Director & State Geologist
Division of Geology & Mineral Resources
Department of Mines, Minerals & Energy
900 Natural Resources Drive, Suite 500
Charlottesville, VA 22903
P: (434) 951-6341
F: (434) 951-6365
E: david.spears@dmme.virginia.gov

WASHINGTON
Mr. Dave Norman
State Geologist & Division Manager
Division of Geology & Earth Resources, Department of Natural Resources
111 Washington Street, Southeast
P.O. Box 47007
Olympia, WA 98504
P: (360) 902-1450
F: (360) 902-1785
E: dave.norman@dnr.wa.gov

WEST VIRGINIA
Mr. Michael Ed Hohn
Director & State Geologist
Geological & Economic Survey
Department of Commerce
1 Mont Chateau Road
Morgantown, WV 26508
P: (304) 594-2331
F: (304) 594-2575
E: info@geosrv.wvnet.edu

WISCONSIN
Dr. Ken Bradbury
Director & State Geologist
Geological & Natural History Survey
University of Wisconsin
3817 Mineral Point Road
Madison, WI 53705
P: (608) 262-1705
F: (608) 262-8086
E: ken.bradbury@uwex.edu

WYOMING
Mr. Tom Drean
Director & State Geologist
State Geological Survey
P.O. Box 1347
Laramie, WY 82073
P: (307) 766-2286
F: (307) 766-2605
E: tom.drean@wyo.gov

Governor

Information provided by:

National Governors Association
Scott Pattison
Executive Director
Hall of the States
444 North Capitol Street
Suite 267
Washington, DC 20001
P: (202) 624-5300
F: (202) 624-5313
www.nga.org

The Council of State Governments
David Adkins
Executive Director/CEO
1776 Avenue of the States
Lexington, KY 40511
P: (859) 244-8000
F: (859) 244-8001
www.csg.org

ALABAMA
The Honorable Kay Ivey (R)
Governor
Office of the Governor
State Capitol
600 Dexter Avenue
Montgomery, AL 36130
P: (334) 242-7100
F: (334) 353-0004

ALASKA
The Honorable Bill Walker (I)
Governor
Office of the Governor
State Capitol
P.O. Box 110001
Juneau, AK 99811
P: (907) 465-3500
F: (907) 465-3532

AMERICAN SAMOA
The Honorable Lolo Matalasi Moliga (I)
Governor
Office of the Governor
Executive Office Building, Third Floor
Utulei
Pago Pago, AS 96799
P: (684) 633-4116
F: (684) 633-2269

ARIZONA
The Honorable Doug Ducey (R)
Governor
Office of the Governor
State Capitol
1700 West Washington Street
Phoenix, AZ 85007
P: (602) 542-4331
F: (602) 542-7601

ARKANSAS
The Honorable Asa Hutchinson (R)
Governor
Office of the Governor
State Capitol
Room 250
Little Rock, AR 72201
P: (501) 682-2345
F: (501) 682-1382

CALIFORNIA
The Honorable Edmund G. Brown Jr. (D)
Governor
Office of the Governor
State Capitol
Sacramento, CA 95814
P: (916) 445-2841
F: (916) 558-3160

COLORADO
The Honorable John Hickenlooper (D)
Governor
Office of the Governor
136 State Capitol
Denver, CO 80203
P: (303) 866-2471
F: (303) 866-2003

CONNECTICUT
The Honorable Dan Malloy (D)
Governor
Office of the Governor
210 Capitol Avenue
Hartford, CT 06106
P: (800) 406-1527
F: (860) 524-7395

DELAWARE
The Honorable John Carney Jr. (D)
Governor
Office of the Governor
Legislative Hall
Dover, DE 19901
P: (302) 744-4101
F: (302) 739-2775

DISTRICT OF COLUMBIA
The Honorable Muriel Bowser (D)
Mayor
Office of the Mayor
1350 Pennsylvania Avenue, Northwest
Suite 316
Washington, DC 20004
P: (202) 727-6300
F: (202) 727-0505
E: eom@dc.gov

FLORIDA
The Honorable Rick Scott (R)
Governor
Office of the Governor
PL 05, The Capitol
400 South Monroe Street
Tallahassee, FL 32399
P: (850) 488-7146
F: (850) 487-0801

GEORGIA
The Honorable Nathan Deal (R)
Governor
Office of the Governor
203 State Capitol
Atlanta, GA 30334
P: (404) 656-1776
F: (404) 657-7332

GUAM
The Honorable Eddie Baza Calvo (R)
Governor
Office of the Governor
Executive Chamber
P.O. Box 2950
Agana, GU 96932
P: (671) 472-8931
F: (671) 477-4826

HAWAII
The Honorable David Y. Ige (D)
Governor
Office of the Governor
Executive Chambers
State Capitol
Honolulu, HI 96813
P: (808) 586-0034
F: (808) 586-0006

IDAHO
The Honorable C.L. "Butch" Otter (R)
Governor
Office of the Governor
700 West Jefferson, Second Floor
Boise, ID 83702
P: (208) 334-2100
F: (208) 334-2175

ILLINOIS
The Honorable Bruce Rauner (R)
Governor
Office of the Governor
State Capitol
207 Statehouse
Springfield, IL 62706
P: (217) 782-0244
F: (217) 524-4049

INDIANA
The Honorable Eric Holcomb (R)
Governor
Office of the Governor
State Capitol, Room 206
Indianapolis, IN 46204
P: (317) 232-4567
F: (317) 232-43443

IOWA
The Honorable Kim Reynolds (R)
Governor
Office of the Governor
State Capitol
1007 East Grand Avenue
Des Moines, IA 50319
P: (515) 281-5211
F: (515) 725-3527

KANSAS
The Honorable Sam Brownback (R)
Governor
Office of the Governor
300 Southwest 10th Avenue, Suite 212S
Topeka, KS 66612
P: (785) 296-3232
F: (785) 296-7973

KENTUCKY
The Honorable Matt Bevin (R)
Governor
Office of the Governor
700 Capital Avenue, Suite 100
Frankfort, KY 40601
P: (502) 564-2611
F: (502) 564-0437

LOUISIANA
The Honorable John Bel Edwards (D)
Governor
Office of the Governor
P.O. Box 94004
Baton Rouge, LA 70804
P: (225) 342-7015
F: (225) 342-7099

MAINE
The Honorable Paul LePage (R)
Governor
Office of the Governor
#1 State House Station
Augusta, ME 04333
P: (207) 287-3531
F: (207) 287-1034

MARYLAND
The Honorable Larry Hogan (R)
Governor
Office of the Governor
State House
100 State Circle
Annapolis, MD 21401
P: (410) 974-3901
F: (410) 974-3275

MASSACHUSETTS
The Honorable Charles Baker (R)
Governor
Office of the Governor
Room 360
Boston, MA 02133
P: (617) 725-4005
F: (617) 727-9725

MICHIGAN
The Honorable Rick Snyder (R)
Governor
Office of the Governor
P.O. Box 30013
Lansing, MI 48909
P: (517) 373-3400
F: (517) 335-6863

MINNESOTA
The Honorable Mark Dayton (D)
Governor
Office of the Governor
130 State Capitol
75 Rev. Martin Luther King Jr. Boulevard
St. Paul, MN 55155
P: (651) 201-3400
F: (651) 797-1850

MISSISSIPPI
The Honorable Phil Bryant (R)
Governor
Office of the Governor
P.O. Box 139
Jackson, MS 39205
P: (601) 359-3150
F: (601) 359-3741
E: governor@governor.state.ms.us

MISSOURI
The Honorable Eric Greitens (R)
Governor
Office of the Governor
P.O. Box 270
Jefferson City, MO 65102
P: (573) 751-4917
F: (573) 751-1906

MONTANA
The Honorable Steve Bullock (D)
Governor
Office of the Governor
State Capitol
Helena, MT 59620
P: (406) 444-3111
F: (404) 444-5529

NEBRASKA
The Honorable Pete Ricketts (R)
Governor
Office of the Governor
P.O. Box 94848
Lincoln, NE 68509
P: (402) 471-2244
F: (402) 741-6031

NEVADA
The Honorable Brian Sandoval (R)
Governor
Office of the Governor
Capitol Building
Carson City, NV 89701
P: (775) 684-5670
F: (775) 684-5683

NEW HAMPSHIRE
The Honorable Chris Sununu (R)
Governor
Office of the Governor
107 North Main Street, Room 208
Concord, NH 03301
P: (603) 271-2121
F: (603) 271-7640

NEW JERSEY
The Honorable Chris Christie (R)
Governor
Office of the Governor
The State House
P.O. Box 001
Trenton, NJ 08625
P: (609) 292-6000
F: (609) 292-3454

NEW MEXICO
The Honorable Susana Martinez (R)
Governor
Office of the Governor
State Capitol, Fourth Floor
Santa Fe, NM 87501
P: (505) 476-2200
F: (505) 476-2226

NEW YORK
The Honorable Andrew M. Cuomo (D)
Governor
Office of the Governor
State Capitol
Albany, NY 12224
P: (518) 474-7516

NORTH CAROLINA
The Honorable Roy A. Cooper III (D)
Governor
Office of the Governor
20301 Mail Service Center
Raleigh, NC 27699
P: (919) 733-4240
F: (919) 733-2120

NORTH DAKOTA
The Honorable Doug Burgum (R)
Governor
Office of the Governor
600 East Boulevard Avenue
Bismarck, ND 58505
P: (701) 328-2200
F: (701) 328-2205

NORTHERN MARIANA ISLANDS
The Honorable Ralph D.G. Torres (R)
Governor
Office of the Governor
Caller Box 10007
Saipan, MP 96950
P: (670) 664-2280
F: (670) 664-2211

OHIO
The Honorable John Kasich (R)
Governor
Office of the Governor
77 South High Street, 30th Floor
Columbus, OH 43215
P: (614) 466-3555
F: (614) 466-9354

OKLAHOMA
The Honorable Mary Fallin (R)
Governor
Office of the Governor
Capitol Building
2300 Lincoln Boulevard, Room 212
Oklahoma City, OK 73105
P: (405) 521-2342
F: (405) 521-3353

OREGON
The Honorable Kate Brown (D)
Governor
Office of the Governor
State Capitol, Room 160
900 Court Street North
Salem, OR 97301
P: (503) 378-3111
F: (503) 378-8970

PENNSYLVANIA
The Honorable Thomas W. Wolf (D)
Governor
Office of the Governor
Room 225, Main Capitol Building
Harrisburg, PA 17120
P: (717) 787-2500
F: (717) 772-8284

PUERTO RICO
The Honorable Ricky Rosello (NPP)
Governor
Office of the Governor
La Fortaleza
P.O. Box 9020082
San Juan, PR 00902
P: (787) 721-7000
F: (787) 721-5072

RHODE ISLAND
The Honorable Gina M. Raimondo (D)
Governor
Office of the Governor
State House
Providence, RI 02903
P: (401) 222-2080
F: (401) 222-8096
E: governor@governor.ri.gov

SOUTH CAROLINA
The Honorable Henry D. McMaster (R)
Governor
Office of the Governor
1205 Pendleton Street
Columbia, SC 29201
P: (803) 734-2100
F: (803) 734-5167

Governor

SOUTH DAKOTA
The Honorable Dennis Daugaard (R)
Governor
Office of the Governor
500 East Capitol Avenue
Pierre, SD 57501
P: (605) 773-3212
F: (605) 773-4711

TENNESSEE
The Honorable Bill Haslam (R)
Governor
Office of the Governor
State Capitol
Nashville, TN 37243
P: (615) 741-2001
F: (615) 532-9711
E: bill.haslam@tn.gov

TEXAS
The Honorable Greg Abbott (R)
Governor
Office of the Governor
P.O. Box 12428
Austin, TX 78711
P: (512) 463-2000
F: (512) 463-5571

U.S. VIRGIN ISLANDS
The Honorable Kenneth Mapp (I)
Governor
Office of the Governor
Government House
21-22 Kongens Gade
St. Thomas, VI 00802
P: (340) 774-0001
F: (340) 693-4374

UTAH
The Honorable Gary R. Herbert (R)
Governor
Office of the Governor
State Capitol, Suite 200
Salt Lake City, UT 84114
P: (801) 538-1000
F: (801) 538-1557

VERMONT
The Honorable Phil Scott (R)
Governor
Office of the Governor
109 State Street
Montpelier, VT 05609
P: (802) 828-3333
F: (802) 828-3339

VIRGINIA
The Honorable Terry McAuliffe (D)
Governor
Office of the Governor
State Capitol, Third Floor
Richmond, VA 23219
P: (804) 786-2211
F: (804) 371-6351

WASHINGTON
The Honorable Jay Inslee (D)
Governor
Office of the Governor
P.O. Box 40002
Olympia, WA 98504
P: (360) 902-4111
F: (360) 753-4110

WEST VIRGINIA
The Honorable Jim Justice (D)
Governor
Office of the Governor
State Capitol Complex
1900 Kanawha Boulevard East
Charleston, WV 25305
P: (304) 558-2000

WISCONSIN
The Honorable Scott K. Walker (R)
Governor
Office of the Governor
115 East
State Capitol
Madison, WI 53702
P: (608) 266-1212
F: (608) 267-8983

WYOMING
The Honorable Matthew Mead (R)
Governor
Office of the Governor
State Capitol Building, Room 124
Cheyenne, WY 82002
P: (307) 777-7434
F: (307) 632-3909

Governor's Chief of Staff

Manages the office of the governor and assists in all duties performed by the governor.

Information provided by:

National Governors Association
Scott Pattison
Executive Director
Hall of the States
444 North Capitol Street
Suite 267
Washington, DC 20001
P: (202) 624-5300
F: (202) 624-5313
www.nga.org

ALABAMA
Mr. Steve Pelham
Chief of Staff
Office of the Governor
State Capitol
600 Dexter Avenue
Montgomery, AL 36130
P: (334) 242-4738

ALASKA
Mr. Scott Kendall
Chief of Staff
Office of the Governor
State Capitol
P.O. Box 110001
Juneau, AK 99811
P: (907) 465-3500

AMERICAN SAMOA
Mr. John Saelua
Chief of Staff
Office of the Governor
Executive Office Building,
Third Floor
Pago Pago, AS 96799
P: (684) 633-4116
F: (684) 633-2269

ARIZONA
Mr. Kirk Adams
Chief of Staff
Office of the Governor
State Capitol
1700 West Washington
Phoenix, AZ 85007
P: (602) 542-1444
E: kadams@az.gov

ARKANSAS
Ms. Alison Williams
Chief of Staff
Office of the Governor
State Capitol, Suite 250
Little Rock, AR 72201
P: (501) 682-2345

CALIFORNIA
Ms. Nancy McFadden
Chief of Staff
Office of the Governor
State Capitol
Sacramento, CA 95814
P: (916) 445-2841

COLORADO
Mr. Doug Friednash
Chief of Staff
Office of the Governor
136 State Capitol
Denver, CO 80203
P: (303) 866-2471
E: djfriednash@state.co.us

CONNECTICUT
Mr. Brian Durand
Chief of Staff
Office of the Governor
210 Capitol Avenue
Hartford, CT 06106
P: (800) 406-1527
E: brian.durand@ct.gov

DELAWARE
Mr. Doug Gramiak
Chief of Staff
Office of the Governor
Legislative Hall
Dover, DE 19902
P: (302) 577-3210
E: doug.gramiak@state.de.us

FLORIDA
Ms. Kim McDougal
Chief of Staff
Office of the Governor
The Capitol
400 South Monroe Street
Tallahassee, FL 32399
P: (850) 488-7146
E: kim.mcdougal
@eog.myflorida.com

GEORGIA
Mr. Chris Riley
Chief of Staff
Office of the Governor
203 State Capitol
Atlanta, GA 30334
P: (404) 656-1776
F: (404) 657-7332

GUAM
Mr. Mark Calvo
Chief of Staff
Office of the Governor
Executive Chamber
P.O. Box 2950
Agana, GU 96932
P: (671) 472-8931

HAWAII
Mr. Michael J. McCartney
Chief of Staff
Office of the Governor
Executive Chambers
State Capitol
Honolulu, HI 96813
P: (808) 586-0034
E: mike.mccartney
@hawaii.gov

IDAHO
Mr. David Hensley
Chief of Staff
Office of the Governor
700 West Jefferson Street
2nd Floor, West Wing
Boise, ID 83702
P: (208) 334-2100
F: (208) 334-2175
E: dhensley@gov.idaho.gov

ILLINOIS
Mr. Richard Goldberg
Chief of Staff
Office of the Governor
State Capitol
207 Statehouse
Springfield, IL 62706
P: (217) 782-0244
F: (217) 524-4049

INDIANA
Mr. Earl Goode
Chief of Staff
Office of the Governor
State Capitol, Room 206
Indianapolis, IN 46204
P: (317) 232-4567
F: (317) 232-3443
E: egoode@gov.in.gov

IOWA
Mr. Michael Bosselot
Chief of Staff
Office of the Governor
State Capitol
Des Moines, IA 50319
P: (515) 281-5211

KANSAS
Mr. Jon Hummell
Chief of Staff
Office of the Governor
State Capitol, Suite 212S
300 Southwest 10th Avenue
Topeka, KS 66612
P: (785) 296-3232
E: jon.hummell@ks.gov

KENTUCKY
Mr. James Brickman
Chief of Staff
Office of the Governor
700 Capitol Avenue, Suite 100
Frankfort, KY 40601
P: (502) 564-2611

LOUISIANA
Mr. Mark Cooper
Chief of Staff
Office of the Governor
P.O. Box 94004
Baton Rouge, LA 70804
P: (225) 342-7015
E: mark.a.cooper@la.gov

MAINE
Mr. John McGough
Chief of Staff
Office of the Governor
1 State House Station
Augusta, ME 04333
P: (207) 287-3531
F: (207) 287-1034
E: John.McGough@maine.gov

MARYLAND
Mr. Sam Malhotra
Chief of Staff
Office of the Governor
State House
100 State Circle
Annapolis, MD 21401
P: (410) 974-3901
E: sam.malhotra
@maryland.gov

MASSACHUSETTS
Mr. Steven Kadish
Chief of Staff
Office of the Governor
State House, Room 360
Boston, MA 02133
P: (617) 725-4005
E: steven.kadish
@state.ma.us

MICHIGAN
Mr. Dick Posthumus
Chief of Staff
Office of the Governor
P.O. Box 30013
Lansing, MI 48909
P: (517) 373-3400

Governor's Chief of Staff

MINNESOTA
Ms. Jaime Tincher
Chief of Staff
Office of the Governor
130 State Capitol
75 Rev. Martin Luther King Jr. Boulevard
St. Paul, MN 55155
P: (651) 201-3400
E: Jaime.tincher@state.mn.us

MISSISSIPPI
Mr. Joseph Songy
Chief of Staff
Office of the Governor
P.O. Box 139
Jackson, MS 39205
P: (601) 359-3150

MISSOURI
Mr. Michael Roche
Chief of Staff
Office of the Governor
Capitol Building, Room 216
P.O. Box 720
Jefferson City, MO 65102
P: (573) 751-3222

MONTANA
Ms. Tracy Stone-Manning
Chief of Staff
Office of the Governor
State Capitol
Helena, MT 59620
P: (406) 444-3111
F: (406) 444-4386
E: TStone-Manning@mt.gov

NEBRASKA
Mr. Matt Miltenberger
Chief of Staff
Office of the Governor
P.O. Box 94848
Lincoln, NE 68509
P: (402) 471-2244
E: matt.miltenberger@nebraska.gov

NEVADA
Mr. Michael J. Willden
Chief of Staff
Office of the Governor
State Capitol Building
101 North Carson Street
Carson City, NV 89701
P: (775) 684-5670
E: mwillden@gov.nv.gov

NEW HAMPSHIRE
Ms. Jayne Millerick
Chief of Staff
Office of the Governor
State House
107 North Main Street, Room 208
Concord, NH 03301
P: (603) 271-2121

NEW JERSEY
Ms. Amy Cradic
Chief of Staff
Office of the Governor
The State House
P.O. Box 001
Trenton, NJ 08625
P: (609) 292-6000

NEW MEXICO
Mr. Keith J. Gardner
Chief of Staff
Office of the Governor
State Capitol, Fourth Floor
Santa Fe, NM 87501
P: (505) 476-2200
F: (505) 476-2226
E: keith.gardner@state.nm.us

NEW YORK
Ms. Melissa DeRosa
Chief of Staff
Office of the Governor
State Capitol
Albany, NY 12224
P: (518) 474-7516

NORTH CAROLINA
Ms. Kristi Jones
Chief of Staff
Office of the Governor
20301 Mail Service Center
Raleigh, NC 27699
P: (919) 733-4240

NORTH DAKOTA
Ms. JoDee Hanson
Chief Administrative Officer
Office of the Governor
State Capitol, Department 101
600 East Boulevard Avenue
Bismarck, ND 58505
P: (701) 328-2200

Ms. Jodi Uecker
Chief Operating Officer
Office of the Governor
State Capitol, Department 101
600 East Boulevard Avenue
Bismarck, ND 58505
P: (701) 328-2200

NORTHERN MARIANA ISLANDS
Mr. Matt Deleon Guerrero
Chief of Staff
Office of the Governor
Caller Box 10007, Capitol Hill
Saipan, MP 96950
P: (670) 237-2231
F: (670) 664-2211

OHIO
Ms. Beth Hansen
Chief of Staff
Office of the Governor
77 South High Street, 30th Floor
Columbus, OH 43215
P: (614) 466-3555
F: (614) 466-9354
E: beth.hansen@governor.ohio.gov

OKLAHOMA
Mr. Chris Benge
Chief of Staff
Office of the Governor
State Capitol Building
2300 Lincoln Boulevard, Room 212
Oklahoma City, OK 73105
P: (405) 521-2342

OREGON
Nik Blosser
Chief of Staff
Office of the Governor
State Capitol, Room 160
900 Court Street, Northeast
Salem, OR 97301
P: (503) 373-1565

PENNSYLVANIA
Mr. Mike Brunelle
Chief of Staff
Office of the Governor
Room 225, Main Capitol Building
Harrisburg, PA 17120
P: (717) 787-2500

PUERTO RICO
Mr. William Villafane
Chief of Staff
Office of the Governor
La Fortaleza
P.O. Box 9020082
San Juan, PR 00902
P: (787) 721-7000

RHODE ISLAND
Mr. Brett Smiley
Chief of Staff
Office of the Governor
State House
Providence, RI 02903
P: (401) 222-8144

SOUTH CAROLINA
Mr. Trey Walker
Chief of Staff
Office of the Governor
1205 Pendleton Street
Columbia, SC 29201
P: (803) 734-2100

SOUTH DAKOTA
Mr. Tony Venhuizen
Chief of Staff
Office of the Governor
500 East Capitol Avenue
Pierre, SD 57501
P: (605) 773-3212
E: tony.venhuizen@state.sd.us

TENNESSEE
Mr. James M. Henry
Chief of Staff
Office of the Governor
State Capitol
Nashville, TN 37243
P: (615) 741-2001
F: (615) 532-9711
E: jim.henry@tn.gov

TEXAS
Mr. Daniel Hodge
Chief of Staff
Office of the Governor
P.O. Box 12428
Austin, TX 78711
P: (512) 463-2000

U.S. VIRGIN ISLANDS
Ms. Rochelle Corneiro
Chief of Staff
Office of the Governor
Government House, 21-22 Kongens Gade
Charlotte Amalie
St. Thomas, VI 00802
P: (340) 774-0001

UTAH
Mr. Justin Harding
Chief of Staff
Office of the Governor
State Capitol, Suite 200
Salt Lake City, UT 84114
P: (801) 538-1000

VERMONT
Mr. Jason Gibbs
Chief of Staff
Office of the Governor
109 State Street
Pavilion Office Building
Montpelier, VT 05609
P: (802) 828-3333
F: (802) 828-3339

VIRGINIA
Mr. Paul J. Reagan
Chief of Staff
Office of the Governor
State Capitol, 3rd Floor
Richmond, VA 23219
P: (804) 786-2211
F: (804) 371-6351

WASHINGTON
Mr. David Postman
Chief of Staff
Office of the Governor
P.O. Box 40002
Olympia, WA 98504
P: (360) 902-4111

WEST VIRGINIA
Mr. Nick Casey
Chief of Staff
Office of the Governor
1900 Kanawha Street
Charleston, WV 25305
P: (304) 558-2000

WISCONSIN
Mr. Rich Zipperer
Chief of Staff
Office of the Governor
115 East State Capitol
Madison, WI 53707
P: (608) 266-1212

WYOMING
Ms. Kari Gray
Chief of Staff
Office of the Governor
State Capitol Building, Room
124
Cheyenne, WY 82002
P: (307) 777-7434
F: (307) 632-3909

Governor's Legislative Director

Oversees the governor's legislative priorities, aids in legislative administration, and assists the governor in all other legislative matters.

ALASKA
Mr. Darwin Peterson
Legislative Director
Office of the Governor
State Capitol
P.O. Box 110001
Juneau, AK 99811
P: (907) 465-3500
F: (907) 465-3532
E: darwin.peterson@alaska.gov

ARIZONA
Ms. Katie Fischer
Director, Legislative Affairs
Office of the Governor
1700 West Washington
Phoenix, AZ 85007
P: (602) 542-7585

ARKANSAS
Mr. Rett Hatcher
Director of Legislative & Agency Affairs
Office of the Governor
State Capitol, Room 250
500 Woodlane Avenue
Little Rock, AR 72201
P: (501) 682-2345

CALIFORNIA
Ms. Camille Wagner
Legislative Affairs Secretary
Office of the Governor
State Capitol
Sacramento, CA 95814
P: (916) 445-2841
F: (916) 445-4633

COLORADO
Mr. Kurtis Morrison
Legislative Director
Office of the Governor
136 State Capitol
Denver, CO 80203
P: (303) 866-2471
F: (303) 866-2003
E: kurt.morrison@state.co.us

FLORIDA
Mr. Kevin Reilly
Legislative Affairs Director
Office of the Governor
The Capitol
400 South Monroe Street
Tallahassee, FL 32399
P: (850) 488-7146

GEORGIA
Ms. Julia Ayers
Deputy Chief of Staff for Legislative & External Affairs
Office of the Governor
142 State Capitol
Atlanta, GA 30334
P: (404) 656-1776
F: (404) 656-5947

IDAHO
Mr. David Hensley
Chief of Staff
Office of the Governor
700 West Jefferson Street
2nd Floor, West Wing
Boise, ID 83702
P: (208) 334-2100
F: (208) 334-2175
E: dhensley@gov.idaho.gov

ILLINOIS
Mr. Richard Goldberg
Chief of Staff
Office of the Governor
State Capitol
207 Statehouse
Springfield, IL 62706
P: (217) 782-0244
F: (217) 524-4049

INDIANA
Ms. Allison Karns
Deputy Chief of Staff of Legislative Affairs
Office of the Governor
State House
Indianapolis, IN 46204
P: (317) 234-8895
F: (317) 232-3443
E: akarns@gov.in.gov

KANSAS
Mr. Brandon Smith
Director of Policy
Office of the Governor
State Capitol, 2nd Floor
Topeka, KS 66612
P: (785) 296-3232
F: (785) 296-7973

KENTUCKY
Mr. Brian Sunderland
Legislative Director
Office of the Governor
700 Capitol Avenue, Suite 100
Frankfort, KY 40601
P: (502) 564-2611
F: (502) 564-2517
E: brian.sunderland@ky.gov

LOUISIANA
Mr. Noble E. Ellington
Legislative Affairs Director
Office of the Governor
P.O. Box 94004
Baton Rouge, LA 70804
P: (225) 342-7188
E: noble.ellington@la.gov

MAINE
Mr. John McGough
Chief of Staff
Office of the Governor
1 State House Station
Augusta, ME 04333
P: (207) 287-3531
F: (207) 287-1034
E: John.McGough@maine.gov

MARYLAND
Mr. Sam Malhotra
Chief of Staff
Office of the Governor
State House
100 State Circle
Annapolis, MD 21401
P: (410) 974-3901
E: sam.malhotra@maryland.gov

MASSACHUSETTS
Ms. Kaitlyn Sprague
Legislative Affairs Director
Office of the Governor
State House, Room 360
Boston, MA 02133
P: (617) 725-4005

MICHIGAN
Mr. Dick Posthumus
Chief of Staff
Office of the Governor
P.O. Box 30013
Lansing, MI 48909
P: (517) 373-3400

MINNESOTA
Mr. Linden Zakula
Deputy Chief of Staff for Communications
Office of the Governor
State Capitol, Room 130
St. Paul, MN 55155
P: (651) 201-3441
E: linden.zakula@state.mn.us

MISSOURI
Ms. Jennae Neustadt
Legislative Director
Office of the Governor
Capitol Building, Room 216
Jefferson City, MO 65101
P: (573) 751-3222
F: (573) 526-3291

MONTANA
Mr. Jim Molloy
Senior Policy Advisor
Office of the Governor
P.O. Box 200801
Helena, MT 59620
P: (406) 444-5503
E: jmolloy@mt.gov

NEW YORK
Ms. Valerie Galasso
Senior Policy Advisor
Office of the Governor
State Capitol
Albany, NY 12224
P: (518) 408-2576
F: (518) 474-8390

NORTH CAROLINA
Mr. Brad Adcock
Legislative Director
Office of the Governor
20301 Mail Service Center
Raleigh, NC 27699
P: (919) 814-2000

NORTH DAKOTA
Mr. Robert Lauf
Director & Senior Policy Advisor
Office of the Governor
State Capitol, Department 101
600 East Boulevard Avenue
Bismarck, ND 58505
P: (701) 328-2200
F: (701) 328-2205

OHIO
Mr. Merle Madrid
Director of Legislative Affairs
Office of the Governor
77 South High Street, 30th Floor
Columbus, OH 43215
P: (614) 644-0856
E: merle.madrid@governor.ohio.gov

OREGON
Mr. Ivo Trummer
Legislative Director
Office of the Governor
900 Court Street, Northeast
Salem, OR 97301
P: (503) 378-6548

PENNSYLVANIA
Mr. Will Danowski
Secretary of Legislative Affairs
Office of the Governor
Room 225, Main Capitol
Building
Harrisburg, PA 17120
P: (717) 787-2500

RHODE ISLAND
Mr. R. David Cruise
Director of Legislative Affairs
Office of the Governor
State House
Providence, RI 02903
P: (401) 222-2080
F: (401) 273-5729

SOUTH CAROLINA
Mr. Jason Brown
Director of Legislative Policy
Office of the Governor
P.O. Box 12267
Columbia, SC 29211
P: (803) 734-2100
F: (803) 734-5167

SOUTH DAKOTA
Mr. Matt Konenkamp
Policy Advisor
Office of the Governor
State Capitol
500 East Capitol Avenue
Pierre, SD 57501
P: (605) 773-3212
F: (605) 773-5844

TENNESSEE
Mr. Warren Wells
Director of Legislation
Office of the Governor
State Capitol
Nashville, TN 37243
P: (615) 741-2001
F: (615) 532-9711

TEXAS
Mr. Jay Dyer
Director of Legislative Affairs
Office of the Governor
P.O. Box 12428
Austin, TX 78711
P: (512) 463-1830

VERMONT
Ms. Kendal Smith
Director of Policy & Legislative
Affairs
Office of the Governor
109 State Street
Montpelier, VT 05609
P: (802) 828-3333

WASHINGTON
Mr. Drew Shirk
Executive Director of
Legislative Affairs
Office of the Governor
P.O. Box 40002
Olympia, WA 98504
P: (360) 902-0672
E: drew.shirk@gov.wa.gov

WEST VIRGINIA
Mr. Bob Ashley
Legislative Director
Office of the Governor
State Capitol Complex
1900 Kanawha Boulevard, East
Charleston, WV 25305
P: (304) 558-2000

Governor's Media Contacts

Issues press releases on behalf of the governor, acts as a liaison with the media and public, and serves as the governor's spokesperson.

Information provided by:

National Governors Association
Scott Pattison
Executive Director
Hall of the States
444 North Capitol Street
Suite 267
Washington, DC 20001
P: (202) 624-5300
F: (202) 624-5313
www.nga.org

ALABAMA
Ms. Yasamie August
Communications Director
Office of the Governor
State Capitol, 600 Dexter Avenue
Montgomery, AL 36130
P: (334) 242-7150

ALASKA
Ms. Grace Jang-Trytten
Press Secretary
Office of the Governor
State Capitol
P.O. Box 110001
Juneau, AK 99811
P: (907) 269-3031

AMERICAN SAMOA
Mr. Iu Joseph Pereira
Executive Assistant To the Governor/Press Officer
Office of the Governor
Pago Pago, AS 96799
P: (684) 633-4116

ARIZONA
Mr. Daniel Scarpinato
Deputy Chief of Staff for Communications
Office of the Governor
1700 West Washington
Phoenix, AZ 85007
P: (602) 542-2661

ARKANSAS
Mr. JR Davis
Communications Director
Office of the Governor
State Capitol, Room 250
Little Rock, AR 72201
P: (501) 683-6412

CALIFORNIA
Mr. Evan Westrup
Press Secretary
Office of the Governor
State Capitol, First Floor
Sacramento, CA 95814
P: (916) 445-4571

COLORADO
Ms. Marie Logsden
Director of Communications
Office of the Governor
State Capitol, Room 127
Denver, CO 80203
P: (303) 866-6324

CONNECTICUT
Ms. Kelly Donnelly
Communications Director
Office of the Governor
State Capitol, 210 Capitol Avenue
Hartford, CT 06106
P: (860) 524-7349

DELAWARE
Mr. Jonathon Starkey
Communications Director
Office of the Governor
Tatnall Building
William Penn Street
Dover, DE 19901
P: (302) 577-8495

FLORIDA
Ms. Jackie Schutz
Communications Director
Office of the Governor
State Capitol, Room 206
Tallahassee, FL 32399
P: (850) 488-5394

GEORGIA
Ms. Jenn Talaber Ryan
Deputy Chief of Staff of Communications
Office of the Governor
State Capitol, Room 100
Atlanta, GA 30334
P: (404) 651-7783

GUAM
Oyo Ngirairikl
Communications Director
Office of the Governor
Executive Chamber
P.O. Box 2950
Hagatna, GU 96932
P: (671) 475-9379

HAWAII
Ms. Cindy McMillan
Director of Communications
Office of the Governor
State Capitol
415 South Beretania Street
Honolulu, HI 96813
P: (808) 586-0034

IDAHO
Mr. Mark Warbis
Communications Director
Office of the Governor
State Capitol
700 West Jefferson, 2nd Floor
Boise, ID 83720
P: (208) 334-2100

ILLINOIS
Mr. Brad Hahn
Communications Director
Office of the Governor
James R. Thompson Center
100 West Randolph, Suite 16-100
Chicago, IL 60601
P: (312) 814-4220

INDIANA
Ms. Susana Suarez
Director of Communications
Office of the Governor
206 State House
Indianapolis, IN 46204
P: (317) 232-1622

IOWA
Mr. Benn Hammes
Communications Director
Office of the Governor
State Capitol
Des Moines, IA 50319
P: (515) 725-3507

KANSAS
Ms. Melika Willoughby
Communications Director
Office of the Governor
State Capitol, Second Floor
Topeka, KS 66612
P: (785) 368-7138

KENTUCKY
Ms. Amanda Stamper
Communications Director
Office of the Governor
State Capitol
700 Capitol Avenue Suite 100
Frankfort, KY 40601
P: (502) 564-2611

LOUISIANA
Mr. Richard Carbo
Communications Director
Office of the Governor
P.O. Box 94004
Baton Rouge, LA 70804
P: (225) 342-8006
E: Richard.carbo@la.gov

MAINE
Mr. Peter Steele
Communications Director
Office of the Governor
State House, Station 1
Augusta, ME 04333
P: (207) 287-5086

MARYLAND
Mr. Douglass Mayer
Communications Director
Office of the Governor
State House
Annapolis, MD 21401
P: (410) 974-2316

MASSACHUSETTS
Mr. Tim Buckley
Communications Director
Office of the Governor
State House, Room 265
Boston, MA 02133
P: (617) 483-3395

MICHIGAN
Mr. Ari Adler
Director of Communications
Office of the Governor
P.O. Box 30013
Lansing, MI 48909
P: (517) 335-6397

MINNESOTA
Mr. Linden Zakula
Deputy Chief of Staff for Communications
Office of the Governor
State Capitol, Room 130
St. Paul, MN 55155
P: (651) 201-3441
E: linden.zakula@state.mn.us

MISSISSIPPI
Mr. Clay Chandler
Director of Communications
Office of the Governor
P.O. Box 139
Jackson, MS 39205
P: (601) 576-2802

MISSOURI
Mr. Parker Brian
Director of Communications
Office of the Governor
State Capitol
P.O. Box 720
Jefferson City, MO 65101
P: (573) 751-3222

MONTANA
Ronja Abel
Director of Communications
Office of the Governor
State Capitol
Helena, MT 59620
P: (406) 444-9844

NEBRASKA
Mr. Taylor Gage
Communications Director
Office of the Governor
P.O. Box 94848
Lincoln, NE 68509
P: (402) 471-7047

NEVADA
Ms. Mari St. Martin
Communications Director
Office of the Governor
State Capitol, Governor's Office
101 North Carson Street
Carson City, NV 89701
P: (775) 250-8210

NEW HAMPSHIRE
Mr. David Abrams
Director of Communications
Office of the Governor
State House
Concord, NH 03301
P: (603) 271-2121

NEW JERSEY
Ms. Jacqueline Halldow
Director of Communications
Office of the Governor
125 West State Street
P.O. Box 001
Trenton, NJ 08625
P: (609) 777-2600

NEW MEXICO
Mr. Christian Sanchez
Communications Director
Office of the Governor
State Capitol, Fourth Floor
Santa Fe, NM 87501
P: (505) 476-2259

NEW YORK
Mr. James Allen
Director of Communications
Office of the Governor
State Capitol, Room 200
Albany, NY 12224
P: (518) 474-8418

NORTH CAROLINA
Ms. Sadie Weiner
Communications Director
Office of the Governor
20301 Mail Service Center
Raleigh, NC 27699
P: (908) 814-2100

NORTH DAKOTA
Mr. Mike Nowatzki
Communications Director
Office of the Governor
600 East Boulevard Avenue
Department 101
Bismarck, ND 58505
P: (701) 328-2200

NORTHERN MARIANA ISLANDS
Mr. Matt Deleon Guerrero
Chief of Staff
Office of the Governor
Caller Box 10007, Capitol Hill
Saipan, MP 96950
P: (670) 237-2231
F: (670) 664-2211

OHIO
Mr. Jim Lynch
Communications Director
Office of the Governor
South High Street, 30th Floor
Columbus, OH 43215
P: (614) 466-3555

OKLAHOMA
Mr. Michael McNutt
Communications Director
Office of the Governor
State Capitol
Oklahoma City, OK 73105
P: (405) 522-8878

OREGON
Mr. Chris Pair
Communications Director
Office of the Governor
State Capitol, Room 254
900 Court Street, Northeast
Salem, OR 97310
P: (971) 283-8197

PENNSYLVANIA
Mr. Mark Nicastre
Director of Communications
Office of the Governor
Main Capitol Building, Room 308
Harrisburg, PA 17120
P: (717) 783-1116

PUERTO RICO
Mr. Pedro Cerame
Communications Director
Office of the Governor
La Fortaleza
San Juan, PR 00902
P: (202) 778-0710

RHODE ISLAND
Mr. Michael Raia
Director of Communications
Office of the Governor
State House
Providence, RI 02903
P: (401) 222-8134

SOUTH CAROLINA
Mr. Brian Symmes
Communications Director
Office of the Governor
1205 Pendleton Street
Columbia, SC 29201
P: (803) 734-2100

SOUTH DAKOTA
Mr. Tony Venhuizen
Chief of Staff
Office of the Governor
500 East Capitol Avenue
Pierre, SD 57501
P: (605) 773-3212
E: tony.venhuizen@state.sd.us

TENNESSEE
Mr. David Smith
Director of Communications
Office of the Governor
State Capitol, Room G-9
Nashville, TN 37243
P: (615) 741-3763

TEXAS
Mr. Matt Hirsch
Director of Communications
Office of the Governor
P.O. Box 12428
Austin, TX 78711
P: (512) 936-3349

U.S. VIRGIN ISLANDS
Ms. Kimberly Jones
Press Secretary
Office of the Governor
Government House, 21-22 Kongens Gade
Charlotte Amalie
St. Thomas, VI 00802
P: (340) 693-4361

UTAH
Mr. Paul Edwards
Deputy Chief of Staff, Communications & Policy
Office of the Governor
210 State Capitol, Suite 200
Salt Lake City, UT 84114
P: (801) 538-1503

VERMONT
Ms. Rebecca Kelley
Director of Communications
Office of the Governor
109 State Street
Montpelier, VT 05609
P: (802) 828-6463

VIRGINIA
Mr. Brian Coy
Communications Director
Office of the Governor
Patrick Henry Building, 3rd Floor
1111 East Broad Street
Richmond, VA 23219
P: (804) 225-4260

WEST VIRGINIA
Mr. Carl Antolini
Director of Communications
Office of the Governor
State Capitol
Charleston, WV 25305
P: (304) 558-4977

WISCONSIN
Mr. Jack Jablonski
Communications Director
Office of the Governor
State Capitol
115 East Capitol
Madison, WI 53702
P: (608) 267-7303

WYOMING
Mr. David Bush
Communications Director
Office of the Governor
State Capitol
Cheyenne, WY 82002
P: (307) 777-7437

Hazardous Waste Management

Develops and maintains a comprehensive hazardous waste management program in the state.

ALABAMA
Mr. Stephen A. Cobb
Chief
Governmental Hazardous Waste
Environmental Management,
Land Division
P.O. Box 301463
Montgomery, AL 36130
P: (334) 271-7739
F: (334) 279-3050

ALASKA
Mr. Bob Blankenburg
Program Manager
Solid Waste Program
Division of Environmental Health
555 Cordova Street
Anchorage, AK 99501
P: (907) 269-7802
F: (907) 269-7510
E: bob.blankenburg@alaska.gov

Ms. Kristin Ryan
Director
Division of Spill Prevention & Response
Department of Environmental Conservation
P.O. Box 111800
Anchorage, AK 99811
P: (907) 269-3094
F: (907) 269-7654
E: kristin.ryan@alaska.gov

ARIZONA
Ms. Laura L. Malone
Waste Programs Division Director
Department of Environmental Quality
1110 West Washington Street
Phoenix, AZ 85007
P: (602) 771-4208
F: (602) 771-2302
E: malone.laura@azdeq.gov

ARKANSAS
Ms. Tammie J. Hynum
Senior Manager, Regulated Waste Operations
Hazardous Waste Division
Department of Environmental Quality
5301 Northshore Drive
North Little Rock, AR 72118
P: (501) 682-0831
F: (501) 682-0880
E: hynum@adeq.state.ar.us

CALIFORNIA
Mr. Scott Smithline
Director
Department of Resources, Recycling & Recovery
1001 I Street
P.O. Box 4025
Sacramento, CA 95812
P: (916) 322-4032
F: (916) 319-7227
E: Scott.Smithline@CalRecycle.ca.gov

COLORADO
Mr. Gary Baughman
Director
Hazardous Materials & Waste Management Division
Public Health & Environment
4300 Cherry Creek Drive, South
Denver, CO 80246
P: (303) 692-3338
F: (303) 759-5355
E: gary.baughman@state.co.us

DELAWARE
Ms. Nancy C. Marker
Administrator
Solid & Hazardous Waste Management Section
89 Kings Highway
Dover, DE 19901
P: (302) 739-9403
F: (302) 739-5060
E: nancy.marker@state.de.us

DISTRICT OF COLUMBIA
Dr. LaQuandra S. Nesbitt
Director
Department of Health
899 North Capitol Street, Northeast
Washington, DC 20002
P: (202) 442-5955
F: (202) 442-4795
E: doh@dc.gov

FLORIDA
Mr. Joe Ullo
Director
Division of Waste Management
Department of Environmental Protection
2600 Blair Stone Road
Tallahassee, FL 32399
P: (850) 245-8693
E: joseph.ullo@dep.state.fl.us

GEORGIA
Mr. Jeff Cown
Branch Chief
Land Protection Branch
2 Martin Luther King Jr. Drive Southeast
Suite 1054, East Floyd Tower
Atlanta, GA 30334
P: (404) 463-8509
F: (404) 362-2693
E: jeff.cown@dnr.ga.gov

HAWAII
Mr. Steven Y.K. Chang
Branch Chief
Solid & Hazardous Waste Branch
Department of Health
919 Ala Moana Boulevard, #212
Honolulu, HI 96814
P: (808) 586-4226
F: (808) 586-7509
E: schang@eha.health.state.hi.us

IDAHO
Mr. Michael McCurdy
Administrator
Waste Management & Remediation Division
DEQ State Office
1410 North Hilton
Boise, ID 83706
P: (208) 373-0188
F: (208) 373-0154
E: michael.mccurdy@deq.idaho.gov

ILLINOIS
Dr. Kevin O'Brien
Director
Sustainable Technology Center
One East Hazelwood Drive
Champaign, IL 61820
P: (217) 333-8940
F: (217) 333-8944
E: kcobrien@illinois.edu

INDIANA
Ms. Peggy Dorsey
Assistant Commissioner, Office of Land Quality
Department of Environmental Management
Government Center North
100 North Senate Avenue
Indianapolis, IN 46204
P: (317) 234-0337
F: (317) 233-6647
E: PDorsey@idem.IN.gov

KANSAS
Mr. William L. Bider
Director
Bureau of Waste Management
Department of Health & Environment
1000 Southwest Jackson Street, Suite 320
Topeka, KS 66612
P: (785) 296-1600
F: (785) 296-1612
E: William.Bider@ks.gov

KENTUCKY
Ms. April Webb
Branch Manager
Hazardous Waste Branch
Division of Waste Management
200 Fair Oaks Lane, 2nd Floor
Frankfort, KY 40601
P: (502) 564-6716
F: (502) 564-4049
E: April.Webb@ky.gov

LOUISIANA
Ms. Lourdes Iturralde
Assistant Secretary
Office of Environmental Compliance
Department of Environmental Quality
P.O. Box 4312
Baton Rouge, LA 70821
P: (225) 219-3710
F: (225) 219-3708
E: deqoec@la.gov

MARYLAND
Ms. Hilary Miller
Director
Land Management Administration
Department of the Environment
1800 Washington Boulevard
Baltimore, MD 21230
P: (410) 537-3314
F: (410) 537-3321
E: hilary.miller@maryland.gov

MASSACHUSETTS
Mr. Martin Suuberg
Commissioner
Department of Environmental Protection
One Winter Street
Boston, MA 02108
P: (617) 292-5500
F: (617) 574-6880

MINNESOTA
Mr. John Linc Stine
Commissioner
Pollution Control Agency
520 Lafayette Road, North
St. Paul, MN 55155
P: (651) 757-2014
F: (651) 296-6334
E: john.stine@state.mn.us

MISSISSIPPI
Mr. Mark Williams
Chief
Solid Waste Policy, Planning & Grants Branch
Department of Environmental Quality
P.O. Box 2261
Jackson, MS 39225
P: (601) 961-5304
F: (601) 961-5785
E: mark_williams@deq.state.ms.us

MISSOURI
Ms. Angie McMichael
Acting Director
Hazardous Waste
Department of Natural Resources
P.O. Box 176
Jefferson City, MO 65102
P: (573) 751-3176
E: hazwaste@dnr.mo.gov

MONTANA
Mr. Ed Tinsley
Continuity of Government Program Manager
Office of State Continuity & Emergency Management
P.O. Box 200113
Helena, MT 59620
P: (406) 444-0125
F: (406) 444-2939
E: Continuity@mt.gov

NEBRASKA
Mr. Jim Macy
Director
Department of Environmental Quality
1200 N Street, Suite 400
P.O. Box 98922
Lincoln, NE 68509
P: (402) 471-2186
F: (402) 471-2909
E: Jim.Macy@nebraska.gov

NEVADA
Mr. Eric Noack
Bureau Chief
Bureau of Waste Management
Division of Environmental Protection
901 South Stewart Street, Suite 4001
Carson City, NV 89701
P: (775) 687-9366
F: (775) 687-6396
E: enoack@ndep.nv.gov

NEW HAMPSHIRE
Mr. John Duclos
Bureau Administrator
Hazardous Waste Management Bureau
Department of Environmental Services
29 Hazen Drive, P.O. Box 95
Concord, NH 03301
P: (603) 271-1998
F: (603) 271-2456
E: john.duclos@des.nh.gov

NEW JERSEY
Mr. Ray Bukowski
Assistant Commissioner, Compliance & Enforcement
Department of Environmental Protection
401 East State Street
P.O. Box 420
Trenton, NJ 08625
P: (609) 984-3285
F: (609) 292-9938

NEW MEXICO
Mr. John E. Kielng
Chief
Hazardous Waste Bureau
State Environment Department
2905 Rodeo Park Drive East, Building 1
Santa Fe, NM 87505
P: (505) 476-6035
F: (505) 476-6030
E: john.kielng@state.nm.us

NEW YORK
Mr. Basil Seggos
Commissioner
Department of Environmental Conservation
625 Broadway
Albany, NY 12233
P: (518) 402-8545
F: (518) 402-8541

NORTH CAROLINA
Ms. Liz Cannon
Section Chief for Hazardous Waste
Department of Environment & Natural Resources
Division of Waste Management
1646 Mail Service Center
Raleigh, NC 27699
P: (919) 707-8203
F: (919) 715-0708

Ms. Julie Woosley
Section Chief for Hazardous Waste
Department of Environment & Natural Resources
Division of Waste Management
217 West Jones Street
Raleigh, NC 27603
P: (919) 707-8203
F: (919) 715-0708
E: julie.woosley@ncdenr.gov

NORTH DAKOTA
Mr. Scott Radig
Director
Division of Waste Management
Department of Health
918 East Divide Avenue, 3rd Floor
Bismark, ND 58501
P: (701) 328-5166
F: (701) 328-5200
E: sradig@nd.gov

NORTHERN MARIANA ISLANDS
Mr. Joaquin P. Omar
Deputy Special Assistant for EMO/OHS
Emergency Management Office
Office of the Governor
Caller Box 10007
Saipan, MP 96950
P: (670) 322-8001
F: (670) 322-7743
E: jpomar@cnmiemo.gov.mp

OHIO
Ms. Terrie TerMeer
Chief
Division of Materials & Waste Management
50 West Town Street, Suite 700
P.O. Box 1049
Columbus, OH 43216
P: (614) 728-0017
F: (614) 728-5315
E: terrie.termeer@epa.ohio.gov

OKLAHOMA
Ms. Kelly Dixon
Division Director
Land Protection Division
Department of Environmental Quality
P.O. Box 1677
Oklahoma City, OK 73101
P: (405) 702-5100
F: (405) 702-5101
E: kelly.dixon@deq.ok.gov

OREGON
Ms. Wendy Wiles
Environmental Solutions Division Administrator
Department of Environmental Quality
700 Northeast Multnomah Street
Suite 600
Portland, OR 97232
P: (503) 229-6834
F: (503) 229-6977
E: wiles.wendy@deq.state.or.us

PUERTO RICO
Mr. Nelson J. Santiago Marrero
Executive Director
Solid Waste Management Authority
P.O. Box 40285
San Juan, PR 00940
P: (787) 765-7575
F: (787) 753-2220

RHODE ISLAND
Ms. Janet Coit
Director
Department of Environmental Management
235 Promenade Street
Providence, RI 02908
P: (401) 222-6800
F: (401) 222-6802
E: janet.coit@dem.ri.gov

Hazardous Waste Management

SOUTH CAROLINA
Ms. Myra Reece
Director of Environmental Affairs
Department of Health & Environmental Control
2600 Bull Street
Columbia, SC 29201
P: (803) 898-3432
F: (803) 896-4001
E: info@dhec.sc.gov

SOUTH DAKOTA
Ms. Vonni Kallemeyn
Environmental Scientist Manager
Department of Environment & Natural Resources
Waste Management Program
523 East Capitol Avenue
Pierre, SD 57501
P: (605) 773-3153
F: (605) 773-6035
E: denrinternet@state.sd.us

TENNESSEE
Mr. Patrick J. Flood
Environmental Program Administrator
Division of Solid Waste Management
312 Rosa L. Parks Avenue
Nashville, TN 37243
P: (615) 532-0792
F: (615) 532-0886
E: Pat.Flood@tn.gov

TEXAS
Mr. Brent Wade
Deputy Director
Office of Waste
12100 Park 35 Circle
P.O. Box 13087
Austin, TX 78711
P: (512) 239-6566
F: (512) 239-0659

U.S. VIRGIN ISLANDS
Mr. David Simon
Director
Division of Environmental Protection
Cyril E. King Airport
Terminal Building, 2nd Floor
St. Thomas, VI 00802
P: (340) 774-3320
E: david.simon@dpnr.gov.vi

UTAH
Mr. Scott Anderson
Director
Division of Waste Management & Radiation Control
Department of Environmental Quality
P.O. Box 144880
Salt Lake City, UT 84114
P: (801) 536-0203
F: (801) 536-0222
E: standerson@utah.gov

VERMONT
Mr. Chuck Schwer
Director
Waste Management & Prevention Division
One National Life Drive
Davis Building, 1st Floor
Montpelier, VT 05620
P: (802) 249-5324
F: (802) 828-1011
E: chuck.schwer@vermont.gov

VIRGINIA
Mr. David K. Paylor
Director
Department of Environmental Quality
629 East Main Street
P.O. Box 1105
Richmond, VA 23219
P: (804) 698-4000
F: (804) 698-4019
E: david.paylor@deq.virginia.gov

WASHINGTON
Mr. Darin Rice
Program Manager
Hazardous Waste & Toxics Reduction
Department of Ecology
300 Desmond Drive, Southeast
Lacey, WA 98503
P: (360) 407-6702
F: (360) 407-6715
E: dric461@ecy.wa.gov

WEST VIRGINIA
Ms. Patty Hickman
Director
Division of Land Restoration
Department of Environmental Protection
601 57th Street Southeast, Room 1035
Charleston, WV 25304
P: (304) 926-0499
F: (304) 926-0457
E: Patricia.A.Hickman@wv.gov

WISCONSIN
Mr. Dave Siebert
Bureau Director
Office of Business Support & Sustainability
101 South Webster Street
P.O. Box 7921
Madison, WI 53707
P: (608) 264-6048
F: (608) 267-2768
E: david.siebert@wisconsin.gov

WYOMING
Mr. Luke Esch
Administrator
Solid & Hazardous Waste Division
Department of Environmental Quality
200 West 17th Street, 2nd Floor
Cheyenne, WY 82002
P: (307) 777-7192
F: (307) 635-1784
E: luke.esch1@wyo.gov

Health Services

Manages the development, administration and delivery of all health programs.

ALABAMA
Dr. Thomas M. Miller
State Health Officer
Department of Public Health
RSA Tower, 201 Monroe Street
P.O. Box 303017
Montgomery, AL 36130
P: (334) 206-5300
F: (334) 206-5520

ALASKA
Dr. Jay C. Butler
Chief Medical Officer & Director
Division of Public Health
350 Main Street, Room 508
P.O. Box 110610
Juneau, AK 99811
P: (907) 465-3090
F: (907) 465-4632
E: jay.butler@alaska.gov

AMERICAN SAMOA
Mr. Taufete'e J. Faumuina
Director
Medical Services Authority
LBJ Tropical Medical Center
Pago Pago, AS 96799
P: (684) 633-1222
F: (684) 633-4043
E: taufetee.faumuina@lbj.asg

ARIZONA
Dr. Cara M. Christ
Director
Department of Health Services
150 North 18th Avenue
Phoenix, AZ 85007
P: (602) 542-1025
F: (602) 542-0833

ARKANSAS
Dr. Nathaniel H. Smith
Director & State Health Officer
Department of Health
4815 West Markham Street
Little Rock, AR 72205
P: (501) 661-2000
F: (501) 661-2388
E: Nathaniel.Smith@Arkansas.gov

CALIFORNIA
Dr. Karen Smith
Director
Department of Public Health
P.O. Box 997377
MS 0500
Sacramento, CA 95899
P: (916) 558-1784

COLORADO
Dr. Larry Wolk
Executive Director & Chief Medical Officer
Department of Public Health & Environment
4300 Cherry Creek Drive, South
Denver, CO 80246
P: (303) 692-2000
F: (303) 691-7702
E: larry.wolk@state.co.us

CONNECTICUT
Dr. Raul Pino
Commissioner
Department of Public Health
410 Capitol Avenue
P.O. Box 340308
Hartford, CT 06134
P: (860) 509-8000
E: raul.pino@ct.gov

DELAWARE
Dr. Karyl T. Rattay
Director
Division of Public Health
Thomas Collins Building
540 South DuPont Highway
Dover, DE 19901
P: (302) 744-4701
F: (302) 739-6659

DISTRICT OF COLUMBIA
Dr. LaQuandra S. Nesbitt
Director
Department of Health
899 North Capitol Street, Northeast
Washington, DC 20002
P: (202) 442-5955
F: (202) 442-4795
E: doh@dc.gov

FLORIDA
Dr. Celeste Philip
State Surgeon General
Department of Health
4052 Bald Cypress Way, Bin # A00
Tallahassee, FL 32399
P: (850) 245-4321
F: (850) 922-9453
E: celeste.philip@flhealth.gov

GEORGIA
Dr. Brenda C. Fitzgerald
Commissioner & State Health Officer
Division of Public Health, Department of Community Health
Two Peachtree Street, Northwest
Suite 15-470
Atlanta, GA 30303
P: (404) 657-2703

GUAM
Mr. James W. Gillan
Director
Department of Public Health & Social Services
123 Chalan Kareta
Mangilao, GU 96913
P: (671) 735-7305
F: (671) 734-2066

HAWAII
Dr. Virginia Pressler
Director of Health
State Department of Health
1250 Punchbowl Street
Honolulu, HI 96813
P: (808) 586-4410
F: (808) 586-4444

IDAHO
Ms. Elke Shaw-Tulloch
Public Health Administrator
Division of Public Health
Department of Health and Welfare
450 West State Street, 4th Floor
Boise, ID 83720
P: (208) 334-5950
F: (208) 334-6573
E: elke.shaw-tulloch@dhw.idaho.gov

ILLINOIS
Dr. Nirav D. Shah
Director of Public Health
Department of Public Health
525-535 West Jefferson Street
Springfield, IL 62761
P: (217) 557-2556
F: (217) 782-3987

INDIANA
Dr. Jerome Adams
State Health Commissioner
Department of Health
2 North Meridian
Indianapolis, IN 46204
P: (317) 233-1325

IOWA
Mr. Gerd W. Clabaugh
Director
Department of Public Health
Lucas State Office Building
321 East 12th Street
Des Moines, IA 50319
P: (515) 281-7689
F: (515) 281-4958
E: gerd.clabaugh@idph.iowa.gov

KANSAS
Dr. Susan Mosier
Secretary
Department of Health & Environment
Curtis State Office Building
1000 Southwest Jackson
Topeka, KS 66612
P: (785) 296-0461
F: (785) 368-6368

KENTUCKY
Dr. Hiram C. Polk Jr.
Commissioner
Department of Public Health
275 East Main Street
Frankfort, KY 40621
P: (502) 564-3970

LOUISIANA
Ms. M. Beth Scalco
Assistant Secretary
Office of Public Health
Department of Health
P.O. Box 629
Baton Rouge, LA 70821
P: (225) 342-9500
F: (225) 342-5568
E: bscalco@la.gov

MAINE
Ms. Sheryl Peavey
Chief Operating Officer
State Center for Disease Control & Prevention
286 Water Street
State House Station 11
Augusta, ME 04333
P: (207) 287-8016

MARYLAND
Mr. Dennis R. Schrader
Secretary
Department of Health & Mental Hygiene
Office of the Secretary
201 West Preston Street, 5th Floor
Baltimore, MD 21201
P: (410) 767-4639
E: Dennis.Schrader@maryland.gov

Health Services

MASSACHUSETTS
Dr. Monica Bharel
Commissioner
Department of Public Health
250 Washington Street, 2nd Floor
Boston, MA 02108
P: (617) 624-6000

MICHIGAN
Mr. Nick Lyon
Director
Department of Health & Human Services
333 South Grand Avenue
P.O. Box 30195
Lansing, MI 48909
P: (517) 335-0267
F: (517) 335-6101
E: LyonN2@michigan.gov

MINNESOTA
Dr. Edward Ehlinger
Commissioner of Health
Department of Health
625 North Robert Street
P.O. Box 64975
St. Paul, MN 55164
P: (651) 201-5810
F: (651) 201-4986
E: Ed.Ehlinger@state.mn.us

MISSISSIPPI
Dr. Mary Currier
State Health Officer
State Department of Health
570 East Woodrow Wilson
P.O. Box 1700
Jackson, MS 39215
P: (601) 576-7634
F: (601) 576-7931
E: mary.currier@msdh.state.ms.us

MISSOURI
Dr. Randall W. Williams
Director
Department of Health & Senior Services
912 Wildwood Drive
P.O. Box 570
Jefferson City, MO 65102
P: (573) 751-6001
F: (573) 751-6010
E: info@health.mo.gov

MONTANA
Ms. Sheila Hogan
Director
Department of Public Health & Human Services
111 North Sanders, Room 301
P.O. Box 4210
Helena, MT 59604
P: (406) 444-5622
F: (406) 444-1970
E: sheilahogan@mt.gov

NEBRASKA
Ms. Courtney Phillips
Chief Executive Officer
Department of Health & Human Services
301 Centennial Mall South
P.O. Box 95026
Lincoln, NE 68509
P: (402) 471-9433
F: (402) 471-9449

NEVADA
Ms. Cody Phinney
Administrator
Division of Public & Behavioral Health
4150 Technology Way
Carson City, NV 89706
P: (775) 684-4200
F: (775) 684-4211
E: cphinney@health.nv.gov

NEW HAMPSHIRE
Dr. Jose T. Montero
Director
Division of Public Health Services
Health & Human Services
129 Pleasant Street
Concord, NH 03301
P: (603) 271-4612
F: (603) 217-5199

NEW JERSEY
Ms. Cathleen Bennett
Commissioner
Department of Health
P.O. Box 360
Trenton, NJ 08625
P: (609) 292-7838
F: (609) 292-0053

NEW MEXICO
Ms. K. Lynn Gallagher
Cabinet Secretary
Department of Health
Harold Runnels Building
1190 South St. Francis Drive
Santa Fe, NM 87505
P: (505) 827-2613
E: lynn.gallagher@state.nm.us

NEW YORK
Dr. Howard Zucker
Commissioner
Department of Health
Corning Tower
Empire State Plaza
Albany, NY 12237
P: (518) 474-2011
F: (518) 474-1449

NORTH CAROLINA
Mr. Danny Staley
Director
Division of Public Health
5605 Six Forks Road
Raleigh, NC 27699
P: (919) 707-5000
F: (919) 870-4829
E: danny.staley@dhhs.nc.gov

NORTH DAKOTA
Dr. Mylynn Tufte
State Health Officer
Department of Health
600 East Boulevard Avenue
Bismarck, ND 58505
P: (701) 328-2372
F: (701) 328-4727
E: mylynntufte@nd.gov

NORTHERN MARIANA ISLANDS
Ms. Esther L. Muna
Chief Executive Officer
Commonwealth Healthcare Corporation
P.O. Box 500409 CK
Saipan, MP 96950

OHIO
Mr. Lance Himes
Interim Director
Department of Health
246 North High Street
Columbus, OH 43215
P: (614) 466-2253

OKLAHOMA
Dr. Terry L. Cline
Commissioner of Health
Department of Health
1000 Northeast 10th Street
Oklahoma City, OK 73117
P: (405) 271-5600

OREGON
Mr. Lillian M. Shirley
Public Health Director
Public Health Division
800 Northeast Oregon Street, Suite 930
Portland, OR 97232
P: (971) 673-1222
F: (971) 673-1299
E: lillian.shirley@dhsoha.state.or.us

PENNSYLVANIA
Dr. Karen Murphy
Secretary of Health
Department of Health
Health & Welfare Building
625 Forster Street, 8th Floor West
Harrisburg, PA 17120
P: (717) 787-9857

PUERTO RICO
Dr. Ana Ruis
Secretary
Department of Health
P.O. Box 70184
San Juan, PR 00936
P: (787) 765-2929

RHODE ISLAND
Dr. Nicole Alexander-Scott
Director
Department of Health
3 Capitol Hill
Providence, RI 02908
P: (401) 222-5960
F: (401) 222-6548
E: health@ri.gov

SOUTH CAROLINA
Ms. Catherine Heigel
Director
Department of Health & Environmental Control
2600 Bull Street
Columbia, SC 29201
P: (803) 898-3432
E: info@dhec.sc.gov

SOUTH DAKOTA
Ms. Kim Malsam-Rysdon
Secretary
Department of Health
Robert Hayes Building
600 East Capitol Avenue
Pierre, SD 57501
P: (605) 773-3361
F: (605) 773-5683
E: kim.malsam-rysdon@state.sd.us

TENNESSEE
Dr. John J. Dreyzehner
Commissioner
Department of Health
710 James Robertson Parkway
Nashville, TN 37243
P: (615) 741-3111
F: (615) 741-6230
E: tn.health@tn.gov

TEXAS
Dr. John Hellerstedt
Commissioner
Department of State Health Services
1100 West 49th Street
P.O. Box 149347
Austin, TX 78714
P: (512) 776-7363
F: (512) 776-7477

U.S. VIRGIN ISLANDS
Ms. Michelle Davis
Commissioner
Department of Health
Charles Harwood Complex
3500 Estate Richmond
Christiansted, VI 00820
P: (340) 718-1311

UTAH
Dr. Joseph Miner
Executive Director
Department of Health
P.O. Box 141000
Salt Lake City, UT 84114
P: (801) 538-6111
F: (801) 538-6306
E: joeminer@utah.gov

VERMONT
Dr. Mark Levine
Health Commissioner
Department of Health
108 Cherry Street
Burlington, VT 05402
P: (802) 863-7200
F: (802) 865-7754

VIRGINIA
Dr. Marissa J. Levine
Commissioner of Health
Department of Health
109 Governor Street
P.O. Box 2448
Richmond, VA 23218
P: (804) 864-7009
F: (804) 864-7022
E: Marissa.Levine@vdh.virginia.gov

WASHINGTON
Dr. John M. Wiesman
Secretary of Health
Department of Health
101 Israel Road, Southeast
Tumwater, WA 98504
P: (360) 236-4030
E: Secretary@doh.wa.gov

WEST VIRGINIA
Dr. Rahul Gupta
Commissioner & State Health Officer
Bureau for Public Health
350 Capitol Street, Room 702
Charleston, WV 25301
P: (304) 558-2971
F: (304) 558-1035

WISCONSIN
Ms. Karen D. McKeown
Administrator
Division of Public Health
Department of Health Services
P.O. Box 2659
Madison, WI 53707
P: (608) 266-1251
F: (608) 267-2832

WYOMING
Dr. Wendy E. Braund
State Health Officer
Public Health Division
Department of Health
6101Yellowstone Road
Cheyenne, WY 82002
P: (307) 777-6004
F: (307) 777-8264

Higher Education

Serves as coordinating and planning agency for state-supported post-secondary education.

ALABAMA
Mr. James Purcell
Executive Director
Commission on Higher Education
100 North Union Street, Room 782
Montgomery, AL 36104
P: (334) 242-2139
E: jim.purcell@ache.alabama.gov

ALASKA
Ms. Stephanie Butler
Interim Executive Director
Commission on Postsecondary Education
3030 Vintage Boulevard
Juneau, AK 99801
P: (907) 465-6740
E: stephanie.butler@alaska.gov

Mr. James R. Johnsen
President
University of Alaska System
202 Butrovich
P.O. Box 755000
Fairbanks, AK 99775
P: (907) 450-8009
F: (907) 450-8012
E: ua.president@alaska.edu

ARIZONA
Ms. Eileen Klein
President
Board of Regents
2020 North Central Avenue, Suite 230
Phoenix, AZ 85004
P: (602) 229-2505
F: (602) 229-2555
E: eileen.klein@azregents.edu

ARKANSAS
Ms. Maria Markham
Director
Department of Higher Education
423 Main Street, Suite 400
Little Rock, AR 72201
P: (501) 371-2031
E: Maria.Markham@adhe.edu

CALIFORNIA
Mr. Timothy P. White
Chancellor
State University System
401 Golden Shore
Long Beach, CA 90802
P: (562) 951-4000
E: twhite@calstate.edu

COLORADO
Ms. Kim Hunter Reed
Executive Director
Department of Higher Education
1560 Broadway, Suite 1600
Denver, CO 80202
P: (303) 862-3018
E: Kim.Reed@dhe.state.co.us

CONNECTICUT
Mr. Keith Norton
Acting Executive Director
Office of Higher Education
61 Woodland Street
Hartford, CT 06105
P: (860) 947-1801
F: (860) 947-1311
E: knorton@ctohe.org

Mr. Mark E. Ojakian
President
Board of Regents for Higher Education
39 Woodland Street
Hartford, CT 06105
P: (860) 493-0011
F: (860) 493-0009
E: ojakianm@ct.edu

DELAWARE
Ms. Shana Payne
Director
Higher Education Office
The Townsend Building
401 Federal Street, Suite 2
Dover, DE 19901
P: (302) 735-4120
F: (302) 739-5894
E: Shana.Payne@doe.k12.de.us

DISTRICT OF COLUMBIA
Ms. Antoinette S. Mitchell
Assistant Superintendent, Postsecondary and Career Education
Office of the State Superintendent of Education
810 1st Street Northeast, 3rd Floor
Washington, DC 20002
P: (202) 741-0471
E: Antoinette.Mitchell@dc.gov

FLORIDA
Mr. Marshall Criser III
Chancellor
State University System Board of Governors
325 West Gaines Street, Suite 1614
Tallahassee, FL 32399
P: (850) 245-0466
F: (850) 245-9685
E: Marshall.Criser@flbog.edu

GEORGIA
Mr. Steve Wrigley
Chancellor
Board of Regents of the University System
270 Washington Street, Southwest
Suite 7025
Atlanta, GA 30334
P: (404) 656-2202

HAWAII
Mr. David Lassner
President
University of Hawaii System
2444 Dole Street, Bachman Hall 202
Honolulu, HI 96822
P: (808) 956-8207
F: (808) 956-5286
E: david.lassner@hawaii.edu

IDAHO
Mr. Matt Freeman
Executive Director
State Board of Education
650 West State Street, Room 307
Boise, ID 83702
P: (208) 332-1570
F: (208) 334-2632
E: matt.freeman@osbe.idaho.gov

INDIANA
Ms. Teresa S. Lubbers
Commissioner
Commission for Higher Education
101 West Ohio Street, Suite 550
Indianapolis, IN 46204
P: (317) 464-4400
F: (317) 464-4410
E: teresal@che.in.gov

IOWA
Mr. Robert Donley
Executive Director
Board of Regents
11260 Aurora Avenue
Urbandale, IA 50322
P: (515) 281-6426
F: (515) 281-6420
E: bdonley@iastate.edu

KANSAS
Mr. Blake Flanders
President & CEO
Board of Regents
1000 Southwest Jackson Street, Suite 520
Topeka, KS 66612
P: (785) 296-3421
F: (785) 296-0983
E: bflanders@ksbor.org

KENTUCKY
Mr. Robert L. King
President
Council on Postsecondary Education
1024 Capital Center Drive, Suite 320
Frankfort, KY 40601
P: (502) 573-1652
F: (502) 573-1535
E: robert.king@ky.gov

LOUISIANA
Mr. Joseph Rallo
Commissioner of Higher Education
Board of Regents
P.O. Box 3677
Baton Rouge, LA 70821
P: (225) 342-4253
F: (225) 342-9318
E: joseph.rallo@la.gov

MAINE
Mr. James H. Page
Chancellor
University of Maine System
16 Central Street
Bangor, ME 04401
P: (207) 973-3205
F: (207) 973-3296
E: jpage@maine.edu

MARYLAND
Dr. James D. Fielder Jr.
Secretary of Higher Education
Higher Education Commission
6 North Liberty Street
Baltimore, MD 21201
P: (410) 767-3012
F: (410) 332-0270
E: James.Fielder@maryland.gov

MASSACHUSETTS
Mr. Carlos E. Santiago
Commissioner
Department of Higher Education
One Ashburton Place, Room 1401
Boston, MA 02108
P: (617) 994-6901
F: (617) 727-6397
E: csantiago@bhe.mass.edu

MICHIGAN
Mr. Daniel J. Hurley
Chief Executive Officer
Association of State Universities
101 South Washington Square, Suite 600
Lansing, MI 48933
P: (517) 482-1563
E: dhurley@masu.org

MINNESOTA
Mr. Lawrence J. Pogemiller
Commissioner
Office of Higher Education
1450 Energy Park Drive, Suite 350
St. Paul, MN 55108
P: (651) 259-3900
F: (651) 642-0597
E: larry.pogemiller@state.mn.us

Mr. Steven J. Rosenstone
Chancellor
State Colleges & Universities
Wells Fargo Place
30 7th Street East, Suite 350
St. Paul, MN 55101
P: (651) 201-1696
F: (651) 297-7465
E: steven.rosenstone@so.mnscu.edu

MISSISSIPPI
Mr. Glenn F. Boyce
Commissioner of Higher Education
State Institutions of Higher Learning
3825 Ridgewood Road
Jackson, MS 39211
P: (601) 432-6198
F: (601) 432-6972
E: gboyce@mississippi.edu

MISSOURI
Ms. Zora Mulligan
Commissioner of Higher Education
Department of Higher Education
205 Jefferson Street
Jefferson City, MO 65102
P: (573) 751-2361
F: (573) 751-6635
E: Zora.Mulligan@dhe.mo.gov

MONTANA
Mr. Clayton Christian
Commissioner of Higher Education
State University System
2500 Broadway Street
P.O. Box 203201
Helena, MT 59620
P: (406) 444-0374
F: (406) 444-1469
E: cchristian@montana.edu

NEBRASKA
Mr. Michael Baumgartner
Executive Director
Coordinating Commission for Postsecondary Education
P.O. Box 95005
Lincoln, NE 68509
P: (402) 471-0029
F: (402) 471-2886
E: mike.baumgartner@nebraska.gov

NEVADA
Mr. John Valery White
Acting Chancellor
State System of Higher Education
2601 Enterprise Road
Reno, NV 89512
P: (775) 784-3222
E: john_white@nshe.nevada.edu

NEW HAMPSHIRE
Mr. Todd Leach
Chancellor
University System
5 Chenell Drive, Suite 301
Concord, NH 03301
P: (603) 862-0963
F: (603) 862-0908
E: todd.leach@usnh.edu

Mr. Edward R. MacKay
Director
Department of Education, Division of Higher Education, Higher Education Commission
101 Pleasant Street
Concord,, NH 03301
P: (603) 271-0256
F: (603) 271-1953
E: edward.mackay@doe.nh.gov

NEW JERSEY
Ms. Rochelle Hendricks
Secretary of Higher Education
Office of the Secretary of Higher Education
P.O. Box 542
Trenton, NJ 08625
P: (609) 292-8052
F: (609) 292-7225
E: rochelle.hendricks@njhe.state.nj.us

NEW MEXICO
Ms. Barbara Damron
Cabinet Secretary
Higher Education Department
2044 Galisteo Street
Santa Fe, NM 87505
P: (505) 476-8409
F: (505) 476-8454
E: Barbara.Damron@state.nm.us

NEW YORK
Mr. John D'Agati
Deputy Commissioner
State Education Department
Office of Higher Education
Room 977, Education Building Annex
Albany, NY 12234
P: (518) 486-3633
F: (518) 486-2254
E: john.dagati@nysed.gov

Ms. Nancy Zimpher
Chancellor
The State University of New York
State University Plaza
353 Broadway
Albany, NY 12246
P: (518) 320-1355
E: nancy.zimpher@suny.edu

NORTH CAROLINA
Ms. Margaret Spellings
President
University of North Carolina
910 Raleigh Road
P.O. Box 2688
Chapel Hill, NC 27514
P: (919) 962-4622
F: (919) 843-9695
E: margaret.spellings@northcarolina.edu

NORTH DAKOTA
Mr. Mark Hagerott
Chancellor
State University System
Department 215, 10th Floor
State Capitol
600 East Boulevard Avenue
Bismarck, ND 58505
P: (701) 328-2974
F: (701) 328-2961
E: Mark.Hagerott@ndus.edu

NORTHERN MARIANA ISLANDS
Ms. Carmen Fernandez
President
Northern Marianas College
P.O. Box 501250
Saipan, MP 96950
P: (670) 237-6701
E: carmen.fernandez@marianas.edu

OHIO
Mr. John Carey
Chancellor
State Department of Higher Education
25 South Front Street
Columbus, OH 43215
P: (614) 466-6000
F: (614) 466-5866
E: chancellor@highered.ohio.gov

OKLAHOMA
Mr. Glen D. Johnson Jr.
Chancellor
State System of Higher Education
655 Research Parkway, Suite 200
Oklahoma City, OK 73104
P: (405) 225-9120
F: (405) 225-9235
E: gjohnson@osrhe.edu

Higher Education

OREGON
Mr. Ben Cannon
Executive Director
Higher Education Coordinating Commission
255 Capitol Street, Northeast
3rd Floor
Salem, OR 97301
P: (503) 378-5690
E: ben.cannon@state.or.us

PENNSYLVANIA
Mr. Frank T. Brogan
Chancellor
State System of Higher Education
Dixon University Center
2986 North Second Street
Harrisburg, PA 17110
P: (717) 720-4205
F: (717) 720-4011
E: fbrogan@passhe.edu

Mr. Wil Del Pilar
Deputy Secretary
Office of Postsecondary & Higher Education
Department of Education
333 Market Street, 12th Floor
Harrisburg, PA 17126
P: (717) 783-6744
F: (717) 772-3622
E: widelpilar@pa.gov

PUERTO RICO
Ms. Maria L. Varas Garcia
Acting Executive Director
Council on Education
P.O. Box 19900
San Juan, PR 00910
P: (787) 641-7100
E: mvaras@ce.pr.gov

RHODE ISLAND
Ms. Brenda Dann-Messier
Acting Commissioner of Postsecondary Education
Office of the Postsecondary Commissioner
560 Jefferson Boulevard, Suite 100
Warwick, RI 02886
P: (401) 736-1110
E: Brenda.Dann-Messier@riopc.edu

SOUTH CAROLINA
Mr. Jeff M. Schilz
Interim President & Executive Director
Commission on Higher Education
1122 Lady Street, Suite 300
Columbia, SC 29201
P: (803) 737-2155
E: jschilz@che.sc.gov

SOUTH DAKOTA
Mr. Michael G. Rush
Executive Director & CEO
State Board of Regents
306 East Capitol Avenue, Suite 200
Pierre, SD 57501
P: (605) 773-3455
F: (605) 773-5320
E: mike.rush@sdbor.edu

TENNESSEE
Mr. Mike Krause
Executive Director
State Higher Education Commission
404 James Robertson Parkway, Suite 1900
Nashville, TN 37243
P: (615) 741-7561
E: Mike.Krause@tn.gov

TEXAS
Dr. Raymund A. Paredes
Commissioner of Higher Education
State Higher Education Coordinating Board
1200 East Anderson Lane
P.O. Box 12788
Austin, TX 78752
P: (512) 427-6101
F: (512) 427-6127
E: raymund.paredes@thecb.state.tx.us

UTAH
Mr. David L. Buhler
Commissioner of Higher Education
State System of Higher Education
Board of Regents Building, The Gateway
60 South 400 West
Salt Lake City, UT 84101
P: (801) 321-7162
F: (801) 321-7156
E: dbuhlerl@utahsbr.edu

VERMONT
Mr. Jeb Spaulding
Chancellor
State Colleges
Office of the Chancellor
P.O. Box 7
Montpelier, VT 05601
P: (802) 224-3000
F: (802) 224-3035
E: jeb.spaulding@vsc.edu

Mr. Thomas Sullivan
President
University of Vermont
344-353 Waterman Building
85 South Prospect Street
Burlington, VT 05405
P: (802) 656-7878
F: (802) 656-9220
E: Thomas.Sullivan@uvm.edu

VIRGINIA
Mr. Peter Blake
Director
State Council of Higher Education
101 North 14th Street
James Monroe Building, 10th Floor
Richmond, VA 23219
P: (804) 225-2611
F: (804) 225-2908
E: peterblake@schev.edu

WASHINGTON
Mr. Michael P. Meotti
Executive Director
State Student Achievement Council
917 Lakeridge Way, Southwest
Olympia, WA 98502
P: (360) 753-7812
E: MichaelM@wsac.wa.gov

WEST VIRGINIA
Mr. Paul L. Hill
Chancellor
State Higher Education Policy Commission
1018 Kanawha Boulevard East, Suite 700
Charleston, WV 25301
P: (304) 558-0699
F: (304) 558-1011
E: paul.hill@wvhepc.edu

WISCONSIN
Mr. Ray Cross
President
University of Wisconsin System
1720 Van Hise Hall
1220 Linden Drive
Madison, WI 53706
P: (608) 262-2321
F: (608) 262-3985
E: rcross@uwsa.edu

WYOMING
Ms. Laurie Nichols
President
University of Wyoming
Old Main Room 206, Department 3434
1000 East University Avenue
Laramie, WY 82071
P: (307) 766-4121
E: uwpres@uwyo.edu

Dr. James O. Rose
Executive Director
State Community College Commission
2300 Capitol Avenue, 5th Floor, Suite B
Cheyenne, WY 82002
P: (307) 777-7763
F: (307) 777-6567
E: jim.rose@wyo.gov

Historic Preservation

Surveys, restores and preserves structures and/or sites of historical or architectural significance in the state.

ALABAMA
Ms. Lisa D. Jones
Executive Director
Historic Commission
468 South Perry Street
Montgomery, AL 36130
P: (334) 230-2690
F: (334) 240-3477
E: Lisa.Jones@preserveala.org

ALASKA
Ms. Judith Bittner
State Historic Preservation Officer
Office of History & Archeology
Department of Natural Resources
550 West 7th Avenue, Suite 1310
Anchorage, AK 99501
P: (907) 269-8721
F: (907) 269-8908
E: judy.bittner@alaska.gov

AMERICAN SAMOA
Mr. David J. Herdrich
Historic Preservation Officer
Historic Preservation Office
Executive Offices of the Governor
American Samoa Government
Pago Pago, AS 96799
P: (684) 699-2316
F: (684) 699-2276
E: david.herdrich@go.as.gov

ARIZONA
Ms. Kathryn Leonard
State Historic Preservation Officer
State Parks
1300 West Washington
Phoenix, AZ 85007
P: (602) 542-4009
F: (602) 542-4180
E: kleonard@azstateparks.gov

ARKANSAS
Ms. Stacy Hurst
State Historic Preservation Officer
Department of Arkansas Heritage
323 Center Street
1500 Tower Building
Little Rock, AR 72201
P: (501) 324-9150
F: (501) 324-9154
E: stacy.hurst@arkansasheritage.org

CALIFORNIA
Ms. Julianne Polanco
State Historic Preservation Officer
Office of Historic Preservation
Department of Parks & Recreation
1725 23rd Street, Suite 100
Sacramento, CA 95816
P: (916) 445-7000
F: (916) 445-7053
E: julianne.polanco@parks.ca.gov

COLORADO
Mr. Steve Turner
State Historic Preservation Officer
Historic Colorado
Colorado Historical Society
1200 Broadway
Denver, CO 80202
P: (303) 866-2776
F: (303) 866-4464
E: steve.turner@chs.state.co.us

CONNECTICUT
Ms. Kristina Newman-Scott
State Historic Preservation Officer & Director of Arts and Historic Preservation
Department of Economic & Community Development
One Constitution Plaza, 2nd Floor
Hartford, CT 06103
E: Kristina.newmanscott@ct.gov

DELAWARE
Mr. Timothy A. Slavin
State Historic Preservation Officer
Division of Historical & Cultural Affairs
21 The Green
Dover, DE 19901
P: (302) 736-7400
F: (302) 739-5660
E: timothy.slavin@state.de.us

DISTRICT OF COLUMBIA
Mr. David Maloney
State Historic Preservation Officer
Historic Preservation Office
1100 4th Street, Southwest, Suite E650
Washington, DC 20024
P: (202) 442-8800
F: (202) 442-7638
E: david.maloney@dc.gov

FLORIDA
Dr. Timothy Parsons
Acting State Historic Preservation Officer & Director
Division of Historical Resources
R.A. Gray Building, Room 305
500 South Bronough Street
Tallahassee, FL 32399
P: (850) 245-6300
F: (850) 245-6437
E: timothy.parsons@dos.myflorida.com

GEORGIA
Mr. Mark Williams
Commissioner & State Historic Preservation Officer
Historic Preservation Division, Department of Natural Resources
2 Martin Luther King Jr. Drive Southeast
Suite 1252, East Tower
Atlanta, GA 30334
P: (404) 656-3500
F: (404) 656-0770
E: Mark.Williams@dnr.ga.gov

GUAM
Ms. Lynda Bordallo Aguon
State Historic Preservation Officer
Department of Parks & Recreation
Department of Parks & Recreation
490 Chalan Palasyo
Agana Heights, GU 96910
P: (671) 475-6270
F: (671) 477-2822
E: lynda.aguon@dpr.guam.gov

HAWAII
Ms. Suzanne D. Case
Chairperson
Department of Land & Natural Resources
Kalanimoku Building
1151 Punchbowl Street
Honolulu, HI 96813
P: (808) 587-0400
F: (808) 587-0390
E: dlnr@hawaii.gov

IDAHO
Ms. Janet Gallimore
Executive Director & State Historic Preservation Officer
State Historical Society
2205 Old Penitentiary Road
Boise, ID 83712
P: (208) 334-2682
E: Janet.Gallimore@ishs.idaho.gov

ILLINOIS
Ms. Heidi Brown-McCreery
Director & State Historic Preservation Officer
Historic Preservation Agency
313 South Sixth Street
Springfield, IL 62701
P: (217) 785-7930
F: (217) 524-7525

INDIANA
Mr. Cameron F. Clark
State Historic Preservation Officer & Director
Department of Natural Resources
402 West Washington Street, Room W256
Government Center South
Indianapolis, IN 46204
P: (317) 232-4020
F: (317) 233-6811
E: dhpa@dnr.in.gov

IOWA
Ms. Susan Kloewer
State Historic Preservation Officer & Administrator
State Historical Society, Department of Cultural Affairs
State Historical Building
600 East Locust Street
Des Moines, IA 50319
P: (515) 281-8749

KANSAS
Ms. Jennie Chinn
State Historic Preservation Officer & Executive Director
State Historical Society
6425 Southwest 6th Avenue
Topeka, KS 66615
P: (785) 272-8681 Ext. 205
F: (785) 272-8682
E: jchinn@kshs.org

KENTUCKY
Mr. Craig Potts
Executive Director & State Historic Preservation Officer
State Heritage Council
300 Washington Street
Frankfort, KY 40601
P: (502) 564-7005
F: (502) 564-5820
E: craig.potts@ky.gov

Historic Preservation

LOUISIANA
Mr. Phil Boggan
Acting State Historic Preservation Officer
Department of Culture, Recreation & Tourism
P.O. Box 44247
Baton Rouge, LA 70804
P: (225) 342-8200
F: (225) 342-8173
E: pboggan@crt.state.la.us

MAINE
Mr. Kirk F. Mohney
State Historic Preservation Officer
Historic Preservation Commission
55 Capitol Street
Station 65
Augusta, ME 04333
P: (207) 287-2132
F: (207) 287-2335
E: kirk.mohney@maine.gov

MARYLAND
Ms. Elizabeth Hughes
State Historic Preservation Officer
State Historical Trust
100 Community Place, 3rd Floor
Crownsville, MD 21032
P: (410) 514-7604
F: (410) 514-7678
E: elizabeth.hughes@maryland.gov

MASSACHUSETTS
Ms. Brona Simon
State Historic Preservation Officer & Executive Director
Historical Commission
220 Morrissey Boulevard
Boston, MA 02125
P: (617) 727-8470
F: (617) 727-5128
E: Brona.Simon@state.ma.us

MICHIGAN
Mr. Brian D. Conway
State Historic Preservation Officer
State Housing Development Authority
702 West Kalamazoo Street
P.O. Box 30740
Lansing, MI 48909
P: (517) 373-1630
F: (517) 335-0348
E: conwayb1@michigan.gov

MINNESOTA
Mr. D. Stephen Elliot
State Historic Preservation Officer
State Historical Society
345 Kellogg Boulevard, West
St. Paul, MN 55102
P: (651) 259-3100
F: (651) 282-2374
E: director@mnhs.org

MISSISSIPPI
Mr. David Pilcher
Director
Archives & Records Services Division
P.O. Box 571
Jackson, MS 39205
P: (601) 576-6823
E: dpilcher@mdah.ms.gov

MISSOURI
Ms. Sara Parker Pauley
Director
Department of Natural Resources
2901 West Truman Boulevard
P.O. Box 176
Jefferson City, MO 65102
P: (573) 751-4732
F: (573) 751-7627
E: sara.pauley@ded.mo.gov

MONTANA
Dr. Mark F. Baumler
State Historic Preservation Officer
State Historic Preservation Office
1301 East Lockey Avenue
P.O. Box 201202
Helena, MT 59620
P: (406) 444-7715
F: (406) 444-6575
E: mbaumler@mt.gov

NEBRASKA
Mr. Trevor Jones
Director & State Historic Preservation Officer
State Historical Society
1500 R Street
P.O. Box 82554
Lincoln, NE 68501
P: (402) 471-4745
F: (402) 471-3100
E: trevor.jones@nebraska.gov

Mr. Michael Smith
Director & State Historic Preservation Officer
State Historical Society
1500 R Street
P.O. Box 82554
Lincoln, NE 68501
P: (402) 471-4745
F: (402) 471-3100
E: michael.smith@nebraska.gov

NEW HAMPSHIRE
Ms. Elizabeth H. Muzzey
State Historic Preservation Officer & Director
Division of Historical Resources
19 Pillsbury Street, 2nd Floor
Concord, NH 03301
P: (603) 271-8850
F: (603) 271-3433
E: elizabeth.muzzey@dcr.nh.gov

NEW JERSEY
Mr. Bob Martin
Commissioner & State Historic Preservation Officer
Department of Environmental Protection
401 East State Street, Mail Code 401-07
P.O. Box 402
Trenton, NJ 08625
P: (609) 292-2885
F: (609) 292-7695

NEW MEXICO
Dr. Jeff Pappas
Director & State Historic Preservation Officer
Historic Preservation Division
Department of Cultural Affairs
407 Galisteo Street, Suite 236
Santa Fe, NM 87501
P: (505) 827-4222
F: (505) 827-6338
E: jeff.pappas@state.nm.us

NEW YORK
Ms. Rose Harvey
State Historic Preservation Officer & Commissioner
Office of Parks, Recreation & Historic Preservation
625 Broadway
Albany, NY 12207
P: (518) 474-0443
F: (518) 474-4492

NORTH CAROLINA
Dr. Kevin Cherry
Deputy Secretary
Office of Archives & History
4614 Mail Service Center
Raleigh, NC 27699
P: (919) 807-7339
F: (919) 715-7274
E: kevin.cherry@ncdcr.gov

NORTH DAKOTA
Ms. Claudia Berg
State Historical Preservation Officer
State Historical Society
612 East Boulevard Avenue
Bismarck, ND 58505
P: (701) 328-2666
F: (701) 328-3710
E: cberg@nd.gov

NORTHERN MARIANA ISLANDS
Ms. Mertie T. Kani
Secretary & State Historic Preservation Officer
Department of Community & Cultural Affairs
P.O. Box 500090CK
Aslito Airport Road
Saipan, MP 96950
P: (670) 664-2120
F: (670) 664-2139
E: mtkani@hotmail.com

OHIO
Mr. Burt Logan
State Historic Preservation Officer
Historic Preservation Office
State History Connection
800 East 17th Avenue
Columbus, OH 43211
P: (614) 298-2000
F: (614) 298-2037
E: blogan@ohiohistory.org

OKLAHOMA
Dr. Bob L. Blackburn
State Historic Preservation Officer
Historical Society
History Center
800 Nazih Zuhdi Drive
Oklahoma City, OK 73105
P: (405) 521-6249
F: (405) 522-0816
E: bblackburn@okhistory.org

OREGON
Ms. Lisa Sumption
Director & State Historic Preservation Officer
Parks & Recreation Department
725 Summer Street, Northeast, Suite C
Salem, OR 97301
P: (503) 986-0707
F: (503) 986-0794
E: jen.busey@oregon.gov

PENNSYLVANIA
Mr. James M. Vaughan
Executive Director
Bureau for Historic Preservation
Commonwealth Keystone Building
400 North Street, 2nd Floor
Harrisburg, PA 17120
P: (717) 783-8946
F: (717) 772-0920
E: jvaughan@pa.gov

PUERTO RICO
Mr. Carlos A. Rubio-Cancelar
State Historic Preservation Officer
State Historic Preservation Office
P.O. Box 9023935
San Juan, PR 00902
P: (787) 721-3737
F: (787) 721-3773
E: carubio@prshpo.pr.gov

RHODE ISLAND
Mr. Edward F. Sanderson
Executive Director & State Historic Preservation Officer
Historical Preservation & Heritage Commission
Old State House
150 Benefit Street
Providence, RI 02903
P: (401) 222-4130
F: (401) 222-2968
E: Edward.Sanderson@preservation.ri.gov

SOUTH CAROLINA
Dr. Eric Emerson
State Historic Preservation Officer
Department of Archives & History
8301 Parklane Road
Columbia, SC 29223
P: (803) 896-6187
F: (803) 896-6167
E: eemerson@scdah.state.sc.us

SOUTH DAKOTA
Mr. Jay D. Vogt
Director
State Historic Preservation Office
Cultural Heritage Center
900 Governors Drive
Pierre, SD 57501
P: (605) 773-3458
F: (605) 773-6041
E: jay.vogt@state.sd.us

TENNESSEE
Mr. Patrick McIntyre Jr.
Executive Director & State Historic Preservation Officer
State Historical Commission
2941 Lebanon Road
Nashville, TN 37243
P: (615) 532-1550
F: (615) 532-1549
E: patrick.mcintyre@tn.gov

TEXAS
Mr. Mark S. Wolfe
State Historic Preservation Officer
State Historical Commission
P.O. Box 12276
Austin, TX 78711
P: (512) 463-6100
F: (512) 463-8222
E: mark.wolfe@thc.state.tx.us

U.S. VIRGIN ISLANDS
Mr. Jean-Pierre Oriol
Acting State Historic Preservation Officer
Department of Planning & Natural Resources
Cyril E. King Airport
Terminal Building, 2nd Floor
St. Thomas, VI 00802
P: (340) 776-8605
F: (340) 776-7236
E: jp.oriol@dpnr.vi.gov

UTAH
Mr. Brad Westwood
State Historic Preservation Officer
Division of State History
300 Rio Grande
Salt Lake City, UT 84101
P: (801) 245-7248
F: (801) 533-3503
E: bradwestwood@utah.gov

VERMONT
Ms. Laura Trieschmann
State Historic Preservation Officer
Department of Housing & Community Development
National Life North Building
1 National Life Drive, 6th Floor
Montpelier, VT 05620
P: (802) 828-5216
F: (802) 828-3258
E: noelle.mackay@state.vt.us

VIRGINIA
Ms. Julie Langan
State Historic Preservation Officer
Department of Historic Resources
2801 Kensington Avenue
Richmond, VA 23221
P: (804) 482-6087
F: (804) 367-2391
E: julie.langan@dhr.virginia.gov

WASHINGTON
Dr. Allyson Brooks
State Historic Preservation Officer
Department of Archaeology & Historic Preservation
1063 South Capitol Way, Suite 106
P.O. Box 48343
Olympia, WA 98504
P: (360) 586-3065
F: (360) 586-3067
E: allyson.brooks@dahp.wa.gov

WEST VIRGINIA
Mr. Randall Reid-Smith
State Historic Preservation Officer
Division of Culture & History
Historic Preservation Office
1900 Kanawha Boulevard East
Charleston, WV 25305
P: (304) 558-0220
F: (304) 558-2779

WISCONSIN
Mr. Jim Draeger
State Historic Preservation Officer
State Historical Society
816 State Street
Madison, WI 53706
P: (608) 264-6464
F: (608) 264-6504
E: jim.draeger@wisconsinhistory.org

WYOMING
Ms. Mary Hopkins
State Historic Preservation Officer
State Historic Preservation Office
2301 Central Avenue, 3rd Floor
Cheyenne, WY 82002
P: (307) 777-7697
F: (307) 777-6421
E: hopkins@uwyo.edu

Housing Finance

Administers the state's housing assistance programs, provides low and moderate income housing by financing low interest loans.

ALASKA
Mr. Bryan Butcher
Executive Director/CEO
Housing Finance Corporation
4300 Boniface Parkway
P.O. Box 101020
Anchorage, AK 99510
P: (907) 330-8452
F: (907) 338-9218
E: wmathias@ahfc.us

AMERICAN SAMOA
The Honorable Lolo Matalasi Moliga (I)
Governor
Development Bank of American Samoa
Executive Office Building, Third Floor
Utulei
Pago Pago, AS 96799
P: (684) 633-4116
F: (684) 633-2269

ARIZONA
Mr. Michael Trailor
Director
Department of Housing
1110 West Washington #280
Phoenix, AZ 85007
P: (602) 771-1007
F: (602) 771-1002
E: michael.trailor@azhousing.gov

ARKANSAS
Mr. Aaron Burkes
President
Development Finance Authority
900 West Capitol, Suite 310
Little Rock, AR 72201
P: (501) 682-5900
F: (501) 682-5939
E: aaron.burkes@adfa.arkansas.gov

CALIFORNIA
Ms. Tia Boatman Patterson
Executive Director
Housing Finance Agency
500 Capitol Mall, Suite 1400
P.O. Box 4034
Sacramento, CA 95812
P: (916) 326-8000
F: (916) 324-8640

COLORADO
Mr. Cris A. White
Executive Director/CEO
Housing & Finance Authority
7595 Technology Way, Suite 300
P.O. Box 60
Denver, CO 80201
P: (303) 297-2432
E: cwhite@chfainfo.com

CONNECTICUT
Mr. Karl Kilduff
Director
Housing Finance Authority
999 West Street
Rocky Hill, CT 06067
P: (860) 571-4240
E: karl.kilduff@chfa.org

DELAWARE
Mr. Anas Ben Addi
Director
State Housing Authority
18 The Green
Dover, DE 19901
P: (302) 739-4263
F: (302) 739-6122

DISTRICT OF COLUMBIA
Ms. Polly Donaldson
Director
Department of Housing & Community Development
1800 Martin Luther King Jr. Avenue
Southeast
Washington, DC 20020
P: (202) 442-7200
E: dhcd@dc.gov

FLORIDA
Mr. Harold L. Price
Executive Director
Housing Finance Corporation
227 North Bronough Street
Suite 5000
Tallahassee, FL 32301
P: (850) 488-4197

GEORGIA
Ms. Carmen Chubb
Deputy Commissioner, Housing
Department of Community Affairs
60 Executive Park South, Northeast
Atlanta, GA 30329
P: (404) 679-0607
F: (404) 679-4837
E: carmen.chubb@dca.ga.gov

GUAM
Mr. Michael J. Duenas
Executive Director
Housing & Urban Renewal Authority
117 Bien Venida Avenue
Sinajana, GU 96910
P: (671) 477-9851
F: (671) 300-7565
E: mjduenas@ghura.org

HAWAII
Mr. Craig K. Hirai
Executive Director
Housing Finance & Development Corporation
677 Queen Street
Honolulu, HI 96813
P: (808) 587-0620
F: (808) 587-0600

ILLINOIS
Ms. Audra Hamernik
Executive Director/Assistant Secretary
Housing Development Authority
111 East Wacker Drive, Suite 1000
Chicago, IL 60601
P: (312) 836-5200
F: (312) 832-2170
E: ahamernik@ihda.org

IOWA
Mr. Dave Jamison
Executive Director
Finance Authority
2015 Grand Avenue
Des Moines, IA 50312
P: (515) 725-4977
F: (515) 725-4901
E: dave.jamison@iowa.gov

KANSAS
Mr. Dennis L. Mesa
Executive Director
Housing Resources Corporation
611 South Kansas Avenue, Suite 300
Topeka, KS 66603
P: (785) 217-2001
F: (785) 232-8084
E: dmesa@kshousingcorp.org

KENTUCKY
Ms. J. Kathryn Peters
Executive Director/Chief Executive Officer
Department of Housing & Economic Development
100 Cambridge Street, Suite 300
Frankfort, KY 40601
P: (617) 573-1100
F: (502) 564-5708
E: kpeters@kyhousing.org

LOUISIANA
Mr. Keith Cunningham
Executive Director
Housing Corporation
2415 Quail Drive
Baton Rouge, LA 70808
P: (225) 763-8700

MAINE
Mr. John Gallagher
Director
State Housing Authority
353 Water Street
Augusta, ME 04330
P: (207) 626-4600
F: (207) 626-4678
E: jgallagher@mainehousing.org

MARYLAND
Mr. Kenneth C. Holt
Secretary
Department of Housing & Community Development
7800 Harkins Road
Lanham, MD 20706
P: (301) 429-7400
F: (410) 987-4070
E: kenneth.holt@maryland.gov

MASSACHUSETTS
Ms. Chrystal Kornegay
Undersecretary of Housing & Community Development
Executive Office of Housing & Economic Development
Housing & Community Development
100 Cambridge Street, Suite 300
Boston, MA 02110
P: (617) 573-1000
F: (617) 573-1120

MICHIGAN
Mr. Earl Poleski
Executive Director
State Housing Development Authority
735 East Michigan Avenue
P.O. Box 30044
Lansing, MI 48909
P: (517) 373-8370
E: PoleskiE@michigan.gov

MINNESOTA
Ms. Mary Tingerthal
Commissioner
Housing Finance Agency
400 Sibley Street, Suite 300
St. Paul, MN 55101
P: (651) 296-5738
F: (651) 296-8139
E: Mary.Tingerthal@state.mn.us

MISSISSIPPI
Mr. Scott Spivey
Executive Director
Home Corporation
735 Riverside Drive
Jackson, MS 39202
P: (601) 718-4642
F: (601) 718-4643
E: scott.spivey@mshc.com

MISSOURI
Mr. Kip Stetzler
Executive Director
Housing Development Commission
920 Main Street, Suite 1400
Kansas City, MO 64105
P: (816) 759-6600
F: (816) 759-6608

NEBRASKA
Ms. Courtney Dentlinger
Director
Department of Economic Development
301 Centennial Mall South
P.O. Box 94666
Lincoln, NE 68509
P: (402) 471-3746
F: (402) 471-3778
E: courtney.dentlinger@nebraska.gov

NEVADA
Mr. C.J. Manthe
Administrator
Housing Division
1830 College Parkway, Suite 200
Carson City, NV 89706
P: (775) 687-2040
F: (775) 687-4040
E: cjmanthe@housing.nv.gov

NEW HAMPSHIRE
Mr. Dean J. Christon
Executive Director
Housing Finance Authority
P.O. Box 5087
Bedford, NH 03108
P: (603) 472-8623
F: (603) 472-2663
E: dean.christon@nhhfa.org

NEW JERSEY
Mr. Anthony L. Marchetta
Executive Director
Housing & Mortgage Finance Agency
637 South Clinton Avenue
P.O. Box 18550
Trenton, NJ 08650
P: (609) 278-7440
F: (609) 278-1754
E: amarchetta@njhmfa.gov

NEW MEXICO
Mr. Jay Czar
Executive Director
Mortgage Finance Authority
334 Fourth Street Southwest
Albuquerque, NM 87102
P: (505) 843-6880
F: (505) 243-3289
E: jczar@housingnm.org

NEW YORK
Ms. RuthAnne Visnauskas
Commissioner/CEO
Homes & Community Renewal
641 Lexington Avenue
New York, NY 10022
P: (866) 275-3427
E: hcrinfo@nyshcr.org

NORTH CAROLINA
Mr. Scott Farmer
Executive Director
Housing Finance Agency
3508 Bush Street
P.O. Box 28066
Raleigh, NC 27611
P: (919) 877-5700
E: bsfarmer@nchfa.com

NORTH DAKOTA
Ms. Jolene Kline
Executive Director
Housing Finance Agency
2624 Vermont Avenue
P.O. Box 1535
Bismarck, ND 58502
P: (701) 328-8072
F: (701) 328-8090
E: jkline@ndhfa.org

NORTHERN MARIANA ISLANDS
Mr. Jesse S. Palacios
Corporate Director
Housing Corporation
P.O. Box 500514
Saipan, MP 96950
P: (670) 234-6866
F: (670) 234-7144
E: jspalacios@nmhc.gov.mp

OHIO
Mr. Sean W. Thomas
Executive Director
Housing Finance Agency
57 East Main Street
Columbus, OH 43215
P: (614) 644-5772
E: ohfa@ohiohome.org

OKLAHOMA
Mr. Dennis Shockley
Executive Director
Housing Finance Agency
100 Northwest 63rd Street, Suite 200
P.O. Box 26720
Oklahoma City, OK 73126
P: (405) 848-1144
F: (405) 840-1109

OREGON
Ms. Margaret Salazar
Director
Housing & Community Services
North Mall Office Building
725 Summer Street, Northeast, Suite B
Salem, OR 97301
P: (503) 986-2000

PUERTO RICO
Mr. Edwin R. Carreras-Rivera
Executive Director
Housing Finance Authority
P.O. Box 71361
San Juan, PR 00936
P: (787) 765-7577

RHODE ISLAND
Ms. Barbara Fields
Executive Director
Rhode Island Housing
44 Washington Street
Providence, RI 02903
P: (401) 457-1234
F: (401) 222-2803
E: bfields@rhodeislandhousing.org

SOUTH CAROLINA
Ms. Valarie Williams
Executive Director
State Housing Finance & Development Authority
300-C Outlet Point Boulevard
Columbia, SC 29210
P: (803) 896-9006
F: (803) 551-4876
E: Valarie.Williams@schousing.com

SOUTH DAKOTA
Mr. Mark Lauseng
Executive Director
Housing Development Authority
3060 East Elizabeth Street
P.O. Box 1237
Pierre, SD 57501
P: (605) 773-3181
F: (605) 773-5154
E: mark@sdhda.org

TENNESSEE
Mr. Ralph Perrey
Executive Director
Housing Development Agency
Jackson Building, Third Floor
502 Deaderick Street
Nashville, TN 37243
P: (615) 815-2200
F: (615) 564-2700
E: rperrey@thda.org

TEXAS
Mr. Tim Irvine
Executive Director
Department of Housing & Community Affairs
221 East 11th Street
P.O. Box 13941
Austin, TX 78711
P: (512) 475-3800
F: (512) 469-9606
E: tim.irvine@tdhca.state.tx.us

U.S. VIRGIN ISLANDS
Mr. Daryl Griffith
Acting Executive Director/Chief Financial Officer
Housing Finance Authority
3202 Demarara Plaza, Suite 200
St. Thomas, VI 00802
P: (340) 777-4432

UTAH
Mr. Grant S. Whitaker
President & CEO
Housing Corporation
2479 South Lake Park Boulevard
West Valley City, UT 84120
P: (801) 902-8200
F: (801) 902-8325
E: gwhitaker@uthc.org

VERMONT
Ms. Sarah E. Carpenter
Executive Director
Housing Finance Agency
164 St. Paul Street
P.O. Box 408
Burlington, VT 05402
P: (802) 652-3421
F: (802) 864-5746
E: scarpenter@vhfa.org

VIRGINIA
Ms. Susan F. Dewey
Executive Director
Housing Development Authority
601 South Belvidere Street
Richmond, VA 23220
P: (804) 782-1986
F: (804) 783-6704
E: susan.dewey@vhda.com

Mr. William C. Shelton
Director
Department of Housing &
Community Development
Main Street Centre
600 East Main Street, Suite 300
Richmond, VA 23219
P: (804) 371-7000
F: (804) 371-6524
E: bill.shelton
@dhcd.virginia.gov

WEST VIRGINIA
Ms. Erica L. Boggess
Executive Director
Housing Development Fund
5710 MacCorkle Avenue,
Southeast
Charleston, WV 25304
P: (304) 391-8600

WISCONSIN
Mr. Wyman B. Winston
Executive Director
Housing & Economic
Development Authority
201 West Washington Avenue,
Suite 700
P.O. Box 1728
Madison, WI 53703
P: (608) 266-7884
F: (608) 267-1099
E: info@wheda.com

WYOMING
Mr. Scott Hoversland
Executive Director
Community Development
Authority
155 North Beech Street
P.O. Box 634
Casper, WY 82602
P: (307) 265-0603
F: (307) 266-5414
E: info@wyomingcda.com

Human Services

Manages the development, administration, and delivery of all human and social service programs.

ALABAMA
Ms. Nancy T. Buckner
Commissioner
Department of Human Resources
Gordon Persons Building, Suite 2104
50 North Ripley Street
Montgomery, AL 36130
P: (334) 242-1310
F: (334) 353-1115
E: Nancy.Buckner@dhr.alabama.gov

ALASKA
Ms. Valerie Davidson
Commissioner
Department of Health & Social Services
3601 C Street, Suite 902
P.O. Box 240249
Anchorage, AK 99503
P: (907) 269-7800
F: (907) 269-0060
E: val.davidson@alaska.gov

AMERICAN SAMOA
Dr. Taeaoafua Meki Solomona
Director
Department of Human & Social Services
P.O. Box 997534
Pago Pago, AS 96799
P: (684) 633-1664
F: (684) 633-7449
E: mtsolomona@dhss.as

ARKANSAS
Ms. Cindy Gillespie
Director
Department of Human Services
Donaghey Plaza
P.O. Box 1437
Little Rock, AR 72203
P: (501) 682-8650
F: (501) 682-6836
E: Cindy.Gillespie@dhs.arkansas.gov

CALIFORNIA
Ms. Diana S. Dooley
Secretary
Health & Human Services Agency
1600 Ninth Street, Room 460
Sacramento, CA 95814
P: (916) 654-3454
F: (916) 654-3343

COLORADO
Mr. Reginald L. Bicha
Executive Director
Department of Human Services
1575 Sherman Street
Denver, CO 80203
P: (303) 866-3475
F: (303) 866-2606
E: reginald.bicha@state.co.us

CONNECTICUT
Mr. Roderick L. Bremby
Commissioner
Department of Social Services
55 Farmington Avenue
Hartford, CT 06105
P: (860) 424-5053
E: roderick.bremby@ct.gov

DELAWARE
Ms. Kara Odom Walker
Secretary
Department of Health & Social Services
1901 North DuPont Highway
Main Building
New Castle, DE 19720
P: (302) 255-9040
F: (302) 255-4429

DISTRICT OF COLUMBIA
Ms. Laura Zeilinger
Director
Department of Human Services
64 New York Avenue, Northeast
6th Floor
Washington, DC 20002
P: (202) 671-4200
F: (202) 671-4326
E: dhs@dc.gov

FLORIDA
Mr. Mike Carroll
Secretary
Department of Children & Families
1317 Winewood Boulevard
Building 1, Room 202
Tallahassee, FL 32399
P: (850) 487-1111
F: (850) 922-2993
E: mike.carroll@myflfamilies.com

GEORGIA
Ms. Robyn A. Crittenden
Commissioner
Department of Human Services
2 Peachtree Street, Northwest
Suite 29-250
Atlanta, GA 30303
P: (404) 656-5680
F: (404) 651-8669

HAWAII
Mr. Pankaj Bhanot
Director
Department of Human Services
1390 Miller Street, Room 209
P.O. Box 339
Honolulu, HI 96809
P: (808) 586-4993
F: (808) 586-4890
E: dhs@dhs.hawaii.gov

IDAHO
Mr. Richard Armstrong
Director
Department of Health & Welfare
450 West State Street
Boise, ID 83702
P: (208) 334-5500
F: (208) 334-6558
E: dick.armstrong@dhw.idaho.gov

ILLINOIS
Mr. James T. Dimas
Secretary
Department of Human Services
100 South Grand Avenue, 3rd Floor
Springfield, IL 62702
P: (217) 557-2134
F: (217) 557-1647

INDIANA
Ms. Adrienne Shields
Director of Family Resources
Family & Social Services Administration
402 West Washington Street, Room W392
P.O. Box 7083
Indianapolis, IN 46204
P: (317) 234-2373
F: (317) 232-4490
E: Adrienne.Shields@fssa.IN.gov

IOWA
Mr. Charles M. Palmer
Director
Department of Human Services
Hoover State Office Building
1305 East Walnut Street
Des Moines, IA 50319
P: (515) 281-5452
F: (515) 281-4980
E: cpalmer1@dhs.state.ia.us

KANSAS
Ms. Phyllis Gilmore
Secretary
Department for Children & Families
555 South Kansas Avenue
Topeka, KS 66603
P: (785) 296-3274
F: (785) 296-2173

KENTUCKY
Ms. Vickie Yates Brown Glisson
Secretary
Cabinet for Health & Family Services
275 East Main Street, 5W-A
Frankfort, KY 40621
P: (502) 564-7042
F: (502) 564-7091

LOUISIANA
Ms. Marketa Garner Walters
Secretary
Department of Children & Family Services
627 North Fourth Street
Baton Rouge, LA 70802
P: (225) 342-7475
F: (225) 342-8636
E: DCFS.Secretary@la.gov

MAINE
Mr. Ricker Hamilton
Deputy Commissioner of Programs
Department of Health & Human Services
221 State Street
11 State House Station
Augusta, ME 04333
P: (207) 287-3707
F: (207) 287-3005
E: ricker.hamilton@maine.gov

MASSACHUSETTS
Ms. Marylou Sudders
Secretary
Executive Office of Health & Human Services
One Ashburton Place, 11th Floor
Boston, MA 02108
P: (617) 573-1600
F: (617) 727-5134

MICHIGAN
Mr. Nick Lyon
Director
Department of Health & Human Services
333 South Grand Avenue
P.O. Box 30195
Lansing, MI 48909
P: (517) 335-0267
F: (517) 335-6101
E: LyonN2@michigan.gov

Human Services

MISSISSIPPI
Dr. Mary Currier
State Health Officer
State Department of Health
570 East Woodrow Wilson
P.O. Box 1700
Jackson, MS 39215
P: (601) 576-7634
F: (601) 576-7931
E: mary.currier
@msdh.state.ms.us

Mr. John Davis
Director
Department of Human Services
750 North State Street
Jackson, MS 39202
P: (601) 359-4457

MISSOURI
Dr. Randall W. Williams
Director
Department of Health & Senior Services
912 Wildwood Drive
P.O. Box 570
Jefferson City, MO 65102
P: (573) 751-6001
F: (573) 751-6010
E: info@health.mo.gov

MONTANA
Ms. Sheila Hogan
Director
Department of Public Health & Human Services
111 North Sanders, Room 301
P.O. Box 4210
Helena, MT 59604
P: (406) 444-5622
F: (406) 444-1970
E: sheilahogan@mt.gov

NEW HAMPSHIRE
Mr. Jeffrey A. Meyers
Commissioner
Department of Health & Human Services
129 Pleasant Street
Concord, NH 03301
P: (603) 271-9200
F: (603) 271-4912
E: Jeffrey.Meyers
@dhhs.nh.gov

NEW JERSEY
Ms. Elizabeth Connolly
Acting Commissioner
Department of Human Services
222 South Warren Street
P.O. Box 700
Trenton, NJ 08625
P: (609) 292-3717

NEW MEXICO
Mr. Brent Earnest
Cabinet Secretary
Human Services Department
P.O. Box 2348
Santa Fe, NM 87504
P: (505) 827-7750
F: (505) 827-6286

NEW YORK
Mr. Samuel D. Roberts
Commissioner
Office of Temporary & Disability Assistance
40 North Pearl Street
Albany, NY 12243
P: (518) 473-1090
E: nyspio@otda.ny.gov

NORTH CAROLINA
Dr. Mandy K. Cohen
Secretary
Department of Health & Human Services
101 Blair Drive
2001 Mail Service Center
Raleigh, NC 27699
P: (919) 855-4800
F: (919) 715-4645
E: mandy.cohen@dhhs.nc.gov

NORTH DAKOTA
Mr. Christopher Jones
Executive Director
Department of Human Services
600 East Boulevard Avenue
Department 325
Bismarck, ND 58505
P: (701) 328-2538
F: (701) 328-2359
E: dhseo@nd.gov

Dr. Mylynn Tufte
State Health Officer
Department of Health
600 East Boulevard Avenue
Bismarck, ND 58505
P: (701) 328-2372
F: (701) 328-4727
E: mylynntufte@nd.gov

NORTHERN MARIANA ISLANDS
Ms. Roxanne P. Diaz
Director
Division of Public Health Services
P.O. Box 500409
Saipan, MP 96950
P: (670) 236-8703
E: chcpublichealth
@gmail.com

OHIO
Ms. Cynthia C. Dungey
Director
Department of Job & Family Services
30 East Broad Street, 32nd Floor
Columbus, OH 43215
P: (614) 466-6283
F: (614) 466-2815

OREGON
Mr. Clyde Saiki
Director
Department of Human Services
500 Summer Street, Northeast
Salem, OR 97301
P: (503) 945-7001
F: (503) 581-6198
E: clyde.saiki@oregon.gov

PENNSYLVANIA
Mr. Theodore Dallas
Secretary
Department of Human Services
Health & Welfare Building
625 Forster Street, P.O. Box 2675
Harrisburg, PA 17105
P: (717) 787-2600
F: (717) 772-2062

PUERTO RICO
Ms. Glorimar Andujar Matos
Secretary
Department of the Family
P.O. Box 11398
Hato Rey, PR 00917
P: (787) 294-4900
F: (787) 297-0732

RHODE ISLAND
Mr. Eric J. Beane
Acting Director
Department of Human Services
Louis Pasteur Building
57 Howard Avenue
Cranston, RI 2920
P: (401) 462-2121

SOUTH CAROLINA
Ms. V. Susan Alford
Director
Department of Social Services
1535 Confederate Avenue
P.O. Box 1520
Columbia, SC 29202
P: (803) 898-7360
F: (803) 898-7277

SOUTH DAKOTA
Ms. Gloria Pearson
Secretary
Department of Human Services
3800 East Highway 34, Hillsview Plaza
C/o 500 East Capitol Avenue
Pierre, SD 57501
P: (605) 773-5990
F: (605) 773-5483
E: infodhs@state.sd.us

TENNESSEE
Ms. Danielle W. Barnes
Commissioner
Department of Human Services
400 Deaderick Street
Nashville, TN 37243
P: (615) 313-4700
F: (615) 741-4165
E: danielle.w.barnes@tn.gov

TEXAS
Mr. Charles Smith
Executive Commissioner
Health & Human Services Commission
4900 North Lamar Boulevard
P.O. Box 13247
Austin, TX 78711
P: (512) 424-6500
F: (512) 424-6587

Mr. Jon Weizenbaum
Commissioner
Department of Aging & Disability Services
701 West 51st Street
P.O. Box 149030
Austin, TX 78714
P: (512) 438-3011
F: (512) 438-3011

U.S. VIRGIN ISLANDS
Mr. Felicia Blyden
Commissioner
Department of Human Services
3011 Golden Rock
Christiansted
St. Croix, VI 00802
P: (340) 718-2980

UTAH
Ms. Ann S. Williamson
Executive Director
Department of Human Services
195 North 1950 West
Salt Lake City, UT 84116
P: (801) 538-4001
F: (801) 538-4016
E: annwilliamson@utah.gov

VERMONT
Mr. Al Gobeille
Secretary
Agency of Human Services
280 State Drive, Center Building
Waterbury, VT 05671
P: (802) 241-0440
E: al.gobeille@vermont.gov

VIRGINIA
Dr. Bill A. Hazel Jr.
Secretary
Office of the Secretary of
Health & Human Services
1111 East Broad Street
P.O. Box 1475
Richmond, VA 23218
P: (804) 786-7765
F: (804) 786-3389
E: bill.hazel
@governor.virginia.gov

Ms. Margaret Ross Schultze
Commissioner
Department of Social Services
801 East Main Street
Richmond, VA 23219
P: (804) 726-7011
E: margaret.schultze
@dss.virginia.gov

WASHINGTON
Mr. Bill Moss
Acting Secretary
Department of Social & Health
Services
1115 Washington Street,
Southeast
Olympia, WA 98504
P: (800) 737-0617
F: (360) 407-0304

WEST VIRGINIA
Mr. Bill J. Crouch
Cabinet Secretary
Department of Health & Human
Resources
One Davis Square, Suite 100
East
Charleston, WV 25301
P: (304) 558-0684
F: (304) 558-1130
E: DHHRSecretary@wv.gov

WYOMING
Dr. Steve Corsi
Director
Department of Family Services
Hathaway Building, 3rd Floor
2300 Capitol Avenue
Cheyenne, WY 82002
P: (307) 777-6597
F: (307) 777-7747
E: steve.corsi@wyo.gov

Information Systems

Provides statewide computer services or coordinates the operation of various data processing systems within state government.

ALASKA
Mr. Bill Vajda
Chief Information Officer
Office of Information Technology
Department of Administration
333 Willoughby Avenue, 10th Floor
Juneau, AK 99801
P: (907) 465-8461
E: bill.vajda@alaska.gov

AMERICAN SAMOA
The Honorable Ueli Tonumaipea
Treasurer
Department of Treasury
American Samoa Government
Pago Pago, AS 96799
P: (684) 633-4155
F: (684) 633-4100
E: ueli.tonumaipea@tr.as.gov

ARIZONA
Mr. Morgan Reed
Chief Information Officer
Strategic Enterprise Technology
100 North 15th Avenue, Suite 400
Phoenix, AZ 85007
P: (602) 540-8831
F: (602) 542-4272

CALIFORNIA
Ms. Amy Tong
Director & Chief Information Officer
Department of Technology
1325 J Street, Suite 1600
Sacramento, CA 95814
P: (916) 319-9223
F: (916) 324-1734
E: amy.tong@state.ca.gov

COLORADO
Ms. Suma Nallapati
Secretary of Technology & Chief Information Officer
Governor's Office of Information Technology
601 East 18th Avenue, Suite 250
Denver, CO 80203
P: (303) 764-7707
E: oit@state.co.us

CONNECTICUT
Mr. Mark D. Raymond
Chief Information Officer
Department of Administrative Services
55 Farmington Avenue
Hartford, CT 06105
P: (860) 622-2419
F: (860) 291-8665
E: mark.raymond@ct.gov

DISTRICT OF COLUMBIA
Ms. Archana Vemulapalli
Acting Chief Technology Officer
Office of the Chief Technology Officer
200 I Street, Southeast
5th Floor
Washington, DC 20003
P: (202) 727-7349
F: (202) 727-6857
E: octo@dc.gov

FLORIDA
Mr. Eric Larson
Acting Executive Director & Chief Information Officer & Chief Operations Officer
Agency for State Technology
4050 Esplanade Way, Suite 115
Tallahassee, FL 32399
P: (850) 717-9506

GEORGIA
Mr. Calvin Rhodes
Executive Director & Chief Information Officer
Technology Authority
47 Trinity Avenue, Southwest
Atlanta, GA 30334
P: (404) 463-2300
F: (404) 463-2380
E: calvn.rhodes@gta.ga.gov

GUAM
Ms. Christine Baleto
Director
Department of Administration
P.O. Box 884
Hagatna, GU 96928
P: (671) 475-1101
F: (671) 477-6788

HAWAII
Mr. Todd Nacapuy
Chief Information Officer
Office of Enterprise Technology Services
P.O. Box 119
Honolulu, HI 96810
P: (808) 586-1910

IDAHO
Mr. Greg Zickau
Chief Information Officer
Department of Administration
650 West State Street, Suite 100
Boise, ID 83720
P: (208) 332-1875
F: (208) 334-2307
E: greg.zickau@cio.idaho.gov

ILLINOIS
Mr. Hardik Bhatt
Chief Information Officer
Department of Innovation & Technology
100 West Randolph, 4th Floor
Chicago, IL 60601
P: (217) 785-1943

INDIANA
Mr. Dewand Neely
Chief Information Officer & Director
Office of Technology
1000 North Senate Avenue
IGCN, Room N551
Indianapolis, IN 46204
P: (317) 234-0835

KANSAS
Mr. Loren Westerdale
Director
Division of Information Systems
Information Technology Services
700 Southwest Harrison Street, Room 1015
Topeka, KS 66603
P: (785) 296-6236
E: loren.westerdale@ks.gov

LOUISIANA
Mr. Richard Howze
State Chief Information Officer
Office of Technology Services
Division of Administration
Claiborne Building, Suite 2-130
Baton Rouge, LA 70804
P: (225) 342-7105
F: (225) 219-9465
E: cio@la.gov

MAINE
Mr. Jim Smith
Chief Information Officer
Office of Information Technology
Administrative & Financial Services
51 Commerce Drive
Augusta, ME 04330
P: (207) 624-7568

MARYLAND
Mr. Michael Leahy
Acting Secretary of Information Technology
Department of Information Technology
100 Community Place
Annapolis, MD 21032
P: (410) 697-9406

MASSACHUSETTS
Mr. Mark Nunnelly
Executive Director
Executive Office for Administration & Finance
MassIT
One Ashburton Place, Room 804
Boston, MA 02108
P: (617) 626-4671

MICHIGAN
Mr. David Behen
Director
Department of Technology, Management & Budget
320 South Walnut Street, 2nd Floor
P.O. Box 30026
Lansing, MI 48909
P: (517) 373-1004
E: behend@michigan.gov

MINNESOTA
Mr. Matt Massman
Commissioner
Department of Administration
116 Veterans Service Building
20 West 12 Street
St. Paul, MN 55155
P: (651) 201-3421
F: (651) 297-7909
E: Matt.Massman@state.mn.us

MISSISSIPPI
Dr. Craig P. Orgeron
Chief Information Officer & Executive Director
Department of Information Technology Services
3771 Eastwood Drive
Jackson, MS 39211
P: (601) 432-8000
F: (601) 713-6380
E: craig.orgeron@its.ms.gov

MISSOURI
Mr. Rich Kliethermes
Chief Information Officer
Information Technology Services Division
Office of Administration
301 West High Street, Suite 270
Jefferson City, MO 65101
P: (573) 526-7742

MONTANA
Mr. Ron Baldwin
Chief Information Officer
Information Technology Services Division
Department of Administration
P.O. Box 200113
Helena, MT 59620
P: (406) 444-2777
F: (406) 444-2701

NEBRASKA
Mr. Ed Toner
Chief Information Officer
Office of the Chief Information Officer
501 South 14th Street
P.O. Box 95045
Lincoln, NE 68508
P: (402) 471-3717
E: ed.toner@nebraska.gov

NEW HAMPSHIRE
Mr. Denis Goulet
Commissioner
Department of Information Technology
27 Hazen Drive
Concord, NH 03301
P: (603) 223-5701
E: Denis.Goulet@Doit.nh.gov

NEW JERSEY
Mr. Dave Weinstein
Chief Information Officer
Office of Information Technology
300 Riverview Plaza
Trenton, NJ 08625
P: (609) 777-5865

NEW MEXICO
Mr. Darryl Ackley
Secretary & Chief Information Officer
Department of Information Technology
P.O. Box 22550
Santa Fe, NM 87505
P: (505) 476-3070
F: (505) 827-2948

NORTH CAROLINA
Mr. Eric Boyette
Secretary & State Chief Information Officer
Department of Information Technology
P.O. Box 17209
Raleigh, NC 27619
P: (919) 707-2134
E: eric.boyette@nc.gov

NORTH DAKOTA
Mr. Shawn Riley
Chief Information Officer
Information Technology Department
4201 Normandy Street
Bismarck, ND 58503
P: (701) 328-1001
F: (701) 328-1075
E: sriley@nd.gov

NORTHERN MARIANA ISLANDS
Mr. Joe I. Quitugua
Director
Commonwealth of Northern Mariana Islands
P.O. Box 5234 CHRB
Saipan, MP 96950
P: (670) 664-1400
F: (670) 664-1415
E: finanedp02@gtepacifica.net

OHIO
Mr. Stuart R. Davis
Chief Information Officer & Assistant Director
Office of Information Technology
Department of Administrative Services
30 East Broad Street, 39th Floor
Columbus, OH 43215
P: (614) 644-6446
F: (614) 728-5297
E: Stu.Davis@das.ohio.gov

OREGON
Mr. Alex Pettit
Chief Information Officer
Department of Administrative Services
Executive Building
155 Cottage Street Northeast, 4th Floor
Salem, OR 97301
P: (503) 378-2128
F: (503) 378-3795
E: alex.pettit@das.state.or.us

PENNSYLVANIA
Mr. John MacMillan
Deputy Secretary for Information Technology & Chief Information Officer
Office for Information Technology
Governor's Office of Administration
613 North Street, Room 210
Harrisburg, PA 17109
P: (717) 787-5440
F: (717) 787-4523
E: cio@pa.gov

RHODE ISLAND
Mr. Christopher Antonellis
Chief Information Officer
Office of Information Technology
Department of Administration
50 Service Avenue
Warwick, RI 02886
P: (401) 462-2185

SOUTH CAROLINA
Mr. Keith Osman
Chief Information Officer
Division of Technology
Department of Administration
4430 Broad River Road
Columbia, SC 29210
P: (803) 896-0222

SOUTH DAKOTA
Mr. David Zolnowsky
Commissioner
Bureau of Information & Telecommunications
Kneip Building
700 Governors Drive
Pierre, SD 57501
P: (605) 773-5110
F: (605) 773-6040

TENNESSEE
Mr. Mark Bengel
Chief Information Officer
Office for Information Resources
Department of Finance & Administration
901 5th Avenue, North
Nashville, TN 37243
P: (615) 741-7951
F: (615) 532-0471

TEXAS
Ms. Stacey Napier
Executive Director
Department of Information Resources
300 West 15th Street, Suite 1300
P.O. Box 13564
Austin, TX 78711
P: (512) 475-4700
F: (512) 475-4759

U.S. VIRGIN ISLANDS
Mr. Angelo Riddick
Director & Chief Information Officer
Bureau of Information Technology
9059 Estate Castle Coakley
Christiansted, VI 00820
P: (340) 713-0354
F: (340) 719-1623

UTAH
Mr. Michael Hussey
Chief Information Officer
Department of Technology Services
1 State Office Buidling, Floor 6
Salt Lake City, UT 84114
P: (801) 538-3298
F: (801) 538-3622
E: mhussey@utah.gov

VERMONT
Mr. John Quinn
Secretary & Chief Information Officer
Agency of Digital Services
Department of Information & Innovation
133 State Street
Montpelier, VT 05633
P: (802) 828-2316
E: john.quinn@vermont.gov

VIRGINIA
Ms. Karen R. Jackson
Secretary of Technology
Office of the Secretary of Technology
1111 East Broad Street
P.O. Box 1475
Richmond, VA 23218
P: (804) 786-9579
F: (804) 786-9584
E: karen.jackson@virginia.goveror.gov

Information Systems

WASHINGTON
Mr. Rob St. John
Deputy Director, Office of the Chief Information Officer
State Technology Solution
1500 Jefferson Street, Southeast
Olympia, WA 98501
P: (360) 407-8700
F: (360) 586-5885
E: rob.st.john@cts.wa.gov

WEST VIRGINIA
Mr. John Dunlap
Chief Technology Officer
Office of Technology
Capitol Complex, Building 5, 10th Floor
Charleston, WV 25305
P: (304) 558-8100
F: (304) 558-0136
E: John.D.Dunlap@wv.gov

WISCONSIN
Mr. David Cagigal
Chief Information Officer
Division of Enterprise Technology
Department of Administration
101 East Wilson Street
Madison, WI 53707
P: (608) 264-9502
F: (608) 267-0626
E: David.Cagigal@wisconsin.gov

WYOMING
Mr. Rick Imbrogno
Administrator
Information Technology Division
Emerson Building, Room 237
2001 Capitol Avenue
Cheyenne, WY 82002
P: (307) 777-5101
F: (307) 777-6725

Insurance

Licenses and regulates insurance agents and insurance and title companies in the state.

ALABAMA
Mr. Jim L. Ridling
Commissioner
Department of Insurance
201 Monroe Street, Suite 502
P.O. Box 303351
Montgomery, AL 36130
P: (334) 269-3550
F: (334) 241-4192

ALASKA
Ms. Lori K. Wing-Heier
Director
Department of Commerce, Community & Economic Development
Division of Insurance
550 West 7th Avenue, Suite 1560
Anchorage, AK 99501
P: (907) 269-7900
F: (907) 269-7910

AMERICAN SAMOA
Mr. Peter Fuimaono
Insurance Commissioner
Office of the Governor
American Samoa Government
A.P. Lutali Executive Office Building
Pago Pago, AS 96799
P: (684) 633-4116

ARIZONA
Ms. Leslie R. Hess
Interim Director
Department of Insurance
2910 North 44th Street, Suite 210
Phoenix, AZ 85018
P: (602) 364-3100
F: (602) 364-3470

ARKANSAS
Mr. Allen Kerr
Commissioner
State Insurance Department
1200 West Third Street
Little Rock, AR 72201
P: (501) 371-2600
F: (501) 371-2618

CALIFORNIA
Mr. Dave Jones
Commissioner
State Department of Insurance
300 Capitol Mall, Suite 1700
Sacramento, CA 95814
P: (916) 492-3500
F: (916) 445-5280

COLORADO
Ms. Marguerite Salazar
Commissioner
Division of Insurance
Department of Regulatory Agencies
1560 Broadway, Suite 850
Denver, CO 80202
P: (303) 894-7499
F: (303) 894-7455

CONNECTICUT
Ms. Katharine L. Wade
Commissioner
State Insurance Department
153 Market Street, 7th Floor
P.O. Box 816
Hartford, CT 06142
P: (860) 297-3800
F: (860) 566-7410

DELAWARE
The Honorable Trinidad Navarro (D)
Commissioner
Department of Insurance
841 Silver Lake Boulevard
Dover, DE 19904
P: (302) 674-7300
F: (302) 739-5280

DISTRICT OF COLUMBIA
Mr. Stephen C. Taylor
Commissioner
Department of Insurance, Securities & Banking
Government of the District of Columbia
810 First Street Northeast, Suite 701
Washington, DC 20002
P: (202) 727-8000
F: (202) 535-1196
E: disb@dc.gov

FLORIDA
Mr. David M. Altmaier
Commissioner
Office of Insurance Regulation
The Larson Building
200 East Gaines Street, Room 101A
Tallahassee, FL 32399
P: (850) 413-5914
F: (850) 488-3334

GEORGIA
The Honorable Ralph T. Hudgens (R)
Commissioner
Office of Insurance & Safety Fire Commissioner
2 Martin Luther King Jr. Drive
West Tower, Suite 704
Atlanta, GA 30334
P: (404) 656-2070
F: (404) 657-8542

GUAM
Mr. Artemio B. Ilagan
Banking & Insurance Commissioner
Regulatory Division
Department of Revenue & Taxation
P.O. Box 23607
GMF Barrigada, GU 96921
P: (671) 635-1817
F: (671) 633-2643
E: art.ilagan@revtax.gov.gu

HAWAII
Mr. Gordon I. Ito
Commissioner, Insurance Division
Department of Commerce & Consumer Affairs
335 Merchant Street, Room 213
P.O. Box 3614
Honolulu, HI 96811
P: (808) 586-2790
F: (808) 586-2806
E: insurance@dcca.hawaii.gov

IDAHO
Mr. Dean L. Cameron
Director
Department of Insurance
700 West State Street, 3rd Floor
P.O. Box 83720
Boise, ID 83720
P: (208) 334-4250
F: (208) 334-4398

ILLINOIS
Ms. Jennifer Hammer
Director
Department of Insurance
320 West Washington Street
Springfield, IL 62767
P: (217) 782-4515

INDIANA
Mr. Stephen W. Robertson
Commissioner
State Department of Insurance
311 West Washington Street, Suite 103
Indianapolis, IN 46204
P: (317) 232-2385
F: (317) 232-5251

IOWA
Mr. Doug Ommen
Commissioner
State Insurance Division
Two Ruan Center
601 Locust, 4th Floor
Des Moines, IA 50309
P: (515) 281-5575

KANSAS
The Honorable Ken Selzer (R)
Commissioner
State Insurance Department
420 Southwest 9th Street
Topeka, KS 66612
P: (785) 296-3071
F: (785) 296-7805
E: commissioner@ksinsurance.org

KENTUCKY
Mr. Brian Maynard
Commissioner
State Department of Insurance
215 West Main Street
P.O. Box 517
Frankfort, KY 40602
P: (502) 564-3630
F: (502) 564-1453

LOUISIANA
The Honorable James J. Donelon (R)
Commissioner
State Department of Insurance
1702 North 3rd Street
P.O. Box 94214
Baton Rouge, LA 70804
P: (225) 342-5900
F: (225) 342-8622

MAINE
Mr. Eric A. Cioppa
Superintendent
State Bureau of Insurance
Professional & Financial Regulation
34 State House Station
Augusta, ME 04333
P: (207) 624-8475
F: (207) 624-8599

MARYLAND
Mr. Alfred Redmer Jr.
Commissioner
State Insurance Administration
200 St. Paul Place, Suite 2700
Baltimore, MD 21202
P: (410) 468-2090
F: (410) 468-2020

MASSACHUSETTS
Mr. Gary Anderson
Acting Commissioner
State Division of Insurance
Consumer Affairs & Business Regulation
1000 Washington Street, 8th Floor
Boston, MA 02118
P: (617) 521-7794
E: gary.anderson@state.ma.us

Insurance

MICHIGAN
Mr. Patrick M. McPharlin
Director
Department of Insurance & Financial Services
530 West Allegan Street, 7th Floor
P.O. Box 30220
Lansing, MI 48909
P: (517) 284-8800
F: (517) 284-8837
E: difs-info@michigan.gov

MINNESOTA
Mr. Mike Rothman
Commissioner
Department of Commerce
85 7th Place East, Suite 280
St. Paul, MN 55101
P: (651) 539-1441
F: (651) 539-1547
E: commerce.commissioner@state.mn.us

MISSISSIPPI
The Honorable Mike Chaney (R)
Commissioner
State Insurance Department
1001 Woolfolk State Office Building
501 North West Street, P.O. Box 79
Jackson, MS 39205
P: (601) 359-3569
F: (601) 359-2474
E: mike.chaney@mid.state.ms.us

MISSOURI
Ms. Chlora Lindley-Myers
Acting Director
Department of Insurance, Financial Institutions & Professional Registration
301 West High Street, Room 530
P.O. Box 690
Jefferson City, MO 65102
P: (573) 751-4126

MONTANA
The Honorable Matt Rosendale (R)
Commissioner of Securities & Insurance, State Auditor
Office of the State Auditor
840 Helena Avenue
Helena, MT 59601
P: (406) 444-2040
F: (406) 444-3497
E: stateauditor@mt.gov

NEBRASKA
Mr. Bruce R. Ramge
Director
State Department of Insurance
941 O Street, Suite 400
P.O. Box 82089
Lincoln, NE 68501
P: (402) 471-2201
F: (402) 471-4610

NEVADA
Ms. Barbara Richardson
Commissioner
Division of Insurance
Department of Business & Industry
1818 East College Parkway, Suite 103
Carson City, NV 89706
P: (775) 687-0700
F: (775) 687-0787

NEW HAMPSHIRE
Mr. Roger A. Sevigny
Commissioner
State Insurance Department
21 South Fruit Street, Suite 14
Concord, NH 03301
P: (603) 271-2261
F: (603) 271-1406
E: roger.sevigny@ins.nh.gov

NEW JERSEY
Mr. Richard J. Badolato
Commissioner
Department of Banking & Insurance
State of New Jersey
20 West State Street, P.O. Box 325
Trenton, NJ 08625
P: (609) 292-7272
F: (609) 984-5273
E: commissioner@dobi.state.nj.us

NEW MEXICO
Mr. John G. Franchini
Superintendent
Office of Superintendent of Insurance
P.E.R.A. Building
1120 Paseo De Peralta, P.O. Box 1689
Santa Fe, NM 87504
P: (505) 827-4601
F: (505) 827-4734

NEW YORK
Ms. Maria T. Vullo
Superintendent
State Department of Financial Services
One State Street
New York, NY 10004
P: (212) 709-3500
F: (212) 709-3520

NORTH CAROLINA
The Honorable Mike Causey (R)
Commissioner
State Department of Insurance
430 North Salisburg Street
Dobbs Building, 1201 Mail Service Center
Raleigh, NC 27699
P: (919) 807-6000
F: (919) 733-6495

NORTH DAKOTA
The Honorable John Godfread (R)
Commissioner
State Department of Insurance
State Capitol, 5th Floor
600 East Boulevard Avenue
Bismarck, ND 58505
P: (701) 328-2440
F: (701) 328-4880

NORTHERN MARIANA ISLANDS
Mr. Mark O. Rabauliman
Secretary of Commerce
Department of Commerce
Office of the Insurance Commissioner
Caller Box 10007 CK
Saipan, MP 96950
P: (670) 664-3077
F: (670) 664-3067
E: info@commerce.gov.mp

OHIO
Ms. Jillian Froment
Director
State Department of Insurance
50 West Town Street
Third Floor, Suite 300
Columbus, OH 43215
P: (614) 644-2658

OKLAHOMA
The Honorable John D. Doak
Commissioner
State Insurance Department
Five Corporate Plaza
3625 Northwest 56th Street, Suite 100
Oklahoma City, OK 73112
P: (405) 521-2828
F: (405) 521-6635

OREGON
Ms. Laura N. Cali Robison
Insurance Commissioner/Chief Actuary
Department of Consumer & Business Services
Financial Regulation, P.O. Box 14480
350 Winter Street, Northeast
Salem, OR 97309
P: (503) 947-7980
F: (503) 378-4351
E: laura.n.cali@oregon.gov

PENNSYLVANIA
Ms. Teresa D. Miller
Commissioner
State Insurance Department
1326 Strawberry Square
Harrisburg, PA 17120
P: (717) 787-7000
F: (717) 772-1969

PUERTO RICO
Mr. Javier Rivera Rios
Commissioner of Insurance
Office of the Commissioner of Insurance
B5 Calle Tabonuco
Suite 216 PMB 356
Guaynabo, PR 00968
P: (787) 304-8686

RHODE ISLAND
Ms. Elizabeth Kelleher Dwyer
Superintendent
Division of Insurance
Department of Business Regulation
1511 Pontiac Avenue, Building 69-2
Cranston, RI 02920
P: (401) 462-9617
F: (401) 462-9602
E: elizabeth.dwyer@dbr.ri.gov

SOUTH CAROLINA
Mr. Raymond G. Farmer
Director
Department of Insurance
1201 Main Street, Suite 1000
P.O. Box 100105
Columbia, SC 29202
P: (803) 737-6160
F: (803) 737-6205

SOUTH DAKOTA
Mr. Larry Deiter
Director
Division of Insurance
State Department of Labor & Regulation
124 South Euclid Avenue, 2nd Floor
Pierre, SD 57501
P: (605) 773-3563
F: (605) 773-5369

TENNESSEE
Ms. Julie Mix McPeak
Commissioner
State Department of Commerce & Insurance
Davy Crockett Tower
500 James Robertson Parkway
Nashville, TN 37243
P: (615) 741-2241
F: (615) 532-6934
E: ask.tdci@tn.gov

TEXAS
Ms. David Mattax
Commissioner
Department of Insurance
333 Guadalupe Street
P.O. Box 149104
Austin, TX 78714
P: (512) 676-6000
F: (512) 490-1045

U.S. VIRGIN ISLANDS
The Honorable Osbert Potter (I)
Lieutenant Governor/Commissioner
Division of Banking, Insurance & Financial Regulation
1331 Kings Street, Suite101
St. Croix, VI 00802
P: (340) 773-6449
F: (340) 773-0330

VERMONT
Mr. Michael Pieciak
Commissioner
Department of Financial Regulation
89 Main Street
Montpelier, VT 05620
P: (802) 828-3301
F: (802) 828-3306
E: michael.pieciak@vermont.gov

VIRGINIA
Ms. Jacqueline K. Cunningham
Commissioner
Bureau of Insurance
State Corporation Commission
1300 East Main Street, P.O. Box 1157
Richmond, VA 23218
P: (804) 371-9741
F: (804) 371-9873

WASHINGTON
The Honorable Mike Kreidler (D)
Commissioner
Office of the Insurance Commissioner
P.O. Box 40256
Olympia, WA 98504
P: (360) 725-7000
F: (360) 586-3535
E: askMike@oic.wa.gov

WEST VIRGINIA
Mr. Allan L. McVey
Insurance Commissioner
Offices of the Insurance Commissioner
900 Pennsylvania Avenue
P.O. Box 50540
Charleston, WV 25305
P: (304) 558-3354
F: (304) 558-4965
E: Allan.L.McVey@wv.gov

WISCONSIN
Mr. Ted Nickel
Commissioner
Office of the Commissioner of Insurance
125 South Webster Street
GEF III, Second Floor, P.O. Box 7873
Madison, WI 53707
P: (608) 266-3585
F: (608) 266-9935

WYOMING
Mr. Tom Glause
Commissioner
State Insurance Department
106 East 6th Avenue
Cheyenne, WY 82002
P: (307) 777-7401
F: (307) 777-2446

International Trade

Promotes state exports, attracts overseas investments in the state and directs trade and investment missions.

ALABAMA
Ms. Hilda Lockhart
Director, International Trade Division
Department of Commerce
401 Adams Avenue, Suite 630
Montgomery, AL 36130
P: (334) 242-0442
F: (334) 242-0415
E: hilda.lockhart@commerce.alabama.gov

ARIZONA
Mr. Kevin O'Shea
Vice President, International Trade
State Commerce Authority
333 North Central, Suite 1900
Phoenix, AZ 85004
P: (602) 845-1217
E: kevino@azcommerce.com

ARKANSAS
Mr. W. Dan Hendrix
President & CEO
Arkansas World Trade Center
3300 Market Street, Suite 400
Rogers, AR 72758
P: (479) 418-4800
E: dhendrix@arwtc.org

CALIFORNIA
Mr. Jeff Williamson
Statewide Director
International Affairs & Business Development
Business & Economic Development
980 9th Street, Suite 2450
Sacramento, CA 95814
P: (909) 556-6639
F: (916) 323-5440
E: jeff.williamson@rccd.edu

COLORADO
Ms. Stacy Feeney
International Outreach Manager
Office of Economic Development & International Trade
1625 Broadway, Suite 2700
Denver, CO 80202
P: (303) 892-3858
F: (303) 892-3848

CONNECTICUT
Ms. Beatriz Gutierrez
International Business Development Manager
Office of International & Domestic Business Development
Economic & Community Development
505 Hudson Street
Hartford, CT 06106
P: (860) 270-8068
F: (860) 707-1809
E: Beatriz.Gutierrez@ct.gov

DELAWARE
Ms. Andrea Tinianow
Director of Corporate & International Development
International Trade & Development
820 North French Street
Wilmington, DE 19801
P: (302) 577-8285
F: (302) 577-1176
E: andrea.tinianow@state.de.us

DISTRICT OF COLUMBIA
Mr. Jonathan Brady
Manager
Export DC
Small & Local Business Development
441 4th Street Northwest, Suite 850N
Washington, DC 20001
P: (202) 741-0824
E: jonathan.brady@dc.gov

FLORIDA
Mr. Manuel Mencia
Senior Vice President
Division of International Trade & Development
Enterprise Florida
201 Alhambra Circle, Suite 610
Coral Gables, FL 33134
P: (305) 808-3660
F: (305) 808-3660
E: mmencia@eflorida.com

GEORGIA
Ms. Mary Waters
Deputy Commissioner, International Trade
International Trade
Department of Economic Development
75 Fifth Street Northwest, Suite 1200
Atlanta, GA 30308
P: (404) 962-4120
F: (404) 962-4121
E: mwaters@georgia.org

HAWAII
Mr. Luis P. Salaveria
Director
Department of Business, Economic Development & Tourism
250 South Hotel Street, 5th Floor
Honolulu, HI 96813
P: (808) 586-2355
F: (808) 586-2377
E: director@dbedt.hawaii.gov

IDAHO
Ms. Jennifer Verdon
Manager
Idaho Commerce
700 West State Street
Boise, ID 83702
P: (208) 287-3165
F: (208) 794-9191
E: jennifer.verdon@commerce.idaho.gov

ILLINOIS
Ms. Margo Markopoulos
Director
Office of Trade & Investment
Commerce & Economic Opportunity
100 West Randolph, Suite 3-400
Chicago, IL 60601
P: (312) 814-2319
F: (312) 814-6581
E: Margo.Markopoulos@illinois.gov

INDIANA
Mr. Kent Anderson
Vice President of Business Development
Economic Development Corporation
One North Capitol, Suite 700
Indianapolis, IN 46204
P: (812) 390-4816
F: (317) 232-4146
E: KAnderson@iedc.in.gov

IOWA
Ms. Kathy Hill
International Trade Office Team Leader & Marketing Manager
International Trade Office
Economic Development Authority
200 East Grand Avenue
Des Moines, IA 50309
P: (515) 725-3141
F: (515) 725-3010
E: kathy.hill@iowa.gov

KANSAS
Mr. Randi Tveitaraas Jack
International Development Manager
Department of Commerce, Business & Community Development Division
1000 Southwest Jackson Street
Curtis State Office Building, Suite 100
Topeka, KS 66612
P: (785) 296-7868
E: rjack@kansascommerce.com

KENTUCKY
Ms. Darlene Barber
Project Manager/STEP Program Director
Cabinet for Economic Development
300 West Broadway
Old Capitol Annex
Frankfort, KY 40601
P: (502) 782-1940
F: (502) 564-3256
E: Darlene.Barber@ky.gov

LOUISIANA
Mr. Larry Collins
Executive Director, International Commerce
State Economic Development
1051 North Third Street
Baton Rouge, LA 70802
P: (225) 342-4323
F: (225) 342-5349
E: larry.collins@la.gov

MARYLAND
Ms. Signe Pringle
Managing Director
Department of Commerce
World Trade Center
401 East Pratt Street, 7th Floor
Baltimore, MD 21202
P: (410) 767-3542
F: (410) 333-4302
E: signe.pringle@maryland.gov

MASSACHUSETTS
Mr. Mark S. Sullivan
Executive Director
Office of International Trade & Investment
State Transportation Building
10 Park Plaza, Suite 4510
Boston, MA 02116
P: (617) 973-8650
F: (617) 227-3488
E: mark.f.sullivan@state.ma.us

MICHIGAN
Ms. Jeanne Broad
Director, International Trade
Economic Development Corporation
International Trade Office
300 North Washington Square
Lansing, MI 48913
P: (313) 258-7947
E: broadj@michigan.org

MINNESOTA
Ms. Kathleen Motzenbecker
Executive Director
Trade Office
1st National Bank Building, Suite E200
332 Minnesota Street
St. Paul, MN 55101
P: (651) 259-7489
F: (651) 296-3555
E: kathleen.motzenbecker@state.mn.us

MISSISSIPPI
Ms. Rose Boxx
International Trade Director
State Development Authority
P.O. Box 849
Jackson, MS 39205
P: (601) 594-6582
F: (601) 359-3605
E: rboxx@mississippi.org

MISSOURI
Ms. Ann Pardalos
Manager
International Trade & Investment Office
Harry S. Truman Building
301 West High Street, Suite 750
Jefferson City, MO 65101
P: (573) 751-6605
F: (573) 526-1567
E: ann.pardalos@ded.mo.gov

MONTANA
Ms. Angelyn DeYoung
International Trade Manager
Office of Trade & International Relations
Department of Commerce
P.O. Box 200505
Helena, MT 59620
P: (406) 841-2783
F: (406) 841-2728
E: adeyoung@mt.gov

NEBRASKA
Ms. Susan Rouch
International Export Manager
Office of International Trade & Investment
Department of Economic Development
301 Centennial Mall, South
Lincoln, NE 68509
P: (402) 471-4668
F: (402) 471-3778
E: susan.rouch@nebraska.gov

NEVADA
Mr. Kristopher J. Sanchez
Director of International Trade
International Trade Division
Office of Economic Development
555 East Washington Avenue, Suite 5400
Las Vegas, NV 89101
P: (702) 486-2700
F: (775) 486-2701
E: ksanchez@diversifynevada.com

NEW HAMPSHIRE
Ms. Tina Kasim
Program Manager
Office of International Commerce
Division of Economic Development
172 Pembroke Road
Concord, NH 03301
P: (603) 271-8444
F: (603) 271-6784
E: tina.kasim@dred.nh.gov

NEW JERSEY
Mr. Eddy S. Mayen
Director
Office of International Business Development & Protocol
Department of State
P.O. Box 820
Trenton, NJ 08625
P: (609) 633-1182
F: (609) 292-5509
E: eddy.mayen@sos.nj.gov

NEW MEXICO
Mr. Edward Herrera
Director
Office of International Trade
Economic Development Department
1100 South St. Francis Drive, Room 1244
Santa Fe, NM 87505
P: (505) 827-0278
F: (505) 827-0328
E: Edward.Herrera@state.nm.us

NEW YORK
Ms. Erin M. Cole
Senior Vice President
Global New York Division
Empire State Development
633 Third Avenue, 36th Floor
New York, NY 10017
P: (212) 803-2300
E: Erin.Cole@esd.ny.gov

NORTH CAROLINA
Mr. Rick Hill
Director, International Trade
International Trade Division
Economic Development Partnership
15000 Weston Parkway
Cary, NC 27513
P: (919) 447-7757
E: Rick.hill@edpnc.com

NORTH DAKOTA
Mr. Dean Gorder
Executive Director
State Trade Office
811 2nd Avenue, North
Suite 284
Fargo, ND 58108
P: (701) 231-1159
F: (701) 231-1151
E: dean@ndto.com

OHIO
Mr. Tom Bainbridge
Export Assistance Program Manager
State Development Services Agency
77 South High Street
P.O. Box 1001
Columbus, OH 43216
P: (614) 728-3120
E: Tom.Bainbridge@development.ohio.gov

OKLAHOMA
Ms. Jennifer Springer
Director of Global Services
Global Business Services
Department of Commerce
900 North Stiles Avenue
Oklahoma City, OK 73104
P: (405) 815-5158
E: Jennifer.Springer@commerce.ok.gov

OREGON
Ms. Amanda Welker
Global Strategies Officer
Business Oregon
One World Trade Center
121 Southwest Salmon, Suite 205
Portland, OR 97204
P: (503) 229-6063
F: (503) 222-5050
E: amanda.welker@oregon.gov

PENNSYLVANIA
Mr. Joseph Burke
Deputy Secretary
Office of International Business Development
Community & Economic Development
400 North Street, 4th Floor
Harrisburg, PA 17120
P: (717) 787-7190
E: jburke@pa.gov

RHODE ISLAND
Ms. Katherine Therieau
Director, International Trade Programs
State Commerce Corporation
315 Iron Horse Way, Suite 101
Providence, RI 02908
P: (401) 278-9100 Ext. 139
F: (401) 273-8270
E: ktherieau@commerceri.com

SOUTH CAROLINA
Mr. Clarke Thompson
International Trade Director
Department of Commerce
1201 Main Street, Suite 1600
Columbia, SC 29201
P: (803) 737-0438
F: (803) 737-0538
E: cthompson@sccommerce.com

SOUTH DAKOTA
Ms. Ann Gesick-Johnson
Workforce Training Coodinator
Governor's Office of Economic Development
711 East Wells Avenue
Pierre, SD 57501
P: (605) 773-3301
E: Ann.Gesick-Johnson@sdreadytowork.com

International Trade

TENNESSEE
Ms. Leslee Alexander
International Director
Department of Economic & Community Development
312 Rosa L. Parks Avenue, 26th Floor
Nashville, TN 37243
P: (615) 483-7293
F: (615) 741-5829
E: leslee.alexander@tn.gov

TEXAS
Mr. Michael Treyger
Manager, Department of Business Assistance
Economic Development & Tourism
Office of the Governor
P.O. Box 12428
Austin, TX 78711
P: (512) 936-0530
F: (512) 936-0445
E: michael.treyger@gov.texas.gov

UTAH
Mr. Brett Heimburger
Director
International Trade & Diplomacy Office
Office of Economic Development
60 East South Temple, 3rd Floor
Salt Lake City, UT 84111
P: (801) 538-8651
F: (801) 538-8888
E: bheimburger@utah.gov

VERMONT
Ms. Katie Corrigan
International Trade Manager
Global Trade Partnership
1 National Life Drive, 6th Floor
Montpelier, VT 05620
P: (802) 828-1744
F: (802) 828-3258

WASHINGTON
Mr. Mark Calhoon
Senior Managing Director
Department of Commerce
2001 6th Avenue, Suite 2600
Seattle, WA 98121
P: (206) 256-6100
F: (206) 256-6158
E: mark.calhoon@commerce.wa.gov

WISCONSIN
Ms. Katy Sinnott
Vice President, International Business Development
Economic Development Corporation
201 West Washington Avenue
Madison, WI 53703
P: (608) 210-6838
F: (608) 266-5551
E: Katy.sinnott@wedc.org

WYOMING
Mr. Ben Avery
Business and Industry Division Director
Business & Industry Division
State Business Council
214 West 15th Street
Cheyenne, WY 82002
P: (307) 777-2863
F: (307) 777-2838
E: ben.avery@wyo.gov

Juvenile Rehabilitation

Administers rehabilitative facilities and programs for delinquent youth committed by the courts.

ALABAMA
Mr. Steven P. Lafreniere
Executive Director
Department of Youth Services
P.O. Box 66
Mount Meigs, AL 36057
P: (334) 215-3800
F: (334) 215-1453

ALASKA
Ms. Barbara Murray
Acting Director
Division of Juvenile Justice
Department of Health & Social Services
P.O. Box 110635
Juneau, AK 99811
P: (907) 465-2212
F: (907) 465-2333
E: Hss.djj@alaska.gov

AMERICAN SAMOA
Mr. Le'i S. Thompson
Commissioner
Department of Public Safety
American Samoa Government
P.O. Box 1086
Pago Pago, AS 96799
P: (684) 633-1111
F: (684) 633-7296
E: lei.thompson@dps.as.gov

ARIZONA
Mr. Jeff Hood
Interim Director
Department of Juvenile Corrections
1624 West Adams Street
Phoenix, AZ 85007
P: (602) 364-4051
F: (602) 542-5156
E: Director@azdjc.gov

ARKANSAS
Ms. Betty Guhman
Director
Division of Youth Services
Department of Human Services
700 Main Street
Little Rock, AR 72203
P: (501) 682-8755
F: (501) 682-1351
E: betty.guhman@dhs.arkansas.gov

CALIFORNIA
Mr. Anthony Lucero
Director
Division of Juvenile Justice
P.O. Box 588501
Elk Grove, CA 95758
P: (916) 683-7460
F: (916) 683-7770

COLORADO
Mr. Anders Jacobson
Director
Division of Youth Corrections
Office of Children, Youth and Families
4255 South Knox Court
Denver, CO 80236
P: (303) 866-7345
F: (303) 866-7344

CONNECTICUT
Mr. Scott Semple
Commissioner
Department of Correction
24 Wolcott Hill Road
Wethersfield, CT 06109
P: (860) 692-7480

DELAWARE
Ms. Nancy S. Dietz
Director
Division of Youth Rehabilitative Services
1825 Faulkland Road
Wilmington, DE 19805
P: (302) 633-2620
F: (302) 633-2636
E: yrs.dscyf@state.de.us

DISTRICT OF COLUMBIA
Mr. Clinton Lacey
Director
Department of Youth Rehabilitation Services
450 H Street, Northwest
Washington, DC 20001
P: (202) 299-5362
F: (202) 299-5608
E: dyrs@dc.gov

FLORIDA
Ms. Christy Daly
Secretary
Department of Juvenile Justice
Knight Building
2737 Centerview Drive
Tallahassee, FL 32399
P: (850) 488-1850
F: (850) 922-2992
E: christy.daly@djj.state.fl.us

GEORGIA
Mr. Avery D. Niles
Commissioner
Department of Juvenile Justice
3408 Covington Highway
Decatur, GA 30032
P: (404) 508-7200
F: (404) 508-7340
E: averyniles@djj.state.ga.us

IDAHO
Ms. Sharon Harrigfeld
Director
Department of Juvenile Corrections
954 West Jefferson Street
P.O. Box 83720
Boise, ID 83720
P: (208) 334-5100
F: (208) 334-5120
E: sharon.harrigfeld@idjc.idaho.gov

INDIANA
Ms. Christine Blessinger
Executive Director
Division of Youth Services
Department of Correction
302 West Washington Street, Room E-334
Indianapolis, IN 46204
P: (317) 234-2969
F: (317) 233-6912
E: CBlessinger@idoc.in.gov

IOWA
Ms. Wendy Rickman
Administrator
Division of Adult, Children & Family Services
Department of Human Services
1305 East Walnut
Des Moines, IA 50319
P: (515) 281-5521
F: (515) 242-6036
E: wrickma@dhs.state.ia.us

KANSAS
Mr. Randy Bowman
Deputy Secretary
Juvenile Services Division
Department of Corrections
714 Southwest Jackson Street, Suite 300
Topeka, KS 66603
P: (785) 296-0042
F: (785) 296-1412
E: Hope.Burns@ks.gov

LOUISIANA
Dr. James Bueche
Deputy Secretary
Office of Juvenile Justice
7919 Independence Boulevard
P.O. Box 66458
Baton Rouge, LA 70896
P: (225) 287-7944
F: (225) 287-7987

MAINE
Mr. Colin O'Neill
Associate Commissioner
Division of Juvenile Services
Department of Corrections
111 State House Station
Augusta, ME 04333
P: (207) 287-4362
F: (207) 287-4370
E: Colin.O'Neill@maine.gov

MARYLAND
Mr. Sam Abed
Secretary
Department of Juvenile Services
One Center Plaza
120 West Fayette Street
Baltimore, MD 21201
P: (410) 230-3100
F: (410) 333-4199
E: Sam.Abed@maryland.gov

MASSACHUSETTS
Mr. Peter Forbes
Commissioner
Department of Youth Services
Office of Health & Human Services
600 Washington Street, 4th Floor
Boston, MA 02111
P: (617) 960-3304
F: (617) 727-0696

MICHIGAN
Mr. Nick Lyon
Director
Department of Health & Human Services
333 South Grand Avenue
P.O. Box 30195
Lansing, MI 48909
P: (517) 335-0267
F: (517) 335-6101
E: LyonN2@michigan.gov

Mr. Steve Yager
Executive Director
Children's Services Agency
Department of Health & Human Services
P.O. Box 30195
Lansing, MI 48909
P: (517) 373-3740
E: YagerS@michigan.gov

Juvenile Rehabilitation

MINNESOTA
Mr. Tom Roy
Commissioner
Department of Corrections
1450 Energy Park Drive, Suite 200
St. Paul, MN 55108
P: (651) 361-7200
F: (651) 642-0414
E: tom.roy@state.mn.us

MISSISSIPPI
Ms. Joyce Word
Director
Office of Justice Programs
Department of Public Safety
P.O. Box 958
Jackson, MS 39205
P: (601) 977-3700
E: jword@dps.ms.gov

MISSOURI
Mr. Tim Decker
Director
Division of Youth Services
3418 Knipp, Suite A-1
P.O. Box 447
Jefferson City, MO 65102
P: (573) 751-3324
F: (573) 526-4494
E: tim.decker@dss.mo.gov

MONTANA
Ms. Loraine Wodnik
Interim Director
Department of Corrections
5 South Last Chance Gulch
P.O. Box 201301
Helena, MT 59620
P: (406) 444-3930
F: (406) 444-4920

NEBRASKA
Mr. Douglas J. Weinberg
Director
Division of Children & Family Services
Department of Health & Human Services
P.O. Box 95026
Lincoln, NE 60509
P: (402) 471-1757
E: doug.weinberg@nebraska.gov

NEVADA
Ms. Kelly Wooldridge
Administrator
Division of Child & Family Services
Department of Health & Human Services
4126 Technology Way, 3rd Floor
Carson City, NV 89706
P: (775) 684-4400
F: (775) 684-4455

NEW JERSEY
Mr. Kevin M. Brown
Executive Director
Juvenile Justice Commission
1001 Spruce Street, Suite 202
P.O. Box 107
Trenton, NJ 08625
P: (609) 292-1400
F: (609) 943-4611

NEW MEXICO
Ms. Monique Jacobson
Cabinet Secretary
Children, Youth & Families Department
P.O. Drawer 5160
Santa Fe, NM 87502
P: (505) 827-7602
F: (505) 827-4053
E: monique.jacobson@state.nm.us

NEW YORK
Ms. Sheila Poole
Acting Commissioner
Office of Children & Family Services
Capitol View Office Park
52 Washington Street
Rensselaer, NY 12144
P: (518) 473-7793
F: (518) 486-7550

NORTH CAROLINA
Mr. William Lassiter
Deputy Secretary for Juvenile Justice
Division of Juvenile Justice
3010 Hammond Business Place
4212 Mail Service Center
Raleigh, NC 27699
P: (919) 733-3388

NORTH DAKOTA
Ms. Lisa Bjergaard
Director
Department of Corrections & Rehabilitation
Division of Juvenile Services
701 16th Avenue, Southwest
Bismarck, ND 58554
P: (701) 328-6390
F: (701) 667-1414
E: lbjergaa@nd.gov

NORTHERN MARIANA ISLANDS
Ms. Vivian Sablan
Administrator
Division of Youth Services
Building #1263, Capital Hill
Saipan, MP 96950
P: (670) 664-2550
F: (670) 664-2566

OHIO
Mr. Harvey J. Reed
Director
Department of Youth Services
30 West Spring Street, 5th Floor
Columbus, OH 43215
P: (614) 466-8783
F: (614) 387-2606

OKLAHOMA
Mr. Steven Buck
Executive Director
Office of Juvenile Affairs
3812 North Santa Fe Suite 400
Oklahoma City, OK 73118
P: (405) 530-2806
E: steven.buck@oja.ok.gov

OREGON
Fariborz Pakseresht
Director
Youth Authority
530 Center Street, Northeast, Suite 500
Salem, OR 97301
P: (503) 373-7212
F: (503) 373-7622
E: Fariborz.Pakseresht@oya.state.or.us

PUERTO RICO
Mr. Jesus Gonzalez Cruz
Administrator
Juvenile Institutions Administration
P.O. Box 19175
San Juan, PR 00910
P: (787) 767-9600
F: (787) 765-3394

RHODE ISLAND
Dr. Trista Piccola
Director
Department of Children, Youth & Families
101 Friendship Street
Providence, RI 02903
P: (401) 528-3502

SOUTH CAROLINA
Mr. Freddie Pough
Director
Department of Juvenile Justice
4900 Broad River Road
P.O. Box 21069
Columbia, SC 29221
P: (803) 896-9749
F: (803) 896-6932

SOUTH DAKOTA
Mr. Doug Herrmann
Director, Juvenile Services
Department of Corrections
3200 East Highway 34
500 East Capitol Avenue
Pierre, SD 57501
P: (605) 773-3478
F: (605) 773-3194
E: doug.herrmann@state.sd.us

TENNESSEE
Ms. Bonnie Hommrich
Commissioner
Department of Childrens Services
UBS Tower, 315 Deaderick, 10th Floor
Nashville, TN 37243
P: (615) 741-9701
E: DCS.Custsrv@tn.gov

TEXAS
Mr. David Reilly
Executive Director
Juvenile Justice Department
11209 Metric Boulevard, Building H
Suite A, P.O. Box 12757
Austin, TX 78758
P: (512) 490-7130
F: (512) 490-7717
E: tyc@tyc.state.tx.us

U.S. VIRGIN ISLANDS
Mr. Felicia Blyden
Commissioner
Department of Human Services
3011 Golden Rock
Christiansted
St. Croix, VI 00802
P: (340) 718-2980

UTAH
Ms. Susan Burke
Director
Division of Juvenile Justice Services
Department of Human Services
195 North 1950 West
Salt Lake City, UT 84116
P: (801) 538-8224
F: (801) 538-4334
E: sburke@utah.gov

VERMONT
Ms. Karen Shea
Deputy Commissioner
Family Services Division
Department for Children & Families
280 State Drive, HC 1 North
Waterbury, VT 05671
P: (802) 241-0904
F: (802) 241-2407
E: Karen.Shea@vermont.gov

VIRGINIA
Mr. Andrew K. Block Jr.
Executive Director
Department of Juvenile Justice
600 East Main Street, 20th Floor
P.O. Box 1110
Richmond, VA 23218
P: (804) 371-0700
F: (804) 371-6497
E: andrew.block@djj.virginia.gov

WASHINGTON
Ms. Marybeth Queral
Assistant Secretary
Juvenile Rehabilitation
14th & Jefferson Street
P.O. Box 45045
Olympia, WA 98504
P: (360) 902-7957
F: (360) 902-7848
E: ContactJRA@dshs.wa.gov

WEST VIRGINIA
Ms. Stephanie Bond
Director
Division of Juvenile Services
1200 Quarrier Street
Charleston, WV 25301
P: (304) 558-9800
F: (304) 558-6032
E: stephanie.j.bond@wv.gov

WISCONSIN
Mr. John D. Paquin
Administrator
Division of Juvenile Corrections
P.O. Box 7925
Madison, WI 53707
P: (608) 240-5900
F: (608) 240-3371
E: John.Paquin@Wisconsin.gov

WYOMING
Mr. Ed Heimer
Administrator, Social Services Division
Department of Family Services
Hathaway Building, 3rd Floor
2300 Capitol Avenue
Cheyenne, WY 82002
P: (307) 777-7564

Labor

Overall responsibility for administering and enforcing the state's labor laws.

ALABAMA
Mr. Fitzgerald Washington
Secretary
Department of Labor
649 Monroe Street
Montgomery, AL 36131
P: (334) 242-8055
E: fwashington@labor.alabama.gov

ALASKA
Ms. Heidi Drygas
Commissioner
Department of Labor & Workforce Development
P.O. Box 111149
Juneau, AK 99811
P: (907) 465-2700
F: (907) 465-2784
E: heidi.drygas@alaska.gov

ARIZONA
Mr. Steve Welker
Director, Labor Department
Industrial Commission
800 West Washington Street
Phoenix, AZ 85007
P: (602) 542-4515
E: LaborAdmin@azica.gov

ARKANSAS
Mr. Leon Jones Jr.
Director
Department of Labor
10421 West Markham Street
Little Rock, AR 72205
P: (501) 682-4541
E: leon.jones@arkansas.gov

CALIFORNIA
Mr. David M. Lanier
Secretary
Labor & Workforce Development Agency
800 Capitol Mall, MIC-55
Sacramento, CA 95814
P: (916) 653-9900

COLORADO
Ms. Ellen Golombek
Executive Director
Department of Labor & Employment
633 17th Street, Suite 201
Denver, CO 80202
P: (303) 318-8017
F: (303) 318-8047
E: Ellen.Golombek@state.co.us

CONNECTICUT
Mr. Scott D. Jackson
Commissioner
Department of Labor
200 Folly Brook Boulevard
Westerfield, CT 06109
P: (860) 263-6000
F: (850) 263-6529
E: scott.jackson@ct.gov

DELAWARE
Mr. John McMahon
Secretary of Labor
Department of Labor
4425 North Market Street
Wilmington, DE 19802
P: (302) 761-8000
F: (302) 761-6621
E: john.mcmahon@state.de.us

DISTRICT OF COLUMBIA
Mr. Odie Donald II
Director
Department of Employment Services
4058 Minnesota Avenue, Northeast
Washington, DC 20019
P: (202) 724-7000
F: (202) 673-6993
E: does@dc.gov

FLORIDA
Ms. Cissy Proctor
Director
Department of Economic Opportunity
107 East Madison Street
Caldwell Building
Tallahassee, FL 32399
P: (850) 245-7105
F: (850) 921-3223
E: cissy.proctor@deo.myflorida.com

GEORGIA
The Honorable Mark Butler (R)
Commissioner
Department of Labor
148 International Boulevard Northeast
Atlanta, GA 30303
P: (404) 232-7300
F: (404) 656-2683
E: commissioner@gdol.ga.gov

GUAM
Mr. Manuel Q. Cruz
Director
Department of Labor
Government of Guam
P.O. Box 9970
Tamuning, GU 96931
P: (671) 475-7044
F: (671) 674-6517

HAWAII
Ms. Linda Chu Takayama
Director
Department of Labor & Industrial Relations
830 Punchbowl Street
Honolulu, HI 96813
P: (808) 586-8844
F: (808) 586-9099
E: dlir.director@hawaii.gov

IDAHO
Mr. Kenneth D. Edmunds
Director
Department of Labor
317 West Main Street
Boise, ID 83735
P: (208) 332-3570
F: (208) 334-6430
E: kenneth.edmunds@labor.idaho.gov

ILLINOIS
Mr. Joe Beyer
Acting Director
Department of Labor
160 North LaSalle Street, Suite C-1300
Chicago, IL 60601
P: (312) 793-2800

INDIANA
Mr. Rick J. Ruble
Commissioner
Department of Labor
402 West Washington Street, Room W195
Indianapolis, IN 46204
P: (317) 232-2655
F: (317) 233-3790
E: rruble@dol.in.gov

IOWA
Mr. Michael A. Mauro
Commissioner
Division of Labor Services
150 Des Moines Street
Des Moines, IA 50309
P: (515) 725-5601
F: (515) 281-4698
E: michael.mauro@iwd.iowa.gov

KANSAS
Ms. Lana Gordon
Secretary of Labor
Department of Labor
401 Southwest Topeka Boulevard
Topeka, KS 66603
P: (785) 296-5000
F: (785) 368-5289
E: lana.gordon@dol.ks.gov

KENTUCKY
Mr. Derrick Ramsey
Secretary
Labor Cabinet
U.S. 127 South Building
Frankfort, KY 40601
P: (502) 564-3070
F: (502) 564-5387
E: derrick.ramsey@ky.gov

LOUISIANA
Ms. Ava Dejoie
Executive Director
Workforce Commission
1001 North 23rd Street
P.O. Box 94094
Baton Rouge, LA 70804
P: (225) 342-3111
F: (225) 342-3778
E: owd@lwc.la.gov

MAINE
Ms. Jeanne Paquette
Commissioner
Department of Labor
54 State House Station
Augusta, ME 04333
P: (207) 623-7900
F: (207) 623-7934
E: jeanne.paquette@maine.gov

MARYLAND
Ms. Kelly M. Schulz
Secretary
Department of Labor, Licensing & Regulation
500 North Calvert Street
Baltimore, MD 21202
P: (410) 230-6020
F: (410) 333-0853
E: kelly.schulz@maryland.gov

MASSACHUSETTS
Mr. Ronald L. Walker II
Secretary
Executive Office of Labor & Workforce Development
One Ashburton Place, Suite 2112
Boston, MA 02108
P: (617) 626-7122

MINNESOTA
Mr. Ken Peterson
Commissioner
Department of Labor & Industry
443 Lafayette Road North
St. Paul, MN 55155
P: (651) 284-5010
F: (651) 284-5720
E: DLI.workcomp@state.mn.us

MISSISSIPPI
Mr. Mark Henry
Executive Director
Department of Employment Security
1235 Echelon Parkway
P.O. Box 1699
Jackson, MS 39215
P: (601) 321-6000
F: (601) 321-6104
E: mhenry@mdes.ms.gov

MISSOURI
Ms. Anna Hui
Director
Department of Labor & Industrial Relations
421 East Dunklin Street
P.O. Box 504
Jefferson City, MO 65102
P: (573) 751-4091
F: (573) 751-4135
E: diroffice@labor.mo.gov

MONTANA
Ms. Pam Bucy
Commissioner
Department of Labor & Industry
P.O. Box 1728
Helena, MT 59624
P: (406) 444-2840
F: (406) 444-1419
E: dliquestions@mt.gov

NEBRASKA
Ms. Courtney Dentlinger
Director
Department of Economic Development
301 Centennial Mall South
P.O. Box 94666
Lincoln, NE 68509
P: (402) 471-3746
F: (402) 471-3778
E: courtney.dentlinger@nebraska.gov

NEVADA
Ms. Shannon M. Chambers
Commissioner
Office of the Labor Commissioner
1818 College Parkway, Suite 102
Carson City, NV 89706
P: (775) 684-1890
F: (775) 687-6409
E: mail1@laborcommissioner.com

NEW HAMPSHIRE
Mr. Ken Merrifield
Commissioner
Department of Labor
95 Pleasant Street
Concord, NH 03301
P: (603) 271-3176

NEW JERSEY
Dr. Aaron R. Fichtner
Acting Commissioner
Department of Labor & Workforce Development
1 John Fitch Plaza
P.O. Box 110
Trenton, NJ 08625
P: (609) 292-1070
E: aaron.fichtner@dol.state.nj.us

NEW MEXICO
Ms. Celina Bussey
Secretary
Department of Workforce Solutions
401 Broadway, Northeast
P.O. Box 1928
Albuquerque, NM 87103
P: (505) 841-8405
F: (505) 841-8491
E: celina.bussey@state.nm.us

NEW YORK
Ms. Roberta Reardon
Commissioner
Department of Labor
W. Averell Harriman State Office Campus
Building 12
Albany, NY 12240
P: (518) 457-9000
F: (518) 485-6297
E: roberta.reardon@labor.state.ny.us

NORTH CAROLINA
The Honorable Cherie K. Berry (R)
Commissioner
Department of Labor
1101 Mail Service Center
Raleigh, NC 27699
P: (919) 733-7166
F: (919) 733-7640
E: cherie.berry@labor.nc.gov

NORTH DAKOTA
Ms. Michelle Kommer
Commissioner of Labor
Department of Labor & Human Rights
600 East Boulevard Avenue
Department 406
Bismarck, ND 58505
P: (701) 328-2660
F: (701) 328-2031
E: mkommer@nd.gov

OHIO
Ms. Shannon Himes
Superintendent
Division of Industrial Compliance
Department of Commerce
P.O. Box 4009
Reynoldsburg, OH 43068
P: (614) 644-2223
E: ic@com.state.oh.us

OKLAHOMA
Ms. Melissa McLawhorn Houston
Commissioner of Labor
Department of Labor
3017 North Stiles, Suite 100
Oklahoma City, OK 73105
P: (405) 521-6101
F: (405) 521-6018
E: labor.info@labor.ok.gov

OREGON
The Honorable Brad Avakian (D)
Commissioner
Bureau of Labor & Industries
800 Northeast Oregon Street
Suite 1045
Portland, OR 97232
P: (971) 673-0781
F: (971) 673-0762
E: brad.avakian@state.or.us

PENNSYLVANIA
Ms. Kathy M. Manderino
Secretary
Department of Labor & Industry
651 Boas Street
Harrisburg, PA 17121
P: (717) 787-5279
F: (717) 787-8826

PUERTO RICO
Mr. Carlos J. Saavedra Gutierrez
Secretary
Department of Labor & Human Resources
P.O. Box 195540
San Juan, PR 00919
P: (787) 754-5353
F: (787) 753-9550

RHODE ISLAND
Mr. Scott Jensen
Director
Department of Labor & Training
Center General Complex
1511 Pontiac Avenue
Cranston, RI 02920
P: (401) 462-8000
F: (401) 462-8872
E: director-dlt@dlt.ri.gov

SOUTH CAROLINA
Ms. Emily Farr
Director
Department of Labor, Licensing & Regulation
110 Centerview Drive
P.O. Box 11329
Columbia, SC 29211
P: (803) 896-4300
F: (803) 896-4393
E: ContactLLR@llr.sc.gov

SOUTH DAKOTA
Ms. Marcia Hultman
Cabinet Secretary
Department of Labor & Regulation
123 West Missouri Avenue
Pierre, SD 57501
P: (605) 773-5395
F: (605) 773-6184
E: marcia.hultman@state.sd.us

TENNESSEE
Mr. Burns Phillips
Commissioner
Department of Labor & Workforce Development
220 French Landing Drive
Nashville, TN 37243
P: (844) 224-5818
F: (615) 741-5078
E: burns.phillips@tn.gov

TEXAS
Mr. Julian Alvarez III
Commissioner Representing Labor
Workforce Commission
101 East 15th Street
Austin, TX 78778
P: (800) 832-2829
F: (512) 475-2152
E: laborinfo@twc.state.tx.us

Labor

Mr. Larry E. Temple
Executive Director
Workforce Commission
101 East 15th Street
Austin, TX 78778
P: (512) 463-0735
F: (512) 475-2321
E: larry.temple@twc.state.tx.us

U.S. VIRGIN ISLANDS
Ms. Catherine Ann Hendry
Commissioner of Labor
Department of Labor
4401 Sion Farm, Suite 1
Christiansted, VI 00820
P: (340) 773-1994
F: (340) 713-3415
E: chendry@vidol.gov

UTAH
Mr. Jaceson Maughan
Commissioner
Labor Commission
P.O. Box 146600
Salt Lake City, UT 84114
P: (801) 530-6800
E: laborcom@utah.gov

VERMONT
Ms. Lindsay H. Kurrle
Commissioner
Department of Labor
5 Green Mountain Drive
P.O. Box 488
Montpelier, VT 05601
P: (802) 828-4301
F: (802) 828-4022
E: Labor.WebInput@vermont.gov

VIRGINIA
Mr. Todd Haymore
Secretary of Commerce & Trade
Office of Commerce & Trade
1111 East Broad Street
P.O. Box 1475
Richmond, VA 23218
P: (804) 786-7831
F: (804) 371-0250
E: Todd.Haymore@governor.virginia.gov

WASHINGTON
Mr. Joel Sacks
Director
Department of Labor & Industries
P.O. Box 44000
Olympia, WA 98504
P: (360) 902-5800
F: (360) 902-5798
E: joel.sacks@lni.wa.gov

WEST VIRGINIA
Mr. David W. Mullins
Commissioner
Division of Labor
Department of Commerce
749 B, Building 6, Capitol Complex
Charleston, WV 25305
P: (304) 558-7890
F: (304) 558-2415

WISCONSIN
Mr. Ray Allen
Secretary
Department of Workforce Development
201 East Washington Avenue (GEF-1)
Room A-400, P.O. Box 7946
Madison, WI 53707
P: (608) 266-3131
F: (608) 266-1784
E: sec@dwd.wisconsin.gov

WYOMING
Mr. John F. Cox
Director
Department of Workforce Services
614 South Greeley Highway
Cheyenne, WY 82002
P: (307) 777-8728
F: (307) 777-5857
E: john.cox@wyo.gov

Law Enforcement

Conducts state-level criminal investigations.

ALABAMA
Mr. Stan Stabler
Acting Secretary of Law Enforcement
Law Enforcement Agency
301 South Ripley Street
P.O. Box 1511
Montgomery, AL 36102
P: (334) 517-2800
F: (334) 242-0512

ALASKA
Mr. Walt Monegan
Commissioner
Department of Public Safety
5700 East Tudor Road
Anchorage, AK 99507
P: (907) 269-5086
F: (907) 269-4543
E: walt.monegan@alaska.gov

AMERICAN SAMOA
Mr. Le'i S. Thompson
Commissioner
Department of Public Safety
American Samoa Government
P.O. Box 1086
Pago Pago, AS 96799
P: (684) 633-1111
F: (684) 633-7296
E: lei.thompson@dps.as.gov

ARIZONA
Colonel Frank Milstead
Director
Department of Public Safety
2222 West Encanto Boulevard
Phoenix, AZ 85009
P: (602) 223-2000
F: (602) 223-2917

COLORADO
Mr. Michael Rankin
Director
Bureau of Investigation
690 Kipling Street, Suite 4000
Lakewood, CO 80215
P: (303) 239-4203
F: (303) 235-0568
E: michael.rankin@state.co.us

CONNECTICUT
Mr. Kevin T. Kane
Chief State's Attorney
Division of Criminal Justice
300 Corporate Place
Rocky Hill, CT 06067
P: (860) 258-5800
F: (860) 258-5858
E: conndcj@ct.gov

DELAWARE
Colonel Nathaniel McQueen Jr.
Commissioner
State Police
1441 North DuPont Highway
Dover, DE 19901
P: (302) 739-5960

DISTRICT OF COLUMBIA
Mr. Peter Newsham
Chief of Police
Metropolitan Police Department
300 Indiana Avenue, Northwest
Room 5059
Washington, DC 20001
P: (202) 727-9099
F: (202) 727-4106
E: mpd@dc.gov

FLORIDA
Mr. Rick Swearingen
Commissioner
Department of Law Enforcement
2331 Phillips Road
P.O. Box 1489
Tallahassee, FL 32302
P: (850) 410-7011
E: RickSwearingen@fdle.state.fl.us

GEORGIA
Mr. Vernon M. Keenan
Director
Bureau of Investigation
3121 Panthersville Road
Decatur, GA 30034
P: (404) 244-2501
F: (404) 270-8352
E: vernon.keenan@gbi.ga.gov

GUAM
Mr. Joseph I. Cruz
Chief of Police
Police Department
#13-16A Mariner Avenue
P.O. Box 23909
Tiyan, GU 96913
P: (671) 475-8508
F: (671) 472-4036
E: chief@gpd.guam.gov

HAWAII
Ms. Renee Sonobe Hong
Deputy Director of Law Enforcement
Department of Public Safety
919 Ala Moana Boulevard, 4th Floor
Honolulu, HI 96814
P: (808) 587-1288
F: (808) 587-1282
E: psd.office.of.the.director@hawaii.gov

ILLINOIS
Mr. Leo P. Schmitz
Director
State Police
801 South 7th Street, Suite 1100 – S
Springfield, IL 62703
P: (217) 782-7263
E: askisp@isp.state.il.us

INDIANA
Mr. Douglas G. Carter
Superintendent
State Police
Indiana Government Center North
100 North Senate Avenue
Indianapolis, IN 46204
P: (317) 232-8248
E: ISP@isp.in.gov

IOWA
Ms. Roxann M. Ryan
Commissioner
Department of Public Safety
215 East 7th Street
Des Moines, IA 50319
P: (515) 725-6182
E: dpsinfo@dps.state.ia.us

KANSAS
Mr. Kirk D. Thompson
Director
Bureau of Investigation
1620 Southwest Tyler Street
Topeka, KS 66612
P: (785) 296-8200

KENTUCKY
Mr. Richard Sanders
Commissioner
State Police
919 Versailles Road
Frankfort, KY 40601
F: (502) 573-1479

LOUISIANA
Lieutenant Colonel Murphy Paul
Deputy Superintendent
Bureau of Investigations
State Police
7919 Independence Boulevard
Baton Rouge, LA 70806
P: (800) 434-8007

MAINE
The Honorable Janet T. Mills (D)
Attorney General
Office of the Attorney General
State House Station 6
Augusta, ME 04333
P: (207) 626-8800

MARYLAND
Colonel William Pallozzi
Superintendent
Department of State Police
1201 Reisterstown Road
Pikesville, MD 21208
P: (410) 653-4219
E: msp.superintendent@maryland.gov

MASSACHUSETTS
Colonel Richard D. McKeon
Superintendent
State Police
Office of Public Safety & Security
470 Worcester Road
Framingham, MA 01702
P: (508) 820-2300
F: (617) 727-6874

MICHIGAN
Colonel Kriste Kibbey Etue
Director
State Police
P.O. Box 30634
Lansing, MI 48909
P: (517) 332-2521
F: (517) 241-0991
E: EtueK@michigan.gov

MINNESOTA
Ms. Ramona Dohman
Commissioner
Department of Public Safety
445 Minnesota Street, Suite 199
St. Paul, MN 55101
P: (651) 201-7160
F: (651) 297-5728
E: Mona.Dohman@state.mn.us

Law Enforcement

MISSISSIPPI
Mr. Marshall Fisher
Commissioner
Department of Public Safety
P.O. Box 958
Jackson, MS 39205
P: (601) 987-1212
F: (601) 987-1488
E: commissioner
@mdps.state.ms.us

MISSOURI
Mr. Anne L. Precythe
Director
Department of Corrections
2729 Plaza Drive
P.O. Box 236
Jefferson City, MO 65102
P: (573) 751-2389
F: (573) 751-4099

MONTANA
The Honorable Tim Fox (R)
Attorney General
Department of Justice
Justice Building
215 North Sanders
Helena, MT 59620
P: (406) 444-2026
F: (406) 444-3549
E: contactdoj@mt.gov

NEBRASKA
Colonel Bradley Rice
Superintendent of Law
Enforcement & Public Safety
State Patrol
1600 Highway 2
Lincoln, NE 68502
P: (402) 471-4545
F: (402) 479-4002
E: Brad.Rice@nebraska.gov

NEVADA
Mr. Patrick J. Conmay
Chief
Investigations Division
Department of Public Safety
555 Wright Way
Carson City, NV 89711
P: (775) 684-7412
F: (775) 687-4405
E: NDIHQC@dps.state.nv.us

NEW HAMPSHIRE
Colonel Robert L. Quinn
Director
Division of State Police
Department of Safety
33 Hazen Drive
Concord, NH 03305
P: (603) 223-8813
F: (603) 271-0336
E: SPHeadquarters
@dos.nh.gov

NEW JERSEY
Colonel Joseph R. Fuentes
Superintendent
State Police
P.O. Box 7068
West Trenton, NJ 08628
P: (609) 882-2000
F: (609) 530-4383

NEW MEXICO
Mr. Pete N. Kassetas
Chief of Police
Department of Public Safety
4491 Cerrillos Road
P.O. Box 1628
Santa Fe, NM 87504
P: (505) 827-9219
F: (505) 827-3395
E: NMSP.Chief@state.nm.us

NEW YORK
Mr. Joseph D'Amico
Superintendent
State Police
1220 Washington Avenue,
Building 22
Albany, NY 12226
P: (518) 457-6721
E: nyspmail@troopers.ny.gov

NORTH CAROLINA
Mr. Bob Schurmeier
Director
State Bureau of Investigation
512 North Salisbury Street
Raleigh, NC 27604
P: (919) 662-4500
E: rschurmeier@ncsbi.gov

NORTH DAKOTA
Mr. Dallas Carlson
Director
Bureau of Criminal
Investigation
Office of the Attorney General
600 East Boulevard Avenue
Bismark, ND 58505
P: (701) 328-5500
F: (701) 328-5510
E: dcarlson@nd.gov

Colonel Michael Gerhart
Superintendent
Highway Patrol
600 East Boulevard Avenue
Department 504
Bismarck, ND 58505
P: (701) 328-2455
F: (701) 328-1717
E: ndhpinfo@nd.gov

OHIO
Colonel John Born
Director
Department of Public Safety
1970 West Broad Street
P.O. Box 182081
Columbus, OH 43218
P: (614) 466-3383
F: (614) 466-0433

OKLAHOMA
Mr. Michael C. Thompson
Commissioner
Department of Public Safety
P.O. Box 11415
Oklahoma City, OK 73136
P: (405) 425-2424
E: mike.thompson
@dps.state.ok.us

PUERTO RICO
Ms. Michelle M.
Hernandez De Fraley
Superintendent
Puerto Rico Police
601 Franklin Delano Roosevelt
Avenue
San Juan, PR 00936
P: (787) 793-1234

RHODE ISLAND
Colonel Ann Claire
Assumpico
Director
Department of Public Safety
311 Danielson Pike
North Scituate, RI 02857
P: (401) 444-1000
F: (401) 444-1105

SOUTH CAROLINA
Mr. Mark A. Keel
Chief
State Law Enforcement Division
4400 Broad River Road
Columbia, SC 29210
P: (803) 896-9223
F: (803) 896-7588

SOUTH DAKOTA
Mr. Bryan Gortmaker
Director
Division of Criminal
Investigation
Office of the Attorney General
1302 East Highway 14, Suite 5
Pierre, SD 57501
P: (605) 773-3331
F: (605) 773-4629
E: atghelp@state.sd.us

TENNESSEE
Mr. Mark Gwyn
Director
Bureau of Investigation
901 R.S. Gass Boulevard
Nashville, TN 37216
P: (615) 744-4000

TEXAS
Mr. Kim Vickers
Executive Director
Commission on Law
Enforcement
6330 East Highway 290, Suite
200
Austin, TX 78723
P: (512) 936-7700 Ext. 7713
F: (512) 936-7766
E: kim.vickers
@tcole.texas.gov

U.S. VIRGIN ISLANDS
Mr. Delroy Richards Sr.
Commissioner
Police Department
Farrelly Criminal Justice Center
Charlotte Amalie
St. Thomas, VI 00802
P: (340) 774-2211
F: (340) 715-5517

UTAH
Mr. Michael Rapich
Superintendent
State Highway Patrol
Department of Public Safety
South 4501 South 2700 West
Salt Lake City, UT 84129
P: (801) 965-4458
E: mrapich@utah.gov

VIRGINIA
Colonel W. Steven Flaherty
Superintendent
Department of State Police
7700 Midlothian Turnpike
P.O. Box 27472
Richmond, VA 23261
P: (804) 674-2000
F: (804) 674-2936
E: steve.flaherty
@vsp.virginia.gov

WASHINGTON
Mr. John R. Batiste
Chief
State Patrol
General Administration Building
P.O. Box 42600
Olympia, WA 98504
P: (360) 596-4000
F: (360) 596-4128
E: john.batiste@wsp.wa.gov

WEST VIRGINIA
Colonel J. L. Cahill
Superintendent
State Police
725 Jefferson Road
South Charleston, WV 25309
P: (304) 746-2115

WISCONSIN
Mr. Brian O'Keefe
Administrator
Division of Criminal
Investigation
Department of Justice
P.O. Box 7857
Madison, WI 53707
P: (608) 266-1221
F: (608) 267-2779

WYOMING
Mr. Steve Woodson
Director
Division of Criminal
Investigation
Combined Laboratories Building
208 South College Drive
Cheyenne, WY 82002
P: (307) 777-7181
F: (307) 777-7252

Law Library

Legal resource for the state's highest court.

ALABAMA
Mr. Timothy A. Lewis
Director & State Law Librarian
State Law Library
300 Dexter Avenue
Montgomery, AL 36104
P: (334) 229-0560
F: (334) 229-0543
E: tim.lewis@alappeals.gov

ALASKA
Ms. Susan Falk
State Law Librarian
State Court Law Library
303 K Street
Anchorage, AK 99501
P: (907) 264-0585
F: (907) 264-0733
E: sfalk@akcourts.us

AMERICAN SAMOA
The Honorable Talauega V. Ale
Attorney General
Office of the Attorney General
American Samoa Government
Executive Office Building, Utulei
Pago Pago, AS 96799
P: (684) 633-4163

ARIZONA
Ms. Holly Henley
State Librarian
State Library, Archives & Public Records
State Capitol, Room 200
1700 West Washington
Phoenix, AZ 85007
P: (602) 926-3366
F: (602) 256-7983

ARKANSAS
Ms. Ava Hicks
Director
Supreme Court Library
Justice Building
625 Marshall Street, Suite 1500
Little Rock, AR 72201
P: (501) 682-2041
F: (501) 682-6877
E: ava.hicks@arcourts.gov

COLORADO
Mr. Dan Cordova
Librarian
Supreme Court Library
Ralph L. Carr Judicial Center
2 East 14th Avenue
Denver, CO 80203
P: (720) 625-5100
F: (720) 625-5110
E: library@judicial.state.co.us

CONNECTICUT
Ms. Ann Doherty
Deputy Director
Law Libraries
Judicial Branch
90 Washington Street, Third Floor
Hartford, CT 06106
P: (860) 706-5145
F: (860) 706-5086
E: ann.doherty@jud.ct.gov

DELAWARE
Ms. Patricia Burris
Law Librarian
State Law Library
38 The Green, Suite 100
414 Federal Street
Dover, DE 19901
P: (302) 674-7470
F: (302) 674-7471
E: patricia.burris@state.de.us

DISTRICT OF COLUMBIA
Ms. Letty Limbach
Librarian
Court of Appeals
500 Indiana Avenue, Northwest
Washington, DC 20001
P: (202) 879-2767

FLORIDA
Ms. Billie J. Blaine
Librarian
Supreme Court Library
500 South Duvall Street
Tallahassee, FL 32399
P: (850) 488-8919
F: (850) 922-5219
E: library@flcourts.org

GUAM
Ms. Geraldine Amparo Cepeda
Executive Director/Librarian
Law Library
141 San Ramon Street
Hagatna, GU 96910
P: (671) 477-7623
F: (671) 472-1246
E: gll@guamlawlibrary.org

HAWAII
Ms. Jenny Silbiger
Law Librarian
Supreme Court Law Library
Ali'iolani Hale, Room 115
417 South King Street
Honolulu, HI 96813
P: (808) 539-4964
F: (808) 539-4974
E: LawLibrary@courts.hawaii.gov

ILLINOIS
Mr. Geoffrey Pelzek
Librarian
Supreme Court Library
Supreme Court Building
200 East Capitol Avenue
Springfield, IL 62701
P: (217) 782-2424
F: (217) 782-5287

INDIANA
Ms. Terri Ross
Law Librarian
Supreme Court Law Library
200 West Washington Street
State House, Room 316
Indianapolis, IN 46204
P: (317) 232-2557
F: (317) 233-8693
E: terri.ross@courts.in.gov

IOWA
Mr. Cory Quist
Law Librarian
State Law Library
Capitol Building, Second Floor
1007 East Grand Avenue
Des Moines, IA 50319
P: (515) 281-5125
F: (515) 281-5405
E: Cory.Quist@iowa.gov

KENTUCKY
Ms. Jennifer Frazier
State Law Librarian
State Law Library
State Capitol, Suite 200
700 Capitol Avenue
Frankfort, KY 40601
P: (502) 564-4848
F: (502) 564-5041

LOUISIANA
Ms. Miriam Childs
Director
Law Library
Supreme Court
400 Royal Street, 2nd Floor
New Orleans, LA 70130
P: (504) 310-2403
F: (504) 310-2419
E: library@lasc.org

MAINE
Mr. John R. Barden
Director
State Law & Legislative Reference Library
43 State House Station
Augusta, ME 04333
P: (207) 287-1600
F: (207) 287-6467
E: lawlib.office@legislature.maine.gov

MARYLAND
Mr. Steve P. Anderson
Director
State Law Library
Murphy Courts of Appeal Building
361 Rowe Boulevard
Annapolis, MD 21401
P: (410) 260-1432
F: (410) 260-1572
E: lawlibrary@mdcourts.gov

MICHIGAN
Ms. Kim Koscielniak
Law Librarian
State Law Library
702 West Kalamazoo Street
Lansing, MI 48909
P: (517) 373-4697
F: (517) 373-3915
E: koscielniakk@michigan.gov

MINNESOTA
Ms. Liz Reppe
State Law Librarian
State Law Library
Room G25, Judicial Center
25 Rev. Dr. Martin Luther King Jr. Blvd.
St. Paul, MN 55155
P: (651) 297-2089
F: (651) 296-6740
E: liz.reppe@courts.state.mn.us

MISSISSIPPI
Mr. Stephen Parks
State Librarian
State Law Library
Gartin Justice Building, 450 High Street
P.O. Box 1040
Jackson, MS 39215
P: (601) 359-3672
F: (601) 359-2912
E: sparks@courts.ms.gov

MISSOURI
Ms. Gail Miller
Director of Library & Public Services
Supreme Court Library
207 West High Street, Second Floor
Jefferson City, MO 65101
P: (573) 751-2636
F: (573) 751-2573

MONTANA
Ms. Sarah McClain
Director
State Law Library
215 North Sanders Street
P.O. Box 203004
Helena, MT 59620
P: (406) 444-3660
F: (406) 444-3603
E: SMcClain@mt.gov

NEBRASKA
Mr. Corey Steel
State Court Administrator
Supreme Court
1445 K Street, Room 1213
P.O. Box 98910
Lincoln, NE 68509
P: (402) 471-3730
F: (402) 471-2854
E: corey.steel@nebraska.gov

NEVADA
Ms. Christine Timko
Law Librarian
Supreme Court Law Library
201 South Carson Street
Carson City, NV 89701
P: (775) 684-1640
F: (775) 684-1662
E: Reference@nvcourts.nv.gov

NEW HAMPSHIRE
Ms. Mary S. Searles
Director
State Law Library
Supreme Court Building
One Charles Doe Drive
Concord, NH 03301
P: (603) 271-3777
F: (603) 513-5450
E: msearles@courts.state.nh.us

NORTH CAROLINA
Mr. Thomas P. Davis
Librarian
Supreme Court Library
500 Justice Building
2 East Morgan Street
Raleigh, NC 27601
P: (919) 831-5709
E: tpd@sc.state.nc.us

NORTH DAKOTA
Mr. Ted Smith
Law Librarian
Supreme Court Law Library
600 East Boulevard Avenue
Judicial Wing Second Floor
Pierre, ND 58505
P: (701) 328-4594
F: (701) 328-3609
E: TSmith@ndcourts.gov

NORTHERN MARIANA ISLANDS
Ms. Margarita M. Palacios
Court Administrator
Supreme Court
P.O. Box 502165
Saipan, MP 96950
P: (670) 236-9800
F: (670) 236-9702
E: supreme.court@saipan.com

OHIO
Mr. Kenneth Kozlowski
Director
Law Library
Supreme Court of Ohio
65 South Front Street, 11th Floor
Columbus, OH 43215
P: (614) 387-9680
F: (614) 387-9689
E: libref@sc.ohio.gov

OKLAHOMA
Mr. Douglas Amos
Law Librarian
Cartwright Memorial Library
200 Northeast 18th Street
Oklahoma City, OK 73105
P: (405) 522-3213
F: (405) 521-2753

OREGON
Ms. Cathryn E. Bowie
State Law Librarian
State Law Library
Supreme Court Building
1163 State Street
Salem, OR 97301
P: (503) 986-5921
F: (503) 986-5623
E: cathryn.e.bowie@ojd.state.or.us

PENNSYLVANIA
Mr. Glenn Miller
Deputy Secretary/Commissioner for Libraries/State Librarian
State Library
Department of Education
Forum 203, 607 South Drive
Harrisburg, PA 17120
P: (717) 783-2466
F: (717) 223-3121
E: glennmille@pa.gov

RHODE ISLAND
Ms. Colleen Hanna
Acting State Law Librarian
State Law Library
Main Library
250 Benefit Street
Providence, RI 02903
P: (401) 222-3275
F: (401) 222-3865
E: channa@courts.ri.gov

SOUTH CAROLINA
Ms. Janet Meyer
Librarian
Supreme Court Library
Supreme Court Building
1231 Gervais Street
Columbia, SC 29211
P: (803) 734-1080
F: (803) 734-0519

TEXAS
Mr. Dale W. Propp
Director
State Law Library
205 West 14th , Room G01
P.O. Box 12367
Austin, TX 78711
P: (512) 463-1722
F: (512) 463-1728
E: library@sll.texas.gov

U.S. VIRGIN ISLANDS
Mr. Richard Buckley
Law Librarian
Law Library
Justice Center, 5400 Veteran's Drive
3rd Floor, East Wing, Room E311
St. Thomas, VI 00802
P: (340) 774-6680 Ext. 6419
F: (340) 776-9889
E: richard.buckley@visuperiorcourt.org

UTAH
Ms. Jessica Van Buren
Director
State Law Library
450 South State Street
P.O. Box 140220
Salt Lake City, UT 84114
P: (801) 238-7991
F: (801) 238-7993
E: jessicavb@utcourts.gov

VERMONT
Mr. Scott Murphy
Acting State Librarian
Department of Libraries
109 State Street
Montpelier, VT 05609
P: (802) 828-3261
F: (802) 828-2199
E: scott.murphy@vermont.gov

VIRGINIA
Ms. Gail Warren
State Law Librarian
Supreme Court
100 North Ninth Street
Richmond, VA 23219
P: (804) 786-2075
F: (804) 786-4542
E: LawLibrary@courts.state.va.us

WASHINGTON
Mr. Rob Mead
State Law Librarian
State Law Library
415 12th Avenue, Southwest
P.O. Box 40751
Olympia, WA 98504
P: (360) 357-2136
F: (360) 357-2153
E: library.requests@courts.wa.gov

WEST VIRGINIA
Ms. Kaye L. Maerz
State Law Librarian
State Law Library
Building One, Room E-404
1900 Kanawha Boulevard East
Charleston, WV 25305
P: (304) 558-2607
F: (304) 558-3673
E: kaye.maerz@courtswv.gov

WISCONSIN
Ms. Julie Tessmer
State Law Librarian
State Law Library
120 Martin Luther King Jr. Boulevard
P.O. Box 7881
Madison, WI 53707
P: (608) 261-2340
F: (608) 267-2319
E: julie.tessmer@wicourts.gov

Law Library

WYOMING
Mr. Matt Swift
State Law Librarian
State Law Library
Supreme Court Building
2301 Capitol Avenue
Cheyenne, WY 82002
P: (307) 777-7509
F: (307) 777-7240

Licensing (Occupational and Professional)

Licenses and regulates the function of various professions in the state. Since there are hundreds of autonomous boards in the states, it is the centralized agencies that are represented in this listing.

ALASKA
Ms. Janey Hovenden
Division Director
Division of Corporations, Business & Professional Licensing
P.O. Box 110806
Juneau, AK 99811
P: (907) 465-2550
F: (907) 465-2974
E: janey.hovenden@alaska.gov

CALIFORNIA
Mr. Dean Grafilo
Director
Department of Consumer Affairs
1625 North Market Boulevard
Sacramento, CA 95834
P: (916) 574-8200
F: (916) 574-8613
E: dean.grafilo@dca.ca.gov

COLORADO
Ms. Ronne Hines
Division Director
Division of Professions & Occupations
Department of Regulatory Agencies
1560 Broadway, Suite 1350
Denver, CO 80202
P: (303) 894-7800
F: (303) 894-7693
E: ronne.hines@dora.state.co.us

CONNECTICUT
Mr. Richard Hurlburt
Director
Occupational & Professional Licensing Division
165 Capitol Avenue
Hartford, CT 06106
P: (860) 713-6135
F: (860) 713-7230
E: richard.hurlburt@ct.gov

DISTRICT OF COLUMBIA
Mr. Clifford Cooks
Program Manager
Department of Consumer & Regulatory Affairs
1100 Fourth Street, Southwest
Washington, DC 20024
P: (202) 442-4400
F: (202) 698-4329
E: dcra@dc.gov

Ms. Sharon Williams Lewis
Senior Deputy Director
Health Regulation & Licensing Administration
Department of Health
899 North Capitol, Northeast, 2nd Floor
Washington, DC 20002
P: (202) 724-4900
F: (202) 724-5145

FLORIDA
Ms. Lucy C. Gee
Division Director
Division of Medical Quality Assurance/Licensure Services
Department of Health
4052 Bald Cypress Way
Tallahassee, FL 32399
P: (850) 245-4224
F: (850) 245-4791
E: lucy_gee@doh.state.fl.us

Ms. Matilde Miller
Interim Secretary
Department of Business & Professional Regulation
1940 North Monroe Street
Tallahassee, FL 32399
P: (850) 487-1395
F: (850) 488-1830
E: matilde.miller@myfloridalicense.com

GEORGIA
Mr. Randall D. Vaughn
Division Director
Professional Licensing Boards Division
Office of Secretary of State
237 Coliseum Drive
Macon, GA 31217
P: (478) 207-2440
F: (478) 207-1363
E: rvaughn@sos.state.ga.us

HAWAII
Ms. Celia Suzuki
Licensing Administrator
Professional & Vocational Licensing Division
Dept. of Commerce & Consumer Affairs
P.O. Box 3469
Honolulu, HI 96801
P: (808) 586-2690
F: (808) 586-2689
E: pvl@dcca.hawaii.gov

IDAHO
Ms. Tana Cory
Bureau Chief
Bureau of Occupational Licenses
1109 Main Street, Suite 220
Boise, ID 83702
P: (208) 334-3233
F: (208) 334-3945
E: tcory@ibol.idaho.gov

ILLINOIS
Mr. Bryan A. Schneider
Secretary
Department of Financial & Professional Regulation
320 West Washington Street
Springfield, IL 62786
P: (217) 785-0820
F: (217) 558-6001

INDIANA
Ms. Deborah J. Frye
Executive Director
Professional Licensing Agency
402 West Washington Street, Room W072
Indianapolis, IN 46204
P: (317) 232-2960
F: (317) 233-4236
E: defrye@pla.IN.gov

IOWA
Ms. Barbara Huey
Bureau Chief
Bureau of Professional Licensure
Lucas State Office Building
321 East 12th Street, 5th Floor
Des Moines, IA 50266
P: (515) 281-0254
F: (515) 281-3121
E: barbara.huey@idph.iowa.gov

KENTUCKY
Mr. Larry Brown
Commissioner
Department of Professional Licensing
P.O. Box 1360
Frankfort, KY 40601
P: (502) 564-8805
F: (502) 564-4818
E: Larry.Brown@ky.gov

MAINE
Ms. Anne L. Head
Commissioner
Department of Professional & Financial Regulation
35 State House Station
Augusta, ME 04333
P: (207) 624-8511
F: (207) 624-8690
E: anne.l.head@maine.gov

MARYLAND
Mr. Dennis R. Schrader
Secretary
Department of Health & Mental Hygiene
Office of the Secretary
201 West Preston Street, 5th Floor
Baltimore, MD 21201
P: (410) 767-4639
E: Dennis.Schrader@maryland.gov

MASSACHUSETTS
Mr. Charles Borstel
Commissioner
Division of Professional Licensure
Consumer Affairs & Business Regulation
1000 Washington Street, Suite 710
Boston, MA 02118
P: (617) 727-3074
F: (617) 727-1944

MICHIGAN
Ms. Shelly Edgerton
Director
Department of Licensing & Regulatory Affairs
P.O. Box 30004
Lansing, MI 48909
P: (517) 373-1820
F: (517) 241-3683
E: EdgertonS1@michigan.gov

Licensing (Occupational and Professional)

MISSOURI
Ms. Jane A. Rackers
Division Director
Division of Professional Regulation
3605 Missouri Boulevard
P.O. Box 1335
Jefferson City, MO 65102
P: (573) 751-1081
F: (573) 751-4176
E: jane.rackers@pr.mo.gov

MONTANA
Mr. Todd Younkin
Division Administrator
Business Standards Division
Department of Labor & Industry
P.O. Box 200513
Helena, MT 59620
P: (406) 841-2300
E: dlibsdhelp@mt.gov

NEBRASKA
Ms. Becky Wisell
Administrator
Health & Human Services Regulation & Licensure
301 Centennial Mall South
P.O. Box 94986
Lincoln, NE 68509
P: (402) 471-2155
F: (402) 471-3577
E: becky.wisell@hhss.ne.gov

NEW JERSEY
Mr. Steve C. Lee
Director
Division of Consumer Affairs
Office of the Attorney General
124 Halsey Street
Newark, NJ 07102
P: (973) 504-6200
F: (973) 273-8035
E: askconsumeraffairs@lps.state.nj.us

NEW MEXICO
Mr. Robert Mike Unthank
Superintendent
Regulation & Licensing Department
2550 Cerrillos Road, 3rd Floor
Sante Fe, NM 87505
P: (505) 476-4508
F: (505) 476-4511

NEW YORK
Ms. Susan Naccarato
Director
Division of Professional Licensing Services
State Education Department
89 Washington Avenue
Albany, NY 12234
P: (518) 474-3817
F: (518) 402-5265
E: opdpls@nysed.gov

OREGON
Ms. Sylvie Donaldson
Director
Health Licensing Office
700 Summer Street, Northeast
Suite 320
Salem, OR 97301
P: (503) 373-1974
F: (503) 370-9004
E: sylvie.donaldson@state.or.us

PENNSYLVANIA
Mr. Ian J. Harlow
Commissioner
Bureau of Professional & Occupational Affairs
Department of State
P.O. Box 2649
Harrisburg, PA 17105
P: (717) 787-8503
F: (717) 783-0510
E: RA-BPOA@pa.gov

SOUTH CAROLINA
Ms. Emily Farr
Director
Department of Labor, Licensing & Regulation
110 Centerview Drive
P.O. Box 11329
Columbia, SC 29211
P: (803) 896-4300
F: (803) 896-4393
E: ContactLLR@llr.sc.gov

TENNESSEE
Mr. Brian McCormack
Assistant Commissioner
Division of Regulatory Boards
Department of Commerce & Insurance
500 James Robertson Parkway, 2nd Floor
Nashville, TN 37243
P: (615) 741-3449
F: (615) 741-6470

Ms. Elizabeth Miller
Director
Division of Health Related Boards
Department of Health
227 French Landing, Suite 300
Nashville, TN 37243
P: (615) 741-2040
F: (615) 532-5369
E: elizabeth.miller@state.tn.us

TEXAS
Mr. Brian Francis
Executive Director
Department of Licensing & Regulation
P.O. Box 12157
Austin, TX 78711
P: (512) 463-3173
F: (512) 475-2874
E: executive.director@license.state.tx.us

Mr. Jon Huss
Interim Assistant Commissioner
Division of Regulatory Services
Department of State Health Services
P.O.Box 149347
Austin, TX 78714
P: (512) 834-6660
F: (512) 834-6635

UTAH
Mr. Mark B. Steinagel
Director
Division of Occupational & Professional Licensing
160 East 300 South, 4th Floor
P.O. Box 146741
Salt Lake City, UT 84114
P: (801) 530-6628
F: (801) 530-6511
E: msteinagel@utah.gov

VERMONT
Mr. Colin Benjamin
Director
Office of Professional Regulation
Secretary of State's Office
89 Main Street, 3rd Floor
Montpelier, VT 05620
P: (802) 828-2367
F: (802) 828-2396
E: colin.benjamin@sec.state.vt.us

VIRGINIA
Mr. David E. Brown
Director
Department of Health Professions
9960 Mayland Drive, Suite 300
Richmond, VA 23233
P: (804) 662-9919
F: (804) 662-9114

Mr. Jay W. DeBoer
Director
Department of Professional & Occupational Regulation
9960 Mayland Drive, Suite 400
Richmond, VA 23233
P: (804) 367-8519
F: (804) 367-9537
E: director@dpor.virginia.gov

WASHINGTON
Ms. Pat Kohler
Agency Director
Department of Licensing
P.O. Box 9020
Olympia, WA 98507
P: (360) 902-3600
F: (360) 902-4042
E: doldirector@dol.wa.gov

Mr. Martin Mueller
Assistant Secretary
State Health Systems Quality Assurance
P.O. Box 47830
Olympia, WA 98504
P: (360) 236-4601
F: (360) 236-4626

WISCONSIN
Ms. Laura Gutierrez
Secretary
Department of Safety & Professional Services
P.O. Box 8935
Madison, WI 53708
P: (608) 266-2112
F: (608) 266-9946

Lieutenant Governor

The statewide elected official who is next in line of succession to the governorship. (In Maine, New Hampshire, Tennessee and West Virginia, the presidents (or speakers) of the Senate are the next in line of succession to the governorship. In Tennessee, the speaker of the Senate bears the statutory title of lieutenant governor. In Arizona, Oregon, and Wyoming, the secretary of state is next in line of succession to the governorship.)

Information provided by:

National Lieutenant Governors Association
Julia Hurst
Executive Director
71 Cavalier Boulevard
Suite 223
Florence, KY 41042
P: (859) 283-1400
jhurst@nlga.us
www.nlga.us

ALABAMA
Vacant
Lieutenant Governor
Office of the Lieutenant Governor
State Capitol
600 Dexter Avenue
Montgomery, AL 36130
P: (334) 242-7100
F: (334) 353-0004

ALASKA
The Honorable Byron Mallot (I)
Lieutenant Governor
Office of the Lieutenant Governor
550 West 7th Street, Suite 1700
Anchorage, AK 99501
P: (907) 269-7460
F: (907) 269-0263

AMERICAN SAMOA
The Honorable Lemanu Peleti Mauga (I)
Lieutenant Governor
Office of the Lieutenant Governor
Territory of American Samoa
Pago Pago, AS 96799
P: (684) 633-4116
F: (684) 633-2269

ARKANSAS
The Honorable Tim Griffin (R)
Lieutenant Governor
Office of the Lieutenant Governor
270 State Capitol
Little Rock, AR 72201
P: (501) 682-2144
F: (501) 682-2894

CALIFORNIA
The Honorable Gavin Newsom (D)
Lieutenant Governor
Office of the Lieutenant Governor
State Capitol, Room 1114
Sacramento, CA 95814
P: (916) 445-8994
F: (916) 323-4998

COLORADO
The Honorable Donna Lynne (D)
Lieutenant Governor
Office of the Lieutenant Governor
130 State Capitol
Denver, CO 80203
P: (303) 866-2087
F: (303) 866-5469

CONNECTICUT
The Honorable Nancy Wyman (D)
Lieutenant Governor
Office of the Lieutenant Governor
State Capitol, Room 304
210 Capitol Avenue
Hartford, CT 06106
P: (860) 524-7384
F: (860) 524-7304

DELAWARE
The Honorable Bethany A. Hall-Long (D)
Lieutenant Governor
Office of the Lieutenant Governor
150 Martin Luther King Jr., South
3rd Floor
Dover, DE 19901
P: (302) 744-4333
E: bethany.hall-long@state.de.us

FLORIDA
The Honorable Carlos Lopez-Cantera (R)
Lieutenant Governor
Office of the Lieutenant Governor
The State Capitol
Tallahassee, FL 32399
P: (850) 488-4711
F: (850) 921-6114

GEORGIA
The Honorable Casey Cagle (R)
Lieutenant Governor
Office of the Lieutenant Governor
240 State Capitol
Atlanta, GA 30334
P: (404) 656-5030
F: (404) 656-6739

GUAM
The Honorable Ray Tenorio (R)
Lieutenant Governor
Office of the Lieutenant Governor
R.J. Bordallo Governor's Complex
P.O. Box 2950
Hagatna, GU 96932
P: (671) 475-9380
F: (671) 477-2007
E: webmaster@guamletgovernor.net

HAWAII
The Honorable Shan S. Tsutsui (D)
Lieutenant Governor
Office of the Lieutenant Governor
Executive Chambers
State Capitol
Honolulu, HI 96813
P: (808) 586-0255
F: (808) 586-0231
E: shan.tsusui@hawaii.gov

IDAHO
The Honorable Brad Little (R)
Lieutenant Governor
Office of the Lieutenant Governor
State Capitol
Boise, ID 83720
P: (208) 334-2200
F: (208) 334-3259

ILLINOIS
The Honorable Evelyn Sanguinetti (R)
Lieutenant Governor
Office of the Lieutenant Governor
214 State House
Springfield, IL 62706
P: (217) 558-3085
F: (217) 558-3086

INDIANA
The Honorable Suzanne Crouch (R)
Lieutenant Governor
Office of the Lieutenant Governor
State Capitol, Room 333
Indianapolis, IN 46204
P: (317) 232-4545
F: (317) 234-1916

IOWA
Mr. Adam Gregg
Lieutenant Governor
Office of the Lieutenant Governor
State Capitol
321 East 12th Street
Des Moines, IA 50319
P: (515) 281-5211
E: agregg@spd.state.ia.us

KANSAS
The Honorable Jeff Colyer (R)
Lieutenant Governor
Office of the Lieutenant Governor
State Capitol, 2nd Floor
300 Southwest 10th Avenue
Topeka, KS 66612
P: (785) 296-2214
F: (785) 296-5669

KENTUCKY
The Honorable Jenean Hampton (R)
Lieutenant Governor
Office of the Lieutenant Governor
700 Capital Avenue, Suite 142
Frankfort, KY 40601
P: (502) 564-2611
F: (502) 564-2849

Lieutenant Governor

LOUISIANA
The Honorable Billy Nungesser (R)
Lieutenant Governor
Office of the Lieutenant Governor
1051 North 3rd Street, Capitol Annex
P.O. Box 44243
Baton Rouge, LA 70804
P: (225) 342-7009
F: (225) 342-1949
E: ltgov@crt.la.gov

MARYLAND
The Honorable Boyd Rutherford (R)
Lieutenant Governor
Office of the Lieutenant Governor
100 State Circle
Annapolis, MD 21401
P: (410) 974-2804
E: ltgov@gov.state.md.us

MASSACHUSETTS
The Honorable Karyn E. Polito (R)
Lieutenant Governor
Office of the Lieutenant Governor
State House, Suite 109B
24 Beacon Street
Boston, MA 02133
P: (617) 727-7030
F: (617) 742-4528

MICHIGAN
The Honorable Brian Calley (R)
Lieutenant Governor
Office of the Lieutenant Governor
P.O. Box 30013
Lansing, MI 48909
P: (517) 373-6800
F: (517) 241-5026

MINNESOTA
The Honorable Tina Smith (D)
Lieutenant Governor
Office of the Lieutenant Governor
130 State Capitol
75 Rev. Martin Luther King Jr. Boulevard
St. Paul, MN 55155
P: (651) 201-3400
F: (651) 797-1850

MISSISSIPPI
The Honorable Tate Reeves (R)
Lieutenant Governor
Office of the Lieutenant Governor
New Capitol, Room 315
P.O. Box 1018
Jackson, MS 39215
P: (601) 359-3200
F: (601) 359-2001
E: ltgov@senate.ms.gov

MISSOURI
The Honorable Michael Parson (R)
Lieutenant Governor
Office of the Lieutenant Governor
State Capitol, Room 224
Jefferson City, MO 65101
P: (573) 751-4727
F: (573) 526-8793

MONTANA
The Honorable Mike Cooney (D)
Lieutenant Governor
Office of the Lieutenant Governor
Capitol Station, Room 207
P.O. Box 200801
Helena, MT 59620
P: (406) 444-5665
F: (406) 444-4648

NEBRASKA
The Honorable Mike Foley (R)
Lieutenant Governor
Office of the Lieutenant Governor
State Capitol, Room 2315
P.O. Box 94863
Lincoln, NE 68509
P: (402) 471-2256
F: (402) 471-6031
E: mike.foley@nebraska.gov

NEVADA
The Honorable Mark Hutchison (R)
Lieutenant Governor
Office of the Lieutenant Governor
101 North Carson Street, Suite 2
Carson City, NV 89701
P: (775) 684-7111
F: (775) 684-7110

NEW JERSEY
The Honorable Kim Guadagno (R)
Lieutenant Governor
Office of the Secretary of State
P.O. Box 300
125 West 8th Street
Trenton, NJ 08625
P: (609) 292-6000
F: (609) 292-3454
E: lt.governor@gov.state.nj.us

NEW MEXICO
The Honorable John A. Sanchez (R)
Lieutenant Governor
Office of the Lieutenant Governor
State Capitol, Suite 417
Santa Fe, NM 87501
P: (505) 476-2250
F: (505) 476-2257

NEW YORK
The Honorable Kathy Hochul (D)
Lieutenant Governor
Office of the Lieutenant Governor
State Capitol
Albany, NY 12224
P: (518) 474-8390
F: (518) 474-1513

NORTH CAROLINA
The Honorable Dan Forest (R)
Lieutenant Governor
Office of the Lieutenant Governor
310 North Blount Street
Raleigh, NC 27601
P: (919) 733-7350
F: (919) 733-6595
E: lt.gov@nc.gov

NORTH DAKOTA
The Honorable Brent Sanford (R)
Lieutenant Governor
Office of the Lieutenant Governor
State Capitol
Bismarck, ND 58505
P: (701) 328-2200
F: (701) 328-2205

NORTHERN MARIANA ISLANDS
The Honorable Victor B. Hocog (R)
Lieutenant Governor
Office of the Lieutenant Governor
Caller Box 10007
Capitol Hill
Saipan, MP 96950
P: (670) 664-2300
F: (670) 664-2311

OHIO
The Honorable Mary Taylor (R)
Lieutenant Governor
Office of the Lieutenant Governor
77 High Street, 30th Floor
Columbus, OH 43215
P: (614) 644-0935
F: (614) 466-9354

OKLAHOMA
The Honorable Todd Lamb (R)
Lieutenant Governor
Office of the Lieutenant Governor
State Capitol, Room 211
Oklahoma City, OK 73105
P: (405) 521-2161
F: (405) 522-8694

PENNSYLVANIA
The Honorable Michael J. Stack (D)
Lieutenant Governor
Office of the Lieutenant Governor
200 Main Capitol Building
Harrisburg, PA 17120
P: (717) 787-3300
F: (717) 783-0150

RHODE ISLAND
The Honorable Daniel McKee (D)
Lieutenant Governor
Office of the Lieutenant Governor
116 State House
Providence, RI 02903
P: (401) 222-2371
F: (401) 222-2012

SOUTH CAROLINA
The Honorable Kevin L. Bryant (R)
Lieutenant Governor
Office of the Lieutenant Governor
P.O. Box 142
Columbia, SC 29202
P: (803) 734-2080
F: (803) 734-2082
E: KevinBryant@scsenate.gov

SOUTH DAKOTA
The Honorable Matthew Michels (R)
Lieutenant Governor
Office of the Lieutenant Governor
500 East Capitol Street
Pierre, SD 57501
P: (605) 773-3661
F: (605) 773-4711

TENNESSEE
The Honorable Randy McNally (R)
(elected by the Senate)
Lieutenant Governor/Speaker of the Senate
Office of the Lieutenant Governor
One Legislative Plaza
Nashville, TN 37243
P: (615) 741-4524
F: (615) 253-0285
E: lt.gov.randy.mcnally@capitol.tn.gov

TEXAS
The Honorable Dan Patrick (R)
Lieutenant Governor
Office of the Lieutenant Governor
Capitol Station
P.O. Box 12068
Austin, TX 78711
P: (512) 463-0001
F: (512) 463-0677

U.S. VIRGIN ISLANDS
The Honorable Osbert Potter (I)
Lieutenant Governor/Commissioner
Office of the Lieutenant Governor
1331 Kings Street, Suite101
St. Croix, VI 00802
P: (340) 773-6449
F: (340) 773-0330

UTAH
The Honorable Spencer J. Cox (R)
Lieutenant Governor
Office of the Lieutenant Governor
P.O. Box 142325
Salt Lake City, UT 84114
P: (801) 538-1133
F: (801) 538-1133

VERMONT
The Honorable David Zuckerman (D)
Lieutenant Governor
Office of the Lieutenant Governor
115 State Street
Monpelier, VT 05633
P: (802) 828-2226
F: (802) 828-3198
E: dzuckerman@leg.state.vt.us

VIRGINIA
The Honorable Ralph S. Northam (D)
Lieutenant Governor
Office of the Lieutenant Governor
102 Governor Street
Richmond, VA 23219
P: (804) 786-2078
F: (804) 786-7514
E: ltgov@ltgov.virginia.gov

WASHINGTON
The Honorable Cyrus Habib (D)
Lieutenant Governor
Office of the Lieutenant Governor
416 14th Avenue Southwest
P.O. Box 40400
Olympia, WA 98504
P: (360) 786-7700
F: (360) 786-7749

WEST VIRGINIA
Senator Mitch Carmichael (R)
Senate President/Lieutenant Governor
Office of the Senate President/Lieutenant Governor
Room 227M, Building 1
Capitol Complex
Charleston, WV 25305
P: (304) 357-7801
E: mitch.carmichael@wvsenate.gov

WISCONSIN
The Honorable Rebecca Kleefisch (R)
Lieutenant Governor
Office of the Lieutenant Governor
Room 19, East State Capitol
P.O. Box 2043
Madison, WI 53702
P: (608) 266-3516
F: (608) 267-3571

Lobby Law Administration

Administers registration and reporting requirements for lobbyists.

ALABAMA
The Honorable John Merrill (R)
Secretary of State
Office of the Secretary of State
P.O. Box 5616
Montgomery, AL 36103
P: (334) 242-7200
F: (334) 242-4993
E: john.merrill@sos.alabama.gov

ALASKA
Ms. Heather Hebdon
Executive Director
Public Offices Commission
Department of Administration
2221 East Northern Lights, Room 128
Anchorage, AK 99508
P: (907) 276-4176
F: (907) 276-7018
E: heather.hebdon@alaska.gov

ARKANSAS
The Honorable Mark Martin (R)
Secretary of State
Office of the Secretary of State
256 State Capitol Building
Little Rock, AR 72201
P: (501) 682-1010
F: (501) 682-3510
E: info@sos.arkansas.gov

CALIFORNIA
Ms. Jana Lean
Chief of Elections
Elections Division
1500 11th Street, 5th Floor
Sacramento, CA 95814
P: (916) 657-2166
F: (916) 653-3214
E: jana.lean@sos.ca.gov

COLORADO
The Honorable Wayne Williams (R)
Secretary of State
Office of the Secretary of State
1700 Broadway, Suite 200
Denver, CO 80290
P: (303) 894-2200
F: (303) 869-4860
E: secretary@sos.state.co.us

CONNECTICUT
Ms. Carol Carson
Executive Director
Office of State Ethics
18-20 Trinity Street, Suite 205
Hartford, CT 06106
P: (860) 263-2384
F: (860) 263-2402
E: carol.carson@ct.gov

DELAWARE
Ms. Deborah Moreau
Commission's Legal Counsel
Public Integrity Commission
Margaret O'Neill Building
410 Federal Street, Suite 3
Dover, DE 19901
P: (302) 739-2399
F: (302) 739-2398
E: deborah.moreau@state.de.us

DISTRICT OF COLUMBIA
Ms. Cecily E. Collier-Montgomery
Director
Office of Campaign Finance
Frank D. Reeves Municipal Building
2000 14th Street, Northwest, Suite 433
Washington, DC 20009
P: (202) 671-0547
F: (202) 671-0658
E: ocf@dc.gov

FLORIDA
Ms. Angela Bonds
Legislative Affairs Director
Office of Legislative Affairs
R. A. Gray Building, Suite 115
500 South Bronough Street
Tallahassee, FL 32399
P: (850) 245-6512
F: (850) 245-6125
E: Angela.Bonds@dos.myflorida.com

Ms. Virlindia Doss
Executive Director
Commission on Ethics
P.O. Drawer 15709
Tallahassee, FL 32317
P: (850) 488-7864
F: (904) 488-3077
E: doss.virlindia@leg.state.fl.us

HAWAII
Mr. Reynaldo D. Graulty
Chair
State Ethics Commission
1001 Bishop Street, Suite 970
Honolulu, HI 96813
P: (808) 587-0460
F: (808) 587-0470
E: ethics@hawaiiethics.org

IDAHO
The Honorable Lawerence Denney (R)
Secretary of State
Office of the Secretary of State
P.O. Box 83720
Boise, ID 83720
P: (208) 334-2300
F: (208) 334-2282
E: ldenney@sos.idaho.gov

ILLINOIS
Mr. David Weisbaum
Director
Index Department
Office of the Secretary of State
111 East Monroe Street
Springfield, IL 62756
P: (217) 782-7017
F: (217) 524-0930

INDIANA
Mr. Charles W. Harris
Executive Director & General Counsel
Lobby Registration Commission
10 West Market Street, Suite 2940
Indianapolis, IN 46204
P: (317) 232-9860
F: (317) 233-0077
E: charris@lrc.in.gov

IOWA
Mr. Michael E. Marshall
Secretary of the Senate
General Assembly
State Capitol
1007 East Grand Avenue
Des Moines, IA 50319
P: (515) 281-5307
E: Mike.Marshall@legis.iowa.gov

KANSAS
Mr. Bryan Caskey
Election Director
Office of the Secretary of State
120 Southwest 10th Avenue
Memorial Hall, 1st Floor
Topeka, KS 66612
P: (785) 296-4561
F: (785) 291-3051
E: election@sos.ks.gov

KENTUCKY
The Honorable Alison L. Grimes (D)
Secretary of State
Office of the Secretary of State
700 Capital Avenue, Suite 152
Frankfort, KY 40601
P: (502) 564-3490
F: (502) 564-5687
E: sos.secretary@ky.gov

LOUISIANA
Ms. Kathleen Allen
Ethics Administrator
Ethics Administration Program
617 North Third Street, Suite 10-36
P.O. Box 4368
Baton Rouge, LA 70821
P: (225) 219-5600
F: (225) 381-7271
E: kathleen.allen@la.gov

MAINE
Mr. Jonathan Wayne
Executive Director
Commission on Governmental Ethics & Election Practices
135 State House Station
Augusta, ME 04333
P: (207) 287-4179
F: (207) 287-6775
E: Jonathan.Wayne@maine.gov

MARYLAND
Ms. Jennifer K. Allgair
General Counsel
State Ethics Commission
45 Calvert Street, 3rd Floor
Annapolis, MD 21401
P: (410) 260-7770
F: (410) 260-7746
E: Jennifer.Allgair@Maryland.gov

Mr. Michael W. Lord
Executive Director
State Ethics Commission
45 Calvert Street, 3rd Floor
Annapolis, MD 21401
P: (410) 260-7770
F: (410) 260-7746
E: Michael.Lord@Maryland.gov

MASSACHUSETTS
The Honorable William F. Galvin (D)
Secretary of the Commonwealth
Office of the Secretary of the Commonwealth
State House, Room 337
24 Beacon Street
Boston, MA 02133
P: (617) 727-9180
F: (617) 742-4722
E: cis@sec.state.ma.us

MICHIGAN
Mr. Christopher M. Thomas
Director
Bureau of Elections
Department of State
Lansing, MI 48918
P: (517) 335-2789
F: (517) 373-0941
E: ChristopherT@michigan.gov

MINNESOTA
Mr. Jeff Sigurdson
Executive Director
Campaign Finance & Public Disclosure Board
Centennial Office Building, Suite 190
658 Cedar Street
St. Paul, MN 55155
P: (651) 539-1190
F: (651) 539-1196
E: jeff.sigurdson@state.mn.us

The Honorable Steve Simon (DFL)
Secretary of State
Office of the Secretary of State
180 State Office Building
100 Martin Luther King Jr. Boulevard
St. Paul, MN 55155
P: (651) 201-1324
F: (651) 269-9073
E: secretary.state@state.mn.us

MISSISSIPPI
Ms. Kimberly P. Turner
Assistant Secretary of State
Elections Division
Secretary of State's Office
401 Mississippi Street, P.O. Box 136
Jackson, MS 39205
P: (601) 359-5137
F: (601) 576-2545
E: Kim.Turner@sos.ms.gov

MISSOURI
Mr. James Klahr
Executive Director
Ethics Commission
3411A Knipp Drive
P.O. Box 1370
Jefferson City, MO 65102
P: (573) 751-2020
F: (573) 526-4506
E: helpdesk@mec.mo.gov

MONTANA
Mr. Jeff Mangan
Commissioner
Commissioner of Political Practices
1209 8th Avenue
P.O. Box 202401
Helena, MT 59620
P: (406) 444-2942
F: (406) 444-1643

NEBRASKA
Mr. Patrick J. O'Donnell
Clerk of the Legislature
State Legislature
State Capitol, Room 2018
P.O. Box 94604
Lincoln, NE 68509
P: (402) 471-2271
F: (402) 471-2126
E: podonnell@leg.ne.gov

NEVADA
Mr. Rick Combs
Director
Legislative Counsel Bureau
Legislative Building
401 South Carson Street
Carson City, NV 89701
P: (775) 684-6800
F: (775) 684-6600
E: combs@lcb.state.nv.us

NEW HAMPSHIRE
The Honorable William M. Gardner (D)
Secretary of State
Office of the Secretary of State
State House, Room 204
Concord, NH 03301
P: (603) 271-3242
F: (603) 271-6316
E: kladd@sos.state.nh.us

NEW JERSEY
Mr. Jeffrey M. Brindle
Executive Director
Election Law Enforcement Commission
P.O. Box 185
Trenton, NJ 08625
P: (609) 292-8700
F: (609) 777-1448
E: jeff.brindle@elec.state.nj.us

NEW MEXICO
The Honorable Dianna J. Duran (R)
Secretary of State
Office of the Secretary of State
325 Don Gaspar, Suite 300
Capitol Annex
Santa Fe, NM 87501
P: (505) 827-3600
F: (505) 827-8081
E: diannaj.duran@state.nm.us

NEW YORK
Mr. Seth H. Agata
Director
Joint Commission on Public Ethics
540 Broadway
Albany, NY 12207
P: (518) 408-3976
F: (518) 408-3975

NORTH CAROLINA
The Honorable Elaine F. Marshall (D)
Secretary of State
Office of the Secretary of State
P.O. Box 29622
Raleigh, NC 27626
P: (919) 807-2005
F: (919) 807-2010
E: emarshal@sosnc.com

NORTH DAKOTA
The Honorable Alvin A. Jaeger (R)
Secretary of State
Office of the Secretary of State
600 East Boulevard
Department 108
Bismarck, ND 58505
P: (701) 328-2900
F: (701) 328-1690
E: ajaeger@nd.gov

OHIO
Mr. Tony W. Bledsoe
Legislative Inspector General/Executive Director
Office of the Legislative Inspector General
50 West Broad Street, Suite 1308
Columbus, OH 43215
P: (614) 728-5100
F: (614) 728-5074
E: info@jlec-olig.state.oh.us

OREGON
Mr. Ronald A. Bersin
Executive Director
Government Ethics Commission
3218 Pringle Road, Southeast, Suite 220
Salem, OR 97302
P: (503) 378-5105
F: (503) 373-1456
E: ron.a.bersin@oregon.gov

SOUTH CAROLINA
Mr. Steven W. Hamm
Interim Executive Director
State Ethics Commission
5000 Thurmond Mall, Suite 250
Columbia, SC 29201
P: (803) 253-4192
F: (803) 253-7539

The Honorable Mark Hammond (R)
Secretary of State
Office of the Secretary of State
1205 Pendleton Street, Suite 525
Columbia, SC 29201
P: (803) 734-2170
F: (803) 734-1661
E: rdaggerhart@sos.sc.gov

TENNESSEE
Mr. Drew Rawlins
Executive Director
Ethics Commission
Registry of Election Finance
404 James Robertson Parkway, Suite 104
Nashville, TN 37243
P: (615) 741-7959
F: (615) 532-8905
E: registry.info@tn.gov

TEXAS
Mr. Keith Ingram
Director of Elections
Elections Division
Office of the Secretary of State
P.O. Box 12060
Austin, TX 78711
P: (512) 463-5650
F: (512) 475-2811
E: elections@sos.texas.gov

VERMONT
The Honorable Jim Condos (D)
Secretary of State
Office of the Secretary of State
128 State Street
Montpelier, VT 05633
P: (802) 828-2148
F: (802) 828-2496
E: jim.condos@sec.state.vt.us

WASHINGTON
B.G. Sandahl
Acting Executive Director
Public Disclosure Commission
711 Capitol Way, Room 206
P.O. Box 40908
Olympia, WA 98504
P: (360) 586-1042
F: (360) 753-1112
E: pdc@pdc.wa.gov

Lobby Law Administration

WEST VIRGINIA
Ms. Rebecca L. Stepto
Executive Director
Ethics Commission
210 Brooks Street, Suite 300
Charleston, WV 25301
P: (304) 558-0664
F: (304) 558-2169
E: rebecca.l.stepto@wv.gov

WISCONSIN
Mr. Michael Haas
Administrator
Elections Commission
212 East Washington Avenue,
3rd Floor
P.O. Box 7984
Madison, WI 53707
P: (608) 266-0136
F: (608) 267-0500
E: Michael.Haas@wi.gov

WYOMING
The Honorable Ed Murray (R)
Secretary of State
Office of the Secretary of State
2020 Carey Avenue, Suite 600 &
700
Cheyenne, WY 82002
P: (307) 777-7378
F: (307) 777-6217
E: secofstate@wyo.gov

Lottery

Administers the state lottery system.

ARIZONA
Mr. Gregory Edgar
Executive Director
State Lottery
4740 East University
Phoenix, AZ 85034
P: (480) 921-4400

ARKANSAS
Mr. William Bishop Woosley
Director
State Lottery Commission
124 West Capitol, Suite 1400
Little Rock, AR 72201
P: (501) 683-2000

CALIFORNIA
Mr. Hugo Lopez
Director
State Lottery Commission
700 North 10th Street
Sacramento, CA 95811
P: (800) 568-8379

COLORADO
Ms. Laura Solano
Director
State Lottery
225 North Main Street
Pueblo, CO 81003
P: (719) 546-2400
E: colorado.lottery
@state.co.us

CONNECTICUT
Mr. Frank Farricker
Acting President & CEO
State Lottery Corporation
777 Brook Street
Rocky Hill, CT 06067
P: (860) 713-2700

DELAWARE
Mr. Vernon Kirk
Director
State Lottery
McKee Business Park
1575 McKee Road, Suite 102
Dover, DE 19904
P: (302) 739-5291
F: (302) 739-6706

DISTRICT OF COLUMBIA
Ms. Tracey Cohen
Acting Executive Director
Lottery & Charitable Games
2235 Shannon Place, Southeast
Washington, DC 20020
P: (202) 645-8000

FLORIDA
Mr. Tom Delacenserie
Secretary
State Lottery
250 Marriott Drive
Tallahassee, FL 32399
P: (850) 487-7777

GEORGIA
Ms. Debbie D. Alford
President & CEO
State Lottery Corporation
Inforum, Suite 3000
250 Williams Street
Atlanta, GA 30303
P: (404) 215-5000
F: (404) 215-8871
E: glottery@galottery.org

IDAHO
Mr. Jeffrey R. Anderson
Director
State Lottery
1199 Shoreline Lane, Suite 100
P.O. Box 6537
Boise, ID 83707
P: (208) 334-2600
F: (208) 947-9401
E: info@idaholottery.com

ILLINOIS
Mr. Gregory Smith
Acting Director
Department of the Lottery
122 South Michigan Avenue
19th Floor
Chicago, IL 60603
P: (312) 793-3030

INDIANA
Ms. Sarah Taylor
Executive Director
Hoosier Lottery
1302 North Meridian Street,
Suite 100
Indianapolis, IN 46202
P: (317) 264-4800
E: info@hoosierlottery.com

IOWA
Mr. Terry Rich
President & CEO
State Lottery Authority
13001 University Avenue
Clive, IA 50325
P: (515) 725-7900
F: (515) 725-7905
E: wmaster@ialottery.com

KANSAS
Mr. Terry Presta
Executive Director
State Lottery
128 North Kansas Avenue
Topeka, KS 66603
P: (785) 296-5700
E: lotteryinfo
@kslottery.net

KENTUCKY
Ms. Margaret Gibbs
Acting President & CEO
State Lottery Corporation
1011 West Main Street
Louisville, KY 40202
P: (502) 560-1500
F: (502) 560-1532

LOUISIANA
Ms. Rose Hudson
President & CEO
State Lottery Corporation
555 Laurel Street
Baton Rouge, LA 70801
P: (225) 297-2000
F: (225) 297-2005
E: info
@louisianalottery.com

MAINE
Mr. Gregg Mineo
Director
State Lottery
10 Water Street
Hallowell, ME 04333
P: (207) 287-3721

MARYLAND
Mr. Gordon Medenica
Director
Lottery & Gaming Control
Agency
1800 Washington Boulevard,
Suite 330
Baltimore, MD 21230
P: (410) 230-8800
E: ask.lotteryandgaming
@maryland.gov

MASSACHUSETTS
Mr. Mike Sweeney
Executive Director
State Lottery Commission
60 Columbian Street
Braintree, MA 02184
P: (781) 849-5555

MINNESOTA
Mr. Mike Vekich
Interim Executive Director
State Lottery
2645 Long Lake Road
Roseville, MN 55113
P: (651) 635-8100
E: lottery@mnlottery.com

MISSOURI
Ms. May Scheve Reardon
Executive Director
State Lottery Commission
P.O. Box 1603
Jefferson City, MO 65102
P: (573) 751-4050

MONTANA
Ms. Angela Wong
Director
State Lottery
2525 North Montana Avenue
Helena, MT 59601
P: (406) 444-5825
F: (406) 444-5830

NEBRASKA
Mr. Brian Rockey
Director
State Lottery
P.O. Box 98901
Lincoln, NE 68509
P: (402) 471-6100

NEW HAMPSHIRE
Mr. Charles McIntyre
Executive Director
State Lottery Commission
P.O. Box 1208
Concord, NH 03301
P: (603) 271-3391

NEW JERSEY
Ms. Carole Hedinger
Executive Director
Division of State Lottery
P.O. Box 041
Trenton, NJ 08625
P: (609) 599-5800
E: publicinfo
@lottery.state.nj.us

NEW MEXICO
Mr. David M. Barden
CEO
State Lottery Authority
P.O. Box 93130
Albuquerque, NM 87199
P: (505) 342-7600
E: custservice
@nmlottery.com

NEW YORK
Ms. Gwen Dean
Director
State Gaming Commission
One Broadway Center
P.O. Box 7500
Schenectady, NY 12301
P: (518) 388-3300

Lottery

NORTH CAROLINA
Ms. Alice Garland
Executive Director
Education Lottery
2100 Yonkers Road
Raleigh, NC 27604
P: (919) 301-3300
F: (919) 715-8833
E: playerinfo@lotterync.net

NORTH DAKOTA
Mr. Randall Miller
Director
State Lottery
1050 East Interstate Avenue, Suite 200
Bismarck, ND 58503
P: (701) 328-1574

OHIO
Mr. Dennis Berg
Director
State Lottery Commission
615 West Superior Avenue
Cleveland, OH 44113
P: (800) 686-4208
E: olcwebmail@olc.state.oh.us

OKLAHOMA
Mr. Rollo Daniel Redburn
Executive Director
State Lottery Commission
3817 North Santa Fe
Oklahoma City, OK 73118
P: (405) 522-7700
F: (405) 521-0528

OREGON
Mr. Barry Pack
Director
State Lottery
P.O. Box 12649
500 Airport Road Southeast
Salem, OR 97309
P: (503) 540-1000
E: webcenter@state.or.us

PENNSYLVANIA
Mr. Drew Svitko
Executive Director
State Lottery
1200 Fulling Mill Road, Suite 2
Middletown, PA 17057
P: (717) 702-8000
F: (717) 702-8024
E: info@palottery.com

PUERTO RICO
Mr. Armando Perez-Cruz
Director
Electronic Lottery
Fundacion Angel Ramos Building
383 Roosevelt Avenue, Suite 107
San Juan, PR 00918
P: (787) 250-8150
E: info@loteriaelectronicapr.com

RHODE ISLAND
Mr. Gerald Aubin
Executive Director
State Lottery
1425 Pontiac Avenue
Cranston, RI 02920
P: (401) 463-6500
F: (401) 463-5669
E: mferriola@rilot.ri.gov

SOUTH CAROLINA
Mr. Hogan Brown
Interim Executive Director
State Education Lottery
1333 Main Street, Suite 400
Columbia, SC 29201
P: (803) 737-2002

SOUTH DAKOTA
Mr. Norman Lingle
Director
State Lottery
P.O. Box 7107
Pierre, SD 57501
P: (605) 773-5770
F: (605) 773-5786
E: lottery@state.sd.us

TENNESSEE
Ms. Rebecca Paul Hargrove
President & CEO
State Education Lottery
26 Century Boulevard, Suite 200
Nashville, TN 37214
P: (615) 324-6500
F: (615) 324-6512

TEXAS
Mr. Gary Grief
Executive Director
State Lottery Commission
611 East Sixth Street
Austin, TX 78701
P: (512) 344-5000
F: (512) 478-3682
E: gary.grief@lottery.state.tx.us

U.S. VIRGIN ISLANDS
Mr. Juan Figueroa
Executive Director
State Lottery
5800 Krondprindsens Gade
St. Thomas, VI 00802
P: (340) 774-2502

VIRGINIA
Ms. Paula I. Otto
Executive Director
State Lottery
900 East Main Street
Richmond, VA 23219
P: (804) 692-7000
F: (804) 692-7102
E: info@valottery.com

WASHINGTON
Mr. Bill Hanson
Director
State Lottery
814 East 4th Avenue
Olympia, WA 98506
P: (360) 664-4800
F: (360) 586-1039
E: director's_office@walottery.com

WEST VIRGINIA
Mr. Alan Larrick
Director
State Lottery
900 Pennsylvania Avenue
Charleston, WV 25302
P: (304) 558-0500

WISCONSIN
Ms. Cindy Polzin
Department of Revenue
2135 Rimrock Road, #231
Madison, WI 53713
P: (608) 261-8800

WYOMING
Mr. Jon Clontz
CEO
State Lottery
1620 Central Avenue, Suite #100
Cheyenne, WY 82001
P: (307) 432-9300

Medicaid

Administers the medical assistance program that finances medical care for income assistance recipients and other eligible medically needy persons.

ALABAMA
Ms. Stephanie Azar
Commissioner
Medicaid Agency
501 Dexter Avenue
P.O. Box 5624
Montgomery, AL 36103
P: (334) 242-5600
E: stephanie.azar@medicaid.alabama.gov

ALASKA
Ms. Margaret Brodie
Director
Health Care Services
Department of Health & Social Services
4501 Business Park Boulevard, Building L
Anchorage, AK 99504
P: (907) 334-2520

AMERICAN SAMOA
Ms. Sandra King Young
Medicaid Director
Medicaid State Agency
American Samoa Government
Pago Pago, AS 96799
P: (684) 633-4818

ARIZONA
Mr. Thomas J. Betlach
Director
Health Care Cost Containment System
Department of Health Services
801 East Jefferson, MD 4100
Phoenix, AZ 85034
P: (602) 417-4711
F: (602) 252-6536
E: thomas.betlach@azahcccs.gov

ARKANSAS
Ms. Dawn Stehle
Deputy Director
Division of Health & Medicaid Services
Department of Human Services
112 West 8th Street, Slot S401
Little Rock, AR 72201
P: (501) 682-8740
F: (501) 682-1197

CALIFORNIA
Ms. Mari Cantwell
Chief Deputy Director, Health Care Programs
Department of Health Care Services
1501 Capitol Avenue, 6th Floor
MS 0000
Sacramento, CA 95814
P: (916) 440-7418
F: (916) 440-7404

COLORADO
Ms. Gretchen Hammer
Medicaid Director
Department of Health Care Policy & Financing
Medicaid & Child Health Plan (CHP+)
1570 Grant Street
Denver, CO 80203
P: (303) 866-5929
F: (303) 866-4411

CONNECTICUT
Ms. Kate McEvoy
State Medicaid Director
Department of Social Services
55 Farmington Avenue
Hartford, CT 06105
P: (860) 424-5067
E: mark.schaefer@ct.gov

DELAWARE
Mr. Stephen Groff
Medicaid Director
Department of Health & Social Services
1901 North DuPont, The Lewis Building
P.O. Box 906
New Castle, DE 19720
P: (302) 255-9626

DISTRICT OF COLUMBIA
Ms. Claudia Schlosberg
Medicaid Director
District of Columbia
One Judiciary Square
441 4th Street, Northwest
Washington, DC 20001
P: (202) 442-9075

FLORIDA
Ms. Beth Kidder
Interim Deputy Secretary for Medicaid
Agency for Healthcare Administration
2727 Mahan Drive, Mail Stop 8
Tallahassee, FL 32308
P: (850) 412-4006

GEORGIA
Ms. Linda Wiant
Chief of the Medicaid Assistance Plans
Department of Community Health
2 Peachtree Street, Northwest
Suite 36450
Atlanta, GA 30303
P: (404) 651-8681

GUAM
Ms. Alyssa Uncangco
Administrator
Bureau of Health Care Financing Administration, Medicaid Program
Public Health & Social Services
123 Chalan Kareta
Mangilcio, GU 96913
P: (671) 735-7282

HAWAII
Ms. Judy Mohr Peterson
Acting Med-QUEST Division Administrator
Department of Human Services
601 Kamokila Boulevard, Room 518
P.O. Box 700190
Kapolei, HI 96709
P: (808) 692-8050

IDAHO
Ms. Lisa Hettinger
Administrator
Department of Health & Welfare
450 West State Street
PTC Building, 10th Floor
Boise, ID 83705
P: (208) 334-1804

ILLINOIS
Ms. Teresa Hursey
Acting Administrator
Division of Medical Programs
Healthcare & Family Services
201 South Grand Avenue East, 3rd Floor
Springfield, IL 62763
P: (217) 782-2570

INDIANA
Mr. Joe Moser
Director of Medicaid
Family & Social Services Administration
402 West Washington Street
P.O. Box 7083
Indianapolis, IN 46207
P: (317) 233-4454
E: Joe.Moser@fssa.IN.gov

IOWA
Ms. Mikki Stier
Medicaid Director
Department of Human Services
100 Army Post Road
Des Moines, IA 50315
P: (515) 256-4640
F: (515) 725-1360

KANSAS
Mr. Mike Randol
Medicaid Director
Department of Health & Environment
900 Southwest Jackson, Suite 900
Topeka, KS 66612
P: (785) 296-3512

KENTUCKY
Mr. Stephen P. Miller
Commissioner
Department for Medicaid Services
Cabinet for Health & Family Services
275 East Main Street, 6 West A
Frankfort, KY 40621
P: (502) 564-4321

LOUISIANA
Ms. Jen Steele
Medicaid Director
Department of Health & Hospitals
628 North 4th Street
Baton Rouge, LA 70802
P: (225) 342-9240

MAINE
Ms. Stefanie Nadeau
Director
Office of MaineCare Services
Department of Health & Human Services
11 State House Station
Augusta, ME 04333
P: (207) 287-2674
F: (207) 287-2675
E: Stefanie.Nadeau@maine.gov

MARYLAND
Ms. Shannon McMahon
Deputy Secretary, Health Care Financing
Department of Health & Mental Hygiene
201 West Preston Street, Room 525
Baltimore, MD 21201
P: (410) 767-4139

Medicaid

MASSACHUSETTS
Mr. Daniel Tsai
Assistant Secretary for MassHealth
Office of Medicaid
Department of Health & Human Services
1 Ashburn Place, 11th Floor, Room 1109
Boston, MA 02108
P: (617) 573-1770
F: (617) 573-1894

MICHIGAN
Mr. Chris Priest
Medicaid Director
Department of Community Health
400 South Pine Street
Lansing, MI 48913
P: (517) 241-7882

MINNESOTA
Ms. Marie Zimmerman
Medicaid Director
Department of Human Services
540 Cedar Street
P.O. Box 64983
St. Paul, MN 55167
P: (651) 431-2182
F: (651) 431-7421

MISSISSIPPI
Dr. David J. Dzielak
Executive Director, Division of Medicaid
Department of Human Services
550 High Street, Suite 1000
Walters Sillers Building
Jackson, MS 39201
P: (601) 359-9562

MISSOURI
Mr. Jay Ludlam
Acting Director
HealthNet Division
615 Howerton Court
P.O. Box 6500
Jefferson City, MO 65102
P: (573) 751-6922

MONTANA
Ms. Mary Dalton
State Medicaid Director
Department of Public Health & Human Services
111 North Sanders
P.O. Box 4210
Helena, MT 59604
P: (406) 444-4084
F: (406) 444-1970
E: mary.dalton@mt.gov

NEBRASKA
Mr. Calder Lynch
Director, Division of Medicaid & Long-Term Care
Department of Health & Human Services
301 Centennial Mall South, 3rd Floor
P.O. Box 95026
Lincoln, NE 68509
P: (402) 471-2135

NEVADA
Ms. Marta Jensen
Acting Administrator
Division of Health Care Financing & Policy
Department of Health & Human Services
1100 East William Street, Suite 101
Carson City, NV 89710
P: (775) 684-3677

NEW HAMPSHIRE
Ms. Deb Fournier
Medicaid Director
Office of Medicaid Business & Policy
Department of Health & Human Services
129 Pleasant Street
Concord, NH 03301
P: (603) 271-9434

NEW JERSEY
Ms. Meghan Davey
Director
Division of Medical Assistance & Health Services
Department of Human Services
7 Quakerbridge Plaza, P.O. Box 712
Trenton, NJ 08625
P: (609) 588-2600
F: (609) 588-3583

NEW MEXICO
Ms. Nancy Smith-Leslie
Director
Medical Assistance Division
Department of Human Services
P.O. Box 2348
Santa Fe, NM 87504
P: (505) 827-6253

NEW YORK
Mr. Jason Helgerson
State Medicaid Director, Deputy Commissioner
Department of Health
Empire State Plaza
Corning Tower, Room 1466
Albany, NY 12237
P: (518) 474-3018

NORTH CAROLINA
Mr. Dave Richard
Deputy Secretary for Medical Assistance
Department of Health & Human Services
1985 Umstead Drive
2501 Mail Service Center
Raleigh, NC 27699
P: (919) 855-4100
E: dave.richard@dhhs.nc.gov

NORTH DAKOTA
Ms. Maggie D. Anderson
Executive Director
Department of Human Services
600 East Boulevard Avenue
Department 325
Bismarck, ND 58505
P: (701) 328-2538
F: (701) 328-2359
E: dhseo@nd.gov

NORTHERN MARIANA ISLANDS
Ms. Helen Sablan
Medicaid Director
Medicaid Program
Caller Box 10007
Saipan, MP 96950
P: (670) 664-4890
F: (670) 664-4885
E: dlnrgov@vzpacifica.net

OHIO
Ms. Barbara Sears
Director
Department of Medicaid
50 West Town Street, 4th Floor
Columbus, OH 43215
P: (614) 466-4443

OKLAHOMA
Ms. Becky Pasternik-Ikard
Medicaid Director
Health Care Authority
4345 North Lincoln Boulevard
Oklahoma City, OK 73105
P: (405) 522-7365

OREGON
Ms. Lori Coyner
Medicaid Director
State Health Authority
500 Summer Street, Northeast, E49
Salem, OR 97301
P: (503) 945-5768

PENNSYLVANIA
Ms. Leesa M. Allen
Executive Medicaid Director
Department of Public Welfare
Office of the Secretary
331 Health & Welfare Building
Harrisburg, PA 17120
P: (717) 787-2600

PUERTO RICO
Ms. Luz E. Cruz-Romero
Interim Executive Director
Medicaid Program
Department of Health
P.O. Box 70184
San Juan, PR 00936
P: (787) 765-2929 Ext. 6700

RHODE ISLAND
Mr. Patrick Tigue
Medicaid Director
Executive Office, Health & Human Services
74 West Road, 1st Floor
Hazard Building
Cranston, RI 02920
P: (401) 462-2121

SOUTH CAROLINA
Ms. Deirdra Singleton
Acting Director
Department of Health & Human Services
1801 Main Street
P.O. Box 8206
Columbia, SC 29201
P: (803) 898-2504

SOUTH DAKOTA
Ms. Johanna Barraza-Cannon
Interim Director, Medical Services
Department of Social Services
700 Governors Drive Kneip Building
Pierre, SD 57501
P: (605) 773-3495

TENNESSEE
Dr. Wendy Long
Director of TennCare & Deputy Commissioner
Department of Finance & Administration
310 Great Circle Road
Nashville, TN 37243
P: (800) 342-3145

TEXAS
Ms. Jami Snyder
Associate Commissioner, Medicaid/CHIP Division
Medical & Social Services
Health & Human Services Commission
4900 Lamar Boulevard
Austin, TX 78751
P: (512) 424-6500

U.S. VIRGIN ISLANDS
Ms. Renee Joseph-Rhymer
Director
Medical Assistance Program
Department of Human Services
1303 Hospital Ground, Building A
St. Thomas, VI 00802
P: (340) 774-0930

UTAH
Mr. Nathan Checketts
Interim Deputy Director
Department of Health
P.O. Box 143101
Salt Lake City, UT 84114
P: (801) 538-6689

VERMONT
Mr. Cory Gustafson
Commissioner
Department of State Health Access
280 State Drive
Waterbury, VT 05671
P: (802) 879-5901

VIRGINIA
Ms. Cynthia B. Jones
Director
Department of Medical Assistance Services
600 East Broad Street, Suite 1300
Richmond, VA 23219
P: (804) 786-8099
E: cindi.jones@dmas.virginia.gov

WASHINGTON
Ms. MaryAnne Lindeblad
Director
Health Care Authority
626 8th Avenue
P.O. Box 45502
Olympia, WA 98504
P: (360) 725-1040

WEST VIRGINIA
Ms. Cynthia Beane
Acting Commissioner
Bureau of Medical Services
Department of Health & Human Resources
350 Capitol Street, Room 251
Charleston, WV 25301
P: (304) 558-1700

WISCONSIN
Mr. Michael Heifetz
Medicaid Director
Department of Health Services
1 West Wilson Street, Room 350
P.O. Box 309
Madison, WI 53701
P: (608) 266-5151
E: michael.heifetz@wisconsin.gov

WYOMING
Ms. Teri Green
State Medicaid Agent
Department of Health
6101 Yellowstone Road, Suite 210
Cheyenne, WY 82009
P: (307) 777-7531
F: (307) 777-6964

Mental Health

Administers the mental services of the state and/or plans and coordinates programs for persons with mental illness.

ALABAMA
Mr. James Perdue
Commissioner
Department of Mental Health
100 North Union Street
Montgomery, AL 36130
P: (334) 242-3640
F: (334) 242-0684
E: James.perdue@mh.alabama.gov

ALASKA
Mr. Randall Burns
Director
Division of Behavioral Health
Department of Health & Social Services
3601 C Street, Suite 878
Anchorage, AK 99503
P: (907) 269-3600
F: (907) 269-3623
E: randall.burns@alaska.gov

AMERICAN SAMOA
Dr. Taeaoafua Meki Solomona
Director
Department of Human & Social Services
P.O. Box 997534
Pago Pago, AS 96799
P: (684) 633-1664
F: (684) 633-7449
E: mtsolomona@dhss.as

ARIZONA
Mr. Thomas J. Betlach
Director
Division of Behavioral Health Services
Department of Health Services
801 East Jefferson, MD 4100
Phoenix, AZ 85034
P: (602) 417-4711
F: (602) 252-6536
E: thomas.betlach@azahcccs.gov

ARKANSAS
Ms. Paula Stone
Interim Director
Division of Behavioral Health Services
305 South Palm Street
Little Rock, AR 72205
P: (501) 686-9981
F: (501) 686-9182
E: paula.stone@dhs.arkansas.gov

CALIFORNIA
Ms. Dina Kokkos-Gonzales
Chief
Mental Health Services Division
Department of Health Care Services
1501 Capitol Avenue, MS 2702
Sacramento, CA 95899
P: (916) 440-7974
E: dina.kokkos-gonzales@dhcs.ca.gov

COLORADO
Dr. Nancy VanDeMark
Director
Office of Behavioral Health
Department of Human Services
1575 Sherman Street, 8th Floor
Denver, CO 80203
P: (303) 866-5700
F: (303) 866-5563
E: nancy.vandemark@state.co.us

CONNECTICUT
Dr. Miriam E. Delphin-Rittmon
Commissioner
Department of Mental Health & Addiction Services
410 Capitol Avenue
P.O. Box 341431
Hartford, CT 06134
P: (860) 418-6676
F: (860) 418-6691
E: Miriam.delphin-rittmon@ct.gov

DELAWARE
Dr. Michael A. Barbieri
Director, Division of Substance Abuse & Mental Health
Health & Social Services
1901 North DuPont Highway
Main Building
New Castle, DE 19720
P: (302) 255-9399
F: (302) 255-4427
E: michael.barbieri@state.de.us

DISTRICT OF COLUMBIA
Dr. Tanya Royster
Director
Department of Behavioral Health
64 New York Avenue, Northeast
Washington, DC 20002
P: (202) 673-2246
E: tanya.royster@dc.gov

FLORIDA
Mr. John Bryant
Director
Substance Abuse & Mental Health
Department of Children & Families
1317 Winewood, Building 6, Room 291
Tallahassee, FL 32399
P: (850) 921-9355
E: john.bryant@myflfamilies.com

GEORGIA
Ms. Judy Fitzgerald
Commissioner
Department of Behavioral Health & Developmental Disabilities
2 Peachtree Street, Northwest
Suite 24.290
Atlanta, GA 30303
P: (404) 463-7945
F: (770) 408-5480
E: judy.fitzgerald@dbhdd.ga.gov

GUAM
Mr. Rey Vega
Director
Department of Mental Health & Substance Abuse
790 Gov. Carlos Camancho Road
Tamuing, GU 96913
P: (671) 647-1901
F: (671) 647-6948
E: rey.vega@mail.dmhsa.guam.gov

HAWAII
Ms. Lynn N. Fallin
Deputy Director
Behavioral Health Administration
Department of Health
1250 Punchbowl Street, Director's Office
Honolulu, HI 96813
P: (808) 586-4416
F: (808) 586-4368
E: lynn.fallin@doh.hawaii.gov

IDAHO
Mr. Ross Edmunds
Administrator
Division of Behavioral Health
Department of Health & Welfare
450 West State Street
Boise, ID 83720
P: (208) 334-5726
F: (208) 334-5998
E: edmundsr@dhw.idaho.gov

ILLINOIS
Ms. Diana Knaebe
Director
Division of Mental Health
Department of Human Services
319 East Madison, Suite 3B
Springfield, IL 60601
P: (217) 782-0071
E: diana.knaebe@illinois.gov

INDIANA
Mr. Kevin Moore
Director
Division of Mental Health & Addiction
Family & Social Services Administration
402 West Washington Street, Room W353
Indianapolis, IN 46204
P: (317) 232-7860
F: (317) 233-1986
E: kevin.moore@fssa.in.gov

IOWA
Mr. Rick Shults
Division Administrator
Division of Mental Health & Disability Services
Department of Human Services
Hoover Building 5SE, 1305 East Walnut
Des Moines, IA 50319
P: (515) 281-8580
F: (515) 242-6036
E: rshults@dhs.state.ia.us

KANSAS
Ms. Susan Fout
Commissioner
Behavioral Health Services
Aging & Disability Services
503 South Kansas Avenue
Topeka, KS 66603
P: (785) 368-7338
E: susan.fout@ks.gov

KENTUCKY
Ms. Wendy Morris
Commissioner
Department for Behavioral Health, Development & Intellectual Disabilities
100 Fair Oaks Lane
Frankfort, KY 40601
P: (502) 564-4527
E: wendy.morris@ky.gov

LOUISIANA
Dr. James Hussey
Assistant Secretary/Medical Director; MH Commissioner
Office of Behavioral Health
Department of Health
P.O. Box 629
Baton Rouge, LA 70821
P: (225) 342-8916
F: (225) 342-3875
E: James.Hussey@LA.gov

MAINE
Mr. Sheldon Wheeler
Director
Office of Substance Abuse & Mental Health Services
Department of Health & Human Services
41 Anthony Avenue
Augusta, ME 04333
P: (207) 287-2595
F: (207) 287-4334
E: Sheldon.wheeler@maine.gov

MARYLAND
Dr. Barbara Bazron
Executive Director
Behavioral Health Administration, Department of Health & Mental Hygiene
Spring Grove Hospital Center
Dix Building, 55 Wade Avenue
Catonsville, MD 21228
P: (410) 402-8452
F: (410) 402-8441
E: barbara.bazron@maryland.gov

MASSACHUSETTS
Ms. Joan Mikula
Commissioner
Department of Mental Health
25 Staniford Street
Boston, MA 02114
P: (617) 626-8123
F: (617) 626-8225
E: joan.mikula@massmail.state.ma.us

MICHIGAN
Ms. Lynda Zeller
Deputy Director
Behavioral Health & Developmental Disabilities Administration
Department of Community Health
320 South Walnut Street
Lansing, MI 48913
P: (517) 335-0196
F: (517) 335-4798
E: zellerl2@michigan.gov

MINNESOTA
Ms. Claire Wilson
Assistant Commissioner
Department of Human Services
P.O. Box 64988
Saint Paul, MN 55164
P: (651) 431-2323
E: claire.wilson@state.mn.us

MISSISSIPPI
Ms. Diana Mikula
Executive Director
Department of Mental Health
1101 Robert E. Lee Building
239 North Lamar Street
Jackson, MS 39201
P: (601) 359-1288
F: (601) 359-6295
E: diana.mikula@dmh.state.ms.us

MISSOURI
Mr. Mark G. Stringer
Director
Department of Mental Health
1706 East Elm Street
Jefferson City, MO 65102
P: (573) 522-1475
F: (573) 751-7814
E: mark.stringer@dmh.mo.gov

MONTANA
Ms. Zoe Barnard
Administrator
Addictive & Mental Disorders Division
100 North Park
Helena, MT 59620
P: (406) 444-7044
E: zbarnard@mt.gov

NEBRASKA
Ms. Sheri Dawson
Acting Director
Division of Behavioral Health
Department of Health & Human Services
301 Centennial Mall South, 3rd Floor
Lincoln, NE 68509
P: (402) 471-8553
F: (402) 471-9449
E: sheri.dawson@nebraska.gov

NEVADA
Ms. Cody Phinney
Administrator
Division of Public & Behavioral Health
4150 Technology Way
Carson City, NV 89706
P: (775) 684-4200
F: (775) 684-4211
E: cphinney@health.nv.gov

NEW HAMPSHIRE
Ms. Michele Harlan
Director of Mental Health
Department of Health & Human Services
105 Pleasant Street
Concord, NH 03301
P: (603) 271-8376
E: michele.a.harlan@dhhs.state.nh.us

NEW JERSEY
Ms. Valerie Mielke
Assistant Commissioner
Division of Mental Health & Addiction Services
Department of Human Services
P.O. Box 700
Trenton, NJ 08625
P: (609) 292-3717
F: (609) 341-2302
E: Valerie.mielke@dhs.state.nj.us

NEW MEXICO
Dr. Wayne W. Lindstrom
Director
Behavioral Health Services Division
Department of Health
P.O. Box 2348
Santa Fe, NM 87504
P: (505) 476-9295
F: (505) 476-9272
E: wayne.lindstrom@state.nm.us

NEW YORK
Dr. Ann Marie T. Sullivan
Commissioner
State Office of Mental Health
44 Holland Avenue
Albany, NY 12229
P: (518) 474-4403
F: (518) 474-2149
E: ann.sullivan@omh.ny.gov

NORTH CAROLINA
Dr. Jason Vogler
Interim Senior Director
Mental Health, Developmental Disabilities & Substance Abuse Services
306 North Wilmington Street
Raleigh, NC 27601
P: (919) 715-2019
E: jason.vogler@dhhs.nc.gov

NORTH DAKOTA
Ms. Pam Sagness
Director
Division of Behavioral Health
Department of Human Services
1237 West Divide Avenue, Suite 1C
Bismarck, ND 58501
P: (701) 328-8824
F: (701) 328-8969
E: psagness@nd.gov

OHIO
Ms. Tracy J. Plouck
Director
Department of Mental Health & Addiction Services
30 East Broad Street, 36th Floor
Columbus, OH 43215
P: (614) 466-2337
F: (614) 752-9453
E: tracy.plouck@mha.ohio.gov

OKLAHOMA
Ms. Terri White
Commissioner
Department of Mental Health & Substance Abuse Services
Executive Department
P.O. Box 53277
Oklahoma City, OK 73152
P: (405) 522-3877
F: (405) 522-0637
E: tlwhite@odmhsas.org

Mental Health and Mental Retardation

OREGON
Mr. Royce Bowlin
Behavioral Health Director
State Health Authority
Health Policy & Analytics
421 Southwest Oak Street, Suite 775
Portland, OR 97204
P: (614) 466-2337
E: royce.a.bowlin@state.or.us

PENNSYLVANIA
Mr. Dennis Marion
Deputy Secretary
Office of Mental Health & Substance Abuse Services
Department of Public Welfare
20 Azalea Drive
Harrisburg, PA 17105
P: (717) 787-6443
F: (717) 787-5394
E: dmarion@pa.gov

PUERTO RICO
Ms. Carmen Graulau
Administrator
Mental Health Services
P.O. Box 607087
Bayamon, PR 00960
P: (787) 763-7575
F: (787) 765-5858
E: tquintana@assmca.pr.gov

RHODE ISLAND
Ms. Rebecca Boss
Acting Director
Department of Behavioral Healthcare
14 Harrington Road
Cranston, RI 02920
P: (401) 462-0917
E: rebecca.boss@bhddh.ri.gov

SOUTH CAROLINA
Mr. John H. Magill
State Director
Department of Mental Health
Office of State Director
2414 Bull Street, Suite 321
Columbia, SC 29201
P: (803) 898-8319
F: (803) 898-1383
E: jhm03@scdmh.org

SOUTH DAKOTA
Ms. Tiffany Wolfgang
Division Director
Behavioral Health
Department of Social Services
811 East 10th Street, Department 9
Sioux Falls, SD 57103
P: (605) 367-5078
F: (605) 367-5239
E: Tiffany.Wolfgang@state.sd.us

TENNESSEE
Ms. Marie Williams
Commissioner
Department of Mental Health & Substance Abuse Services
Andrew Jackson Building
Nashville, TN 37243
P: (615) 253-3049
F: (615) 532-6514
E: Marie.Williams@tn.gov

TEXAS
Ms. Lauren Lacefield Lewis
Assistant Commissioner of Mental Health & Substance Abuse
Department of State Health Services
P.O. Box 149347
Austin, TX 78714
P: (512) 206-5145
F: (512) 206-5306
E: lauren.lacefieldlewis@dshs.state.tx.us

U.S. VIRGIN ISLANDS
Ms. Berlina Wallace-Berube
Director of Mental Health
Department of Health
3500 Estate Richmond
Charles Harwood Complex
Christiansted, VI 00802
P: (340) 718-1311 Ext. 3755
E: berlina.wallace-berube@doh.vi.gov

UTAH
Mr. Doug Thomas
Director
Division of Substance Abuse & Mental Health
Department of Human Services
195 North 1950 West
Salt Lake City, UT 84116
P: (801) 538-4298
F: (801) 538-9892
E: dothomas@utah.gov

VERMONT
Ms. Meliss Bailey
Commissioner
Department of Mental Health
280 State Drive, NOB 2 North
Waterbury, VT 05671
P: (802) 241-0137
E: melissa.bailey@vermont.gov

VIRGINIA
Mr. Daniel Herr
Assistant Commissioner of Behavioral Health Services
Department of Behavioral Health & Developmental Services
1220 Bank Street
P.O. Box 1797
Richmond, VA 23218
E: daniel.herr@dbhds.virginia.gov

WASHINGTON
Chris Imhoff
Director
Division of Behavioral Health & Recovery
Department of Social & Health Services
P.O. Box 45050
Lacey, WA 98504
P: (360) 725-3770
F: (360) 725-2280
E: Chris.imhoff@dshs.wa.gov

WEST VIRGINIA
Ms. Beth J. Morrison
Director, Mental Health Services
DHHR/Bureau for Behavioral Health & Health Facilities
350 Capitol Street, Room 350
Charleston, WV 25301
P: (304) 356-4976
E: beth.j.morrison@wv.gov

WISCONSIN
Ms. Joyce Allen
Director, Bureau of Prevention Treatment & Recovery
Division of Mental Health & Substance Abuse Services,
Department of Health Services
1 West Wilson Street, Room #850
Madison, WI 53707
P: (608) 266-1351
F: (608) 266-2579
E: joyce.allen@wisconsin.gov

WYOMING
Ms. Chris Newman
Senior Administrator
Behavioral Health Division
Department of Health
6101 Yellowstone Road, Suite 220
Cheyenne, WY 82002
P: (307) 777-6494
F: (307) 777-5849
E: chris.newman@wyo.gov

Minority Affairs

Serves as an advocate for state minority communities and promotes minority business enterprises within the state.

AMERICAN SAMOA
Dr. Taeaoafua Meki Solomona
Director
Department of Human & Social Services
P.O. Box 997534
Pago Pago, AS 96799
P: (684) 633-1664
F: (684) 633-7449
E: mtsolomona@dhss.as

ARIZONA
Ms. Sandra Watson
President & CEO
Commerce Authority
118 North 7th Avenue, Suite 400
Phoenix, AZ 85007
P: (602) 845-1215
F: (602) 845-1201
E: commerce@azcommerce.com

CONNECTICUT
Ms. Melody A. Currey
Commissioner
Department of Administrative Services
450 Columbus Boulevard
Hartford, CT 06103
P: (860) 713-5100
F: (860) 713-7481
E: Melody.Currey@ct.gov

IDAHO
Ms. Linda L. Goodman
Administrator
Human Rights Commission
317 West Main Street, Second Floor
Boise, ID 83735
P: (208) 334-2873
F: (208) 334-2664
E: Linda.Goodman@labor.idaho.gov

INDIANA
Ms. Terrie F. Daniel
Deputy Commissioner
Minority & Women's Business Enterprises
Department of Administration
402 West Washington Street, Room W479
Indianapolis, IN 46204
P: (317) 232-3061
F: (317) 233-6921
E: mwbe@idoa.in.gov

IOWA
Ms. Kristin H. Johnson
Executive Director
Civil Rights Commission
Grimes State Office Building
400 East 14th Street
Des Moines, IA 50319
P: (515) 281-4576
F: (515) 242-5840
E: Kristin.Johnson2@iowa.gov

KANSAS
Ms. Adrienne Foster
Executive Director
Hispanic & Latino American Affairs Commission
900 Southwest Jackson, Room 100
Topeka, KS 66612
P: (785) 296-3465
F: (785) 296-8118
E: khlaac@ks.gov

KENTUCKY
Mr. John J. Johnson
Executive Director
Commission on Human Rights
332 West Broadway, 7th Floor
Louisville, KY 40202
P: (502) 595-4024
F: (502) 595-4801
E: john.johnson@ky.gov

LOUISIANA
Mr. Patrick Bell
Assistant Commissioner
Division of Diversity & Opportunity
Department of Insurance
P.O. Box 94214
Baton Rouge, LA 70802
P: (225) 342-8393
F: (225) 342-4652
E: pbell@ldi.la.gov

MAINE
Ms. Joyce Oreskovich
Director
Bureau of Human Resources
#4 State House Station
Burton M. Cross Building, 4th Floor
Augusta, ME 04333
P: (207) 624-7761
F: (207) 287-4414
E: joyce.a.oreskovich@maine.gov

MARYLAND
Mr. Jimmy Rhee
Special Secretary
Governor's Office of Small, Minority & Women Business Affairs
100 Community Place, 3rd Floor
Crownsville, MD 21032
P: (410) 697-9600
E: jimmy.rhee@maryland.gov

MASSACHUSETTS
Ms. Sandra E. Borders
Director
Office of Diversity & Equal Opportunity
One Ashburton Place, Room 213
Boston, MA 02108
P: (617) 727-7441
F: (617) 878-9830

MINNESOTA
Mr. Kevin Lindsey
Commissioner
Department of Human Rights
Freeman Building
625 Robert Street, North
St. Paul, MN 55155
P: (651) 539-1100
F: (651) 296-9042
E: Kevin.Lindsey@state.mn.us

MISSOURI
Mr. Seth Bauman
Director
Office of Equal Opportunity
301 West High Street, Room 630
P.O. Box 809
Jefferson City, MO 65102
P: (573) 751-8130
F: (573) 522-8078

NORTH DAKOTA
Ms. Michelle Kommer
Commissioner of Labor
Department of Labor & Human Rights
600 East Boulevard Avenue
Department 406
Bismarck, ND 58505
P: (701) 328-2660
F: (701) 328-2031
E: mkommer@nd.gov

OHIO
Mr. G. Michael Payton
Executive Director
Civil Rights Commission
Rhodes State Office Tower
30 East Broad Street, 5th Floor
Columbus, OH 43215
P: (614) 466-2785
F: (614) 644-8776
E: paytonm@ocrc.state.oh.us

OKLAHOMA
Ms. Lucinda Meltabarger
Administrator
Human Capital Management Division
2101 North Lincoln Boulevard
Room G-80
Oklahoma City, OK 73105
P: (405) 521-3928
F: (405) 524-6942
E: lucinda.meltabarger@omes.ok.gov

OREGON
Ms. Serena Stoudamire-Wesley
Director of Diversity, Equity and Inclusion
Office of the Governor
160 State Capitol, 900 Court Street
Salem, OR 97301
P: (503) 378-6833

SOUTH CAROLINA
Mr. Thomas J. Smith
Executive Director
Commission for Minority Affairs
2221 Devine Street, Suite 408
Columbia, SC 29205
P: (803) 832-8160
F: (803) 333-9627
E: tsmith@cfma.sc.gov

SOUTH DAKOTA
Mr. Steve Emery
Secretary of Tribal Relations
Department of Tribal Relations
302 East Dakota Street
Pierre, SD 57501
P: (605) 773-3415
F: (605) 773-6592

TENNESSEE
Ms. Beverly L. Watts
Executive Director
Human Rights Commission
312 Rosa L. Parks Avenue, 23rd Floor
Nashville, TN 37243
P: (615) 741-5825
F: (615) 253-1886
E: ask.thrc@tn.gov

VIRGINIA
Ms. Tracey Wiley
Director
Department of Small Business & Supplier Diversity
101 North 14th Street, 11th Floor
Richmond, VA 23219
P: (804) 786-6585
F: (804) 786-9736
E: tracey.jeter@sbsd.virginia.gov

Minority Affairs

WEST VIRGINIA
Dr. Darrell Cummings
Chair
Human Rights Commission
1321 Plaza East, Room 108A
Charleston, WV 25301
P: (304) 558-2616
F: (304) 558-0085

WISCONSIN
Mr. Robert A. Rodriguez
Administrator
Division of Equal Rights
201 East Washington Avenue
P.O. Box 8928
Madison, WI 53708
P: (608) 266-3345
F: (608) 267-4592
E: erinfo@dwd.wisconsin.gov

Motor Vehicle Administration

Issues and maintains all records related to motor vehicle registration, operators' licenses and certificates of titles in the state.

ALABAMA
Mr. Stan Stabler
Acting Secretary of Law Enforcement
Law Enforcement Agency
301 South Ripley Street
P.O. Box 1511
Montgomery, AL 36102
P: (334) 517-2800
F: (334) 242-0512

ALASKA
Colonel James Cockrell
Director
Division of State Troopers
Department of Public Safety
5700 East Tudor Road
Anchorage, AK 99507
P: (907) 269-5511
F: (907) 337-2059
E: james.cockrell@alaska.gov

Ms. Marla Thompson
Director
Division of Motor Vehicles
Department of Administration
1300 West Benson Boulevard, Suite 900
Anchorage, AK 99503
P: (907) 269-5559
E: marla.thompson@alaska.gov

AMERICAN SAMOA
Mr. Le'i S. Thompson
Commissioner
Department of Public Safety
American Samoa Government
P.O. Box 1086
Pago Pago, AS 96799
P: (684) 633-1111
F: (684) 633-7296
E: lei.thompson@dps.as.gov

ARIZONA
Mr. Eric Jorgensen
Director
Motor Vehicle Division
Department of Transportation
P.O. Box 2100, MD 555M
Phoenix, AZ 85001
P: (602) 255-0072
F: (602) 712-6539

Colonel Frank Milstead
Director
Department of Public Safety
2222 West Encanto Boulevard
Phoenix, AZ 85009
P: (602) 223-2000
F: (602) 223-2917

ARKANSAS
Mr. Roger Duren
Administrator of Motor Vehicles
Office of Motor Vehicles
Ragland Building
1900 West 7th Street, Suite 1100
Little Rock, AR 72201
P: (501) 682-4692
F: (501) 682-4756
E: roger.duren@dfa.arkansas.gov

Ms. Tonie Shields
Administrator of Driver Services
Office of Driver Services
Ragland Building
1900 West 7th Street, Room 2067
Little Rock, AR 72201
P: (501) 371-5581
F: (501) 682-7688
E: tonie.shields@dfa.arkansas.gov

Mr. Larry Walther
Director
Department of Finance & Administration
1509 West 7th Street
DFA Building, Room 401
Little Rock, AR 72201
P: (501) 682-2242
F: (501) 682-1029
E: larry.walther@dfa.arkansas.gov

CALIFORNIA
Mr. Joseph A. Farrow
Commissioner
Highway Patrol
601 North 7th Street
P.O. Box 942898
Sacramento, CA 94298
P: (916) 843-3001
F: (916) 843-3264

Ms. Jean Shiomoto
Director
Department of Motor Vehicles
2415 1st Avenue, Mail Station F101
Sacramento, CA 95818
P: (916) 657-6940
F: (916) 657-2096
E: jshiomoto@dmv.ca.gov

DELAWARE
Colonel Nathaniel McQueen Jr.
Commissioner
State Police
1441 North DuPont Highway
Dover, DE 19901
P: (302) 739-5960

Mr. Scott Vien
Director
Division of Motor Vehicles
303 Transportation Circle
P.O. Box 698
Dover, DE 19903
P: (302) 744-2500

DISTRICT OF COLUMBIA
Ms. Lucinda M. Babers
Director
Department of Motor Vehicles
P.O. Box 90120
Washington, DC 20090
P: (202) 737-4404
E: dmv@dc.gov

FLORIDA
Ms. Terry L. Rhodes
Executive Director
Department of Highway Safety & Motor Vehicles
2900 Apalachee Parkway, M.S. 01
Tallahassee, FL 32399
P: (850) 617-3100
F: (850) 922-6274
E: executivedirector@flhsmv.gov

GEORGIA
Mr. Spencer R. Moore
Commissioner
Department of Driver Services
2206 East View Parkway
P.O. Box 80447
Conyers, GA 30013
P: (678) 413-8654
F: (678) 413-8661
E: smoore3@dds.ga.gov

Ms. Georgia Steele
Director
Motor Vehicle Division
Department of Revenue
4125 Welcome All Road
Atlanta, GA 30354
P: (404) 417-7680
E: georgia.steele@dor.ga.gov

GUAM
Mr. Steve Aguon
Supervisor, Vehicle Registration
Department of Revenue & Taxation
Motor Vehicle Division
P.O. Box 23607
GMF, GU 96921
P: (671) 635-7652
F: (671) 633-2643
E: steve.aguon@revtax.guam.gov

HAWAII
Mr. Ford Fuchigami
Director
Department of Transportation
869 Punchbowl Street
Honolulu, HI 96813
P: (808) 587-2150
F: (808) 587-2167
E: ford.n.fuchigami@hawaii.gov

IDAHO
Mr. Alan Frew
Administrator
Motor Vehicles Division
3311 West State Street
P.O. Box 7129
Boise, ID 83707
P: (208) 334-4443
F: (208) 332-2063
E: alan.frew@itd.idaho.gov

ILLINOIS
Mr. Ernie Dannenberger
Director
Vehicle Services Department
Michael J. Howlett Building
501 South Second Street, Room 312
Springfield, IL 62756
P: (217) 785-3000
F: (217) 785-4727
E: edannenberger@ilsos.net

Mr. Rick Kurnick
Metro Director
Driver Services Department
17 North State, Suite 1100
Chicago, IL 60602
P: (312) 793-1010
F: (312) 814-2974

Mr. Michael J. Mayer
Downstate Director
Driver Services Department
2701 South Dirksen Parkway
Springfield, IL 62723
P: (217) 782-6212
F: (217) 785-2472
E: mmayer@lisos.net

Motor Vehicle Administration

Mr. Leo P. Schmitz
Director
State Police
801 South 7th Street, Suite 1100 – S
Springfield, IL 62703
P: (217) 782-7263
E: askisp@isp.state.il.us

INDIANA
Mr. Douglas G. Carter
Superintendent
State Police
Indiana Government Center North
100 North Senate Avenue
Indianapolis, IN 46204
P: (317) 232-8248
E: ISP@isp.in.gov

Mr. Peter Lacy
Commissioner
Bureau of Motor Vehicles
Government Center North
100 North Senate Avenue
Indianapolis, IN 46204
P: (317) 234-6846
E: PLacy@bmv.IN.gov

IOWA
Colonel Patrick J. Hoye
Bureau Chief
Governor's Traffic Safety Bureau
Department of Public Safety
215 East 7th Street
Des Moines, IA 50319
P: (515) 725-6120
F: (515) 725-6133
E: hoye@dps.state.ia.us

Mr. Mark Lowe
Director
Department of Transportation
800 Lincoln Way
Ames, IA 50010
P: (515) 237-3210
F: (515) 817-6508
E: mark.lowe@dot.iowa.gov

Ms. Roxann M. Ryan
Commissioner
Department of Public Safety
215 East 7th Street
Des Moines, IA 50319
P: (515) 725-6182
E: dpsinfo@dps.state.ia.us

KANSAS
Colonel Mark Bruce
Superintendent
Highway Patrol
122 Southwest 7th Street
Topeka, KS 66603
P: (785) 296-6800
F: (785) 296-3049

Mr. Samuel Williams
Secretary
Department of Revenue
Docking State Office Building, 2nd Floor
915 Southwest Harrison Street
Topeka, KS 66612
P: (785) 296-3909
F: (785) 296-7928

KENTUCKY
Mr. John-Mark Hack
Commissioner
Department of Vehicle Regulation
Transportation Cabinet
P.O. Box 2014
Frankfort, KY 40602
P: (502) 564-7000
F: (502) 564-6403

Mr. Greg Thomas
Acting Secretary
Transporation Cabinet
200 Mero Street
Frankfort, KY 40622
P: (502) 564-4890
F: (502) 564-4809
E: gregory.thomas@ky.gov

LOUISIANA
Colonel Kevin W. Reeves
Superintendent
State Police
Public Safety Services
7919 Independence Boulevard
Baton Rouge, LA 70806
P: (225) 925-6118

MAINE
Colonel Robert A. Williams
Chief
State Police
42 State House Station
45 Commerce Drive
Augusta, ME 04333
P: (207) 624-7200
E: robert.a.williams@maine.gov

MARYLAND
Colonel William Pallozzi
Superintendent
Department of State Police
1201 Reisterstown Road
Pikesville, MD 21208
P: (410) 653-4219
E: msp.superintendent@maryland.gov

Mr. Kevin C. Reigrut
Executive Secretary
Transportation Authority
2310 Broening Highway, Suite 150
Baltimore, MD 21224
P: (410) 537-1001 Ext. 71001
E: kcreigrut@mdta.state.md.us

MASSACHUSETTS
Ms. Erin C. Deveney
Registrar
Registry of Motor Vehicles
Department of Transportation
10 Park Plaza, Suite 4160
Boston, MA 02116
P: (857) 368-4636
F: (857) 368-0601

MICHIGAN
Colonel Kriste Kibbey Etue
Director
State Police
P.O. Box 30634
Lansing, MI 48909
P: (517) 332-2521
F: (517) 241-0991
E: EtueK@michigan.gov

The Honorable Ruth Johnson (R)
Secretary of State
Office of the Secretary of State
430 West Allegan Street, 4th Floor
Lansing, MI 48918
P: (517) 373-2510
F: (517) 373-0727
E: secretary@michigan.gov

MINNESOTA
Mr. Dawn Olson
Director
Driver & Vehicle Services Division
445 Minnesota Street, Suite 190
St. Paul, MN 55101
P: (651) 282-6555
F: (651) 296-3141
E: dawn.m.olson@state.mn.us

MISSISSIPPI
Mr. Marshall Fisher
Commissioner
Department of Public Safety
P.O. Box 958
Jackson, MS 39205
P: (601) 987-1212
F: (601) 987-1488
E: commissioner@mdps.state.ms.us

Mr. Herb Frierson
Commissioner
Department of Revenue
P.O. Box 1033
Jackson, MS 39215
P: (601) 923-7000
F: (601) 923-7423

MONTANA
Ms. Sarah Garcia
Administrator
Motor Vehicle Division
Department of Justice
302 North Roberts, P.O. Box 201430
Helena, MT 59620
P: (406) 444-3933
F: (406) 444-2086
E: mvd@mt.gov

Mr. Duane Williams
Administrator
Motor Carrier Services Division
Department of Transportation
P.O. Box 4639
Helena, MT 59604
P: (406) 444-7312
F: (406) 444-0800
E: duwilliams@mt.gov

NEBRASKA
Ms. Rhonda Lahm
Director
Department of Motor Vehicles
301 Centennial Mall South
P.O. Box 94789
Lincoln, NE 68509
P: (402) 471-2281
F: (402) 471-3920
E: rhonda.lahm@nebraska.gov

NEVADA
Ms. Terri L. Albertson
Director
Department of Motor Vehicles
555 Wright Way
Carson City, NV 89711
P: (775) 684-4549
F: (775) 684-4692

Colonel Dennis S. Osborn
Chief
Highway Patrol
Department of Public Safety
555 Wright Way
Carson City, NV 89711
P: (775) 687-5300

Mr. James Wright
Director
Department of Public Safety
555 Wright Way
Carson City, NV 89711
P: (775) 684-4808
F: (775) 684-4809

NEW HAMPSHIRE
Mr. John J. Barthelmes
Commissioner
Department of Safety
James H. Hayes Safety Building
33 Hazen Drive
Concord, NH 03305
P: (603) 223-3889
F: (603) 271-3903
E: john.barthelmes
@dos.nh.gov

Ms. Elizabeth Bielecki
Director
Division of Motor Vehicles
Department of Safety
23 Hazen Drive
Concord, NH 03305
P: (603) 227-4000
F: (603) 271-3903
E: nh.dmvhelp@dos.nh.gov

NEW JERSEY
Mr. Raymond P. Martinez
Chief Administrator
Motor Vehicle Commission
P.O. Box 160
Trenton, NJ 08666
P: (609) 292-6500
F: (609) 777-4171
E: raymond.martinez
@dot.state.nj.us

NEW MEXICO
Mr. John Monforte
Acting Secretary
Taxation & Revenue
Department
1100 South St. Francis Drive
Santa Fe, NM 87504
P: (505) 827-0700
F: (505) 827-0331

NEW YORK
Mr. Joseph D'Amico
Superintendent
State Police
1220 Washington Avenue,
Building 22
Albany, NY 12226
P: (518) 457-6721
E: nyspmail@troopers.ny.gov

Ms. Theresa L. Egan
Executive Deputy Commissioner
Department of Motor Vehicles
6 Empire State Plaza
Albany, NY 12228
P: (518) 474-0846
F: (518) 474-9578

NORTH CAROLINA
Mr. David Howard
Acting Commissioner & Chief
Deputy Secretary
Division of Motor Vehicles
Department of Transportation
1501 Mail Service Center
Raleigh, NC 27699
P: (919) 707-2800
F: (919) 733-9150
E: dlhoward@ncdot.gov

NORTH DAKOTA
Mr. Grant Levi
Director
Department of Transportation
608 East Boulevard Avenue
Bismarck, ND 58505
P: (701) 328-2581
F: (701) 328-0310
E: glevi@nd.gov

Mr. Mark Nelson
Deputy Director
Driver & Vehicle Services
Department of Transportation
608 East Boulevard Avenue
Bismarck, ND 58505
P: (701) 328-2500
F: (701) 328-0310
E: mnelson@nd.gov

NORTHERN MARIANA ISLANDS
Mr. Robert A. Guerrero
Commissioner
Department of Public Safety
Jose M. Sablan Building
Caller Box 10007
Saipan, MP 96950
P: (670) 664-9022
F: (670) 664-9027

OHIO
Colonel John Born
Director
Department of Public Safety
1970 West Broad Street
P.O. Box 182081
Columbus, OH 43218
P: (614) 466-3383
F: (614) 466-0433

Mr. Don Petit
Registrar
Bureau of Motor Vehicles
1970 West Broad Street
P.O. Box 16520
Columbus, OH 43216
P: (614) 387-3000
F: (614) 261-9601

Colonel Paul A. Pride
Superintendent
State Highway Patrol
1970 West Broad Street
P.O. Box 182074
Columbus, OH 43223
P: (614) 466-2990
E: wwwohp@dps.ohio.gov

OKLAHOMA
Mr. Roy Dockum
Executive Director
Motor Vehicle Commission
4334 Northwest Expressway
Suite 183
Oklahoma City, OK 73116
P: (405) 607-8227 Ext. 102
F: (405) 607-8989

OREGON
Mr. Thomas McClellan
Administrator
Division of Driver & Motor
Vehicle
1905 Lana Avenue, Northeast
Salem, OR 97314
P: (503) 945-5100
F: (503) 945-0893
E: thomas.l.mcclellan
@state.or.us

Ms. Amy Ramsdell
Administrator
Motor Carrier Transportation
Division
Department Of Transportation
3930 Fairview Industrial Drive
Southeast
Salem, OR 97302
P: (503) 373-1638
E: Amy.J.Ramsdell
@odot.state.or.us

PENNSYLVANIA
Colonel Tyree C. Blocker
Commissioner
State Police
1800 Elmerton Avenue
Harrisburg, PA 17110
P: (717) 783-5599
F: (717) 787-2948

Ms. Leslie S. Richards
Secretary
Department of Transportation
Keystone Building
400 North Street, Fifth Floor
Harrisburg, PA 17120
P: (717) 787-2838
F: (717) 787-5491
E: lsrichards@pa.gov

PUERTO RICO
Ms. Michelle M.
Hernandez De Fraley
Superintendent
Puerto Rico Police
601 Franklin Delano Roosevelt
Avenue
San Juan, PR 00936
P: (787) 793-1234

RHODE ISLAND
Mr. Walter Craddock
Administrator
Division of Motor Vehicles
Department of Revenue
600 New London Avenue
Cranston, RI 02920
P: (401) 462-5705
F: (401) 462-5784
E: walter.craddock
@dmv.ri.gov

SOUTH CAROLINA
Ms. Marcia S. Adams
Executive Director
Department of Administration
1200 Senate Street, Suite 600
Columbia, SC 29201
P: (803) 734-8120
F: (803) 734-2117
E: marcia.adams
@admin.sc.gov

Mr. Mark A. Keel
Chief
State Law Enforcement Division
4400 Broad River Road
Columbia, SC 29210
P: (803) 896-9223
F: (803) 896-7588

Motor Vehicle Administration

Colonel Michael Oliver
Commander
Highway Patrol
10311 Wilson Boulevard
P.O. Box 1993
Blythewood, SC 29016
P: (803) 896-7920
F: (803) 896-7922

SOUTH DAKOTA
Ms. Debra Hillmer
Director
Motor Vehicles Division
Department of Revenue
445 East Capitol Avenue
Pierre, SD 57501
P: (605) 773-3541
F: (605) 773-2550
E: motorv@state.sd.us

TENNESSEE
Ms. Paula Shaw
Executive Director
Motor Vehicle Commission
500 James Robertson Parkway
Nashville, TN 37243
P: (615) 741-2711
F: (615) 741-0651
E: Paula.J.Shaw@state.tn.us

Colonel Tracy Trott
Director
Highway Patrol
1150 Foster Avenue
Nashville, TN 37243
P: (615) 251-5175
F: (615) 532-1051

TEXAS
Ms. Whitney Brewster
Director
Department of Motor Vehicles
4000 Jackson Avenue
Austin, TX 78731
P: (512) 465-3000
F: (512) 465-4129

Mr. Steve McCraw
Director
Department of Public Safety
5805 North Lamar Boulevard
P.O. Box 4087
Austin, TX 78773
P: (512) 424-2000
F: (512) 483-5708

U.S. VIRGIN ISLANDS
Mr. Delroy Richards Sr.
Commissioner
Police Department
Farrelly Criminal Justice Center
Charlotte Amalie
St. Thomas, VI 00802
P: (340) 774-2211
F: (340) 715-5517

UTAH
Mr. Brad L. Simpson
Division Director
Division of Motor Vehicles
Tax Commission
210 North 1950 West
Salt Lake City, UT 84134
P: (801) 297-2200
F: (801) 297-3570
E: bsimpson@utah.gov

VERMONT
Colonel Matthew Birmingham
Director
State Police
45 State Drive
Waterbury, VT 05671
P: (802) 241-5260
E: Matthew.Birmingham@vermont.gov

Mr. Robert Ide
Commissioner
Department of Motor Vehicles
Agency of Transportation
120 State Street
Montpelier, VT 05602
P: (802) 828-2011
F: (802) 828-2170
E: Robert.Ide@vermont.gov

VIRGINIA
Mr. Richard D. Holcomb
Commissioner
Department of Motor Vehicles
P.O. Box 27412
Richmond, VA 23269
P: (804) 497-7100
F: (804) 367-2296
E: richard.holcomb@dmv.virginia.gov

WASHINGTON
Mr. John R. Batiste
Chief
State Patrol
General Administration Building
P.O. Box 42600
Olympia, WA 98504
P: (360) 596-4000
F: (360) 596-4128
E: john.batiste@wsp.wa.gov

Ms. Pat Kohler
Agency Director
Department of Licensing
P.O. Box 9020
Olympia, WA 98507
P: (360) 902-3600
F: (360) 902-4042
E: doldirector@dol.wa.gov

WEST VIRGINIA
Pat Reed
Commissioner
Division of Motor Vehicles
5707 MacCorkle Avenue, Southeast
Charleston, WV 25317
P: (304) 558-3900
F: (304) 926-3884
E: dot.dmvcommissioner@wv.gov

WISCONSIN
Ms. Kristina Boardman
Administrator
Division of Motor Vehicles
4802 Sheboygan Avenue
Madison, WI 53705
P: (608) 261-8605
F: (608) 267-3812
E: kristina.boardman@dot.wi.gov

Mr. J.D. Lind
Superintendent
Division of State Patrol
4802 Sheboygan Avenue, Room 551
P.O. Box 7912
Madison, WI 53707
P: (608) 266-3212
F: (608) 267-4495
E: JD.Lind@dot.wi.gov

WYOMING
Colonel Kebin Haller
Administrator
Highway Patrol
5300 Bishop Boulevard
Cheyenne, WY 82009
P: (307) 777-4301
F: (307) 777-3897

Mr. Bill Panos
Director
Department of Transportation
5300 Bishop Boulevard
Cheyenne, WY 82009
P: (307) 777-4484
F: (307) 777-4163
E: bill.panos@wyo.gov

Natural Resources

Formulates and coordinates policies to protect, develop, utilize, restore and enhance the state's natural resources.

ALABAMA
Mr. N. Gunter Guy Jr.
Commissioner of Conservation
Department of Conservation & Natural Resources
64 North Union Street
Montgomery, AL 36130
P: (334) 242-3486
E: dcnr.commissioner@dcnr.alabama.gov

ALASKA
Mr. Andrew T. Mack
Commissioner
Department of Natural Resources
550 West 7th Avenue, Suite 1400
Anchorage, AK 99501
P: (907) 269-8431
F: (907) 269-8918
E: andrew.mack@alaska.gov

AMERICAN SAMOA
Mr. Va'amua Henry Sespasara
Director
Department of Marine & Wildlife Resources
American Samoa Government
Pago Pago, AS 96799
P: (684) 633-4465
F: (684) 633-7552

ARIZONA
Mr. Fred Breedlove
Director
State Land Department, Natural Resources
1616 West Adams Street
Phoenix, AZ 85007
P: (602) 542-2693

ARKANSAS
Mr. Bruce Holland
Executive Director
Natural Resources Commission
101 East Capitol Avenue, Suite 350
Little Rock, AR 72201
P: (501) 682-3961
F: (501) 682-3991
E: bruce.holland@arkansas.gov

CALIFORNIA
Mr. John Laird
Secretary of Energy & Environment
Natural Resources Agency
1416 Ninth Street, Room 1311
Sacramento, CA 95814
P: (916) 653-5656
F: (916) 653-8102
E: secretary@resources.ca.gov

COLORADO
Mr. Bob Randall
Interim Executive Director
Department of Natural Resources
1313 Sherman Street, Room 718
Denver, CO 80203
P: (303) 866-3311
F: (303) 866-2115
E: Robert.Randall@state.co.us

CONNECTICUT
Mr. William Hyatt
Bureau Chief
Bureau of Natural Resources
79 Elm Street
Hartford, CT 06106
P: (860) 424-3010
F: (860) 424-4070
E: william.hyatt@ct.gov

DELAWARE
Mr. Shawn Garvin
Secretary
Department of Natural Resources & Environmental Control
89 Kings Highway
Dover, DE 19901
P: (302) 739-9000

DISTRICT OF COLUMBIA
Dr. Hamid Karimi
Deputy Director
Natural Resources Administration
1200 First Street Northeast
Washington, DC 20002
P: (202) 535-2277
E: hamid.karimi@dc.gov

FLORIDA
Mr. Ryan Matthews
Interim Secretary
Department of Environmental Protection
3900 Commonwealth Boulevard, M.S. 49
Tallahassee, FL 32399
P: (850) 245-2011

GEORGIA
Mr. Mark Williams
Commissioner & State Historic Preservation Officer
Department of Natural Resources
2 Martin Luther King Jr. Drive Southeast
Suite 1252, East Tower
Atlanta, GA 30334
P: (404) 656-3500
F: (404) 656-0770
E: Mark.Williams@dnr.ga.gov

GUAM
Ms. Mariquita F. Taitague
Director
Department of Agriculture
163 Dairy Road
Mangilao, GU 96913
P: (671) 734-3942
F: (671) 734-6569

HAWAII
Ms. Suzanne D. Case
Chairperson
Department of Land & Natural Resources
Kalanimoku Building
1151 Punchbowl Street
Honolulu, HI 96813
P: (808) 587-0400
F: (808) 587-0390
E: dlnr@hawaii.gov

IDAHO
Mr. John Tippets
Director
Department of Environmental Quality
1410 North Hilton
Boise, ID 83706
P: (208) 373-0240
F: (208) 373-0417
E: john.tippets@deq.idaho.gov

ILLINOIS
Mr. Wayne Rosenthal
Director
Department of Natural Resources
One Natural Resources Way
Springfield, IL 62702
P: (217) 782-6302
F: (217) 785-9236
E: wayne.rosenthal@illinois.gov

INDIANA
Mr. Cameron F. Clark
State Historic Preservation Officer & Director
Department of Natural Resources
402 West Washington Street, Room W256
Government Center South
Indianapolis, IN 46204
P: (317) 232-4020
F: (317) 233-6811
E: dhpa@dnr.in.gov

IOWA
Mr. Chuck Gipp
Director
Department of Natural Resources
4th Floor, Wallace Building
502 East 9th Street
Des Moines, IA 50319
P: (515) 725-8282
F: (515) 281-8895
E: chuck.gipp@dnr.iowa.gov

KANSAS
Mr. Rob Reschke
Executive Director
Division of Conservation
Department of Agriculture
1320 Research Park Drive
Manhattan, KS 66502
P: (785) 564-6621
F: (785) 564-6778
E: robert.reschke@kda.ks.gov

KENTUCKY
Mr. Allen Luttrell
Commissioner
Department of Natural Resources
2 Hudson Hollow
Frankfort, KY 40601
P: (502) 564-6940
F: (502) 564-5698
E: allten.luttrell@ky.gov

LOUISIANA
Mr. Thomas Harris
Secretary
Department of Natural Resources
P.O. Box 94396
Baton Rouge, LA 70804
P: (225) 342-2710
F: (225) 342-3790
E: thomas.harris@la.gov

Natural Resources

MAINE
Mr. Walter E. Whitcomb
Commissioner
Department of Agriculture, Conservation & Forestry
Harlow Building - AMHI Complex
28 State House Station
Augusta, ME 04333
P: (207) 287-3419
F: (207) 287-7548
E: dacf@maine.gov

MARYLAND
Mr. Mark Belton
Secretary
Department of Natural Resources
Tawes State Office Building C4
580 Taylor Avenue
Annapolis, MD 21401
P: (410) 260-8101
F: (410) 260-8111

MASSACHUSETTS
Mr. Leo Roy
Commissioner
Department of Conservation & Recreation
Office of Energy & Environmental Affairs
251 Causeway Street, Suite 600
Boston, MA 02114
P: (617) 626-1250
F: (617) 626-1351
E: mass.parks@state.ma.us

MICHIGAN
Mr. Keith Creagh
Director
Department of Natural Resources
Executive Division
P.O. Box 30028
Lansing, MI 48909
P: (517) 284-6367
E: DNR-Director@michigan.gov

MINNESOTA
Mr. Tom Landwehr
Commissioner
Department of Natural Resources
500 Lafayette Road
St. Paul, MN 55155
P: (651) 296-6157
F: (651) 296-4799
E: Tom.Landwehr@state.mn.us

MISSISSIPPI
Mr. Gary Rikard
Executive Director
Department of Environmental Quality
P. O. Box 2261
Jackson, MS 39225
P: (601) 961-5000
F: (601) 961-5093
E: gary_rikard@deq.state.ms.us

MISSOURI
Ms. Carol S. Comer
Director
Department of Natural Resources
1101 Riverside Drive
P.O. Box 176
Jefferson City, MO 65102
P: (573) 751-4732
F: (573) 751-7627
E: carol.comer@ded.mo.gov

MONTANA
Mr. John Tubbs
Director
Department of Natural Resources & Conservation
1539 Eleventh Avenue
P.O. Box 201601
Helena, MT 59620
P: (406) 444-2074
F: (406) 444-2684

NEBRASKA
Mr. Gordon W. Fassett
Director
Department of Natural Resources
301 Centennial Mall South
P.O. Box 94676
Lincoln, NE 68509
P: (402) 471-2366
F: (402) 471-2900
E: jeff.fassett@nebraska.gov

NEVADA
Mr. Bradley Crowell
Director
Department of Conservation & Natural Resources
901 South Stewart Street, Suite 1003
Carson City, NV 89701
P: (775) 684-2700
F: (775) 684-2715
E: bcrowell@dcnr.nv.gov

NEW JERSEY
Mr. Rich Boornazian
Assistant Commissioner
Natural & Historic Resources
Mail Code 501-03A
P.O. Box 420
Trenton, NJ 08625
P: (609) 292-3541
E: richard.boornazian@dep.state.nj.us

NEW MEXICO
Mr. Ken McQueen
Cabinet Secretary
Energy, Minerals & Natural Resources Department
1220 South St. Francis Drive
Santa Fe, NM 87505
P: (505) 476-3200
F: (505) 476-3220
E: ken.mcqueen@state.nm.us

NEW YORK
Mr. Basil Seggos
Commissioner
Department of Environmental Conservation
625 Broadway
Albany, NY 12233
P: (518) 402-8545
F: (518) 402-8541

NORTH CAROLINA
Ms. Susi H. Hamilton
Secretary
Department of Natural & Cultural Resources
109 East Jones Street
Mail Service Center 4601
Raleigh, NC 27601
P: (919) 807-7300

NORTH DAKOTA
Mr. Greg Link
Division Chief
Conservation & Communications Division
Game & Fish Department
100 North Bismarck Expressway
Bismarck, ND 58501
P: (701) 328-6331
F: (701) 328-6352
E: ndgf@nd.gov

OHIO
Mr. James J. Zehringer
Director
Department of Natural Resources
2045 Morse Road
Columbus, OH 43229
P: (614) 265-6565
F: (614) 261-9601

OKLAHOMA
Mr. Michael Teague
Secretary of Energy & Environment
Office of the Secretary of Energy & Environment
204 North Robinson, Suite 1010
Oklahoma City, OK 73102
P: (405) 522-7099
F: (405) 530-8999
E: ee@ee.ok.gov

OREGON
Mr. Ray Jaindl
Director of Natural Resources Program Area
Department of Agriculture
635 Capitol Street, Northeast
Salem, OR 97301
P: (503) 986-4713
E: rjaindl@oda.state.or.us

PENNSYLVANIA
Ms. Cindy Adams Dunn
Secretary
Department of Conservation & Natural Resources
400 Market Street, 7th Floor
Harrisburg, PA 17105
P: (717) 787-2869
F: (717) 705-2832

PUERTO RICO
Ms. Tania Vazquez Rivera
Secretary
Department of Natural & Environmental Resources
P.O. Box 366147
San Juan, PR 00936
P: (787) 999-2200
F: (787) 999-2303

RHODE ISLAND
Mr. Larry Mouradjian
Associate Director
Department of Environmental Management
Bureau of Natural Resources
235 Promenade Street
Providence, RI 02908
P: (401) 222-4700 Ext. 2414
F: (401) 222-3162
E: larry.mouradjian@dem.ri.gov

SOUTH CAROLINA
Mr. Alvin A. Taylor
Director
Department of Natural Resources
1000 Assembly Street
P.O. Box 167
Columbia, SC 29202
P: (803) 734-4007
F: (803) 734-9809
E: taylora@dnr.sc.gov

SOUTH DAKOTA
Mr. Steven M. Pirner
Secretary
Department of Environment & Natural Resources
Joe Foss Building
523 East Capital Avenue
Pierre, SD 57501
P: (605) 773-5559
F: (605) 773-6035
E: denrinternet@state.sd.us

TENNESSEE
Mr. Brock Hill
Deputy Commissioner
Bureau of Parks & Conservation
312 Rosa L. Parks Avenue
Nashville, TN 37243
P: (615) 532-0696
F: (615) 741-8858

TEXAS
Dr. Bryan W. Shaw
Chair
Commission on Environmental Quality
12100 Park 35 Circle
P.O. Box 13087
Austin, TX 78711
P: (512) 239-5510
F: (512) 239-5533
E: bryan.shaw@tceq.texas.gov

U.S. VIRGIN ISLANDS
Mr. Lloyd Bough Jr.
Commissioner
Department of Planning & Natural Resources
Cyril E. King Airport
Terminal Building, 2nd Floor
St. Thomas, VI 00802
P: (340) 774-3320
F: (340) 773-1082

VERMONT
Ms. Julie Moore
Secretary
Agency of Natural Resources
103 South Main Street, Center Building
Waterbury, VT 05671
P: (802) 828-1294
F: (802) 244-1102
E: julie.moore@vermont.gov

VIRGINIA
Ms. Molly Ward
Secretary
Office of the Secretary of Natural Resources
1111 East Broad Street
P.O. Box 1475
Richmond, VA 23218
P: (804) 786-0044
F: (804) 371-8333
E: molly.ward@governor.virginia.gov

WASHINGTON
The Honorable Hilary Franz (D)
Commissioner of Public Lands
Department of Natural Resources
111 Washington Street, Southeast
P.O. Box 47000
Olympia, WA 98504
P: (360) 902-1000
F: (360) 902-1775
E: cpl@dnr.wa.gov

WEST VIRGINIA
Mr. Stephen S. McDaniel
Director
Division of Natural Resources
324 Fourth Avenue, Building 74
South Charleston, WV 25303
P: (304) 558-2754
F: (304) 558-2768

WISCONSIN
Ms. Cathy Stepp
Secretary
Department of Natural Resources
101 South Webster Street
P.O. Box 7921
Madison, WI 53707
P: (608) 266-2121
F: (608) 266-6983
E: DNRSecretary@Wisconsin.gov

WYOMING
Mr. Bob Budd
Executive Director
Wildlife & Natural Resource Trust
Hathaway Building, 1st Floor
2300 Capitol Avenue, Suite 117
Cheyenne, WY 82002
P: (307) 777-8024

Occupational Safety

Enforces safety standards for the protection of employees in places of employment.

ALABAMA
Mr. Fitzgerald Washington
Secretary
Department of Labor
649 Monroe Street
Montgomery, AL 36131
P: (334) 242-8055
E: fwashington@labor.alabama.gov

ALASKA
Ms. Deborah Kelly
Director
Division of Labor Standards & Safety
Labor & Workforce Development
P.O. Box 111149
Juneau, AK 99811
P: (907) 465-4855
F: (907) 465-6012
E: deborah.kelly@alaska.gov

AMERICAN SAMOA
Mr. Esenaeiaso J. Liu
Director
Department of Human Resources
Executive Office Building
AP Lutali, 2nd Floor
Pago Pago, AS 96799
P: (684) 644-4485
F: (684) 633-1139
E: eseneiaso.liu@hr.as.gov

ARIZONA
Mr. James Ashley
Director
Industrial Commission
800 West Washington Street
Phoenix, AZ 85007
P: (602) 542-4411
F: (602) 542-7889

CALIFORNIA
Ms. Juliann Sum
Acting Chief
Division of Occupational Safety & Health
Department of Industrial Relations
1515 Clay Street, 19th Floor
Oakland, CA 94612
P: (510) 286-7000
F: (510) 286-7037
E: jsum@dir.ca.gov

CONNECTICUT
Mr. Scott D. Jackson
Commissioner
Department of Labor
200 Folly Brook Boulevard
Westerfield, CT 06109
P: (860) 263-6000
F: (850) 263-6529
E: scott.jackson@ct.gov

DELAWARE
Mr. James G. Cagle Jr.
Director
Division of Industrial Affairs
Department of Labor
4425 North Market Street, 3rd Floor
Wilmington, DE 19802
P: (302) 761-8200
F: (302) 761-6601

DISTRICT OF COLUMBIA
Mr. Odie Donald II
Director
Department of Employment Services
4058 Minnesota Avenue, Northeast
Washington, DC 20019
P: (202) 724-7000
F: (202) 673-6993
E: does@dc.gov

FLORIDA
Mr. Tanner Holloman
Director
Division of Workers' Compensation
Department of Financial Services
200 East Gaines Street
Tallahassee, FL 32399
P: (850) 413-1600
E: Tanner.Holloman@myfloridacfo.com

GUAM
Mr. Manuel Q. Cruz
Director
Department of Labor
Government of Guam
P.O. Box 9970
Tamuning, GU 96931
P: (671) 475-7044
F: (671) 674-6517

HAWAII
Ms. Linda Chu Takayama
Director
Department of Labor & Industrial Relations
830 Punchbowl Street
Honolulu, HI 96813
P: (808) 586-8844
F: (808) 586-9099
E: dlir.director@hawaii.gov

ILLINOIS
Ms. Carolyn Parks
Executive Director
Workers' Compensation Commission
100 West Randolph Street, Suite 8-200
Chicago, IL 60601
P: (312) 814-6638
E: carolyn.parks@illinois.gov

INDIANA
Mr. Rick J. Ruble
Commissioner
Department of Labor
402 West Washington Street, Room W195
Indianapolis, IN 46204
P: (317) 232-2655
F: (317) 233-3790
E: rruble@dol.in.gov

IOWA
Mr. Michael A. Mauro
Commissioner
Division of Labor Services
150 Des Moines Street
Des Moines, IA 50309
P: (515) 725-5601
F: (515) 281-4698
E: michael.mauro@iwd.iowa.gov

KANSAS
Ms. Lana Gordon
Secretary of Labor
Department of Labor
401 Southwest Topeka Boulevard
Topeka, KS 66603
P: (785) 296-5000
F: (785) 368-5289
E: lana.gordon@dol.ks.gov

Mr. Terri Sanchez
Director
Industrial Safety & Health Division
Department of Labor
401 Southwest Topeka Boulevard
Topeka, KS 66603
P: (785) 296-4386
F: (785) 296-1775
E: indsafetyhealth@dol.ks.gov

KENTUCKY
Mr. Mike Dixon
Executive Director
Occupational Safety & Health Program
1047 US Highway 127 South
Suite 4
Frankfort, KY 40601
P: (502) 564-3070
F: (502) 696-1902

LOUISIANA
Ms. Sheral Kellar
Director
Office of Workers' Compensation Administration
Workforce Commission
P.O. Box 94040
Baton Rouge, LA 70804
P: (225) 342-7555
F: (225) 342-5665
E: owca@lwc.la.gov

MAINE
Mr. Steve Greeley
Director
Workplace Safety Division
Department of Labor
45 State House Station
Augusta, ME 04333
P: (207) 623-7900
F: (207) 623-7934
E: mdol@maine.gov

MARYLAND
Mr. William E. Dallas
Assistant Commissioner
Department of Labor, Licensing & Regulation
Occupational Safety & Health
10946 Golden West Drive, Suite 160
Hunt Valley, MD 21031
P: (410) 527-2065
F: (410) 527-4481
E: william.dallas@maryland.gov

MASSACHUSETTS
Mr. Daniel Bennett
Secretary
Executive Office of Public Safety & Security
One Ashburton Place, Suite 2133
Boston, MA 02108
P: (617) 727-7775
F: (617) 727-4764
E: eopsinfo@state.ma.us

MICHIGAN
Mr. Bart Pickelman
Acting Director
Occupational Safety & Health Administration
530 West Allegan Street
P.O. Box 30643
Lansing, MI 48909
P: (517) 284-7771
F: (517) 322-1775
E: pickelmanb@michigan.gov

MINNESOTA
Mr. Ken Peterson
Commissioner
Department of Labor & Industry
443 Lafayette Road North
St. Paul, MN 55155
P: (651) 284-5010
F: (651) 284-5720
E: DLI.workcomp@state.mn.us

MISSOURI
Ms. Anna Hui
Director
Department of Labor & Industrial Relations
421 East Dunklin Street
P.O. Box 504
Jefferson City, MO 65102
P: (573) 751-4091
F: (573) 751-4135
E: diroffice@labor.mo.gov

MONTANA
Ms. Pam Bucy
Commissioner
Department of Labor & Industry
P.O. Box 1728
Helena, MT 59624
P: (406) 444-2840
F: (406) 444-1419
E: dliquestions@mt.gov

NEBRASKA
Ms. Courtney Dentlinger
Director
Department of Economic Development
301 Centennial Mall South
P.O. Box 94666
Lincoln, NE 68509
P: (402) 471-3746
F: (402) 471-3778
E: courtney.dentlinger@nebraska.gov

NEVADA
Mr. Joseph D. Decker
Administrator
Division of Industrial Relations
400 West King Street, Suite 400
Carson City, NV 89703
P: (775) 684-7270
F: (775) 687-6305

NEW HAMPSHIRE
Mr. Ken Merrifield
Commissioner
Department of Labor
95 Pleasant Street
Concord, NH 03301
P: (603) 271-3176

NEW JERSEY
Mr. Howard Black
Director
Division of Public Safety & Occupational Safety & Health
Labor & Workforce Development
P.O. Box 110
Trenton, NJ 08625
P: (609) 292-0501

NEW MEXICO
Mr. Bob Genoway
Bureau Chief
Occupational Health & Safety Bureau
525 Camino De Los Marquez, Suite 3
P.O. Box 5469
Santa Fe, NM 87505
P: (505) 476-8718
F: (505) 476-8734
E: Robert.Genoway@state.nm.us

NEW YORK
Ms. Roberta Reardon
Commissioner
Department of Labor
W. Averell Harriman State Office Campus
Building 12
Albany, NY 12240
P: (518) 457-9000
F: (518) 485-6297
E: roberta.reardon@labor.state.ny.us

NORTH CAROLINA
Mr. Kevin Beauregard
Director
Occupational Safety & Health Division
Department of Labor
1101 Mail Service Center
Raleigh, NC 27699
P: (919) 807-2900
E: kevin.beauregard@labor.nc.gov

NORTH DAKOTA
Mr. Nick Jolliffe
Director
Loss Control Department
Workforce Safety & Insurance
1600 East Century Avenue, Suite 1
Bismarck, ND 58503
P: (800) 777-5033
F: (701) 328-3820
E: njolliffe@nd.gov

OHIO
Ms. Jacqueline Williams
Director
Department of Commerce
77 South High Street, 23rd Floor
Columbus, OH 43215
P: (614) 644-7047
E: director.office@com.state.oh.us

OKLAHOMA
Ms. Betsey Kulakowski
Assistant Director, Public Employee Occupational Safety and Health
Department of Labor
3017 North Stiles, Suite 100
Oklahoma City, OK 73105
P: (405) 521-6277
F: (405) 521-6018
E: betsey.kulakowski@labor.ok.gov

OREGON
Mr. Michael Wood
Division Administrator
Occupational Safety & Health Division
350 Winter Street, Northeast, Room 430
P.O. Box 14480
Salem, OR 97309
P: (503) 947-7400
F: (503) 947-7461
E: michael.wood@oregon.gov

PENNSYLVANIA
Ms. Jennifer Berrier
Director
Bureau of Occupational & Industrial Safety
1613 Labor & Industry Building
651 Boas Street
Harrisburg, PA 17121
P: (717) 783-6304
F: (717) 787-8363

PUERTO RICO
Mr. Carlos J. Saavedra Gutierrez
Secretary
Department of Labor & Human Resources
P.O. Box 195540
San Juan, PR 00919
P: (787) 754-5353
F: (787) 753-9550

RHODE ISLAND
Mr. Scott Jensen
Director
Department of Labor & Training
Center General Complex
1511 Pontiac Avenue
Cranston, RI 02920
P: (401) 462-8000
F: (401) 462-8872
E: director-dlt@dlt.ri.gov

SOUTH CAROLINA
Ms. Emily Farr
Director
Department of Labor, Licensing & Regulation
110 Centerview Drive
P.O. Box 11329
Columbia, SC 29211
P: (803) 896-4300
F: (803) 896-4393
E: ContactLLR@llr.sc.gov

SOUTH DAKOTA
Mr. James E. Marsh
Director
Division of Labor & Management
Department of Labor & Regulation
700 Governors Drive
Pierre, SD 57501
P: (605) 773-3681
F: (605) 773-4211
E: james.marsh@state.sd.us

TENNESSEE
Mr. Steve Hawkins
Administrator
Occupational Safety & Health Administration
Labor and Workforce Development
220 French Landing Drive
Nashville, TN 37243
P: (615) 741-2793
F: (615) 741-3325
E: Steve.Hawkins@tn.gov

Occupational Safety

Mr. Burns Phillips
Commissioner
Department of Labor &
Workforce Development
220 French Landing Drive
Nashville, TN 37243
P: (844) 224-5818
F: (615) 741-5078
E: burns.phillips@tn.gov

TEXAS
Dr. John Hellerstedt
Commissioner
Department of State Health
Services
1100 West 49th Street
P.O. Box 149347
Austin, TX 78714
P: (512) 776-7363
F: (512) 776-7477

U.S. VIRGIN ISLANDS
Ms. Catherine Ann Hendry
Commissioner of Labor
Department of Labor
4401 Sion Farm, Suite 1
Christiansted, VI 00820
P: (340) 773-1994
F: (340) 713-3415
E: chendry@vidol.gov

UTAH
Mr. Chris Hill
Director
Occupational Safety & Health
Division
Labor Commission
P.O. Box 146650
Salt Lake City, UT 84114
P: (801) 362-3113
F: (801) 530-7606
E: chill@utah.gov

VERMONT
Mr. Dan Whipple
Manager
VOSHA
Department of Labor
P.O. Box 488
Montpelier, VT 05601
P: (802) 828-5084
F: (802) 828-4022
E: dan.whipple@vermont.gov

VIRGINIA
Mr. Todd Haymore
Secretary of Commerce & Trade
Office of Commerce & Trade
1111 East Broad Street
P.O. Box 1475
Richmond, VA 23218
P: (804) 786-7831
F: (804) 371-0250
E: Todd.Haymore
@governor.virginia.gov

WASHINGTON
Ms. Anne Soiza
Assistant Director
Division of Occupational Safety
& Health
Department of Labor &
Industries
P.O. Box 44600
Olympia, WA 98504
P: (360) 902-5090
F: (360) 902-5619
E: Anne.Soiza@LNI.wa.gov

WEST VIRGINIA
Mr. David W. Mullins
Commissioner
Division of Labor
Department of Commerce
749 B, Building 6, Capitol
Complex
Charleston, WV 25305
P: (304) 558-7890
F: (304) 558-2415

WISCONSIN
Ms. Laura Gutierrez
Secretary
Department of Safety &
Professional Services
P.O. Box 8935
Madison, WI 53708
P: (608) 266-2112
F: (608) 266-9946

WYOMING
Mr. Steven R. Czoschke
Executive Secretary
Workers' Compensation Medical
Commission
CenturyLink Building, Suite 190
6101 Yellowstone Road
Cheyenne, WY 82002
P: (307) 777-5422
F: (307) 777-5201

Oil & Gas Regulation

Regulates the drilling, operation, maintenance and abandonment of oil and gas wells in the state.

ALABAMA
Mr. Berry H. Tew Jr.
State Geologist & Oil and Gas Supervisor
Geological Survey of Alabama
State Oil & Gas Board
P.O. Box 869999
Tuscaloosa, AL 35486
P: (205) 349-2852
F: (205) 247-3676
E: ntew@gsa.state.al.us

ALASKA
Ms. Chantal Walsh
Director
Division of Oil & Gas
Department of Natural Resources
550 West 7th Avenue, Suite 1100
Anchorage, AK 99501
P: (907) 269-8800
F: (907) 269-8939
E: chantal.walsh@alaska.gov

ARKANSAS
Mr. Lawrence Bengal
Director
Oil & Gas Commission
301 Natural Resources Drive, Suite 102
Little Rock, AR 72205
P: (501) 683-5814
F: (501) 683-5818
E: Larry.Bengal@aogc.state.ar.us

CALIFORNIA
Mr. Ken Harris
State Oil & Gas Supervisor
Division of Oil, Gas & Geothermal Resources
801 K Street, MS 18-01
Sacramento, CA 95814
P: (916) 323-1779
F: (916) 323-0424

COLORADO
Mr. Matt Lepore
Director
Oil & Gas Conservation Commission
Department of Natural Resources
1120 Lincoln Street, Suite 801
Denver, CO 80203
P: (303) 894-2100
F: (303) 894-2109
E: Matt.Lepore@state.co.us

FLORIDA
Ms. Cindy Mulkey
Program Administrator
Oil & Gas Regulation
Department of Environmental Protection
2600 Blair Stone Road, MS 3588
Tallahassee, FL 32399
P: (850) 717-9110
F: (850) 245-8356
E: Cindy.Mulkey@dep.state.fl.us

GEORGIA
Dr. Becky Champion
Program Manager
Regulatory Support Program
Watershed Protection Branch
2 Martin Luther King Jr. Dr., Suite 1152
Atlanta, GA 30334
P: (404) 463-4950
F: (404) 656-2453
E: becky.champion@dnr.ga.gov

GUAM
Mr. Glenn Leon Guerrero
Director
Department of Public Works
542 North Marine Corp Drive
Tamuning, GU 96913
P: (671) 646-3131
F: (671) 649-6178
E: glenn.leonguerrero@dpw.guam.gov

IDAHO
Mr. Tom Schultz
Director
Department of Lands
300 North 6th Street, Suite 103
Boise, ID 83702
P: (208) 334-0200
F: (208) 334-3698
E: tschultz@idl.idaho.gov

ILLINOIS
Mr. Mike Mankowski
Director of Oil & Gas
Division of Oil & Gas
One Natural Resources Way
Springfield, IL 62702
P: (217) 782-7756
E: mike.mankowski@illinois.gov

IOWA
Ms. Geri Huser
Chair
Utilities Board
1375 East Court Avenue, Room 69
Des Moines, IA 50319
P: (515) 725-7888
F: (515) 725-7399
E: geri.huser@iub.iowa.gov

KANSAS
Mr. Ryan Hoffman
Director
Conservation Division (Oil & Gas)
Corporation Commission
266 North Main Street, Suite 220
Wichita, KS 67202
P: (316) 337-6200
F: (316) 337-6211

KENTUCKY
Mr. Dennis Hatfield
Director
Division of Oil & Gas
300 Sower Boulevard, 3rd Floor
Frankfort, KY 40601
P: (502) 782-6214
E: Dennis.Hatfield@ky.gov

LOUISIANA
Mr. David Elfert
Director
Geological Oil & Gas Division
617 North Third Street
P.O. Box 94275
Baton Rouge, LA 70804
P: (225) 342-5501
F: (225) 342-8199
E: David.Elfert@la.gov

MARYLAND
Ms. Hilary Miller
Director
Land Management Administration
Department of the Environment
1800 Washington Boulevard
Baltimore, MD 21230
P: (410) 537-3314
F: (410) 537-3321
E: hilary.miller@maryland.gov

MASSACHUSETTS
Mr. Martin Suuberg
Commissioner
Department of Environmental Protection
One Winter Street
Boston, MA 02108
P: (617) 292-5500
F: (617) 574-6880

MICHIGAN
Mr. Harold R. Fitch
Director
Office of Oil, Gas & Minerals
Department of Environmental Quality
P.O. Box 30256
Lansing, MI 48909
P: (517) 284-6823
F: (517) 241-1595
E: fitchh@michigan.gov

MINNESOTA
Mr. Daniel P. Wolf
Executive Secretary
Public Utilities Commission
121 Seventh Place East, Suite 350
St. Paul, MN 55101
P: (651) 201-2217
F: (651) 297-7073
E: dan.wolf@state.mn.us

MISSISSIPPI
Ms. Lisa Ivshin
Executive Director
Oil & Gas Board
500 Greymont Avenue, Suite E
Jackson, MS 39202
P: (601) 576-4920
F: (601) 352-2201
E: livshin@ogb.state.ms.us

MONTANA
Mr. Jim Halvorson
Administrator/Petroleum Geologist
Board of Oil & Gas
Billings Technical Office
2535 St. Johns Avenue
Billings, MT 59102
P: (406) 656-0040
F: (406) 655-6015

NEBRASKA
Mr. William H. Sydow
Director
Oil & Gas Conservation Commission
922 Illinois
P.O. Box 399
Sidney, NE 69162
P: (308) 254-6919
F: (308) 254-6922
E: bsydow@nogcc.ne.gov

Oil & Gas Regulation

NEW JERSEY
Mr. James P. Giuliano
Director
Division of Reliability & Security
Board of Public Utilities
44 South Clinton Avenue
Newark, NJ 08625
P: (609) 633-7341
F: (609) 341-5782
E: james.giuliano@bpu.state.nj.us

NEW MEXICO
Mr. David Catanach
Division Director
Oil Conservation Division
1220 South St. Francis Drive
Santa Fe, NM 87505
P: (505) 476-3460
F: (505) 476-3462

NEW YORK
Mr. Basil Seggos
Commissioner
Department of Environmental Conservation
625 Broadway
Albany, NY 12233
P: (518) 402-8545
F: (518) 402-8541

NORTH DAKOTA
Mr. Lynn D. Helms
Director
Oil & Gas Division
Industrial Commission, Department 405
600 East Boulevard Avenue
Bismarck, ND 58505
P: (701) 328-8020
F: (701) 328-8022
E: lhelms@nd.gov

OHIO
Mr. Richard Simmers
Chief
Division of Oil & Gas
Department of Natural Resources
2045 Morse Road, Building F-2
Columbus, OH 43229
P: (614) 265-6922
F: (614) 265-6910

OKLAHOMA
Mr. Tim Baker
Director
Oil & Gas Division
Corporation Commission
P.O. Box 52000
Oklahoma City, OK 73152
P: (405) 521-2240

PENNSYLVANIA
Mr. Scott Perry
Deputy Secretary
Office of Oil & Gas Management
Rachel Carson State Office Building
400 Market Street, 16th Floor
Harrisburg, PA 17101
P: (717) 783-9438
F: (717) 705-4087

RHODE ISLAND
Ms. Margaret E. Curran
Chair
Public Utilities Commission
89 Jefferson Boulevard
Warwick, RI 02888
P: (401) 941-4500
F: (401) 941-1691
E: margaret.curran@puc.ri.gov

SOUTH CAROLINA
Mr. Joe Gellici
Section Chief
Hydrology Section
Department of Natural Resources
1000 Assembly Street
Columbia, SC 29201
P: (803) 734-6428
F: (803) 734-9200
E: gellicij@dnr.sc.gov

TENNESSEE
Mr. Mike Burton
Supervisor
Oil & Gas Program
Environmental Field Office
711 R.S. Gass Boulevard
Nashville, TN 37243
P: (615) 687-7120
F: (615) 532-1517
E: Michael.K.Burton@tn.gov

UTAH
Mr. John Rogers
Associate Director
Division of Oil, Gas & Mining
1594 West North Temple, Suite 1210
P.O. Box 145801
Salt Lake City, UT 84114
P: (801) 538-5349
F: (801) 359-3940
E: johnrogers@utah.gov

VERMONT
Ms. Julie Moore
Secretary
Agency of Natural Resources
103 South Main Street, Center Building
Waterbury, VT 05671
P: (802) 828-1294
F: (802) 244-1102
E: julie.moore@vermont.gov

VIRGINIA
Mr. Rick Cooper
Director
Division of Gas & Oil
Department of Mines, Minerals & Energy
P.O. Drawer 159, 135 Highland Drive
Lebanon, VA 24266
P: (276) 415-9700
F: (276) 415-9671
E: DgoInfo@dmme.virginia.gov

WEST VIRGINIA
Mr. James Martin
Chief
Office of Oil & Gas
Department of Environmental Protection
601 57th Street Southeast, Room 2030
Charleston, WV 25304
P: (304) 926-0499
F: (304) 926-0452
E: James.A.Martin@wv.gov

WISCONSIN
Mr. Jeff Ripp
Administrator
Public Service Commission
610 North Whitney Way
Madison, WI 53707
P: (608) 267-9813
F: (608) 267-1381
E: Jeffrey.Ripp@wisconsin.gov

WYOMING
Mr. Mark Watson
Agency Director
Oil & Gas Conservation Commission
2211 King Boulevard
P.O. Box 2640
Casper, WY 82602
P: (307) 234-7147
F: (307) 234-5306
E: mark.watson@wyo.gov

Ombudsman

Investigates citizens' complaints about the administrative acts of any state agency.

ALABAMA
Ms. Pam Bye
Director of Constituent Services
Office of the Governor
600 Dexter Avenue
Montgomery, AL 36130
P: (334) 242-7100
F: (334) 353-0004
E: pam.bye@governor.alabama.gov

ALASKA
Ms. Linda Lord-Jenkins
Ombudsman
Office of the Ombudsman
333 West Fourth Avenue, Suite 305
Anchorage, AK 99501
P: (907) 269-5290
F: (907) 269-5291
E: linda.lord-jenkins@akleg.gov

ARIZONA
Mr. Dennis Wells
Ombudsman-Citizens' Aide
Office of the Ombudsman - Citizen's Aide
3737 North 7th Street, Suite 209
Phoenix, AZ 85014
P: (602) 277-7292
F: (602) 277-7312
E: ombuds@azoca.org

CALIFORNIA
The Honorable Elaine M. Howle
State Auditor
Bureau of State Audits
621 Capitol Mall, Suite 1200
Sacramento, CA 95814
P: (916) 445-0255 Ext. 342
F: (916) 323-0913
E: elaineh@bsa.ca.gov

COLORADO
Mr. Matt Steinkamp
Director
State Employee Assistance Programs
Department of Personnel & Administration
1525 Sherman Street, Suite 117
Denver, CO 80203
P: (303) 866-4314
F: (303) 866-4388
E: matt.steinkamp@state.co.us

DELAWARE
Mr. Joe Bryant
Constituent Relations Director
Office of the Governor
Tatnall Building
150 Martin Luther King Jr. Blvd., South
Dover, DE 19901
P: (302) 744-4101

DISTRICT OF COLUMBIA
Mr. Tommie Jones
Director
Mayor's Office of Community Relations & Services
1350 Pennsylvania Avenue, Northwest, 332
Washington, DC 20004
P: (202) 724-1516
E: tommie.jones@dc.gov

FLORIDA
Mr. Warren Davis
Director of Citizen Services
Office of the Governor
The Capitol
400 South Monroe Street
Tallahassee, FL 32399
P: (850) 488-7146
F: (850) 487-0801
E: Warren.Davis@eog.myflorida.com

HAWAII
Mr. Robin K. Matsunaga
Ombudsman
Office of the Ombudsman
465 South King Street, 4th Floor
Honolulu, HI 96813
P: (808) 587-0770
F: (808) 587-0773
E: complaints@ombudsman.hawaii.gov

IOWA
Ms. Kristie Hirschman
Ombudsman
Office of Ombudsman
Ola Babcock Miller Building
1112 East Grand
Des Moines, IA 50319
P: (515) 281-3592
F: (515) 242-6007
E: kristie.hirschman@legis.iowa.gov

KENTUCKY
Mr. Edward C. Monahan
Public Advocate
Department of Public Advocacy
100 Fair Oaks Lane, Suite 302
Frankfort, KY 40601
P: (502) 564-8006
F: (502) 564-7890

MAINE
Ms. Patricia A. Condon
Director of Constituent Services
Office of the Governor
#1 State House Station
Augusta, ME 04333
P: (207) 287-3531
F: (207) 287-1034

MISSISSIPPI
Mr. James Tucker
State Long-Term Care Ombudsman
Division of Aging & Adult Services
Department of Human Services
750 North State Street
Jackson, MS 39202
P: (601) 359-4927
E: james.tucker@mdhs.ms.gov

MISSOURI
The Honorable Michael Parson (R)
Lieutenant Governor
Office of the Lieutenant Governor
State Capitol, Room 224
Jefferson City, MO 65101
P: (573) 751-4727
F: (573) 526-8793

MONTANA
Mr. Tyler Campbell
Citizens' Advocate
Citizens' Advocate Office
State Capitol, Room 232
P.O. Box 200803
Helena, MT 59620
P: (406) 444-3468
E: citizensadvocate@mt.gov

NEBRASKA
Mr. Marshall Lux
Ombudsman
State Legislature
Room 807, State Capitol
P.O. Box 94604
Lincoln, NE 68509
P: (402) 471-2035
F: (402) 471-4277
E: ombud@leg.ne.gov

NEW HAMPSHIRE
Mr. Charles H. Weatherill
Ombudsman
Department of Health & Human Services
105 Pleasant Street
Concord, NH 03301
P: (603) 271-6941
F: (603) 271-4632
E: cweather@dhhs.state.nh.us

NORTHERN MARIANA ISLANDS
Mr. James Benedetto
Office of the Attorney General
P.O. Box 502452
Saipan, MP 96950
P: (670) 664-2333
F: (670) 664-2349
E: ombudsman@federal.com

PUERTO RICO
Ms. Iris Miriam Ruiz Class
Prosecutor
Office of the Ombudsman
P.O. Box 41088
San Juan, PR 00940
P: (787) 724-7373
F: (787) 724-7386
E: irismiriam.ruiz@opc.gobierno.pr

SOUTH DAKOTA
Ms. Sadie Stevens
Director of Constituent Services
Office of the Governor
500 East Capitol Avenue
Pierre, SD 57501
P: (605) 773-3212
F: (605) 773-4711

TEXAS
Mr. Gregory S. Davidson
Director
Constituent Communication Division
Office of the Governor
P.O. Box 12428
Austin, TX 78711
P: (512) 463-1800
F: (512) 463-1849

U.S. VIRGIN ISLANDS
Ms. Camille Paris
St. John Administrator
Office of the Governor
21-22 Kongens Gade
Charlotte Amalie
St. Thomas, VI 00802
P: (340) 774-0001
F: (340) 774-1361

UTAH
Ms. Tiffeni Wall
Constituent Services Director
Office of the Governor
350 North State Street, Suite 200
P.O. Box 142220
Salt Lake City, UT 84114
P: (801) 538-1000
E: tiffeniwall@utah.gov

Ombudsman

WEST VIRGINIA
Ms. Patricia Burdette
Director of Constituent Services
Office of the Governor
1900 Kanawha Boulevard, East
Charleston, WV 25305
P: (304) 558-2000
F: (304) 342-7025
E: Patricia.A.Burdette
@wv.gov

Parks and Recreation

Manages the state's parks, historical sites and recreational areas.

ALABAMA
Mr. Greg Lein
Director
State Parks Division
64 North Union Street, Room 538
Montgomery, AL 36130
P: (334) 242-3334
E: greg.lein@dcnr.alabama.gov

ALASKA
Mr. Matt Wedeking
Acting Director
Division of Parks & Outdoor Recreation
Department of Natural Resources
550 West 7th Avenue, Suite 1380
Anchorage, AK 99501
P: (907) 269-8700
F: (907) 269-8901
E: matthew.wedeking@alaska.gov

ARIZONA
Ms. Sue Black
Executive Director
State Parks
23751 North 23rd Avenue, #190
Phoenix, AZ 85085
P: (602) 542-4174
F: (602) 542-4188
E: sblack@azstateparks.gov

ARKANSAS
Mr. Grady Spann
Director
Department of Parks & Tourism
1 Capitol Mall, Room 4A-900
Little Rock, AR 72201
P: (501) 682-7777
F: (501) 682-1364
E: grandy.spann@arkansas.gov

CALIFORNIA
Ms. Lisa Mangat
Director
Department of Parks & Recreation
1416 Ninth Street
P.O. Box 942896
Sacramento, CA 94296
P: (916) 653-6995
F: (916) 654-6374
E: info@parks.ca.gov

COLORADO
Mr. Bob Broscheid
Director
Division of Parks & Wildlife
1313 Sherman Street, 6th Floor
Denver, CO 80203
P: (303) 866-3203
F: (303) 866-3206
E: bob.broscheid@state.co.us

CONNECTICUT
Mr. Tom Tyler
Director
DEP, State Parks Division
79 Elm Street
Hartford, CT 06106
P: (860) 424-3099
F: (860) 424-4070
E: tom.tyler@ct.gov

DELAWARE
Mr. Raymond E. Bivens
Director
Division of Parks & Recreation
89 Kings Highway
Dover, DE 19901
P: (302) 739-9200
F: (302) 739-3817
E: raymond.bivens@state.de.us

DISTRICT OF COLUMBIA
Mr. Keith A. Anderson
Director
Department of Parks & Recreation
1250 U Street Northwest, 2nd Floor
Washington, DC 20009
P: (202) 673-7647
F: (202) 673-2087
E: keith.anderson@dc.gov

GEORGIA
Ms. Becky Kelley
Director
State Parks & Historic Sites Division
2600 Highway 155, Southwest
Stockbridge, GA 30281
P: (770) 389-7277
F: (770) 389-7402
E: Becky.Kelley@dnr.ga.gov

HAWAII
Mr. Curt Cottrell
Administrator
Division of State Parks
Department of Land & Natural Resources
1151 Punchbowl Street
Honolulu, HI 96813
P: (808) 587-0290
F: (808) 587-0311

IDAHO
Mr. David Langhorst
Director
Department of Parks & Recreation
5657 Warm Springs Avenue
P.O. Box 83720
Boise, ID 83720
P: (208) 514-2250
F: (208) 334-5232
E: david.langhorst@idpr.idaho.gov

ILLINOIS
Mr. Wayne Rosenthal
Director
Department of Natural Resources
One Natural Resources Way
Springfield, IL 62702
P: (217) 782-6302
F: (217) 785-9236
E: wayne.rosenthal@illinois.gov

INDIANA
Mr. Daniel W. Bortner
Director
State Parks
Department of Natural Resources
402 West Washington Street, Room W298
Indianapolis, IN 46204
P: (317) 232-4136
F: (317) 232-4132
E: dbortner@dnr.IN.gov

IOWA
Mr. Todd Coffelt
Bureau Chief
State Parks
Department of Natural Resources
Wallace State Office Building
Des Moines, IA 50319
P: (515) 725-8485
F: (515) 281-6794
E: todd.coffelt@dnr.iowa.gov

KANSAS
Mr. Robin Jennison
Secretary
Department of Wildlife, Parks & Tourism
1020 South Kansas Avenue, Room 200
Topeka, KS 66612
P: (785) 296-2281
F: (785) 296-6953

KENTUCKY
Mr. Donnie Holland
Commissioner
State Parks
2 Hudson Hollow Road, Unit 1
Frankfort, KY 40601
P: (502) 564-2172
F: (502) 564-7015
E: donnie.holland@ky.gov

LOUISIANA
Mr. Robert J. Barham
Assistant Secretary
Office of State Parks
P.O. Box 44426
Baton Rouge, LA 70804
P: (225) 342-8111
F: (225) 342-8107
E: parks@crt.la.gov

MAINE
Mr. Tom Desjardin
Director of Parks & Lands
Bureau of Parks & Lands
22 State House Station
Augusta, ME 04333
P: (207) 287-4961
F: (207) 287-6170
E: Tom.Desjardin@maine.gov

MARYLAND
Ms. Nita Settina
Superintendent
Park Service
580 Taylor Avenue
Tawes State Office Building, E3
Annapolis, MD 21401
P: (410) 260-8186
F: (410) 260-8191
E: nita.settina@maryland.gov

MASSACHUSETTS
Ms. Priscilla H. Geigis
Director
Division of State Parks & Recreation
Department of Conservation & Recreation
251 Causeway Street, 9th Floor
Boston, MA 02114
P: (617) 626-4986
F: (617) 626-1351

Parks and Recreation

MICHIGAN
Mr. Ronald Olson
Chief
Parks & Recreation Division
Department of Natural Resources
P.O. Box 30257
Lansing, MI 48909
P: (517) 284-7275
F: (517) 373-4625
E: OlsonR@michigan.gov

MINNESOTA
Ms. Erika Rivers
Director
Division of Parks & Trails
500 Lafayette Road
St. Paul, MN 55155
P: (651) 259-5591
F: (651) 297-1157
E: erika.rivers@state.mn.us

NEBRASKA
Mr. Jim Swenson
Division Administrator
Parks Division
Game & Parks Commission
2200 North 33rd Street
Lincoln, NE 68503
P: (402) 471-5499
F: (402) 471-5528
E: jim.swenson@nebraska.gov

NEVADA
Mr. Eric Johnson
Administrator
Division of State Parks
901 South Stewart Street, Suite 5005
Carson City, NV 89701
P: (775) 684-2771
F: (775) 684-2777
E: stparks@parks.nv.gov

NEW HAMPSHIRE
Ms. Gail Wolek
Administrator
Division of Parks & Recreation
172 Pembroke Road
Concord, NH 03301
P: (603) 271-3556
F: (603) 271-3553
E: gail.wolek@DRED.NH.GOV

NEW JERSEY
Mr. Mark Texel
Director
State Park Service
Mail Code: 501-04
P.O. Box 420
Trenton, NJ 08625
P: (609) 292-2773
F: (609) 984-0503
E: Mark.Texel@dep.state.nj.us

NEW MEXICO
Ms. Christy Tafoya
Director
State Park Division
1220 South St. Francis Drive
Santa Fe, NM 87505
P: (505) 476-3355
F: (505) 476-3361
E: nm.parks@state.nm.us

NEW YORK
Ms. Rose Harvey
State Historic Preservation Officer & Commissioner
Office of Parks, Recreation & Historic Preservation
625 Broadway
Albany, NY 12207
P: (518) 474-0443
F: (518) 474-4492

NORTH CAROLINA
Mr. Mike Murphy
Director
State Parks System
121 West Jones Street
1615 Mail Service Center
Raleigh, NC 27699
P: (919) 707-9300
F: (919) 715-3085
E: michael.murphy@ncparks.gov

NORTH DAKOTA
Jesse Hanson
Interim Director
Parks & Recreation Department
1600 East Century Avenue, Suite 3
P.O. Box 5594
Bismarck, ND 58506
P: (701) 328-5357
F: (710) 328-5363
E: parkrec@nd.gov

OHIO
Mr. Michael D. Bailey
Chief
Division of Parks & Watercraft
2045 Morse Road, Building C-3
Columbus, OH 43229
P: (614) 265-6561
E: ohiostateparks@dnr.state.oh.us

OKLAHOMA
Ms. Kris Marek
Director of State Parks
Tourism & Recreation Department
P.O. Box 52002
Oklahoma City, OK 73152
P: (405) 230-8300
F: (405) 230-8500

OREGON
Ms. Lisa Sumption
Director & State Historic Preservation Officer
Parks & Recreation Department
725 Summer Street, Northeast, Suite C
Salem, OR 97301
P: (503) 986-0707
F: (503) 986-0794
E: jen.busey@oregon.gov

PENNSYLVANIA
Mr. John Hallas
Director
Bureau of State Parks
P.O. Box 8551
Harrisburg, PA 17105
P: (717) 787-6640

RHODE ISLAND
Mr. Robert Paquette
Chief
Division of Parks & Recreation
1100 Tower Hill Road
North Kingstown, RI 02852
P: (401) 667 6200
F: (401) 667 3970
E: dem.riparks@dem.ri.gov

SOUTH CAROLINA
Mr. Phil Gaines
Director
State Park Service
1205 Pendleton Street
Columbia, SC 29201
P: (803) 734-0345
F: (803) 734-1017
E: pgaines@scprt.com

SOUTH DAKOTA
Ms. Katie Ceroll
Director
Division of Parks & Recreation
Game, Fish & Parks
523 East Capitol Avenue
Pierre, SD 57501
P: (605) 773-3391
F: (605) 773-6245

TENNESSEE
Mr. Brock Hill
Deputy Commissioner
Bureau of Parks & Conservation
312 Rosa L. Parks Avenue
Nashville, TN 37243
P: (615) 532-0696
F: (615) 741-8858

TEXAS
Mr. Brent Leisure
Director of State Parks
State Parks
4200 Smith School Road
Austin, TX 78744
P: (512) 389-4866
F: (512) 389-4814

UTAH
Mr. Fred Hayes
Director
State Parks Office
Department of Natural Resources
1594 West North Temple, Suite 116
Salt Lake City, UT 84116
P: (801) 538-7336
F: (801) 538-7378
E: fredhayes@utah.gov

VERMONT
Mr. Craig Whipple
Director
Division of State Parks
Forests, Parks & Recreation
1 National Life Drive, Davis 2
Montpelier, VT 05620
P: (802) 343-5318
F: (802) 828-1399
E: craig.whipple@vermont.gov

VIRGINIA
Mr. Craig Seaver
Director
Division of State Parks
600 East Main Street
Richmond, VA 23219
P: (804) 786-5055
F: (804) 786-9294
E: craig.seaver@dcr.virginia.gov

WASHINGTON
Mr. Don Hoch
Director
State Parks & Recreation Commission
P.O. Box 42650
Olympia, WA 98504
P: (360) 902-8501
F: (360) 902-8681
E: Don.Hoch@parks.wa.gov

WEST VIRGINIA
Mr. Sam England
Chief
Parks & Recreation
324 4th Avenue
South Charleston, WV 25303
P: (304) 558-2764
F: (304) 558-0077
E: samuel.a.england@wv.gov

WISCONSIN
Mr. Ben Bergey
Manager
Bureau of Parks & Recreation
101 South Webster Street
P.O. Box 7921
Madison, WI 53707
P: (608) 266-2185
F: (607) 267-7474
E: benjamin.bergey
@wisconsin.gov

WYOMING
Mr. Domenic Bravo
Administrator
State Parks, Historic Sites &
Trails
2301 Central Avenue
Barrett Building, 4th Floor
Cheyenne, WY 82002
P: (307) 777-6323
F: (307) 777-6005

Parole and Probation (Adult)

Determines whether paroles should be granted or revoked and supervises adult parolees and probationers.

For more information contact:
American Probation & Parole Association
Veronica Cunningham
Executive Director
1776 Avenue of the States
Lexington, KY 40511
P: (859) 244-8216
F: (859) 244-8001
vcunningham@csg.org
www.appa-net.org

ALABAMA
Mr. Phil Bryant
Executive Director
Board of Pardons & Paroles
301 South Ripley Street
P.O. Box 302405
Montgomery, AL 36130
P: (334) 353-7771
F: (334) 353-9400

ALASKA
Mr. Jeffrey Edwards
Director
Parole Board
Department of Corrections
550 West Seventh Avenue, Suite 1800
Anchorage, AK 99501
P: (907) 269-4642
F: (907) 269-4697
E: jeffrey.edwards@alaska.gov

AMERICAN SAMOA
Mr. Le'i S. Thompson
Commissioner
Department of Public Safety
American Samoa Government
P.O. Box 1086
Pago Pago, AS 96799
P: (684) 633-1111
F: (684) 633-7296
E: lei.thompson@dps.as.gov

ARIZONA
Ms. Ellen Kirschbaum
Executive Director
Board of Executive Clemency
1645 West Jefferson Street, Suite 101
Phoenix, AZ 85007
P: (602) 542-5656
F: (602) 542-5680

ARKANSAS
Ms. Sheila Sharp
Director
State Community Correction
Two Union National Plaza
105 West Capitol Avenue
Little Rock, AR 72201
P: (501) 682-9510
F: (501) 682-9513
E: sheila.sharp@arkansas.gov

COLORADO
Mr. Joe Morales
Chair
State Board of Parole
1600 West 24th Street, Building 54
Pueblo, CO 81003
P: (719) 583-5800
E: joe.morales@state.co.us

CONNECTICUT
Mr. Richard Sparaco
Executive Director
Board of Pardons & Paroles
55 West Main Street
Waterbury, CT 06702
P: (203) 805-6634
F: (203) 805-6652
E: richard.sparaco@po.state.ct.us

DELAWARE
Mr. David Henderson
Chairperson
Board of Parole
820 North French Street
Carvel State Office Building, 4th Floor
Wilmington, DE 19801
P: (302) 577-5233
F: (302) 577-3501

DISTRICT OF COLUMBIA
Ms. Nancy M. Ware
Director
Court Services & Offender Supervision Agency
633 Indiana Avenue, Northwest
Washington, DC 20004
P: (202) 220-5300
F: (202) 220-5350

GEORGIA
Mr. Terry E. Barnard
Chair
Board of Pardons & Paroles
2 Martin Luther King Jr. Drive Southeast
Suite 458, Balcony Level, East Tower
Atlanta, GA 30334
P: (404) 656-4661
F: (404) 651-8502

GUAM
Mr. John Q. Lizama
Chief Probation Officer
Probation Services Division
Superior Court of Guam
120 West O'Brien Drive
Hagatna, GU 96910
P: (671) 475-3448
F: (671) 477-4944

HAWAII
Mr. Edmund "Fred" Hyun
Interim Chair
Paroling Authority
1177 Alakea Street, Ground Floor
Honolulu, HI 96813
P: (808) 587-1300
F: (808) 587-1314

IDAHO
Ms. Sandy Jones
Executive Director
Commission of Pardons & Parole
3056 Elder Street
Boise, ID 83705
P: (208) 334-2520
F: (208) 334-3501
E: sajones@idoc.idaho.gov

ILLINOIS
Mr. Jason Garnett
Chief of Parole
Parole Division
1301 Concordia Court
P.O. Box 19277
Springfield, IL 62794
P: (217) 558-2200

INDIANA
Ms. Gwen Horth
Chair
Parole Board
402 West Washington Street, Room W466
Indianapolis, IN 46204
P: (317) 232-5737
F: (317) 232-5738
E: GHorth@idoc.IN.gov

IOWA
Ms. Katrina Carter
Interim Deputy Director, Offender Services
Department of Corrections
Jessie Parker Building
510 East 12th Street
Des Moines, IA 50319
P: (515) 314-2645
E: katrina.carter@iowa.gov

KANSAS
Mr. Jonathan Ogletree
Chair
Prisoner Review Board
Department of Corrections
714 Southwest Jackson, Suite 300
Topeka, KS 66603
P: (785) 296-3469
F: (785) 296-7949
E: KDOC_PRB_Public_Commen@ks.gov

KENTUCKY
Ms. Lelia A. Vanhoose
Chair
Parole Board
P.O. Box 2400
Frankfort, KY 40602
P: (502) 564-3620
F: (502) 564-8995

LOUISIANA
Ms. Mary Fuentes
Executive Director
Board of Pardons & Parole
504 Mayflower Street, Building 6
P.O. Box 94304
Baton Rouge, LA 70804
P: (225) 342-6622
F: (225) 342-3701

MAINE
Mr. Willard Goodwin
Director
Adult Community Corrections
Department of Corrections
State House Station 111
Augusta, ME 04333
P: (207) 287-4380
F: (207) 287-4370

MARYLAND
Mr. Joseph F. Clocker
Director
Division of Parole & Probation
Public Safety & Correctional Services
6776 Reisterstown Road, Suite 305
Baltimore, MD 21215
P: (410) 585-3566
F: (410) 764-4091
E: joseph.clocker@maryland.gov

MICHIGAN
Mr. Michael Eagen
Chair
Parole Board
P.O. Box 30003
Lansing, MI 48909
P: (517) 373-0270
F: (517) 335-0039
E: EagenM@michigan.gov

MINNESOTA
Mr. Tom Roy
Commissioner
Department of Corrections
1450 Energy Park Drive, Suite 200
St. Paul, MN 55108
P: (651) 361-7200
F: (651) 642-0414
E: tom.roy@state.mn.us

MISSISSIPPI
Mr. Steve Pickett
Chair
State Parole Board
660 North Street, Suite 100A
Jackson, MS 39202
P: (601) 576-3520
F: (601) 576-3528
E: swpickett@mdoc.state.ms.us

MISSOURI
Ms. Julie Kempker
Chief State Supervisor
Division of Parole & Probation
Department of Corrections
3400 Knipp Drive
Jefferson City, MO 65109
P: (573) 751-8488
F: (573) 751-8501

NEBRASKA
Ms. Rosalyn Cotton
Chair
Board of Parole
P.O. Box 94754
Lincoln, NE 68509
P: (402) 471-2156
F: (402) 471-2453
E: rosalyn.cotton@nebraska.gov

NEVADA
Ms. Connie S. Bisbee
Chair
Board of Parole Commissioners
1677 Old Hot Springs Road, Suite A
Carson City, NV 89706
P: (775) 687-5049
F: (775) 687-6736
E: info@parole.nv.gov

NEW HAMPSHIRE
Mr. Michael McAlister
Director
Division of Field Services
Department of Corrections
P.O. Box 1806
Concord, NH 03302
P: (603) 271-5652
E: michael.mcalister@nhdoc.state.nh.us

NEW JERSEY
Mr. David W. Thomas
Executive Director
State Parole Board
P.O. Box 862
Trenton, NJ 08625
P: (609) 292-4257
F: (609) 943-4769

NEW MEXICO
Ms. Joann Martinez
Executive Director
Parole Board
45 Penitentiary Road
Santa Fe, NM 87508
P: (505) 827-8892
F: (505) 827-8933

NEW YORK
Ms. Tina M. Stanford
Chair
Board of Parole
97 Central Avenue
Albany, NY 12206
P: (518) 473-9548
F: (518) 473-6037
E: nysparole@parole.state.ny.us

NORTH DAKOTA
Ms. Leann Bertsch
Director
Department of Corrections & Rehabilitation
3100 Railroad Avenue
P.O. Box 1898
Bismarck, ND 58502
P: (701) 328-6390
F: (701) 328-6651
E: lbertsch@asca.net

NORTHERN MARIANA ISLANDS
Ms. Ursula I. Lifoifoi Aldan
Chief Probation Officer
Office of Adult Probation
Superior Court
P.O. Box 500307
Saipan, MP 96950
P: (670) 236-9870
F: (670) 236-9866
E: ualdan@hotmail.com

Mr. Eugene Villagomez
Chief Parole Officer
Board of Parole
P.O. Box 502641
Saipan, MP 95950
P: (670) 664-3300
F: (670) 664-3310
E: ualdan@hotmail.com

OKLAHOMA
Ms. Jari Askins
Interim Executive Director
Pardon & Parole Board
2915 North Classen, Suite 405
Oklahoma City, OK 73106
P: (405) 521-6600
F: (405) 602-6437

OREGON
Ms. Brenda Carney
Executive Director
Board of Parole & Post-Prison Supervision
2575 Center Street, Northeast
Suite 100
Salem, OR 97301
P: (503) 945-0919
F: (503) 373-7558
E: brenda.k.carney@doc.state.or.us

PENNSYLVANIA
Mr. Leo Dunn
Chair
Board of Probation & Parole
1101 South Front Street
Harrisburg, PA 17104
P: (717) 787-5699
F: (717) 772-2157

PUERTO RICO
Ms. Mercedes Peguero Moronta
President
Parole Board
Minillas Station
P.O. Box 40945
San Juan, PR 00940
P: (787) 754-8115
F: (787) 754-8181

RHODE ISLAND
Ms. Laura Pisaturo
Chair
Parole Board
Mathias Building, #56
12 Halligan Road
Cranston, RI 02920
P: (401) 462-0900
F: (401) 462-0915
E: parolebd@doc.ri.gov

SOUTH CAROLINA
Mr. Jerry B. Adger
Director
Department of Probation, Parole & Pardon Services
2221 Devine Street, Suite 600
P.O. Box 50666
Columbia, SC 29250
P: (803) 734-9278
F: (803) 734-9440

SOUTH DAKOTA
Mr. Doug Clark
Executive Director
Department of Corrections
Board of Pardons & Paroles
1600 North Drive, P.O. Box 5911
Sioux Falls, SD 57117
P: (605) 367-5040
F: (605) 367-5115

TENNESSEE
Mr. Richard Montgomery
Chair
Board of Parole
404 James Robertson Parkway
Suite 1300
Nashville, TN 37243
P: (615) 741-1150
F: (615) 532-8581
E: BOP.Webmail@tn.gov

TEXAS
Mr. David G. Gutierrez
Chair
Board of Pardons & Paroles
P. O. Box 13401
Austin, TX 78711
P: (512) 936-6351
F: (936) 291-8367
E: bpp_pio@tdcj.texas.gov

U.S. VIRGIN ISLANDS
The Honorable Michael C. Dunston
Presiding Judge
Superior Court
Farrelly Justice Center
P.O. Box 70
St. Thomas, VI 00804
P: (340) 774-6680
F: (340) 777-8187

Mr. Chesley Roebuck
Chair
Board of Parole
P.O. Box 2668
St. Thomas, VI 00802
P: (340) 778-2036
F: (340) 778-1637

Parole and Probation (Adult)

UTAH
Mr. James Hudspeth
Division Director
Adult Probation & Parole
Department of Corrections
14717 South Minuteman Drive
Draper, UT 84020
P: (801) 545-5901
F: (801) 545-5911
E: jhudspeth@utah.gov

VERMONT
Ms. Sue Blair
Director
Parole Board
Department of Corrections
152 South Main Street
Waterbury, VT 05671
P: (802) 241-0970
F: (802) 652-6538

VIRGINIA
Ms. Adrianne L. Bennett
Chair
Parole Board
6900 Atmore Drive
Richmond, VA 23225
P: (804) 674-3081
F: (804) 674-3284
E: Adrianne.Bennett@vpb.virginia.gov

WASHINGTON
Ms. Kecia Rongen
Chair
Indeterminate Sentence Review Board
4317 6th Avenue, Southeast
P.O. Box 40907
Olympia, WA 98504
P: (360) 407-2400
F: (360) 493-9287
E: isrb@doc1.wa.gov

WEST VIRGINIA
Ms. Benita F. Murphy
Chair
Parole Board
1356 Hansford Street, Suite B
Charleston, WV 25301
P: (304) 558-6366
F: (304) 558-5678
E: Benita.F.Murphy@wv.gov

WISCONSIN
Ms. Denise Symdon
Administrator
Division of Community Corrections
P.O. Box 7925
Madison, WI 53707
P: (608) 240-5300
F: (608) 240-3330

WYOMING
Mr. Dan Fetsco
Executive Director
Board of Parole
3120 Old Faithful Road, Suite 300
Cheyenne, WY 82002
P: (307) 777-5444
F: (307) 777-5386
E: daniel.fetsco@wyo.gov

Personnel

Formulates, implements, and enforces personnel management policies and procedures for the state.

Information provided by:

National Association of State Personnel Executives
Leslie Scott
Association Manager
1776 Avenue of the States
Lexington, KY 40511
P: (859) 244-8182
F: (859) 244-8001
lscott@csg.org
www.naspe.net

ALABAMA
Ms. Alice Ann Byrne
Deputy Director
State Personnel Department
313 Folsom Administration Building
64 North Union Street, Suite 300
Montgomery, AL 36130
P: (334) 242-3389
E: aliceann.byrne@personnel.alabama.gov

Ms. Jackie Graham
State Personnel Director
State Personnel Department
313 Folsom Administration Building
64 North Union Street, Suite 300
Montgomery, AL 36130
P: (334) 242-3711
F: (334) 353-3320
E: jackie.graham@personnel.alabama.gov

ALASKA
Ms. Kate Sheehan
Director
Division of Personnel & Labor Relations
Department of Administration
P.O. Box 110201
Juneau, AK 99811
P: (907) 465-4430
F: (907) 465-3415
E: kate.sheehan@alaska.gov

AMERICAN SAMOA
Mr. Esenaeiaso J. Liu
Director
Department of Human Resources
Executive Office Building
AP Lutali, 2nd Floor
Pago Pago, AS 96799
P: (684) 644-4485
F: (684) 633-1139
E: eseneiaso.liu@hr.as.gov

ARIZONA
Ms. Marie Isaacson
Human Resources Director
Benefits Services Division
Department of Administration
100 North 15th Avenue, Suite 261
Phoenix, AZ 85007
P: (602) 542-5482
F: (602) 542-2796
E: marie.isaacson@azdoa.gov

ARKANSAS
Ms. Kay Barnhill Terry
State Personnel Administrator
Office of Personnel Management
Department of Finance & Administration
1509 West 7th Street
Little Rock, AR 72201
P: (501) 682-5122
F: (501) 682-5104
E: kay.terry@dfa.arkansas.gov

CALIFORNIA
Mr. Richard Gillihan
Director
California CalHR
1515 S Street, Suite 400
Sacramento, CA 96814
P: (916) 327-4024
E: richard.gillihan@calhr.ca.gov

COLORADO
Ms. Kim Burgess
Chief Human Resources Officer
Division of Human Resources
Department of Personnel & Administration
1313 Sherman Street, 1st Floor
Denver, CO 80203
P: (303) 866-2105
F: (303) 866-2021
E: kim.burgess@state.co.us

CONNECTICUT
Dr. Pamela L. Libby
Director
Human Resource Management
165 Capitol Avenue, Room 411
Hartford, CT 06106
P: (860) 713-5204
F: (860) 622-2965
E: pamela.libby@po.state.ct.us

DELAWARE
Ms. Brenda Lakeman
Director
Statewide Benefits
Office of Budget & Management
Enterprise Business Park
Dover, DE 19901
P: (302) 739-4195
F: (302) 739-7984
E: brenda.lakeman@state.de.us

DISTRICT OF COLUMBIA
Ms. Ventris C. Gibson
Director
Department of Human Resources
441 4th Street Northwest
Suite 300 South
Washington, DC 20001
P: (202) 442-9700
F: (202) 727-6827
E: ventris.gibson@dc.gov

FLORIDA
Ms. Sharon Larson
Director
Division of Human Resources
Department of Management Services
4050 Esplanade Way, Suite 235
Tallahassee, FL 32399
P: (850) 413-8725
F: (850) 922-6642
E: sharon.larson@dms.myflorida.com

GEORGIA
Ms. Debbie Smith
Deputy Commissioner
Human Resources Administration
West Tower, Room 504
2 Martin Luther King Jr. Drive Southwest
Atlanta, GA 30334
P: (404) 657-0590
F: (404) 656-5979
E: Debbie.Smith@doas.ga.gov

GUAM
Ms. Christine Baleto
Director
Department of Administration
P.O. Box 884
Hagatna, GU 96928
P: (671) 475-1101
F: (671) 477-6788

HAWAII
Mr. James Nishimoto
Director
Department of Human Resources Development
State Office Tower
235 South Beretania Street, 14th Floor
Honolulu, HI 96813
P: (808) 587-1100
E: james.k.nishimoto@hawaii.gov

IDAHO
Ms. Susan Buxton
Administrator
Department of Human Resources
700 West State Street
P.O. Box 83720
Boise, ID 83720
P: (208) 854-3077
E: susan.buxton@dhr.idaho.gov

ILLINOIS
Ms. Elizabeth Whitehorn
Chief of Staff, Bureau of Personnel
Department of Central Management Services
503 William G. Stratton Building
Springfield, IL 62706
P: (217) 524-8773
E: chris.griffin@illnois.gov

INDIANA
Ms. Brandye Hendrickson
Director
State Personnel Department
402 West Washington Street, Room W161
100 North Senate Avenue, Room N 758
Indianapolis, IN 46204
P: (317) 233-5606
E: BHendrickson2@spd.IN.gov

Personnel

IOWA
Ms. Karin Gregor
Chief Operating Officer
Department of Administrative Services
Human Resources Enterprise
Hoover State Office Building
Des Moines, IA 50319
P: (515) 281-5064
E: karin.gregor@iowa.gov

KANSAS
Mr. Kraig Knowlton
Director
Office of Personnel Services
Landon State Office Building
900 Southwest Jackson, Room 251
Topeka, KS 66612
P: (785) 296-4278
F: (785) 296-6793
E: kraig.knowlton@da.ks.gov

KENTUCKY
Mr. Thomas Stephens
Secretary
Personnel Cabinet
State Office Building, 3rd Floor
501 High Street
Frankfort, KY 40601
P: (502) 564-7430
F: (502) 564-7603
E: thomasb.stephens@ky.gov

LOUISIANA
Mr. Byron Decoteau Jr.
Director
Department of State Civil Service
1201 North Third Street
P.O. Box 94111
Baton Rouge, LA 70804
P: (225) 342-8272
F: (225) 342-0966
E: bryon.decoteau@la.gov

MAINE
Ms. Joyce Oreskovich
Director
Bureau of Human Resources
#4 State House Station
Burton M. Cross Building, 4th Floor
Augusta, ME 04333
P: (207) 624-7761
F: (207) 287-4414
E: joyce.a.oreskovich@maine.gov

MARYLAND
Ms. Cynthia Kollner
Executive Director
Office of Personnel Services & Benefits
Department of Budget & Management
301 West Preston Street, Room 609
Baltimore, MD 21201
P: (410) 767-4715
F: (410) 333-5262
E: cindy.kollner@maryland.gov

MASSACHUSETTS
Mr. Ronald Arigo
Chief Human Resources Officer
Human Resources Division
Office for Administration and Finance
1 Ashburton Palce, Room 301
Boston, MA 02108
P: (617) 878-9703
E: ronald.arigo@MassMail.State.MA.US

MICHIGAN
Ms. Janine Winters
State Personnel Director
Civil Service Commission
Capitol Commons Center
400 South Pine Street
Lansing, MI 48933
P: (517) 373-3020
F: (517) 284-9950
E: wintersj@michigan.gov

MINNESOTA
Mr. Edwin Hudson
Assistant Commissioner
Enterprise Human Resources Division
Department of Management & Budget
658 Cedar Street
St. Paul, MN 55155
P: (651) 259-3636
F: (651) 296-8919
E: edwin.hudson@state.mn.us

MISSISSIPPI
Ms. Kelly Hardwick
Executive Director
State Personnel Board
200 East Capitol Street, Suite 800
Jackson, MS 39201
P: (601) 359-2702
F: (601) 359-2729
E: kelly.hardwick@mspb.ms.gov

MISSOURI
Ms. Nancy Johnston
Director, Division of Personnel
Office of Administration
301 West High Street, Suite 430
P.O. Box 388
Jefferson City, MO 65101
P: (573) 751-4162
F: (573) 751-8641
E: persmail@oa.mo.gov

MONTANA
Ms. Anjenette Schafer
Administrator
State Human Resources Division
Department of Administration
P.O. Box 200127
Helena, MT 59620
P: (406) 444-3885
F: (406) 444-0703
E: aschafer2@mt.gov

NEBRASKA
Ms. Marjory Bell
Director
State Personnel Division
Department of Administrative Services
1526 K Street, Suite 100
Lincoln, NE 68508
P: (402) 471-2075
F: (402) 471-3754
E: margie.bell@nebraska.gov

NEVADA
Mr. Peter Long
Administrator
Division of Human Resource Management
Department of Administration
100 North Stewart Street, Suite 200
Carson City, NV 89701
P: (775) 684-0121
F: (775) 684-0122
E: plong@admin.nv.gov

NEW HAMPSHIRE
Ms. Sara J. Willingham
Director
Division of Personnel
Department of Administrative Services
28 School Street
Concord, NH 03301
P: (603) 271-3261
F: (603) 271-1422
E: sara.willingham@nh.gov

NEW JERSEY
Mr. Robert M. Czech
Chair/Chief Executive Officer
State Civil Service Commission
P.O. Box 317
Trenton, NJ 08625
P: (606) 292-4125
E: robert.czech@csc.state.nj.us

Ms. Grace Kelly
Deputy CEO
Civil Service Commission
P.O. Box 317
Trenton, NJ 08625
P: (606) 292-4125
E: grace.kelly@csc.state.nj.us

NEW MEXICO
Mr. Justin Najaka
Director
State Personnel Office
2600 Cerrillos Road
Santa Fe, NM 87505
P: (505) 490-2414
F: (505) 476-7806
E: Justin.Najaka@state.nm.us

NEW YORK
Ms. Lola Brabham
Acting Commissioner
Department of Civil Service
Alfred E. Smith State Office Building
Albany, NY 12239
P: (518) 457-3701
E: lola.brabham@cs.state.ny.us

NORTH CAROLINA
Ms. Barbara Gibson
Director
Office of Human Resources
1331 Mail Service Center
Raleigh, NC 27699
P: (919) 807-4800
F: (919) 715-9750
E: barbara.gibson@nc.gov

NORTH DAKOTA
Ms. Becki Sicble
Interim Director
Human Resource Management Services
Office of Management & Budget
600 East Boulevard Avenue, Dept. 113
Bismarck, ND 58505
P: (701) 328-4735
E: blsicble@nd.gov

NORTHERN MARIANA ISLANDS
Mr. Isidro Seman
Director of Personnel
Office of Personnel Management
P.O. Box 5153 CHRB
Saipan, MP 96950
P: (670) 234-6925 Ext. 101
F: (670) 234-1013

OHIO
Mr. Tom Cruse
Deputy Director
Human Resources Division
30 East Broad Street, 28th Floor
Columbus, OH 43215
P: (614) 728-0732
E: tom.cruse@das.ohio.gov

OKLAHOMA
Ms. Lucinda Meltabarger
Administrator
Human Capital Management Division
2101 North Lincoln Boulevard
Room G-80
Oklahoma City, OK 73105
P: (405) 521-3928
F: (405) 524-6942
E: lucinda.meltabarger@omes.ok.gov

OREGON
Ms. Madilyn Zike
Chief HR Officer
Human Resources Office
Department of Administrative Services
155 Cottage Street, Northeast
Salem, OR 97301
P: (503) 378-3020
F: (503) 373-7684
E: madilyn.zike@state.or.us

PENNSYLVANIA
Mr. Korvin D. Auch
Deputy Secretary for Human Resources & Management
State Human Resources & Management
517 Finance Building
Harrisburg, PA 17110
P: (717) 787-8191
F: (717) 783-4429
E: kauch@pa.gov

PUERTO RICO
Mr. Harry O. Diaz Vega
Director
Labor Affairs & Human Resource Administration
P.O. Box 8476
San Juan, PR 00919
P: (787) 274-4300
F: (787) 250-1145

RHODE ISLAND
Ms. Deborah Dawson
Human Resources Director
Office of Personnel Administration
1 Capitol Hill
Providence, RI 02908
P: (401) 222-2160
F: (401) 222-6391
E: deborah.dawson@hr.ri.gov

SOUTH CAROLINA
Ms. Kim Aydlette
Director
Division of State Human Resources
Department of Administration
8301 Parklane Road, Suite A220
Columbia, SC 29223
P: (803) 896-5300
F: (803) 896-5050
E: kim.aydlette@admin.sc.gov

SOUTH DAKOTA
Ms. Laurie R. Gill
Commissioner
Bureau of Human Resources
500 East Capitol Avenue
Pierre, SD 57501
P: (605) 773-4918
F: (605) 773-6947
E: laurie.gill@state.sd.us

TENNESSEE
Ms. Rebecca R. Hunter
Commissioner
Department of Human Resources
James K. Polk Building, 1st Floor
505 Deaderick Street
Nashville, TN 37243
P: (615) 741-2958
F: (615) 741-7880
E: rebecca.hunter@tn.gov

U.S. VIRGIN ISLANDS
Mr. Milton E. Potter
Director
Division of Personnel
GERS Building, 3rd Floor
3438 Kronprindsens Gade
St. Thomas, VI 00802
P: (340) 774-8588
F: (340) 714-5040
E: info@dopusvi.net

UTAH
Ms. Debbie Cragun
Executive Director
Department of Human Resource Management
2120 State Office Building
P.O. Box 141531
Salt Lake City, UT 84114
P: (801) 538-3403
F: (801) 538-3081
E: dcragun@utah.gov

VERMONT
Ms. Beth Fastiggi
Commissioner
Department of Human Resources
110 State Street
Montpelier, VT 05620
P: (802) 828-3491
E: beth.fastiggi@vermont.gov

VIRGINIA
Mrs. Sara Redding Wilson
Director
Department of Human Resource Management
101 North 14th Street, 12th Floor
Richmond, VA 23219
P: (804) 225-2237
F: (804) 371-7401
E: sara.wilson@dhrm.virginia.gov

WASHINGTON
Mr. Franklin Plaistowe
Assistant Director
State Human Resources
128th 10th Avenue
P.O. Box 47500
Olympia, WA 98504
P: (360) 407-4104
E: StateHR@ofm.wa.gov

WEST VIRGINIA
Mr. Joe F. Thomas
Acting Director
State Division of Personnel
1900 Kanawha Boulevard, East
Charleston, WV 25305
P: (304) 558-3950
E: joe.f.thomas@wv.gov

WISCONSIN
Mr. Gregory L. Gracz
Director
Division of Personnel Management
101 East Wilson Street
P.O. Box 7855
Madison, WI 53707
P: (608) 266-9820
F: (608) 267-1014
E: greg.gracz@wi.gov

WYOMING
Ms. Patricia Bach
Administrator, Human Resources Division
Department of Administration & Information
Emerson Building
2001 Capitol Avenue, Room 128
Cheyenne, WY 82002
P: (307) 777-6722
E: tricia.bach1@wyo.gov

Port Authority

Agency housed under the department of transportation that oversees coastal transportation, international transportation, shipping, and all other acts involving state ports.

ALABAMA
Mr. James K. Lyons
Director/CEO
Port Authority
250 North Water Street
P.O. Box 1588
Mobile, AL 36633
P: (251) 441-7200
E: jlyons@asdd.com

ALASKA
Mr. Michael Lukshin
State Ports & Harbors Engineer
Department of Transportation & Public Facilities
3132 Channel Drive
P.O. Box 112500
Juneau, AK 99811
P: (907) 465-3979
F: (907) 465-3124
E: michael.lukshin@alaska.gov

AMERICAN SAMOA
Dr. Clarie Tuia Poumele
Director
Department of Port Administration
P.O. Box 1539
Pago Pago, AS 96799
P: (684) 633-4612
E: claire.poumele@gmail.com

GEORGIA
Mr. Griffith Lynch
Executive Director
Ports Authority
2 Main Street
Garden City, GA 31408
P: (912) 964-3874
F: (912) 966-3615
E: glynch@gaports.com

HAWAII
Mr. Davis K. Yogi
Harbors Administrator
Harbors Division
Hale Awa Ku Moku Building
79 South Nimitz Highway, Room 310
Honolulu, HI 96813
P: (808) 587-1928
F: (808) 587-1984
E: Davis.Yogi@hawaii.gov

INDIANA
Mr. Rich Cooper
Chief Executive Officer
Ports of Indiana
150 West Market Street, Suite 100
Indianapolis, IN 46204
P: (317) 232-9200
F: (317) 232-0137
E: info@portsofindiana.com

KANSAS
Mr. Richard Carlson
Secretary of Transportation
Department of Transportation
Eisenhower State Office Building
700 Southwest Harrison
Topeka, KS 66603
P: (785) 296-3461
F: (785) 296-1095
E: richard.carlson@ks.gov

MAINE
Mr. John H. Henshaw
Executive Director
Port Authority
16 State House Station
Augusta, ME 04333
P: (207) 624-3564
F: (207) 624-3099
E: john.h.henshaw@maine.gov

MARYLAND
Mr. James J. White
Executive Director
Port Administration
World Trade Center
401 East Pratt Street
Baltimore, MD 21202
P: (410) 385-4400
E: jwhite@marylandports.com

MASSACHUSETTS
Dr. Thomas P. Glynn Jr.
Chief Executive Officer
Port Authority
One Harborside Drive, Suite 200S
East Boston, MA 02128
P: (617) 568-5000

MINNESOTA
Mr. Charles A. Zelle
Commissioner
Department of Transportation
Transportation Building
395 John Ireland Boulevard
St. Paul, MN 55155
P: (651) 366-4800
F: (651) 366-4795
E: charlie.zelle@state.mn.us

MISSISSIPPI
Mr. Mark L. McAndrews
Port Director
Pascagoula Port Authority
P.O. Box 70
Pascagoula, MS 39568
P: (228) 762-4041
F: (228) 762-7476
E: info@portofpascagoula.com

NEW HAMPSHIRE
Mr. Geno Marconi
Director of Ports & Harbors
Division of Ports & Harbors
555 Market Street
Portsmouth, NH 03801
P: (603) 436-8500
F: (603) 436-2780
E: g.marconi@peasedev.org

NEW YORK
Mr. Patrick Foye
Executive Director
The Port Authority of New York & New Jersey
4 World Trade Center
150 Greenwich Street
New York, NY 10007
P: (212) 435-7000

NORTH CAROLINA
Mr. Paul J. Cozza
Executive Director
State Ports Authority
2202 Burnett Boulevard
Wilmington, NC 28401
P: (910) 763-1621
E: paul.cozza@ncports.com

NORTHERN MARIANA ISLANDS
Mr. Christopher Tenorio
Executive Director
Commonwealth Ports Authority
P.O. Box 501055
Saipan, MP 96950
P: (670) 237-6500
F: (670) 234-5962

OHIO
Mr. Jerry Wray
Director
Department of Transportation
1980 West Broad Street
Columbus, OH 43223
P: (614) 466-7170
F: (614) 466-8662
E: Terri.Barnhart@dot.ohio.gov

OKLAHOMA
Mr. Scott Robinson
Director
The Port of Muskogee
P.O. Box 2819
Muskogee, OK 74402
P: (918) 682-7886
F: (918) 683-4811
E: Scott@muskogeeport.com

Mr. David L. Yarbrough
Director
Tulsa Port of Catoosa
5350 Cimarron Road
Catoosa, OK 74015
P: (918) 266-2291
F: (918) 266-7678
E: david@tulsaport.com

SOUTH CAROLINA
Mr. James I. Newsome III
President & CEO
State Ports Authority
176 Concord Street
P.O.Box 22287
Charleston, SC 29413
P: (843) 723-8651
E: scspainfo@scspa.com

U.S. VIRGIN ISLANDS
Mr. David W. Mapp
Acting Executive Director
Port Authority
8074 Lindbergh Bay
P.O. Box 301707
St. Thomas, VI 00803
P: (340) 774-1629
F: (340) 774-0025
E: info@viport.com

UTAH
Mr. Chad Sheppick
Director
Motor Carriers Division
Department of Transportation
4501 South 2700 West, P.O. Box 148240
Salt Lake City, UT 84114
P: (801) 965-4156
F: (801) 965-4847
E: csheppick@utah.gov

VIRGINIA
Mr. John F. Reinhart
CEO & Executive Director
Port Authority
600 World Trade Center
Norfolk, VA 23510
P: (757) 683-2103
F: (757) 683-8500
E: jreinhart@portofvirginia.com

WEST VIRGINIA
Mr. Charles Neal Vance
Director
Public Port Authority
1900 Kanawha Boulevard, East
Building 5, Room A-137
Charleston, WV 25305
P: (304) 558-9386
F: (304) 558-0333
E: Charles.N.Vance@wv.gov

Public Defender

Represents indigent criminal defendants who desire to appeal their convictions to the state's intermediate appellate court or court of last resort.

ALASKA
Mr. Quinlan Steiner
Public Defender
Public Defender Agency
Department of Administration
900 West 5th Avenue, Suite 200
Anchorage, AK 99501
P: (907) 334-4400
F: (907) 269-5476
E: quinlan.steiner@alaska.gov

AMERICAN SAMOA
Mr. Marc Douglas Fiaui
Director
Office of the Public Defender
Executive Office Building
Pago Pago, AS 96799
P: (684) 633-1286
F: (684) 633-4745
E: douglas.fiaui@go.as.gov

ARKANSAS
Mr. Gregg Parrish
Director
Public Defender Commission
101 East Capitol, Suite 201
Little Rock, AR 72201
P: (501) 682-9070
F: (501) 682-9073

CALIFORNIA
Mr. Michael J. Hersek
State Public Defender
Office of the State Public Defender
221 Main Street, 10th Floor
San Francisco, CA 94105
P: (415) 904-5600
F: (510) 452-8712

COLORADO
Mr. Douglas Wilson
State Public Defender
Office of the State Public Defender
1300 Broadway, Suite 400
Denver, CO 80203
P: (303) 764-1400
F: (303) 764-1478
E: doug.wilson@coloradodefenders.us

CONNECTICUT
Ms. Susan O. Storey
Chief Public Defender
Division of Public Defender Services
30 Trinity Street, 4th Floor
Hartford, CT 06106
P: (860) 509-6400
F: (860) 509-6495
E: susan.storey@jud.ct.gov

DELAWARE
Mr. Brendan O'Neill
Chief Defender
Office of Defense Services
Carvel State Office Building
820 North French Street, 3rd Floor
Wilmington, DE 19801
P: (302) 577-5200
F: (302) 577-3995

DISTRICT OF COLUMBIA
Ms. Avis Buchanan
Director
Public Defender Service
633 Indiana Avenue, Northwest
Washington, DC 20004
P: (202) 628-1200
F: (202) 824-2784
E: abuchanan@pdsdc.org

FLORIDA
Fran Gilbert
Executive Director
Public Defender Association
103 North Gadsden Street
Tallahassee, FL 32301
P: (850) 488-6850
F: (850) 488-4720
E: admin@flpda.org

GEORGIA
The Honorable Chris Carr (R)
Attorney General
Office of the Attorney General
40 Capitol Square, Southwest
Atlanta, GA 30334
P: (404) 656-3300
F: (404) 657-8733

GUAM
Mr. Stephen P. Hattori
Executive Director
Public Defender Service Corporation
779 Route 4
Sinajana, GU 96910
P: (671) 475-3100
F: (671) 477-5844
E: sphattori@guampdsc.net

HAWAII
Mr. John M. Tonaki
Public Defender
Office of the Public Defender
1130 North Nimitz Highway
Suite A-254
Honolulu, HI 96817
P: (808) 586-2200
F: (808) 586-2222

ILLINOIS
Mr. Michael J. Pelletier
State Appellate Defender
Office of the State Appellate Defender
400 West Monroe, Suite 202
P.O. Box 5240
Springfield, IL 62705
P: (217) 782-7203
F: (217) 782-5385
E: Michael.Pelletier@osad.state.il.us

KANSAS
Ms. Patricia A. Scalia
Executive Director
Board of Indigents' Defense Services
700 Southwest Jackson Street, Suite 500
Topeka, KS 66603
P: (785) 296-6631
F: (785) 291-3082
E: inquiry@sbids.org

KENTUCKY
Mr. Edward C. Monahan
Public Advocate
Department of Public Advocacy
100 Fair Oaks Lane, Suite 302
Frankfort, KY 40601
P: (502) 564-8006
F: (502) 564-7890

LOUISIANA
Mr. James T. Dixon Jr.
State Public Defender
Public Defender Board
301 Main Street, Suite 700
Baton Rouge, LA 70825
P: (225) 219-9305
F: (225) 219-9326

MARYLAND
Mr. Paul B. DeWolfe Jr.
Public Defender
Public Defender System
William Donald Schefer Tower
6 St. Paul Street, Suite 1400
Baltimore, MD 21202
P: (410) 767-8479
F: (410) 333-8496
E: jsehorn@opd.state.md.us

MASSACHUSETTS
Mr. Anthony J. Benedetti
Chief Counsel
Committee for Public Counsel Services
44 Bromfield Street
Boston, MA 02108
P: (617) 482-6212
F: (617) 988-8495
E: abenedetti@publiccounsel.net

MICHIGAN
Ms. Dawn Van Hoek
Director
State Appellate Defender Office
Suite 3300, Penobscot Building
645 Griswald
Detroit, MI 48226
P: (313) 256-9833
F: (313) 965-0372
E: dvanhoek@sado.org

MINNESOTA
Mr. William Ward
State Public Defender
Board of Public Defense
331 Second Avenue South, Suite 900
Minneapolis, MN 55401
P: (612) 279-3512
E: william.ward@mnpd.us

MISSOURI
Mr. Michael Barrett
State Public Defender
Office of the State Public Defender
Woodrail Centre
1000 West Nifong, Building 7, Suite 100
Columbia, MO 65203
P: (573) 777-9977
F: (573) 777-9976
E: public.defender@mspd.mo.gov

MONTANA
Mr. William F. Hooks
Chief Public Defender
Office of the State Public Defender
44 West Park Street
Butte, MT 59701
P: (406) 444-9546
F: (406) 496-6098
E: opdreceptionist@mt.gov

NEBRASKA
Mr. Jeffery Pickens
Chief Counsel
Commission on Public Advocacy
140 North 8th Street, Suite 270
Lincoln, NE 68508
P: (402) 471-7775
F: (402) 471-8087
E: jpickens@ncpa.ne.gov

NEVADA
Ms. Karin L. Kreizenbeck
State Public Defender
Office of the Public Defender
Department of Health & Human Services
511 East Robinson Street, #1
Carson City, NV 89701
P: (775) 684-1080
F: (775) 687-4993
E: klkreizenbeck@govmail.state.nv.us

NEW HAMPSHIRE
Mr. Chris Johnson
Chief Appellate Defender
Public Defender
10 Ferry Street
Concord, NH 03301
P: (603) 224-1236
F: (603) 227-9367

NEW JERSEY
Mr. Joseph E. Krakora
Public Defender
Office of the Public Defender
Hughes Justice Complex, 25 Market Street
P.O. Box 850
Trenton, NJ 08625
P: (609) 292-7087
F: (609) 777-1795
E: thedefenders@opd.nj.gov

NEW MEXICO
Mr. Bennett J. Baur
Chief Public Defender
Public Defender Department
301 North Guadalupe Street
Santa Fe, NM 87501
P: (505) 395-2888

NORTH CAROLINA
Mr. Thomas K. Maher
Executive Director
Office of Indigent Defense Services
123 West Main Street
Suite 400
Durham, NC 27701
P: (919) 354-7200
F: (919) 354-7201
E: Thomas.K.Maher@nccourts.org

NORTH DAKOTA
The Honorable Wayne Stenehjem (R)
Attorney General
Office of the Attorney General
State Capitol
600 East Boulevard Avenue
Bismarck, ND 58505
P: (701) 328-2210
F: (701) 328-2226
E: wstenehjem@nd.gov

NORTHERN MARIANA ISLANDS
Mr. Doug Hartig
Chief Public Defender
Office of the Public Defender
Civic Center Complex
P.O. Box 5010007
Saipan, MP 96950
P: (670) 234-6503
F: (670) 234-1009
E: hartigd1@gmail.com

OHIO
Mr. Timothy Young
Ohio Public Defender
Office of the Public Defender
250 East Broad Street, Suite 1400
Columbus, OH 43215
P: (614) 644-1610
F: (614) 644-9972
E: Timothy.Young@opd.ohio.gov

OKLAHOMA
Mr. Joe P. Robertson
Executive Director
Indigent Defense System
P.O. Box 926
Norman, OK 73070
P: (405) 801-2601

OREGON
Ms. Nancy Cozine
Executive Director
Office of Public Defense Services
Office of Public Defense Services
1175 Court Street, Northeast
Salem, OR 97301
P: (503) 378-3349
F: (503) 378-4463
E: Nancy.Cozine@opds.state.or.us

RHODE ISLAND
Ms. Mary S. McElroy
Public Defender
Office of the Public Defender
160 Pine Street
Providence, RI 02903
P: (401) 222-3492
F: (401) 222-5225
E: Information@ripd.org

SOUTH DAKOTA
The Honorable Marty J. Jackley (R)
Attorney General
Office of the Attorney General
1302 East Highway 14, Suite 1
Pierre, SD 57501
P: (605) 773-3215
F: (605) 773-4106
E: atghelp@state.sd.us

U.S. VIRGIN ISLANDS
Mr. Samuel L. Joseph
Chief Public Defender
Office of the Territorial Public Defender
P.O. Box 6040
St. Thomas, VI 00804
P: (340) 774-8181
F: (340) 774-3052

VERMONT
Mr. Matthew F. Valerio
Defender General
Office of the Defender General
6 Baldwin Street, 4th Floor
Montpelier, VT 05633
P: (802) 828-3168
F: (802) 828-3163
E: Matthew.Valerio@vermont.gov

VIRGINIA
Mr. David J. Johnson
Executive Director
Indigent Defense Commission
1604 Santa Rosa Road, Suite 200
Richmond, VA 23229
P: (804) 662-7249
F: (804) 662-7359
E: djohnson@adm.idc.virginia.gov

WASHINGTON
Ms. Joanne Moore
Director
State Office of Public Defense
711 Capitol Way South, Suite 106
Evergreen Plaza Building, P.O. Box 40957
Olympia, WA 98504
P: (360) 586-3164, Ext. 112
F: (360) 586-8165
E: opd@opd.wa.gov

WEST VIRGINIA
Ms. Dana F. Eddy
Executive Director
Public Defender Services
One Players Club Drive, Suite 301
Charleston, WV 25311
P: (304) 558-3905
F: (304) 558-1098
E: Dana.F.Eddy@wv.gov

WISCONSIN
Ms. Kelli Thompson
State Public Defender
Office of the State Public Defender
17 South Fairchild Street, Suite 500
Madison, WI 53703
P: (608) 266-0087
F: (608) 267-0584
E: ThompsonK@opd.wi.gov

WYOMING
Ms. Diane M. Lozano
State Public Defender
Office of the State Public Defender
Rogers Building
316 West 22nd Street
Cheyenne, WY 82002
P: (307) 777-7519
F: (307) 777-8742
E: diane.lozano@wyo.gov

Public Lands

Manages state-owned lands.

ALABAMA
Ms. Patti Powell
Director
State Lands Division
Conservation & Natural Resources
64 North Union Street
Montgomery, AL 36130
P: (334) 242-3484
F: (334) 242-0999
E: patti.powell@dcnr.alabama.gov

ALASKA
Mr. Brent Goodrum
Director
Division of Mining, Land & Water
Department of Natural Resources
550 West Seventh Avenue, Suite 1070
Anchorage, AK 99501
P: (907) 269-8600
F: (907) 269-8904
E: brent.goodrum@alaska.gov

ARIZONA
Ms. Lisa Atkins
State Land Commissioner
State Land Department
1616 West Adams Street
Phoenix, AZ 85007
P: (602) 542-4621

ARKANSAS
The Honorable John Thurston
Commissioner
Commissioner of State Lands
State Capitol Building
500 Woodlane Street, Suite 109
Little Rock, AR 72201
P: (501) 324-9422
F: (501) 324-9421
E: land@cosl.org

CALIFORNIA
Ms. Kari Lewis
Program Manager
Wildlife Branch, Lands Program
Department of Fish & Wildlife
1812 9th Street
Sacramento, CA 95811
P: (916) 445-3789
F: (916) 445-4058
E: Kari.Lewis@wildlife.ca.gov

COLORADO
Mr. Bill Ryan
Director
State Land Board
Department of Natural Resources
1127 Sherman Street, Suite 300
Denver, CO 80203
P: (303) 866-3454
F: (303) 866-3152
E: bill.ryan@state.co.us

DELAWARE
Mr. Raymond E. Bivens
Director
Division of Parks & Recreation
89 Kings Highway
Dover, DE 19901
P: (302) 739-9200
F: (302) 739-3817
E: raymond.bivens@state.de.us

DISTRICT OF COLUMBIA
Mr. Keith A. Anderson
Director
Department of Parks & Recreation
1250 U Street Northwest, 2nd Floor
Washington, DC 20009
P: (202) 673-7647
F: (202) 673-2087
E: keith.anderson@dc.gov

GEORGIA
Mr. Mark Williams
Commissioner & State Historic Preservation Officer
Department of Natural Resources
2 Martin Luther King Jr. Drive Southeast
Suite 1252, East Tower
Atlanta, GA 30334
P: (404) 656-3500
F: (404) 656-0770
E: Mark.Williams@dnr.ga.gov

HAWAII
Ms. Suzanne D. Case
Chairperson
Department of Land & Natural Resources
Kalanimoku Building
1151 Punchbowl Street
Honolulu, HI 96813
P: (808) 587-0400
F: (808) 587-0390
E: dlnr@hawaii.gov

IDAHO
Mr. Tom Schultz
Director
Department of Lands
300 North 6th Street, Suite 103
Boise, ID 83702
P: (208) 334-0200
F: (208) 334-3698
E: tschultz@idl.idaho.gov

ILLINOIS
Mr. Wayne Rosenthal
Director
Department of Natural Resources
One Natural Resources Way
Springfield, IL 62702
P: (217) 782-6302
F: (217) 785-9236
E: wayne.rosenthal@illinois.gov

INDIANA
Mr. Mitch Zoll Jr.
Division Director
Historic Preservation & Archaeology
Department of Natural Resources
402 West Washington Street, W274
Indianapolis, IN 46204
P: (317) 232-3492
F: (317) 232-0693
E: mzoll@dnr.in.gov

IOWA
Mr. Chuck Gipp
Director
Department of Natural Resources
4th Floor, Wallace Building
502 East 9th Street
Des Moines, IA 50319
P: (515) 725-8282
F: (515) 281-8895
E: chuck.gipp@dnr.iowa.gov

KANSAS
Mr. Robin Jennison
Secretary
Department of Wildlife, Parks & Tourism
1020 South Kansas Avenue, Room 200
Topeka, KS 66612
P: (785) 296-2281
F: (785) 296-6953

KENTUCKY
Mr. Greg Johnson
Commissioner
Department of Fish & Wildlife Resources
One Sportsman's Lane
Frankfort, KY 40601
P: (502) 564-3400
F: (502) 564-0506

LOUISIANA
Mr. Jonathan Robillard
Administrator
Office of State Lands
Division of Administration
P.O. Box 44124
Baton Rouge, LA 70804
P: (225) 342-4578
E: Jonathan.Robillard@la.gov

MAINE
Mr. Tom Desjardin
Director of Parks & Lands
Bureau of Parks & Lands
22 State House Station
Augusta, ME 04333
P: (207) 287-4961
F: (207) 287-6170
E: Tom.Desjardin@maine.gov

MARYLAND
Mr. Daryl Anthony
Assistant Secretary for Land Resources
Department of Natural Resources
Tawes State Office Building
580 Taylor Avenue
Annapolis, MD 21401
P: (410) 260-8106
F: (410) 260-8111
E: daryl.anthony@maryland.gov

MASSACHUSETTS
Mr. Leo Roy
Commissioner
Department of Conservation & Recreation
Office of Energy & Environmental Affairs
251 Causeway Street, Suite 600
Boston, MA 02114
P: (617) 626-1250
F: (617) 626-1351
E: mass.parks@state.ma.us

MICHIGAN
Mr. Ronald Olson
Chief
Parks & Recreation Division
Department of Natural Resources
P.O. Box 30257
Lansing, MI 48909
P: (517) 284-7275
F: (517) 373-4625
E: OlsonR@michigan.gov

MINNESOTA
Mr. Tom Landwehr
Commissioner
Department of Natural Resources
500 Lafayette Road
St. Paul, MN 55155
P: (651) 296-6157
F: (651) 296-4799
E: Tom.Landwehr@state.mn.us

MISSISSIPPI
Mr. Bill Cheney
Assistant Secretary of State
Public Lands Division
Office of the Secretary of State
125 South Congress Street, P.O. Box 136
Jackson, MS 39205
P: (601) 359-5156
F: (601) 359-1461

MONTANA
Mr. John Tubbs
Director
Department of Natural Resources & Conservation
1539 Eleventh Avenue
P.O. Box 201601
Helena, MT 59620
P: (406) 444-2074
F: (406) 444-2684

NEBRASKA
Mr. Jim Swenson
Division Administrator
Parks Division
Game & Parks Commission
2200 North 33rd Street
Lincoln, NE 68503
P: (402) 471-5499
F: (402) 471-5528
E: jim.swenson@nebraska.gov

NEW HAMPSHIRE
Mr. Brad W. Simpkins
Director/State Forester
Division of Forests & Lands
Resources & Economic Development
172 Pembroke Road
Concord, NH 03301
P: (603) 271-2214
F: (603) 271-6488
E: Brad.Simpkins@dred.nh.gov

NEW JERSEY
Mr. Larry Herrighty
Director
Division of Fish & Wildlife
Department of Environmental Protection
501 East State Street, 3rd Floor
Trenton, NJ 08625
P: (609) 292-9410
F: (609) 292-8207

NEW MEXICO
The Honorable Aubrey Dunn (R)
Commissioner
State Land Office
310 Old Santa Fe Trail
P.O. Box 1148
Santa Fe, NM 87504
P: (505) 827-5761
F: (505) 827-5766
E: adunn@slo.state.nm.us

NEW YORK
Mr. Basil Seggos
Commissioner
Department of Environmental Conservation
625 Broadway
Albany, NY 12233
P: (518) 402-8545
F: (518) 402-8541

NORTHERN MARIANA ISLANDS
Ms. Marianne Concepcion-Teregeyo
Secretary
Department of Public Lands
P.O. Box 500380
Saipan, MP 96950
P: (670) 234-3751
F: (670) 234-3755
E: dpl@dpl.gov.mp

OHIO
Mr. James J. Zehringer
Director
Department of Natural Resources
2045 Morse Road
Columbus, OH 43229
P: (614) 265-6565
F: (614) 261-9601

OKLAHOMA
Ms. Kelly Dixon
Division Director
Land Protection Division
Department of Environmental Quality
P.O. Box 1677
Oklahoma City, OK 73101
P: (405) 702-5100
F: (405) 702-5101
E: kelly.dixon@deq.ok.gov

PENNSYLVANIA
Mr. John Hallas
Director
Bureau of State Parks
P.O. Box 8551
Harrisburg, PA 17105
P: (717) 787-6640

RHODE ISLAND
Ms. Janet Coit
Director
Department of Environmental Management
235 Promenade Street
Providence, RI 02908
P: (401) 222-6800
F: (401) 222-6802
E: janet.coit@dem.ri.gov

SOUTH DAKOTA
The Honorable Ryan Brunner (R)
Commissioner
Department of School & Public Lands
State Capitol, Suite 212
500 East Capitol Avenue
Pierre, SD 57501
P: (605) 773-3303
F: (605) 773-5520
E: ryan.brunner@state.sd.us

TENNESSEE
Mr. Jai Templeton
Commissioner
Department of Agriculture
Melrose Station
P.O. Box 40627
Nashville, TN 37204
P: (615) 837-5100
F: (615) 837-5333

TEXAS
Mr. Brent Leisure
Director of State Parks
State Parks
4200 Smith School Road
Austin, TX 78744
P: (512) 389-4866
F: (512) 389-4814

U.S. VIRGIN ISLANDS
Mr. Lloyd Bough Jr.
Commissioner
Department of Planning & Natural Resources
Cyril E. King Airport
Terminal Building, 2nd Floor
St. Thomas, VI 00802
P: (340) 774-3320
F: (340) 773-1082

Ms. Dawn L. Henry
Commissioner
Department of Planning & Natural Resources
Cyril E. King Airport
Terminal Building, 2nd Floor
St. Thomas, VI 00802
P: (340) 774-3320
F: (340) 773-1082

Mr. David W. Mapp
Acting Executive Director
Port Authority
8074 Lindbergh Bay
P.O. Box 301707
St. Thomas, VI 00803
P: (340) 774-1629
F: (340) 774-0025
E: info@viport.com

UTAH
Mr. Brian Cottham
State Forester/Director
Division of Forestry, Fire & State Lands
Department of Natural Resources
1594 West North Temple, Suite 3520
Salt Lake City, UT 84114
P: (801) 538-5504
F: (801) 533-4111
E: briancottham@utah.gov

VERMONT
Ms. Julie Moore
Secretary
Agency of Natural Resources
103 South Main Street, Center Building
Waterbury, VT 05671
P: (802) 828-1294
F: (802) 244-1102
E: julie.moore@vermont.gov

Public Lands

VIRGINIA
Mr. Christopher L. Beschler
Director
Department of General Services
1100 Bank Street, Suite 420
Richmond, VA 23219
P: (804) 786-3311
E: christopher.beschler@dgs.virginia.gov

WASHINGTON
The Honorable Hilary Franz (D)
Commissioner of Public Lands
Department of Natural Resources
111 Washington Street, Southeast
P.O. Box 47000
Olympia, WA 98504
P: (360) 902-1000
F: (360) 902-1775
E: cpl@dnr.wa.gov

WEST VIRGINIA
Mr. Joe T. Scarberry
Supervisor
Office of Land & Streams
Building 74, Room 200
324 Fourth Avenue
South Charleston, WV 25303
P: (304) 558-3225
F: (304) 558-3680
E: Joe.T.Scarberry@wv.gov

WISCONSIN
Mr. Jonathan Barry
Executive Secretary
Board of Commissioners of Public Lands
101 East Wilson Street, 2nd Floor
P.O. Box 8943
Madison, WI 53708
P: (608) 266-8369
F: (608) 267-2787
E: Jonathan.Barry@wisconsin.gov

WYOMING
Ms. Bridget Hill
Director
Office of State Lands & Investments
Herschler Building, 3rd Floor West
122 West 25th Street
Cheyenne, WY 82002
P: (307) 777-6629
F: (307) 777-3524
E: bridget.hill1@wyo.gov

Public Safety

Provides information and services to insure the protection and safety of citizens and property.

ALABAMA
Mr. Stan Stabler
Acting Secretary of Law Enforcement
Law Enforcement Agency
301 South Ripley Street
P.O. Box 1511
Montgomery, AL 36102
P: (334) 517-2800
F: (334) 242-0512

ALASKA
Mr. Walt Monegan
Commissioner
Department of Public Safety
5700 East Tudor Road
Anchorage, AK 99507
P: (907) 269-5086
F: (907) 269-4543
E: walt.monegan@alaska.gov

AMERICAN SAMOA
Mr. Le'i S. Thompson
Commissioner
Department of Public Safety
American Samoa Government
P.O. Box 1086
Pago Pago, AS 96799
P: (684) 633-1111
F: (684) 633-7296
E: lei.thompson@dps.as.gov

ARIZONA
Colonel Frank Milstead
Director
Department of Public Safety
2222 West Encanto Boulevard
Phoenix, AZ 85009
P: (602) 223-2000
F: (602) 223-2917

ARKANSAS
Colonel Bill Bryant
Director
State Police
1 State Police Plaza Drive
Little Rock, AR 72209
P: (501) 618-8299
F: (501) 618-8222
E: info@asp.arkansas.gov

CALIFORNIA
Mr. John Isaacson
Division Chief
Public Safety Division
Governor's Office of Emergency Services
3650 Schriever Avenue
Mather, CA 95655
P: (916) 845-8644
F: (916) 845-8511
E: john.isaacson@caloes.ca.gov

COLORADO
Mr. Stan Hilkey
Executive Director
Department of Public Safety
700 Kipling Street, #1000
Denver, CO 80215
P: (303) 239-4398
F: (303) 239-4670
E: stan.hilkey@state.co.us

CONNECTICUT
Ms. Dora B. Schriro
Commissioner
Department of Emergency Services & Public Protection
1111 Country Club Road
Middletown, CT 06457
P: (860) 685-8000
F: (860) 685-8354
E: dora.schriro@ct.gov

DELAWARE
Colonel Robert M. Coupe
Cabinet Secretary
Department of Safety & Homeland Security
303 Transportation Circle
P.O. Box 818
Dover, DE 19903
P: (302) 744-2680
F: (302) 739-4874

DISTRICT OF COLUMBIA
Mr. Peter Newsham
Chief of Police
Metropolitan Police Department
300 Indiana Avenue, Northwest
Room 5059
Washington, DC 20001
P: (202) 727-9099
F: (202) 727-4106
E: mpd@dc.gov

FLORIDA
Mr. Rick Swearingen
Commissioner
Department of Law Enforcement
2331 Phillips Road
P.O. Box 1489
Tallahassee, FL 32302
P: (850) 410-7011
E: RickSwearingen@fdle.state.fl.us

GEORGIA
Colonel Mark W. McDonough
Commissioner
Department of Public Safety
959 East Confederate Avenue, Southeast
P.O. Box 1456
Atlanta, GA 30371
P: (404) 624-7477
F: (404) 624-6706

GUAM
Mr. Joseph I. Cruz
Chief of Police
Police Department
#13-16A Mariner Avenue
P.O. Box 23909
Tiyan, GU 96913
P: (671) 475-8508
F: (671) 472-4036
E: chief@gpd.guam.gov

HAWAII
Mr. Nolan Espinda
Director
Department of Public Safety
919 Ala Moana Boulevard, 4th Floor
Honolulu, HI 96814
P: (808) 587-1288
F: (808) 587-1282
E: psd.office.of.the.director@hawaii.gov

ILLINOIS
Ms. Carolyn Gurski
Chief Public Safety Officer
Department of Corrections
1301 Concordia Court
P.O. Box 19277
Springfield, IL 62794
P: (217) 558-2200

INDIANA
Mr. Douglas G. Carter
Superintendent
State Police
Indiana Government Center North
100 North Senate Avenue
Indianapolis, IN 46204
P: (317) 232-8248
E: ISP@isp.in.gov

IOWA
Ms. Roxann M. Ryan
Commissioner
Department of Public Safety
215 East 7th Street
Des Moines, IA 50319
P: (515) 725-6182
E: dpsinfo@dps.state.ia.us

KANSAS
Major General Lee E. Tafanelli (R)
Adjutant General
Adjutant General's Department
5920 Southeast Coyote Drive
Building 2005, Room 229
Topeka, KS 66619
P: (785) 646-1190
F: (785) 274-1682
E: ng.ks.ksarng.list.staff-pao@mail.mil

KENTUCKY
Mr. John Tilley
Secretary
Justice & Public Safety Cabinet
125 Holmes Street
Frankfort, KY 40601
P: (502) 564-7554
F: (502) 564-4840
E: john.tilley@ky.gov

LOUISIANA
Colonel Kevin W. Reeves
Superintendent
State Police
Public Safety Services
7919 Independence Boulevard
Baton Rouge, LA 70806
P: (225) 925-6118

MAINE
Mr. John E. Morris
Commissioner
Department of Public Safety
45 Commerce Drive, Suite 1
104 State House Station
Augusta, ME 04333
P: (207) 626-3800
F: (207) 287-3042
E: john.e.morris@maine.gov

MARYLAND
Mr. Stephen Moyer
Secretary
Department of Public Safety & Correctional Services
300 East Joppa Road, Suite 1000
10th Floor
Towson, MD 21286
P: (410) 339-5000

MASSACHUSETTS
Mr. Daniel Bennett
Secretary
Executive Office of Public Safety & Security
One Ashburton Place, Suite 2133
Boston, MA 02108
P: (617) 727-7775
F: (617) 727-4764
E: eopsinfo@state.ma.us

Public Safety

MICHIGAN
Colonel Kriste Kibbey Etue
Director
State Police
P.O. Box 30634
Lansing, MI 48909
P: (517) 332-2521
F: (517) 241-0991
E: EtueK@michigan.gov

MINNESOTA
Ms. Ramona Dohman
Commissioner
Department of Public Safety
445 Minnesota Street, Suite 199
St. Paul, MN 55101
P: (651) 201-7160
F: (651) 297-5728
E: Mona.Dohman@state.mn.us

MISSISSIPPI
Mr. Marshall Fisher
Commissioner
Department of Public Safety
P.O. Box 958
Jackson, MS 39205
P: (601) 987-1212
F: (601) 987-1488
E: commissioner@mdps.state.ms.us

MISSOURI
Mr. Charles A. Juden
Director
Department of Public Safety
Office of the Director
P.O. Box 749
Jefferson City, MO 65102
P: (573) 751-4905
F: (573) 751-5399

MONTANA
Mr. Ed Tinsley
Continuity of Government Program Manager
Office of State Continuity & Emergency Management
P.O. Box 200113
Helena, MT 59620
P: (406) 444-0125
F: (406) 444-2939
E: Continuity@mt.gov

NEBRASKA
Colonel Bradley Rice
Superintendent of Law Enforcement & Public Safety
State Patrol
1600 Highway 2
Lincoln, NE 68502
P: (402) 471-4545
F: (402) 479-4002
E: Brad.Rice@nebraska.gov

NEVADA
Mr. James Wright
Director
Department of Public Safety
555 Wright Way
Carson City, NV 89711
P: (775) 684-4808
F: (775) 684-4809

NEW HAMPSHIRE
Mr. John J. Barthelmes
Commissioner
Department of Safety
James H. Hayes Safety Building
33 Hazen Drive
Concord, NH 03305
P: (603) 223-3889
F: (603) 271-3903
E: john.barthelmes@dos.nh.gov

NEW JERSEY
Colonel Joseph R. Fuentes
Superintendent
State Police
P.O. Box 7068
West Trenton, NJ 08628
P: (609) 882-2000
F: (609) 530-4383

NEW MEXICO
Mr. Scott Weaver
Cabinet Secretary
Department of Public Safety
4491 Cerrillos Road
P.O. Box 1628
Santa Fe, NM 87504
P: (505) 827-3370
F: (505) 827-3434

NEW YORK
Mr. Michael C. Green
Executive Deputy Commissioner
Division of Criminal Justice Services
Alfred E. Smith Building
80 South Swan Street
Albany, NY 12210
P: (518) 457-5837
F: (518) 473-1271

NORTH CAROLINA
Mr. Erik A. Hooks
Secretary of Public Safety
Department of Public Safety
512 North Salisbury Street
Raleigh, NC 27604
P: (919) 662-4500
E: erik.hooks@ncdps.gov

NORTH DAKOTA
Colonel Michael Gerhart
Superintendent
Highway Patrol
600 East Boulevard Avenue
Department 504
Bismarck, ND 58505
P: (701) 328-2455
F: (701) 328-1717
E: ndhpinfo@nd.gov

NORTHERN MARIANA ISLANDS
Mr. Robert A. Guerrero
Commissioner
Department of Public Safety
Jose M. Sablan Building
Caller Box 10007
Saipan, MP 96950
P: (670) 664-9022
F: (670) 664-9027

OHIO
Colonel John Born
Director
Department of Public Safety
1970 West Broad Street
P.O. Box 182081
Columbus, OH 43218
P: (614) 466-3383
F: (614) 466-0433

OKLAHOMA
Mr. Michael C. Thompson
Commissioner
Department of Public Safety
P.O. Box 11415
Oklahoma City, OK 73136
P: (405) 425-2424
E: mike.thompson@dps.state.ok.us

OREGON
Mr. Eriks Gabliks
Director
Department of Public Safety Standards & Training
4190 Aumsville Highway, Southeast
Salem, OR 97317
P: (503) 378-2332
F: (503) 378-2043
E: eriks.gabliks@state.or.us

PENNSYLVANIA
Colonel Tyree C. Blocker
Commissioner
State Police
1800 Elmerton Avenue
Harrisburg, PA 17110
P: (717) 783-5599
F: (717) 787-2948

PUERTO RICO
Ms. Michelle M. Hernandez De Fraley
Superintendent
Puerto Rico Police
601 Franklin Delano Roosevelt Avenue
San Juan, PR 00936
P: (787) 793-1234

RHODE ISLAND
Colonel Ann Claire Assumpico
Director
Department of Public Safety
311 Danielson Pike
North Scituate, RI 02857
P: (401) 444-1000
F: (401) 444-1105

SOUTH CAROLINA
Mr. Leroy Smith
Director
Department of Public Safety
10311 Wilson Boulevard
P.O. Box 1993
Blythewood, SC 29016
P: (803) 896-7979
F: (803) 896-7881

SOUTH DAKOTA
Mr. Trevor Jones
Secretary
Department of Public Safety
118 West Capitol Avenue
Pierre, SD 57501
P: (605) 773-3178
F: (605) 773-3018
E: DPSInfo@state.sd.us

TENNESSEE
Mr. David Purkey
Commissioner
Department of Safety & Homeland Security
1150 Foster Avenue
P.O. Box 945
Nashville, TN 37202
P: (615) 251-5166
E: email.safety@tn.gov

TEXAS
Mr. Steve McCraw
Director
Department of Public Safety
5805 North Lamar Boulevard
P.O. Box 4087
Austin, TX 78773
P: (512) 424-2000
F: (512) 483-5708

U.S. VIRGIN ISLANDS
Mr. Delroy Richards Sr.
Commissioner
Police Department
Farrelly Criminal Justice Center
Charlotte Amalie
St. Thomas, VI 00802
P: (340) 774-2211
F: (340) 715-5517

UTAH
Mr. Keith D. Squires
Commissioner
Department of Public Safety
South 4501 South 2700 West
Salt Lake City, UT 84129
P: (801) 965-4062
F: (801) 965-4608
E: ksquires@utah.gov

VIRGINIA
Mr. Brian J. Moran
Secretary
Office of the Secretary of Public
Safety & Homeland Security
1111 East Broad Street
P.O. Box 1475
Richmond, VA 23218
P: (804) 786-5351
F: (804) 225-3882
E: brian.moran
@governor.virginia.gov

WASHINGTON
Mr. John R. Batiste
Chief
State Patrol
General Administration Building
P.O. Box 42600
Olympia, WA 98504
P: (360) 596-4000
F: (360) 596-4128
E: john.batiste@wsp.wa.gov

WEST VIRGINIA
Mr. Jeff Sandy
Cabinet Secretary
Department of Military Affairs
& Public Safety
Building 1, Room W-400
1900 Kanawha Boulevard, East
Charleston, WV 25305
P: (304) 558-2930
E: Jeff.Sandy@wv.gov

WISCONSIN
Mr. Brian O'Keefe
Administrator
Division of Criminal
Investigation
Department of Justice
P.O. Box 7857
Madison, WI 53707
P: (608) 266-1221
F: (608) 267-2779

WYOMING
Colonel Kebin Haller
Administrator
Highway Patrol
5300 Bishop Boulevard
Cheyenne, WY 82009
P: (307) 777-4301
F: (307) 777-3897

Public Utility Regulation

Supervises and regulates the electric, gas, telephone and water utilities in the state.

Information provided by:

National Association of Regulatory Utility Commissioners
Greg R. White
Executive Director
1101 Vermont Avenue NW,
Suite 200
Washington, DC 20005
P: (202) 898-2208
F: (202) 898-2213
gwhite@naruc.org
www.naruc.org

ALABAMA
Ms. Twinkle Andress Cavanaugh (R)
President
Public Service Commission
100 North Union Street, Suite 850
Montgomery, AL 36104
P: (334) 242-5297
F: (334) 242-0509
E: twinkle.cavanaugh@psc.alabama.gov

ALASKA
Mr. Robert Pickett
Chair
Regulatory Commission
701 West 8th Avenue, Suite 300
Anchorage, AK 99501
P: (907) 276-6222
F: (907) 276-0160
E: bob.pickett@alaska.gov

ARIZONA
The Honorable Doug Little (R)
Commissioner
Corporation Commission
Commissioner's Wing
1200 West Washington, 2nd Floor
Phoenix, AZ 85007
P: (602) 542-2237
F: (602) 542-0752
E: little-web@azcc.gov

ARKANSAS
Mr. Ted J. Thomas
Chair
Public Service Commission
1000 Center Building
P.O. Box 400
Little Rock, AR 72201
P: (501) 682-5804
F: (501) 682-5731
E: tthomas@psc.state.ar.us

CALIFORNIA
Mr. Michael Picker
President
Public Utilities Commission
California State Building
505 Van Ness Avenue
San Francisco, CA 94102
P: (415) 703-2284
E: mp6@cpuc.ca.gov

COLORADO
Mr. Jeffrey P. Ackermann
Chair
Public Utilities Commission
1560 Broadway, Suite 250
Denver, CO 80202
P: (303) 894-2000
F: (303) 866-2930
E: jeffrey.ackermann@state.co.us

CONNECTICUT
Ms. Katie Scharf Dykes
Chair
Public Utilities Regulatory Authority
Energy & Environmental Protection
10 Franklin Square
New Britain, CT 06051
P: (860) 827-1553
F: (860) 418-6495
E: katie.dykes@ct.gov

DELAWARE
Mr. Dallas Winslow
Chair
Public Service Commission
861 Silver Lake Boulevard
Cannon Building, Suite 100
Dover, DE 19904
P: (302) 736-7500
F: (302) 739-4849
E: dallaswinslow@yahoo.com

DISTRICT OF COLUMBIA
Ms. Betty Ann Kane
Chair
Public Service Commission
1325 G Street, Northwest
Suite 800
Washington, DC 20005
P: (202) 821-9129
F: (202) 626-9212
E: bakane@psc.dc.gov

FLORIDA
Ms. Julie Imanuel Brown
Chair
Public Service Commission
2540 Shumard Oak Boulevard
Gerald Gunter Building
Tallahassee, FL 32399
P: (850) 413-6042
F: (850) 413-6025
E: jibrown@psc.state.fl.us

GEORGIA
Mr. Stan Wise
Chair
Public Service Commission
244 Washington Street
Atlanta, GA 30334
P: (404) 657-4574
F: (404) 657-4576
E: stanwise@psc.state.ga.us

GUAM
Mr. Jeffrey C. Johnson
Chair
Public Utilities Commission
414 West Soledad Avenue, Suite 207
GCIC Building, P.O. Box 862
Hagatna, GU 96910
P: (671) 472-1907
F: (671) 472-1917
E: jjohnson@guampuc.com

HAWAII
Mr. Randall Y. Iwase
Chair
Public Utilities Commission
465 South King Street
Kekuanao'a Building, Room 103
Honolulu, HI 96813
P: (808) 586-2020
F: (808) 586-2066
E: randy.y.iwase@hawaii.gov

IDAHO
Mr. Paul Kjellander
President
Public Utilities Commission
472 West Washington Street
P.O. Box 83720
Boise, ID 83720
P: (208) 334-2898
F: (208) 334-3762
E: paul.kjellander@puc.idaho.gov

ILLINOIS
Mr. Brien J. Sheahan
Chair
Commerce Commission
160 North LaSalle Street, Suite C-800
Chicago, IL 60601
P: (312) 814-8592
F: (312) 814-1818
E: bsheahan@icc.illinois.gov

INDIANA
Mr. Jim D. Atterholt
Chair
Utility Regulatory Commission
PNC Center, Suite 1500 East
101 West Washington Street
Indianapolis, IN 46204
P: (317) 232-2701
E: jatterholt@urc.in.gov

IOWA
Ms. Geri Huser
Chair
Utilities Board
1375 East Court Avenue, Room 69
Des Moines, IA 50319
P: (515) 725-7888
F: (515) 725-7399
E: geri.huser@iub.iowa.gov

KANSAS
Mr. Pat Apple
Corporation Commission
1500 Southwest Arrowhead Road
Topeka, KS 66604
P: (785) 271-3100
E: p.apple@kcc.ks.gov

KENTUCKY
Mr. Michael J. Schmitt
Chair
Public Service Commission
211 Sower Boulevard
Frankfort, KY 40601
P: (502) 782-2555
E: michael.schmitt@ky.gov

LOUISIANA
Mr. Lambert C. Boissiere III
Commissioner
Public Service Commission
602 North Fifth Street
P.O. Box 91154
Baton Rouge, LA 70821
P: (225) 342-4999
F: (504) 680-9536
E: cesily.roberts@la.gov

MAINE
Mr. Mark Vannoy
Chair
Public Utilities Commission
18 State House Station
Augusta, ME 04333
P: (207) 287-3831
F: (207) 287-1039
E: mark.vannoy@maine.gov

MARYLAND
Mr. W. Kevin Hughes
Chair
Public Service Commission
6 St. Paul Street, 16th Floor
Baltimore, MD 21202
P: (410) 767-8073
F: (410) 333-6495
E: kevin.hughes@maryland.gov

MASSACHUSETTS
Ms. Angela M. O'Connor
Chair
Department of Public Utilities
One South Station
Boston, MA 02110
P: (617) 305-3500
F: (617) 345-9102
E: angie.oconnor@state.ma.us

MICHIGAN
Ms. Sally Talberg
Chair
Public Service Commission
P.O. Box 30221
Lansing, MI 48909
P: (517) 284-8075
F: (517) 284-8293
E: talbergs@michigan.gov

MINNESOTA
Ms. Nancy Lange
Chair
Public Utilities Commission
121 7th Place East, Suite 350
St. Paul, MN 55101
P: (651) 201-2240
E: nancy.lange@state.mn.us

MISSISSIPPI
Mr. Brandon Presley
Commissioner
Public Service Commission
501 North West Street
Woolfolk State Office Building
Jackson, MS 39201
P: (662) 963-1471
F: (601) 961-5824
E: brandon.presley@psc.state.ms.us

MISSOURI
Mr. Daniel Hall
Chair
Public Service Commission
200 Maidson Street
Governor Office Building
Jefferson City, MO 65101
P: (573) 751-3243
F: (573) 526-7341
E: daniel.hall@psc.mo.gov

MONTANA
Mr. Brad Johnson
Chair
Public Service Commission
1701 Prospect Avenue
P.O. Box 202601
Helena, MT 59620
P: (406) 444-6169
F: (406) 444-7618
E: bjohnson@mt.gov

NEBRASKA
Mr. Tim Schram
Chair
Public Service Commission
P.O. Box 94927
Lincoln, NE 68509
P: (402) 471-0218
E: tim.schram@nebraska.gov

NEVADA
Mr. Joseph C. Reynolds
Chair
Public Utilities Commission
1150 East William Street
Carson City, NV 89701
P: (775) 684-6123
E: joereynolds@puc.nv.gov

NEW HAMPSHIRE
Mr. Martin Honigberg
Chair
Public Utilities Commission
21 South Fruit Street, Suite 10
Concord, NH 03301
P: (603) 271-2443
E: martin.honigberg@puc.nh.gov

NEW JERSEY
Mr. Richard S. Mroz
President
Board of Public Utilities
44 South Clinton Avenue
P.O. Box 350
Trenton, NJ 08625
P: (609) 777-3310
F: (609) 777-3330
E: richard.mroz@bpu.nj.gov

NEW MEXICO
Mr. Sandy Jones
Chair
Public Regulation Commission
1120 Paseo De Peralta
Santa Fe, NM 87501
P: (505) 827-8020
E: sandy.jones@state.nm.us

NEW YORK
Mr. Gregg Sayre
Chair
Public Service Commission
Three Empire State Plaza
Albany, NY 12223
P: (518) 408-1978
E: gregg.sayre@dps.ny.gov

NORTH CAROLINA
Mr. Edward S. Finley Jr.
Chair
Utilities Commission
430 North Salisbury Street
Raleigh, NC 27603
P: (919) 733-6067
F: (919) 715-5970
E: finley@ncuc.net

NORTH DAKOTA
The Honorable Randy Christmann (R)
Chair
Public Service Commission
600 East Boulevard Avenue
Department 408
Bismarck, ND 58505
P: (701) 328-2400
F: (701) 328-2410
E: rchristmann@nd.gov

OHIO
Mr. Asim Z. Haque
Chair
Public Utilities Commission
180 East Broad Street
Columbus, OH 43215
P: (614) 466-3204
E: asim.haque@puco.ohio.gov

OKLAHOMA
The Honorable Bob Anthony (R)
Chair
Corporation Commission
Jim Thorpe Office Building
2101 North Lincoln Boulevard
Oklahoma City, OK 73105
P: (405) 521-2261
F: (405) 521-4532
E: b.anthony@occemail.com

OREGON
Ms. Lisa Hardie
Chair
Public Utility Commission
201 High Street Southeast, Suite 100
P.O. Box 1088
Salem, OR 97301
P: (503) 378-6611
E: Lisa.Hardie@state.or.us

PUERTO RICO
Mr. Omar E. Negron Judice
Chair
Public Service Commission
P.O. Box 190870
San Juan, PR 00919
P: (787) 756-1919
F: (787) 756-8086
E: onegron@csp.pr.gov

RHODE ISLAND
Ms. Margaret E. Curran
Chair
Public Utilities Commission
89 Jefferson Boulevard
Warwick, RI 02888
P: (401) 941-4500
F: (401) 941-1691
E: margaret.curran@puc.ri.gov

SOUTH CAROLINA
Mr. Swain E. Whitfield
Chair
Public Service Commission
101 Executive Center Drive, Suite 100
Columbia, SC 29210
P: (803) 896-5100
E: swain.whitfield@psc.sc.gov

SOUTH DAKOTA
The Honorable Kristie Fiegen (R)
Chair
Public Utilities Commission
State Capitol
500 East Capitol Avenue
Pierre, SD 57501
P: (605) 773-3201
F: (866) 757-6031
E: kristie.fiegen@state.sd.us

TENNESSEE
Mr. David Jones
Chair
Public Utility Commission
502 Deaderick Street, 4th Floor
Nashville, TN 37243
P: (615) 714-1920
E: david.jones@completeholdingsgroup.com

TEXAS
Ms. Donna L. Nelson
Chair
Public Utility Commission
1701 North Congress Avenue
Austin, TX 78701
P: (512) 936-7015
F: (512) 936-7018
E: donna.nelson@puc.texas.gov

Public Utility Regulation

U.S. VIRGIN ISLANDS
Mr. Andrew Rutnik
Chair
Public Service Commission
P.O. Box 40
Charlotte Amalie
St. Thomas, VI 00804
P: (340) 776-1291
E: andrewrutnik@gmail.com

VERMONT
Mr. James Volz
Chair
Public Service Board
112 State Street, 4th Floor
Montpelier, VT 05620
P: (802) 828-1655
F: (802) 828-3351
E: james.volz@vermont.gov

VIRGINIA
Ms. Judith W. Jagdmann
Chair
State Corporation Commission
1300 East Main Street
Richmond, VA 23219
P: (804) 371-9608
F: (804) 371-9376
E: judy.jagdmann
@scc.virginia.gov

WASHINGTON
Mr. David W. Danner
Chair
Utilities & Transportation
Commission
1300 South Evergreen Park
Drive
P.O. Box 47250
Olympia, WA 98504
P: (360) 664-1208
F: (360) 586-1150
E: ddanner@utc.wa.gov

WEST VIRGINIA
Mr. Michael A. Albert
Chair
Public Service Commission
201 Brooks Street
Charleston, WV 25301
P: (304) 340-0300
F: (304) 340-3758
E: malbert@psc.state.wv.us

WISCONSIN
Ms. Ellen Nowak
Chair
Public Service Commission
610 North Whitney Way
Madison, WI 53705
P: (608) 267-7899
F: (608) 266-1401
E: ellen.nowak
@wisconsin.gov

WYOMING
Mr. Bill Russell
Chair
Public Service Commission
2515 Warren Avenue, Suite 300
Cheyenne, WY 82002
P: (307) 777-7427
E: bill.russell2@wyo.gov

Purchasing

Central screening and acquisition point for supplies, equipment, and/or services for state agencies.

ALABAMA
Mr. Michael Jones
State Purchasing Director
Division of Purchasing
Department of Finance
100 North Union Street, Suite 192
Montgomery, AL 36104
P: (334) 242-7250
F: (334) 242-4419
E: michael.jones@purchasing.alabama.gov

ALASKA
Mr. Jason Soza
Chief Procurement Officer
Division of General Services
333 Willoughby Avenue, Floor 7
State Office Building, P.O. Box 110210
Juneau, AK 99811
P: (907) 465-5684
E: jason.soza@alaska.gov

ARIZONA
Mr. Stephen Nettles
Statewide Procurement Group Manager
State Procurement Office
100 North 15th Avenue, Suite 201
Phoenix, AZ 85007
P: (602) 542-9145
E: steve.nettles@azdoa.gov

ARKANSAS
Mr. Edward Armstrong
State Procurement Director
Office of State Procurement
Department of Finance & Administration
1509 West 7th Street, Floor 3
Little Rock, AR 72201
P: (501) 324-9316
E: edward.armstrong@dfa.arkansas.gov

CALIFORNIA
Mr. Ricardo Martinez
Acting Deputy Director
Procurement Division
Department of General Services
707 Third Street, Floor 2
West Sacramento, CA 95605
P: (916) 375-4563
E: ricardo.martinez@dgs.ca.gov

COLORADO
Ms. Cindy Lombardi
State Purchasing & Contracts Director
Department of Personnel & Administration
1525 Sherman Street, Floor 3
Denver, CO 80203
P: (303) 866-6212
F: (303) 894-7445
E: cindy.lombardi@state.co.us

CONNECTICUT
Ms. Carol Wilson
Director of Procurement
Procurement Division
450 Columbus Boulevard, Suite 1202
Hartford, CT 06103
P: (860) 713-5093
F: (860) 622-2904
E: carol.wilson@ct.gov

DELAWARE
Mr. Dean W. Stotler
Director
Government Support Services
Office of Management & Budget
100 Enterprise Place, Suite 4
Dover, DE 19904
P: (302) 857-4501
F: (302) 739-2564
E: dean.stotler@state.de.us

DISTRICT OF COLUMBIA
Mr. George Schutter
Chief Procurement Officer
Office of Contracting & Procurement
441 4th Street, Northwest
Suite 700S
Washington, DC 20001
P: (202) 724-4242
E: george.schutter@dc.gov

FLORIDA
Ms. Rosalyn Ingram
Director of State Purchasing & Chief Procurement Officer
Division of State Purchasing
4050 Esplanade Way, Suite 360
Tallahassee, FL 32399
P: (850) 488-3049
E: rosalyn.ingram@dms.myflorida.com

GEORGIA
Ms. Lisa Eason
Deputy Commissioner
State Purchasing Division
200 Piedmont Avenue, Suite 1302
West Tower
Atlanta, GA 30334
P: (404) 656-0934
F: (770) 334-4903
E: lisa.eason@doas.ga.gov

HAWAII
Ms. Sarah Allen
Procurement Administrator
State Procurement Office
1151 Punchbowl Street, Room 230A
Honolulu, HI 96813
P: (808) 587-4700
E: sarah.allen@hawaii.gov

IDAHO
Ms. Sarah Hilderbrand
Chief Procurement Officer
Division of Purchasing
650 West State Street, Room B15
Boise, ID 83702
P: (208) 332-1612
F: (208) 327-7320
E: sarah.hilderbrand@adm.idaho.gov

ILLINOIS
Ms. Ellen Daley
Chief Procurement Officer
Chief Procurement Office for General Services
Stratton Building, Room 712
401 South Spring Street
Springfield, IL 62706
P: (217) 558-2231
E: ellen.h.daley@illinois.gov

INDIANA
Ms. Erin Kellam
Interim Deputy Commissioner of Strategic Sourcing
Department of Administration
402 West Washington Street
Room W479
Indianapolis, IN 46204
P: (317) 234-8851
E: ekellam@idoa.in.gov

IOWA
Mr. Kelly Green
Chief Operations Officer
Central Procurement & Fleet Services Enterprise
Hoover State Office Building, Floor 3
1305 East Walnut Street
Des Moines, IA 50319
P: (515) 725-2272
E: kelly.green@iowa.gov

KANSAS
Mr. Tracy Diel
Director of Procurement & Contracts
Office of Procurement & Contracts
Department of Administration
900 Southwest Jackson, Suite 451-S
Topeka, KS 66612
P: (785) 296-2376
F: (785) 296-7240
E: tracy.diel@da.ks.gov

KENTUCKY
Ms. Joan Graham
Executive Director
Office of Procurement Services
702 Capitol Annex, Room 096
Frankfort, KY 40601
P: (502) 564-8624
F: (502) 564-6013
E: joan.graham@ky.gov

LOUISIANA
Ms. Paula Tregre
Interim Director of State Procurement
Office of State Procurement
1201 North 3rd Street, Suite 2-160
P.O. Box 94095
Baton Rouge, LA 70804
P: (225) 342-3793
E: paula.tregre@la.gov

MAINE
Mr. Kevin Scheirer
Director
Division of Purchases
Burton M. Cross Building, Floor 4
9 State House Station, 111 Sewall Street
Augusta, ME 04333
P: (207) 624-7349
E: kevin.scheirer@maine.gov

Purchasing

MARYLAND
Ms. Lauri McGuire
Assistant Secretary,
Procurement & Logistics
Department of General Services
State Office Building
301 West Preston Street, Suite M-10
Baltimore, MD 21201
P: (410) 767-7522
E: lauri.mcguire@maryland.gov

MASSACHUSETTS
Mr. Gary Lambert
Assistant Secretary for Operational Services
Operational Services Division
One Ashburton Place, Room 1017
Boston, MA 02108
P: (617) 720-3330
F: (617) 727-4527
E: gary.lambert@state.ma.us

MICHIGAN
Mr. Jim Colangelo
Chief Procurement Officer
DTMB-Procurement
525 West Allegan Street
Lansing, MI 48913
P: (517) 284-6998
E: colangeloj@michigan.gov

MINNESOTA
Ms. Betsy Hayes
Chief Procurement Officer
Office of State Procurement
Department of Administration
50 Sherburne Avenue, Suite 112
St. Paul, MN 55155
P: (651) 201-2400
F: (651) 297-3996
E: betsy.hayes@state.mn.us

MISSISSIPPI
Ms. Aubry Leigh Goodwin
Chief Procurement Officer
Office of Purchasing, Travel & Fleet Management
Department of Finance & Administration
501 North West Street, Suite 701A
Jackson, MS 39201
P: (601) 359-3409
F: (601) 359-3910
E: aubreyleigh.goodwin@dfa.ms.gov

MISSOURI
Ms. Karen Boeger
Director of Purchasing
Division of Purchasing & Materials Management
301 West High Street, Room 630
Harry S. Truman Building
Jefferson City, MO 65101
P: (573) 751-1699
F: (573) 526-9815
E: karen.boeger@oa.mo.gov

MONTANA
Mr. Brad Sanders
Chief Procurement Officer
State Procurement Bureau
State Financial Services Division
125 North Roberts Street, Room 165
Helena, MT 59601
P: (406) 444-1459
F: (406) 444-2529
E: bsanders@mt.gov

NEBRASKA
Mr. Bo Botelho
Administrator/Chief of Operations
Department of Administrative Services, Materiel Division
1526 K Street, Suite 130
Lincoln, NE 68508
P: (402) 471-0972
F: (402) 471-2089
E: bob.botelho@nebraska.gov

NEVADA
Mr. Jeff Haag
Administrator
Purchasing Division
Department of Administration
515 East Musser Street, Suite 300
Carson City, NV 89701
P: (775) 684-0184
E: jhaag@admin.nv.gov

NEW HAMPSHIRE
Ms. Lisa Pollard
Director of Procurement & Support Services
Bureau of Purchase & Property
25 Capitol Street, Room 102
Concord, NH 03301
P: (603) 271-7272
E: lisa.pollard@nh.gov

NEW JERSEY
Mr. Maurice Griffin
Acting Director
Division of Purchase & Property
Department of Treasury
33 West State Street, 8th Floor
Trenton, NJ 08608
P: (609) 292-4886
E: maurice.griffin@treas.nj.gov

NEW MEXICO
Mr. Lawrence Maxwell
Director of State Purchasing
State Purchasing Division
General Services Department
1100 St. Francis Drive, Room 2016
Santa Fe, NM 87505
P: (505) 827-0472
F: (505) 827-2484
E: Lawrence.Maxwell@state.nm.us

NEW YORK
Mr. Sean Carroll
Chief Procurement Officer
State Procurement
Corning Tower, Floor 38
Empire State Plaza
Albany, NY 12242
P: (518) 473-5294
E: sean.carroll@ogs.ny.gov

NORTH CAROLINA
Ms. Angela Dunaway
Deputy State Purchasing Officer
Division of Purchase & Contract
116 West Jones Street
Raleigh, NC 27603
P: (919) 807-4545
E: angie.dunaway@doa.nc.gov

NORTH DAKOTA
Ms. Sherry Neas
Director
Central Services Division - SPO
Capitol Tower, Floor 14, Department 012
600 East Boulevard Avenue
Bismarck, ND 58505
P: (701) 328-1726
F: (701) 328-1615
E: sneas@nd.gov

OHIO
Ms. Kelly Sanders
Chief Procurement Officer
Office of Procurement Services
4200 Surface Road
Columbus, OH 43228
P: (614) 752-5259
E: kelly.sanders@das.ohio.gov

OKLAHOMA
Mr. Ferris Barger
State Purchasing Director
Central Purchasing Division
Management & Enterprise Services
5005 North Lincoln Street, Suite 300
Oklahoma City, OK 73105
P: (405) 521-2115
E: ferris.barger@omes.ok.gov

OREGON
Ms. Dianne Lancaster
Chief Procurement Officer
Enterprise Goods & Services, Procurement Policy
Department of Administrative Services
155 Cottage Street, Northeast, Floor 3
Salem, OR 97301
P: (503) 378-3529
F: (503) 373-1626
E: dianne.lancaster@oregon.gov

PENNSYLVANIA
Ms. Jennifer Doherty
Chief Procurement Officer
Bureau of Procurement
Department of General Services
555 Walnut Street, Floor 6
Harrisburg, PA 17101
P: (717) 787-5862
E: jedoherty@pa.gov

RHODE ISLAND
Ms. Nancy McIntyre
Purchasing Agent
Division of Purchases
Department of Administration
One Capitol Hill, Floor 2
Providence, RI 02908
P: (401) 574-8126
F: (401) 574-8387
E: nancy.mcintyre@purchasing.ri.gov

SOUTH CAROLINA
Mr. Delbert Singleton
Division Director
Division of Procurement Services
State Fiscal Accountability Authority
1201 Main Street, Suite 600
Columbia, SC 29201
P: (803) 734-2314
F: (803) 734-2117
E: delbert@sfaa.sc.gov

SOUTH DAKOTA
Mr. Steven Berg
Director of Procurement
Office of Procurement Management
Bureau of Administration
523 East Capitol Avenue, PMB 01231
Pierre, SD 57501
P: (605) 773-3405
F: (605) 773-4840
E: steven.berg@state.sd.us

TENNESSEE
Mr. Mike Perry
Chief Procurement Officer
Central Procurement Office
WRS Tennessee Tower, Floor 3
312 Rosa L. Parks Avenue
Nashville, TN 37243
P: (615) 741-3625
E: mike.perry@tn.gov

TEXAS
Ms. Jette Withers
Director
Statewide Procurement Division
Comptroller of Public Accounts
P.O. Box 13186
Austin, TX 78711
P: (512) 463-3938
E: jette.withers@cpa.texas.gov

UTAH
Mr. Kent Beers
Executive Director
Division of Purchasing
3150 State Office Building, Capitol Hill
P.O. Box 141061
Salt Lake City, UT 84114
P: (801) 538-3143
F: (801) 538-3882
E: kbeers@utah.gov

VERMONT
Ms. Deb Damore
Director
Department of Buildings & General Services
Office of Purchasing & Contracting
10 Baldwin Street
Montpelier, VT 05633
P: (802) 828-5784
F: (802) 828-2222
E: deborah.damore@vermont.gov

VIRGINIA
Mr. Robert Gleason
Director
Division of Purchases & Supply
1111 East Broad Street
Richmond, VA 23219
P: (804) 786-3846
F: (804) 371-7877
E: robert.gleason@dgs.virginia.gov

WASHINGTON
Ms. Christine Warnock
Chief Procurement Officer
Contracts & Procurement, Department of Enterprise Services
1500 Jefferson Street, Southeast
Floor 6, P.O. Box 41411
Olympia, WA 98501
P: (360) 407-9398
F: (360) 586-2426
E: christine.warnock@des.wa.gov

WEST VIRGINIA
Mr. David R. Tincher
Director
Purchasing Division
Department of Administration
2019 Washington Street, East
Charleston, WV 25305
P: (304) 558-2538
F: (304) 558-0006
E: david.tincher@wv.gov

WISCONSIN
Mr. Rick Hughes
Bureau Director
Bureau of Procurement
101 East Wilson Street, Floor 6
P.O. Box 7867
Madison, WI 53707
P: (608) 266-1558
F: (608) 267-0600
E: rick.hughes@wisconsin.gov

WYOMING
Ms. Lori Galles
Procurment Manager
Department of Administration & Information
General Services Division
700 West 21st Street
Cheyenne, WY 82002
P: (307) 777-6707
F: (307) 777-5852
E: lori.galles@wyo.gov

Recycling

Responsible for promoting and implementing state oversight of municipal solid waste recycling, source reduction and recycling within state government and industry.

ALABAMA
Mr. Lance R. LeFleur
Director
Department of Environmental Management
P.O. Box 301463
Montgomery, AL 36130
P: (334) 271-7710
F: (334) 279-3043

ALASKA
Mr. Bob Blankenburg
Program Manager
Solid Waste Program
Division of Environmental Health
555 Cordova Street
Anchorage, AK 99501
P: (907) 269-7802
F: (907) 269-7510
E: bob.blankenburg@alaska.gov

ARIZONA
Ms. Laura L. Malone
Waste Programs Division Director
Department of Environmental Quality
1110 West Washington Street
Phoenix, AZ 85007
P: (602) 771-4208
F: (602) 771-2302
E: malone.laura@azdeq.gov

CALIFORNIA
Mr. Scott Smithline
Director
Department of Resources, Recycling & Recovery
1001 I Street
P.O. Box 4025
Sacramento, CA 95812
P: (916) 322-4032
F: (916) 319-7227
E: Scott.Smithline@CalRecycle.ca.gov

COLORADO
Mr. Gary Baughman
Director
Hazardous Materials & Waste Management Division
Public Health & Environment
4300 Cherry Creek Drive, South
Denver, CO 80246
P: (303) 692-3338
F: (303) 759-5355
E: gary.baughman@state.co.us

CONNECTICUT
Ms. Yvonne Bolton
Bureau Chief
Bureau of Materials Management & Compliance Assurance
Energy & Environmental Protection
79 Elm Street
Hartford, CT 06106
P: (860) 424-3021
F: (860) 424-4060
E: yvonne.bolton@ct.gov

DELAWARE
Mr. Richard P. Watson
Chief Executive Officer
Solid Waste Authority
1128 South Bradford Street
Dover, DE 19904
P: (302) 739-5361
F: (302) 739–4287
E: info@dswa.com

DISTRICT OF COLUMBIA
Mr. Christopher Shorter
Director
Department of Public Works
Frank D. Reeves Municipal Center
2000 14th Street, Northwest
Washington, DC 20009
P: (202) 673-6833
F: (202) 671-0642
E: dpw@dc.gov

FLORIDA
Mr. Joe Ullo
Director
Division of Waste Management
Department of Environmental Protection
2600 Blair Stone Road
Tallahassee, FL 32399
P: (850) 245-8693
E: joseph.ullo@dep.state.fl.us

GEORGIA
Mr. Kevin Clark
Executive Director
Environmental Finance Authority
233 Peachtree Street, Northeast
Harris Tower, Suite 900
Atlanta, GA 30303
P: (404) 584-1000
F: (404) 584-1069
E: kclark@gefa.ga.gov

GUAM
Mr. Glenn Leon Guerrero
Director
Department of Public Works
542 North Marine Corp Drive
Tamuning, GU 96913
P: (671) 646-3131
F: (671) 649-6178
E: glenn.leonguerrero@dpw.guam.gov

HAWAII
Mr. Keith Kawaoka
Deputy Director
Environmental Health Administration
Department of Health
1250 Punchbowl Street
Honolulu, HI 96813
P: (808) 586-4424
F: (808) 586-4368

IDAHO
Mr. John Tippets
Director
Department of Environmental Quality
1410 North Hilton
Boise, ID 83706
P: (208) 373-0240
F: (208) 373-0417
E: john.tippets@deq.idaho.gov

ILLINOIS
Mr. Sean McCarthy
Director
Department of Commerce & Economic Opportunity
100 West Randolph Street, Suite 3-400
Chicago, IL 60601
P: (312) 814-2811

KANSAS
Mr. William L. Bider
Director
Bureau of Waste Management
Department of Health & Environment
1000 Southwest Jackson Street, Suite 320
Topeka, KS 66612
P: (785) 296-1600
F: (785) 296-1612
E: William.Bider@ks.gov

KENTUCKY
Mr. Jon Maybriar
Division Director
Division of Waste Management
Department for Environmental Protection
300 Sower Boulevard, 2nd Floor
Frankfort, KY 40601
P: (502) 564-6702
F: (502) 564-4245
E: jon.maybriar@ky.gov

LOUISIANA
Ms. Lourdes Iturralde
Assistant Secretary
Office of Environmental Compliance
Department of Environmental Quality
P.O. Box 4312
Baton Rouge, LA 70821
P: (225) 219-3710
F: (225) 219-3708
E: deqoec@la.gov

MARYLAND
Ms. Hilary Miller
Director
Land Management Administration
Department of the Environment
1800 Washington Boulevard
Baltimore, MD 21230
P: (410) 537-3314
F: (410) 537-3321
E: hilary.miller@maryland.gov

MASSACHUSETTS
Mr. Matthew A. Beaton
Secretary of Energy and Environmental Affairs
Executive Office of Energy & Environmental Affairs
100 Cambridge Street, Suite 900
Boston, MA 02114
P: (614) 626-1000
F: (614) 626-4900
E: env.internet@state.ma.us

MICHIGAN
Ms. Heidi Grether
Director
Department of Environmental Quality
P.O. Box 30473
Lansing, MI 48909
P: (517) 284-6700
F: (517) 241-7401
E: GretherH@michigan.gov

MINNESOTA
Mr. Matt Massman
Commissioner
Department of Administration
116 Veterans Service Building
20 West 12 Street
St. Paul, MN 55155
P: (651) 201-3421
F: (651) 297-7909
E: Matt.Massman@state.mn.us

MISSISSIPPI
Ms. Jennifer Milner
State Recycling Coordinator
Recycling & Solid Waste Reduction Program
Department of Environmental Quality
P.O. Box 2261
Jackson, MS 39225
P: (601) 961-5739
F: (601) 961-5785

MISSOURI
Mr. Chris Nagel
Program Director
Solid Waste Management Program
Department of Natural Resources
P.O. Box 176
Jefferson City, MO 65102
P: (573) 751-5401
F: (573) 526-3902
E: swmp@dnr.mo.gov

MONTANA
Mr. John Lewis
Director
Department of Administration
125 North Roberts Street, Room 155
P.O. Box 200101
Helena, MT 59620
P: (406) 444-3033
F: (406) 444-6194
E: johnlewis@mt.gov

NEBRASKA
Mr. Jim Macy
Director
Department of Environmental Quality
1200 N Street, Suite 400
P.O. Box 98922
Lincoln, NE 68509
P: (402) 471-2186
F: (402) 471-2909
E: Jim.Macy@nebraska.gov

NEVADA
Mr. Eric Noack
Bureau Chief
Bureau of Waste Management
Division of Environmental Protection
901 South Stewart Street, Suite 4001
Carson City, NV 89701
P: (775) 687-9366
F: (775) 687-6396
E: enoack@ndep.nv.gov

NEW HAMPSHIRE
Mr. Thomas S. Burack
Commissioner
Department of Environmental Services
29 Hazen Drive
P.O. Box 95
Concord, NH 03302
P: (603) 271-3449
F: (603) 271-2867
E: thomas.burack@des.nh.gov

NEW JERSEY
Mr. Zafar Billah
Acting Bureau Chief
Bureau of Recycling & Hazardous Waste Management
Department of Environmental Protection
P.O. Box 402
Trenton, NJ 08625
P: (609) 984-3438
F: (609) 633-1112

NEW MEXICO
Ms. Auralie Ashley-Marx
Bureau Chief
Solid Waste Bureau
Harold Runnels Building, Room N2150
1190 St. Francis Drive, P.O. Box 5469
Santa Fe, NM 87502
P: (505) 827-0197
F: (505) 827-2902
E: auralie.ashley-marx@state.nm.us

NEW YORK
Mr. David Vitale
Director
Division of Materials Management
625 Broadway, Floor 9
Albany, NY 12233
P: (518) 402-8678
F: (518) 402-9024
E: dmm@dec.ny.gov

NORTH DAKOTA
Mr. Scott Radig
Director
Division of Waste Management
Department of Health
918 East Divide Avenue, 3rd Floor
Bismark, ND 58501
P: (701) 328-5166
F: (701) 328-5200
E: sradig@nd.gov

NORTHERN MARIANA ISLANDS
Mr. James A. Ada
Secretary
Department of Public Works
Caller Box 10007, Capitol Hill
Saipan, MP 96950
P: (670) 235-5827
F: (670) 235-6346

OHIO
Mr. James J. Zehringer
Director
Department of Natural Resources
2045 Morse Road
Columbus, OH 43229
P: (614) 265-6565
F: (614) 261-9601

OKLAHOMA
Ms. Kelly Dixon
Division Director
Land Protection Division
Department of Environmental Quality
P.O. Box 1677
Oklahoma City, OK 73101
P: (405) 702-5100
F: (405) 702-5101
E: kelly.dixon@deq.ok.gov

OREGON
Mr. George M. Naughton
Chief Financial Officer
Chief Financial Office
Department of Administrative Services
155 Cottage Street, Northeast, U10
Salem, OR 97301
P: (503) 378-5460
F: (503) 373-7643
E: george.m.naughton@oregon.gov

PENNSYLVANIA
Mr. Walt Harner
Bureau Director
Bureau of Waste Management
Department of Environmental Protection
P.O. Box 69170
Harrisburg, PA 17106
P: (717) 783-2388
F: (717) 787-1904
E: ra-epwaste@pa.gov

PUERTO RICO
Mr. Nelson J. Santiago Marrero
Executive Director
Solid Waste Management Authority
P.O. Box 40285
San Juan, PR 00940
P: (787) 765-7575
F: (787) 753-2220

RHODE ISLAND
Mr. Michael O'Connell
Executive Director
Resource Recovery Corporation
65 Shun Pike
Johnston, RI 02919
P: (401) 942-1430
F: (401) 942-3280
E: moconnell@rirrc.org

SOUTH CAROLINA
Ms. Myra Reece
Director of Environmental Affairs
Department of Health & Environmental Control
2600 Bull Street
Columbia, SC 29201
P: (803) 898-3432
F: (803) 896-4001
E: info@dhec.sc.gov

Recycling

SOUTH DAKOTA
Ms. Vonni Kallemeyn
Environmental Scientist Manager
Department of Environment & Natural Resources
Waste Management Program
523 East Capitol Avenue
Pierre, SD 57501
P: (605) 773-3153
F: (605) 773-6035
E: denrinternet@state.sd.us

TENNESSEE
Mr. Robert J. Martineau Jr.
Commissioner
Department of Environment & Conservation
William R. Snodgrass Tennessee Tower
312 Rosa L. Parks Avenue, 2nd Floor
Nashville, TN 37243
P: (615) 532-0109
F: (615) 532-0120

TEXAS
Ms. Gayla D. Davis
Manager
State Leasing Services
Facilities Commission
P.O. Box 13047
Austin, TX 78711
P: (512) 463-3331
F: (512) 239-5533
E: Gayla.Davis@tfc.state.tx.us

U.S. VIRGIN ISLANDS
Mr. Gustav James
Commissioner
Department of Public Works
6002 Estate Anna's Hope
Christiansted
St. Croix, VI 00820
P: (340) 773-1290
F: (340) 778-8906

UTAH
Ms. Donna Spangler
Communications Director
Office of Planning & Public Affairs
Department of Environmental Quality
P.O. Box 144810
Salt Lake City, UT 84114
P: (801) 536-4484
F: (801) 536-4480
E: dspangler@utah.gov

VERMONT
Mr. Marc Roy
Section Chief, Hazardous Materials Management Section
Waste Management & Prevention Division
One National Life Drive
Davis Building, 1st Floor
Montpelier, VT 05620
P: (802) 522-0275
F: (802) 828-1011
E: marc.roy@vermont.gov

VIRGINIA
Mr. David K. Paylor
Director
Department of Environmental Quality
629 East Main Street
P.O. Box 1105
Richmond, VA 23219
P: (804) 698-4000
F: (804) 698-4019
E: david.paylor@deq.virginia.gov

WASHINGTON
Ms. Laurie G. Davies
Program Manager
Waste 2 Resources Program
Department of Ecology
300 Desmond Drive, Southeast
Lacey, WA 98503
P: (360) 407-6103
F: (360) 407-6102
E: ldav461@ecy.wa.gov

WEST VIRGINIA
Mr. Mark Holstine
Executive Director
Solid Waste Management Board
601 57th Street, Southeast
Charleston, WV 25304
P: (304) 926-0499
F: (304) 926-0472
E: mark.d.holstine@wv.gov

WISCONSIN
Mr. Michael Prager
Program Coordinator
Division of Air, Waste, Remediation & Redevelopment
101 South Webster Street
P.O. Box 7921
Madison, WI 53707
P: (608) 261-4927
F: (608) 267-7646
E: Michael.Prager@wisconsin.gov

WYOMING
Mr. Todd Parfitt
Director
Department of Environmental Quality
200 West 17th Street
Cheyenne, WY 82002
P: (307) 777-7937
F: (307) 635-1784
E: todd.parfitt@wyo.gov

Revenue

Administers state tax laws and the collection and processing of state taxes.

ALABAMA
Ms. Julie P. MaGee
Commissioner
Department of Revenue
50 North Ripley Street
Montgomery, AL 36104
P: (334) 242-1175

ALASKA
Mr. Randall Hoffbeck
Commissioner
Department of Revenue
P.O. Box 110400
Juneau, AK 99811
P: (907) 465-2300
F: (907) 465-2389
E: randall.hoffbeck
@alaska.gov

AMERICAN SAMOA
The Honorable Ueli
Tonumaipea
Treasurer
Department of Treasury
American Samoa Government
Pago Pago, AS 96799
P: (684) 633-4155
F: (684) 633-4100
E: ueli.tonumaipea
@tr.as.gov

ARIZONA
Mr. David Briant
Director
Department of Revenue
1600 West Monroe
Phoenix, AZ 85007
P: (602) 716-6090
F: (602) 542-2072

ARKANSAS
Mr. Larry Walther
Director
Department of Finance &
Administration
1509 West 7th Street
DFA Building, Room 401
Little Rock, AR 72201
P: (501) 682-2242
F: (501) 682-1029
E: larry.walther
@dfa.arkansas.gov

CALIFORNIA
Mr. Selvi Stanislaus
Executive Officer
Franchise Tax Board
P.O. Box 1468
Sacramento, CA 95812
P: (916) 845-4543
F: (916) 845-3191
E: selvi.stanislaus
@ftb.ca.gov

COLORADO
Ms. Barbara Brohl
Executive Director
Department of Revenue
1375 Sherman Street
P.O. Box 17087
Denver, CO 80217
P: (303) 866-5610
F: (303) 866-2400
E: barbara.brohl
@state.co.us

CONNECTICUT
Mr. Kevin B. Sullivan
Commissioner
Department of Revenue
Services
25 Sigourney Street, Suite 2
Hartford, CT 06106
P: (860) 297-5962
F: (860) 297-5698
E: kevin.b.sullivan
@po.state.ct.us

DELAWARE
Mr. David Gregor
Director
Division of Revenue
Carvel State Office Building
820 North French Street
Wilmington, DE 19801
P: (302) 577-8686
F: (302) 577-8202
E: david.gregor@state.de.us

DISTRICT OF COLUMBIA
Mr. Stephen M. Cordi
Deputy Chief Financial Officer
Office of Tax & Revenue
1101 4th Street, Southwest
Suite 270 West
Washington, DC 20024
P: (202) 727-4829
F: (202) 442-6890
E: stephen.cordi@dc.gov

FLORIDA
Mr. Leon Biegalski
Executive Director
Department of Revenue
5050 West Tennessee Street
Tallahassee, FL 32399
P: (850) 617-8600
E: EMailDOR@dor.state.fl.us

GEORGIA
Ms. Lynnette Riley
Revenue Commissioner
Department of Revenue
1800 Century Center Boulevard
Atlanta, GA 30345
P: (404) 417-2100

GUAM
Mr. John P. Camacho
Director
Department of Revenue &
Taxation
Director's Office
P.O. Box 23607
GMF, GU 96921
P: (671) 635-1817
F: (671) 633-2643
E: john.camacho
@revtax.guam.gov

HAWAII
Ms. Maria E. Zielinski
Director
Department of Taxation
P.O. Box 259
Honolulu, HI 96809
P: (808) 587-1540
F: (808) 587-1560
E: Tax.Directors.Office
@hawaii.gov

IDAHO
Mr. Ken A. Roberts
Chair
Tax Commission
P.O. Box 36
Boise, ID 83722
P: (208) 334-7660
E: tax-commissioners
@tax.idaho.gov

ILLINOIS
Ms. Connie Beard
Director
Department of Revenue
101 West Jefferson Street
Springfield, IL 62702
P: (217) 782-3336
F: (217) 782-6337

INDIANA
Mr. Adam Krupp
Commissioner
Department of Revenue
100 North Senate Avenue
Room 248N
Indianapolis, IN 46204
P: (317) 232-8039
F: (317) 232-2103
E: akrupp@dor.in.gov

IOWA
Ms. Courtney M. Kay-Decker
Director
Department of Revenue
Hoover State Office Building
1305 East Walnut Street
Des Moines, IA 50319
P: (515) 281-3204
E: courtney.decker@iowa.gov

KANSAS
Mr. Samuel Williams
Secretary
Department of Revenue
Docking State Office Building,
2nd Floor
915 Southwest Harrison Street
Topeka, KS 66612
P: (785) 296-3909
F: (785) 296-7928

KENTUCKY
Mr. Daniel Bork
Commissioner
Department of Revenue
501 High Street
11th Floor, Station 1
Frankfort, KY 40601
P: (502) 564-3226
F: (502) 564-3875

LOUISIANA
Ms. Kimberly Robinson
Secretary of Revenue
Department of Revenue
617 North Third Street
P.O. Box 201
Baton Rouge, LA 70821
P: (855) 307-3893
F: (225) 219-2708
E: Krissy.Thomas@la.gov

MAINE
Mr. Jerome D. Gerard
Executive Director
Revenue Services
24 State House Station
51 Commerce Drive
Augusta, ME 04333
P: (207) 624-9620
E: Jerome.D.Gerard
@maine.gov

MARYLAND
Mr. Wayne Green
Director
Revenue Administration
Division
Comptroller of Maryland
110 Carroll Street, Room 105
Annapolis, MD 21411
P: (410) 260-7445
E: wgreen@comp.state.md.us

Revenue

MICHIGAN
Mr. Gregory Gursky
Deputy Treasurer for Tax Policy
Department of Treasury
Richard H. Austin Building
430 West Allegan Street
Lansing, MI 48922
P: (517) 373-3200

MISSISSIPPI
Mr. Herb Frierson
Commissioner
Department of Revenue
P.O. Box 1033
Jackson, MS 39215
P: (601) 923-7000
F: (601) 923-7423

MONTANA
Mr. Mike Kadas
Director
Department of Revenue
P.O. Box 5805
Helena, MT 59604
P: (406) 444-6900
F: (406) 444-3696

NEBRASKA
Mr. Tony Fulton
Tax Commissioner
Department of Revenue
P.O. Box 94818
Lincoln, NE 68509
P: (402) 471-5605
F: (402) 471-5608
E: tony.fulton@nebraska.gov

NEVADA
Ms. Deonne E. Contine
Executive Director
Department of Taxation
1550 College Parkway, Suite 115
Carson City, NV 89706
P: (775) 684-2000
F: (775) 684-2020

NEW HAMPSHIRE
Mr. John T. Beardmore
Commissioner
Department of Revenue Administration
Governor Hugh Gallen State Office Park
109 Pleasant Street
Concord, NH 03302
P: (603) 230-5000
F: (603) 271-6121
E: john.beardmore@dra.nh.gov

NEW JERSEY
Mr. John J. Ficara
Acting Director
Division of Taxation
P.O. Box 281
Trenton, NJ 08695
P: (609) 292-5185

NEW MEXICO
Mr. John Monforte
Acting Secretary
Taxation & Revenue Department
1100 South St. Francis Drive
Santa Fe, NM 87504
P: (505) 827-0700
F: (505) 827-0331

NEW YORK
Nonie Manion
Acting Commissioner
Department of Taxation & Finance
W.A. Hamman Campus, Building 9
Albany, NY 12227
P: (518) 457-7377

NORTH CAROLINA
Mr. Ronald Penny
Secretary
Department of Revenue
501 North Wilmington Street
P.O. Box 25000
Raleigh, NC 27640
P: (919) 814-1006
F: (919) 733-0023
E: ronald.penny@dornc.com

NORTH DAKOTA
The Honorable Ryan Rauschenberger (R)
Commissioner
Office of the State Tax Commissioner
600 East Boulevard Avenue
Department 127
Bismarck, ND 58505
P: (701) 328-7088
F: (701) 328-3700
E: rrauschenberger@nd.gov

NORTHERN MARIANA ISLANDS
Ms. Larrsa Larson
Secretary
Department of Finance
P.O. Box 5234, CHRB
Saipan, MP 96950
P: (670) 664-1100
F: (670) 664-1115
E: revtax@gtepacifica.net

OHIO
Mr. Joseph W. Testa
Tax Commissioner
Department of Taxation
P.O. Box 530
Columbus, OH 43216
P: (614) 466-2166
F: (614) 466-6401
E: contactthecommissioner@tax.state.oh.us

OKLAHOMA
Mr. Steve Burrage
Chair
Tax Commission
2501 North Lincoln Boulevard
Oklahoma City, OK 73194
P: (405) 521-3160
F: (405) 522-0074

OREGON
Ms. Nia Ray
Director
Department of Revenue
Room 457, Revenue Building
Salem, OR 97301
P: (503) 945-8214
F: (503) 945-8290
E: nia.ray@oregon.gov

PENNSYLVANIA
Mr. C. Daniel Hassell
Acting Secretary
Department of Revenue
Strawberry Square
Harrisburg, PA 17128
P: (717) 783-3683
F: (717) 787-3990

RHODE ISLAND
Mr. Robert Hull
Director of Revenue
Department of Revenue
One Capitol Hill
Providence, RI 02908
P: (401) 574-8999
F: (401) 574-8997

SOUTH CAROLINA
Mr. W. Hartley Powell
Director
Department of Revenue
P.O. Box 125
Columbia, SC 29214
P: (803) 898-5040
E: Director@dor.sc.gov

SOUTH DAKOTA
Mr. Andy Gerlach
Secretary
Department of Revenue
445 East Capital Avenue
Pierre, SD 57501
P: (605) 773-3311
F: (605) 773-5129

TENNESSEE
Mr. David Gerregano
Commissioner
Department of Revenue
500 Deaderick Street
Andrew Jackson Building
Nashville, TN 37242
P: (615) 741-2461
F: (615) 741-2883
E: David.Gerregano@tn.gov

TEXAS
The Honorable Glenn Hegar (R)
Comptroller of Public Accounts
Office of the Comptroller of Public Accounts
LBJ State Office Building, 1st Floor
111 East 17th Street
Austin, TX 78774
P: (512) 463-4444
F: (512) 463-4902
E: glenn.hegar@cpa.state.tx.us

U.S. VIRGIN ISLANDS
Mr. Marvin L. Pickering
Director
Bureau of Internal Revenue
6115 Estate Smith Bay, Suite 225
St. Thomas, VI 00802
P: (340) 715-1040
F: (340) 774-2672

UTAH
Mr. John L. Valentine
Chair
State Tax Commission
210 North 1950 West
Salt Lake City, UT 84134
P: (801) 297-2200
E: taxmaster@utah.gov

VERMONT
Mr. Andrew Pallito
Commissioner
Department of Finance & Management
109 State Street
Montpelier, VT 05609
P: (802) 828-2376
F: (802) 828-2428
E: andy.pallito@vermont.gov

VIRGINIA
Mr. Craig M. Burns
Tax Commissioner
Department of Taxation
Main Street Centre
600 East Main Street, 23rd Floor
Richmond, VA 23219
P: (804) 786-3301
F: (804) 786-4208
E: craig.burns
@tax.virginia.gov

WASHINGTON
Ms. Vikki Smith
Director
Department of Revenue
Executive Office
P.O. Box 47450
Olympia, WA 98504
P: (360) 534-1605

WEST VIRGINIA
Mr. Dave Hardy
Cabinet Secretary
Department of Revenue
State Capitol
Building 1, W-300
Charleston, WV 25305
P: (304) 558-1017
F: (304) 558-2324

WISCONSIN
Mr. Richard G. Chandler
Secretary
Department of Revenue
2135 Rimrock Road
P.O. Box 8933, Mail Stop 624-A
Madison, WI 53713
P: (608) 266-2772
F: (608) 267-0834
E: Richard.Chandler
@revenue.wi.gov

WYOMING
Mr. Dan Noble
Director
Department of Revenue
122 West 25th Street, 2nd Floor
West
Cheyenne, WY 82002
P: (307) 777-5287
F: (307) 777-7722
E: DirectorofRevenue
@wyo.gov

Savings and Loan

Administers laws regulating the operation of savings and loan associations in the state.

ALABAMA
Mr. Mike Hill
Superintendent
Banking Department
P.O. Box 4600
Montgomery, AL 36103
P: (334) 242-3452
F: (334) 242-3500
E: mike.hill@banking.alabama.gov

ALASKA
Ms. Kevin Anselm
Director
Division of Banking & Securities
P.O. Box 110807
Juneau, AK 99811
P: (907) 465-2521
F: (907) 465-1230
E: kevin.anselm@alaska.gov

ARIZONA
Mr. Robert Charlton
Superintendent of Financial Institutions
Department of Financial Institutions
2910 North 44th Street, Suite 310
Phoenix, AZ 85018
P: (602) 771-2770
F: (602) 381-1225
E: rcharlton@azdfi.gov

ARKANSAS
Ms. Candace Franks
Commissioner
State Banking Department
400 Hardin Road, Suite 100
Little Rock, AR 72211
P: (501) 324-9019
F: (501) 324-9028
E: cfranks@banking.state.ar.us

CALIFORNIA
Ms. Jan Lynn Owen
Commissioner
Department of Business Oversight
1515 K Street, Suite 200
Sacramento, CA 95814
P: (866) 275-2677
F: (916) 322-1559

COLORADO
Mr. Chris Myklebust
Commissioner
Division of Financial Services
Department of Regulatory Agencies
1560 Broadway, Suite 950
Denver, CO 80202
P: (303) 894-2336
F: (303) 894-7886
E: chris.myklebust@state.co.us

DELAWARE
Mr. Robert A. Glen
Commissioner
Office of State Bank Commissioner
555 East Lockerman Street
Dover, DE 19901
P: (302) 739-4235
F: (302) 739-3609
E: bankcommissioner@state.de.us

DISTRICT OF COLUMBIA
Mr. Stephen C. Taylor
Commissioner
Department of Insurance, Securities & Banking
Government of the District of Columbia
810 First Street Northeast, Suite 701
Washington, DC 20002
P: (202) 727-8000
F: (202) 535-1196
E: disb@dc.gov

GEORGIA
Mr. Kevin Hagler
Commissioner
Department of Banking & Finance
2990 Brandywine Road, Suite 200
Atlanta, GA 30341
P: (770) 986-1633
F: (770) 986-1654
E: khagler@dbf.state.ga.us

HAWAII
Ms. Iris Ikeda Catalani
Commissioner
Division of Financial Institutions
King Kalakaua Building
335 Merchant Street, Room 221
Honolulu, HI 96813
P: (808) 586-2820
F: (808) 586-2818
E: dfi@dcca.hawaii.gov

IDAHO
Mr. Gavin M. Gee
Director
Department of Finance
800 Park Boulevard, Suite 200
P.O. Box 83720
Boise, ID 83720
P: (208) 332-8010
F: (208) 332-8097
E: gavin.gee@finance.idaho.gov

ILLINOIS
Ms. Kerri Doll
Director
Division of Banking
320 West Washington Street
5th Floor
Springfield, IL 62786
P: (217) 558-4938

INDIANA
Mr. Tom Fite
Public Finance Director
Department of Financial Institutions
30 South Meridian Street
Suite 300
Indianapolis, IN 46204
P: (317) 453-2177
F: (317) 232-7655
E: tfite@dfi.IN.gov

IOWA
Mr. Ronald L. Hansen
Superintendent
Division of Banking
200 East Grand Avenue, Suite 300
Des Moines, IA 50309
P: (515) 281-4014
F: (515) 281-4862
E: rhansen@idob.state.ia.us

KANSAS
Ms. Michelle W. Bowman
Commissioner
Office of the State Banking Commissioner
700 Southwest Jackson, Suite 300
Topeka, KS 66603
P: (785) 296-2266
F: (785) 296-0168

KENTUCKY
Mr. Charles A. Vice
Commissioner
Department of Financial Institutions
1025 Capital Center Drive, Suite 200
Frankfort, KY 40601
P: (502) 573-3390
F: (502) 573-8787
E: charles.vice@ky.gov

MAINE
Mr. Lloyd P. LaFountain III
Superintendent
Bureau of Financial Institutions
Professional & Financial Regulation
36 State House Station
Augusta, ME 04333
P: (207) 624-8570
F: (207) 624-8590
E: lloyd.p.lafountain.III@maine.gov

MARYLAND
Mr. Gordon Cooley
Commissioner of Financial Regulation
Office of the Commissioner Financial Regulation
500 North Calvert Street, Room 402
Baltimore, MD 21202
P: (410) 230-6001
F: (410) 333-0475
E: gordon.cooley@maryland.gov

MASSACHUSETTS
Mr. Terence A. McGinnis
Commissioner
Division of Banking
1000 Washington Street, 10th Floor
Boston, MA 02118
P: (617) 956-1500
F: (617) 956-1599

MICHIGAN
Mr. Patrick M. McPharlin
Director
Department of Insurance & Financial Services
530 West Allegan Street, 7th Floor
P.O. Box 30220
Lansing, MI 48909
P: (517) 284-8800
F: (517) 284-8837
E: difs-info@michigan.gov

MINNESOTA
Mr. Mike Rothman
Commissioner
Department of Commerce
85 7th Place East, Suite 280
St. Paul, MN 55101
P: (651) 539-1441
F: (651) 539-1547
E: commerce.commissioner@state.mn.us

MISSOURI
Ms. Debbie Hardman
Commissioner of Finance
Division of Finance
Truman State Office Building, Room 630
P.O. Box 716
Jefferson City, MO 65102
P: (573) 751-3242
F: (573) 751-9192
E: finance@dof.mo.gov

MONTANA
Ms. Melanie Hall
Commissioner
Division of Banking & Financial Institutions
301 South Park, Suite 316
P.O. Box 200546
Helena, MT 59620
P: (406) 841-2920
F: (406) 841-2930
E: mghall@mt.gov

NEBRASKA
Mr. Mark Quandahl
Director
Department of Banking & Finance
1526 K Street, Suite 300
P.O. Box 95006
Lincoln, NE 68509
P: (402) 471-2845
E: mark.quandahl@nebraska.gov

NEVADA
Mr. George E. Burns
Commissioner
Financial Institutions Division
Department of Business & Industry
2785 East Desert Inn Road, Suite 180
Las Vegas, NV 89121
P: (702) 486-4120
F: (702) 486-4563
E: gburns@fid.state.nv.us

NEW HAMPSHIRE
Mr. Jerry Little
Bank Commissioner
Banking Department
53 Regional Drive, Suite 200
Concord, NH 03301
P: (603) 271-3561

NEW JERSEY
Mr. Richard J. Badolato
Commissioner
Department of Banking & Insurance
State of New Jersey
20 West State Street, P.O. Box 325
Trenton, NJ 08625
P: (609) 292-7272
F: (609) 984-5273
E: commissioner@dobi.state.nj.us

NORTH DAKOTA
Mr. Robert J. Entringer
Commissioner
Department of Financial Institutions
2000 Schafer Street, Suite G
Bismarck, ND 58501
P: (701) 328-9933
F: (701) 328-0290
E: rentring@nd.gov

OHIO
Mr. Kevin R. Allard
Superintendent
Division of Financial Institutions
Department of Commerce
77 South High Street, 21st Floor
Columbus, OH 43215
P: (614) 728-8400
F: (614) 728-0380
E: Web.dfi@com.ohio.gov

OKLAHOMA
Mr. Mick Thompson
Commissioner
State Banking Department
2900 North Lincoln Boulevard
Oklahoma City, OK 73105
P: (405) 521-2782
F: (405) 522-2993
E: mick.thompson@banking.ok.gov

OREGON
Ms. Laura N. Cali Robison
Insurance Commissioner/Chief Actuary
Department of Consumer & Business Services
Financial Regulation, P.O. Box 14480
350 Winter Street, Northeast
Salem, OR 97309
P: (503) 947-7980
F: (503) 378-4351
E: laura.n.cali@oregon.gov

PENNSYLVANIA
Ms. Robin Weissmann
Secretary
Department of Banking & Securities
Market Square Plaza
17 North 2nd Street, Suite 1300
Harrisburg, PA 17101
P: (717) 787-2665
F: (717) 787-8773
E: dobssecretary@pa.gov

SOUTH CAROLINA
Mr. Robert L. Davis
Commissioner of Banking
Office of the Commissioner of Banking
1205 Pendleton Street, Suite 305
Columbia, SC 29201
P: (803) 734-2001
F: (803) 734-2013

Mr. Louie A. Jacobs
Commissioner of Banking
Office of the Commissioner of Banking
1205 Pendleton Street, Suite 305
Columbia, SC 29201
P: (803) 734-2001
F: (803) 734-2013

SOUTH DAKOTA
Mr. Bret Afdahl
Director
Division of Banking
Department of Labor & Regulation
1601 North Harrison Avenue, Suite 1
Pierre, SD 57501
P: (605) 773-3421
F: (866) 326-7504
E: banking@state.sd.us

TENNESSEE
Mr. Greg Gonzales
Commissioner
Department of Financial Institutions
414 Union Street, Suite 1000
Nashville, TN 37219
P: (615) 741-5603
F: (615) 253-6306
E: Greg.Gonzales@tn.gov

TEXAS
Ms. Caroline C. Jones
Commisssioner
Department of Savings & Mortgage Lending
2601 North Lamar Boulevard, Suite 201
Austin, TX 78705
P: (512) 475-1350
F: (512) 475-1505

UTAH
Mr. G. Edward Leary
Commissioner
Department of Financial Institutions
324 South State Street, Suite 201
P.O. Box 146800
Salt Lake City, UT 84114
P: (801) 538-8830
F: (801) 538-8894
E: ELEARY@utah.gov

VERMONT
Ms. Cynthia Stuart
Deputy Commissioner
Banking Division
Department of Financial Regulation
89 Main Street
Montpelier, VT 05620
P: (802) 828-4874
F: (802) 828-3306
E: cynthia.stuart@vermont.gov

VIRGINIA
Mr. E. Joseph Face Jr.
Commissioner of Financial Institutions
Bureau of Financial Institutions
1300 East Main Street, 8th Floor
P.O. Box 640
Richmond, VA 23218
P: (804) 371-9657
F: (804) 371-9416
E: joe.face@scc.virginia.gov

WASHINGTON
Ms. Roberta Hollinshead
Director of Banks
Division of Banks
Department of Financial Institutions
P.O. Box 41200
Olympia, WA 98504
P: (360) 902-8704
F: (360) 753-6070
E: banks@dfi.wa.gov

Savings and Loan

WEST VIRGINIA
Ms. Dawn Holstein
Acting Commissioner &
Director of Depository
Institutions
Division of Financial
Institutions
Board of Banking & Financial
Institution
900 Pennsylvania Avenue, Suite
306
Charleston, WV 25302
P: (304) 558-2294
F: (304) 558-0442
E: dholstein@wvdob.org

WISCONSIN
Ms. Cheryll Olson-Collins
Administrator
Division of Banking
P.O. Box 7876
Madison, WI 53707
P: (608) 261-7578
F: (608) 267-6889
E: cheryll.olsoncollins
@dfi.wisconsin.gov

Secretary of State

Statewide official who oversees a variety of electoral, registration, publication, and legislative duties for the state.

Information provided by:

National Association of Secretaries of State
Leslie Reynolds
Executive Director
444 North Capitol Street, NW
Suite 401
Washington, DC 20001
P: (202) 624-3525
F: (202) 624-3527
reynolds@sso.org
www.nass.org

ALABAMA
The Honorable John Merrill (R)
Secretary of State
Office of the Secretary of State
P.O. Box 5616
Montgomery, AL 36103
P: (334) 242-7200
F: (334) 242-4993
E: john.merrill@sos.alabama.gov

ARIZONA
The Honorable Michele Reagan (R)
Secretary of State
Office of the Secretary of State
1700 West Washington, Suite 1700
Phoenix, AZ 85007
P: (602) 542-4285
F: (602) 542-1575
E: sosadmin@azsos.gov

ARKANSAS
The Honorable Mark Martin (R)
Secretary of State
Office of the Secretary of State
256 State Capitol Building
Little Rock, AR 72201
P: (501) 682-1010
F: (501) 682-3510
E: info@sos.arkansas.gov

CALIFORNIA
Mr. Alex Padilla
Secretary of State
Office of the Secretary of State
1500 11th Street
Sacramento, CA 95814
P: (916) 653-7244
F: (916) 653-4795
E: secretary.padilla@sos.ca.gov

COLORADO
The Honorable Wayne Williams (R)
Secretary of State
Office of the Secretary of State
1700 Broadway, Suite 200
Denver, CO 80290
P: (303) 894-2200
F: (303) 869-4860
E: secretary@sos.state.co.us

CONNECTICUT
The Honorable Denise W. Merrill (D)
Secretary of State
Office of the Secretary of State
Capitol Office
P.O. Box 150470
Hartford, CT 06115
P: (860) 509-6200
F: (860) 509-6209
E: denise.merrill@ct.gov

DELAWARE
The Honorable Jeffrey Bullock (D)
Secretary of State
Office of the Secretary of State
401 Federal Street
Dover, DE 19901
P: (302) 739-4111
F: (302) 739-3811
E: kathy.bradford@state.de.us

DISTRICT OF COLUMBIA
The Honorable Lauren C. Vaughn (appointed)
Secretary of the District
Office of the Secretary of the District
1350 Pennsylvania Avenue, Northwest
Suite 419
Washington, DC 20004
P: (202) 727-6306
F: (202) 727-3582
E: secretary@dc.gov

FLORIDA
The Honorable Kenneth Detzner (R) (appointed)
Secretary of State
Office of the Secretary of State
R.A. Gray Building
500 South Bronough Street, Suite 100
Tallahassee, FL 32399
P: (850) 245-6000
F: (850) 245-6125
E: secretaryofstate@dos.myflorida.com

GEORGIA
The Honorable Brian Kemp (R)
Secretary of State
Office of the Secretary of State
214 State Capitol
Atlanta, GA 30334
P: (404) 656-2881
F: (404) 656-0513
E: soscontact@sos.ga.gov

IDAHO
The Honorable Lawerence Denney (R)
Secretary of State
Office of the Secretary of State
P.O. Box 83720
Boise, ID 83720
P: (208) 334-2300
F: (208) 334-2282
E: ldenney@sos.idaho.gov

ILLINOIS
The Honorable Jesse White (D)
Secretary of State
Office of the Secretary of State
213 State Capitol
Springfield, IL 62756
P: (217) 782-2201
F: (217) 785-0358
E: jessewhite@ilsos.net

INDIANA
The Honorable Connie Lawson (R)
Secretary of State
Office of the Secretary of State
201 State House
Indianapolis, IN 46204
P: (317) 232-6536
F: (317) 233-3283
E: sos@sos.in.gov

IOWA
The Honorable Paul Pate (R)
Secretary of State
Office of the Secretary of State
Lucas Building, First Floor
321 East 12th Street
Des Moines, IA 50319
P: (515) 281-6230
F: (515) 242-5952
E: sos@sos.iowa.gov

KANSAS
The Honorable Kris Kobach (R)
Secretary of State
Office of the Secretary of State
120 Southwest 10th Avenue
Topeka, KS 66612
P: (785) 296-4564
F: (785) 368-8033
E: sos@sos.ks.gov

KENTUCKY
The Honorable Alison L. Grimes (D)
Secretary of State
Office of the Secretary of State
700 Capital Avenue, Suite 152
Frankfort, KY 40601
P: (502) 564-3490
F: (502) 564-5687
E: sos.secretary@ky.gov

LOUISIANA
The Honorable Tom Schedler (R)
Secretary of State
Office of the Secretary of State
P.O. Box 94125
Baton Rouge, LA 70804
P: (225) 922-2880
F: (225) 922-2003
E: admin@sos.la.gov

MAINE
The Honorable Matthew Dunlap (D)
Secretary of State
Office of the Secretary of State
148 State House Station
Augusta, ME 04333
P: (207) 626-8400
F: (207) 287-8598
E: sos.office@maine.gov

MARYLAND
The Honorable John C. Wobensmith (appointed)
Secretary of State
Office of the Secretary of State
16 Francis Street
Annapolis, MD 21401
P: (410) 974-5521
F: (410) 841-5527
E: dlmdsos_sos@maryland.gov

Secretary of State

MASSACHUSETTS
The Honorable William F. Galvin (D)
Secretary of the Commonwealth
Office of the Secretary of the Commonwealth
State House, Room 337
24 Beacon Street
Boston, MA 02133
P: (617) 727-9180
F: (617) 742-4722
E: cis@sec.state.ma.us

MICHIGAN
The Honorable Ruth Johnson (R)
Secretary of State
Office of the Secretary of State
430 West Allegan Street, 4th Floor
Lansing, MI 48918
P: (517) 373-2510
F: (517) 373-0727
E: secretary@michigan.gov

MINNESOTA
The Honorable Steve Simon (DFL)
Secretary of State
Office of the Secretary of State
180 State Office Building
100 Martin Luther King Jr. Boulevard
St. Paul, MN 55155
P: (651) 201-1324
F: (651) 269-9073
E: secretary.state@state.mn.us

MISSISSIPPI
The Honorable C. Delbert Hosemann Jr. (R)
Secretary of State
Office of the Secretary of State
125 South Congress Street
Jackson, MS 39201
P: (601) 359-1350
F: (601) 359-6700
E: delbert.hosemann@sos.ms.gov

MISSOURI
The Honorable Jay Ashcroft (R)
Secretary of State
Office of the Secretary of State
600 West Main
P.O. Box 1767
Jefferson City, MO 65101
P: (573) 751-4936
F: (573) 526-4903

MONTANA
The Honorable Corey Stapleton (R)
Secretary of State
Office of the Secretary of State
P.O. Box 202801
Helena, MT 59620
P: (406) 444-2034
F: (406) 444-4249
E: sos@mt.gov

NEBRASKA
The Honorable John A. Gale (R)
Secretary of State
Office of the Secretary of State
P.O. Box 94608-4608
Lincoln, NE 68509
P: (402) 471-2554
F: (402) 471-3237
E: sos.info@nebraska.gov

NEVADA
The Honorable Barbara Cegavske (R)
Secretary of State
Office of the Secretary of State
101 North Carson Street, Suite 3
Carson City, NV 89701
P: (775) 684-5708
F: (775) 684-5724
E: sosexec@sos.nv.gov

NEW HAMPSHIRE
The Honorable William M. Gardner (D)
(elected by the Legislature)
Secretary of State
Office of the Secretary of State
State House, Room 204
Concord, NH 03301
P: (603) 271-3242
F: (603) 271-6316
E: kladd@sos.state.nh.us

NEW MEXICO
The Honorable Maggie Oliver (D)
Secretary of State
Office of the Secretary of State
325 Don Gaspar, Suite 300
Santa Fe, NM 87501
P: (505) 827-3600

NEW YORK
The Honorable Rossana Rosado
(appointed)
Secretary of State
Office of the Secretary of State
One Commerce Plaza
99 Washington Avenue, Suite 1100
Albany, NY 12231
P: (518) 486-9846
E: info@dos.ny.gov

NORTH CAROLINA
The Honorable Elaine F. Marshall (D)
Secretary of State
Office of the Secretary of State
P.O. Box 29622
Raleigh, NC 27626
P: (919) 807-2005
F: (919) 807-2010
E: emarshal@sosnc.com

NORTH DAKOTA
The Honorable Alvin A. Jaeger (R)
Secretary of State
Office of the Secretary of State
600 East Boulevard
Department 108
Bismarck, ND 58505
P: (701) 328-2900
F: (701) 328-1690
E: ajaeger@nd.gov

OHIO
The Honorable Jon Husted (R)
Secretary of State
Office of the Secretary of State
180 East Broad Street, 16th Floor
Columbus, OH 43215
P: (614) 466-2655
F: (614) 644-0649
E: jhusted@ohiosecretaryofstate.gov

OKLAHOMA
The Honorable Dave Lopez
(appointed)
Secretary of State
Office of the Secretary of State
2300 North Lincoln Boulevard, Suite 101
Oklahoma City, OK 73105
P: (405) 521-3912
E: executivelegislative@sos.ok.gov

OREGON
The Honorable Dennis Richardson (R)
Secretary of State
Office of the Secretary of State
136 State Capitol
Salem, OR 37310
P: (503) 986-1523
F: (503) 986-1616
E: oregon.sos@state.or.us

PENNSYLVANIA
The Honorable Pedro A. Cortes (D)
(appointed)
Secretary of the Commonwealth
Office of the Secretary of the Commonwealth
302 North Office Building
Harrisburg, PA 17120
P: (717) 787-6458
F: (717) 787-1734
E: ST-PRESS@pa.gov

PUERTO RICO
The Honorable Luis Rivera Marín
(appointed)
Secretary of State
Office of the Secretary of State
P.O. Box 9023271
San Juan, PR 00902
P: (787) 722-2121

RHODE ISLAND
The Honorable Nellie Gorbea (D)
(elected by the Legislature)
Secretary of State
Office of the Secretary of State
82 Smith Street, Room 217
Providence, RI 02903
P: (401) 222-2357
F: (401) 222-1356
E: nmgorbea@sos.ri.gov

SOUTH CAROLINA
The Honorable Mark Hammond (R)
Secretary of State
Office of the Secretary of State
1205 Pendleton Street, Suite 525
Columbia, SC 29201
P: (803) 734-2170
F: (803) 734-1661
E: rdaggerhart@sos.sc.gov

SOUTH DAKOTA
The Honorable Shantel Krebs (R)
Secretary of State
Office of the Secretary of State
500 East Capitol Avenue, Suite 204
Pierre, SD 57501
P: (605) 773-3537
F: (605) 773-6580
E: shantel.krebs@state.sd.us

TENNESSEE
The Honorable Tre Hargett (R)
(elected by the Legislature)
Secretary of State
Office of the Secretary of State
State Capitol, First Floor
Nashville, TN 37243
P: (615) 741-2819
F: (615) 741-5962
E: tre.hargett@tn.gov

TEXAS
The Honorable Rolando Pablos (R)
(appointed)
Secretary of State
Office of the Secretary of State
1100 Congress Avenue
Austin, TX 78701
P: (512) 463-5770
E: secretary@sos.state.tx.us

VERMONT
The Honorable Jim Condos (D)
Secretary of State
Office of the Secretary of State
128 State Street
Montpelier, VT 05633
P: (802) 828-2148
F: (802) 828-2496
E: jim.condos@sec.state.vt.us

VIRGINIA
The Honorable Kelly Thomasson
(appointed)
Secretary of the Commonwealth
Office of the Secretary of the Commonwealth
P.O. Box 2454
Richmond, VA 23218
P: (804) 786-2441
F: (804) 371-0017
E: kelly.thomasson@governor.virginia.gov

WASHINGTON
The Honorable Kim Wyman (R)
Secretary of State
Office of the Secretary of State
P.O. Box 40220
Olympia, WA 98503
P: (360) 902-4151
F: (360) 586-5629
E: kim.wyman@sos.wa.gov

WEST VIRGINIA
The Honorable Mac Warner (R)
Secretary of State
Office of the Secretary of State
Building 1, Suite 157K
1900 Kanawha Boulevard
Charleston, WV 25305
P: (304) 558-6000
F: (304) 558-0900
E: wvsos@wvsos.com

WISCONSIN
The Honorable Douglas J. La Follette (D)
Secretary of State
Office of the Secretary of State
P.O. Box 7848
Madison, WI 53707
P: (608) 266-8888
F: (608) 266-3159
E: doug.lafollette@sos.state.wi.us

WYOMING
The Honorable Ed Murray (R)
Secretary of State
Office of the Secretary of State
2020 Carey Avenue, Suite 600 & 700
Cheyenne, WY 82002
P: (307) 777-7378
F: (307) 777-6217
E: secofstate@wyo.gov

Securities

Regulates the sale of securities and registers securities prior to public sale.

ALASKA
Ms. Kevin Anselm
Director
Division of Banking & Securities
P.O. Box 110807
Juneau, AK 99811
P: (907) 465-2521
F: (907) 465-1230
E: kevin.anselm@alaska.gov

ARIZONA
Mr. Matthew J. Neubert
Director
Securities Division
Corporation Commission
1300 West Washington, 3rd Floor
Phoenix, AZ 85007
P: (602) 542-4242
F: (602) 388-1335
E: securitiesdiv@azcc.gov

ARKANSAS
Ms. Candace Franks
Commissioner
State Banking Department
400 Hardin Road, Suite 100
Little Rock, AR 72211
P: (501) 324-9019
F: (501) 324-9028
E: cfranks@banking.state.ar.us

CALIFORNIA
Ms. Jan Lynn Owen
Commissioner
Department of Business Oversight
1515 K Street, Suite 200
Sacramento, CA 95814
P: (866) 275-2677
F: (916) 322-1559

COLORADO
Mr. Gerald Rome
Securities Commissioner
Division of Securities
Department of Regulatory Agencies
1560 Broadway, Suite 900
Denver, CO 80202
P: (303) 894-2320
F: (303) 894-2126
E: gerald.rome@state.co.us

CONNECTICUT
Ms. Lynn McKenna-Krumins
Division Director
Securities & Business Investments Division
Department of Banking
260 Constitution Plaza
Hartford, CT 06103
P: (860) 240-8230
F: (860) 424-4075
E: Lynn.McKenna-Krumins@ct.gov

DISTRICT OF COLUMBIA
Mr. Theodore A. Miles
Associate Commissioner, Securities
Department of Insurance, Securities & Banking
Securities Bureau
810 First Street Northeast, Suite 701
Washington, DC 20002
P: (202) 727-8000
F: (202) 535-1196
E: disb@dc.gov

FLORIDA
Mr. Gregory Luers
Director, Division of Securities
Office of Financial Regulation
200 East Gaines Street
Tallahassee, FL 32399
P: (850) 410-9819
E: gregory.luers@flofr.com

GEORGIA
Noula Zaharis
Securities Director, Securities & Charities Division
Office of the Secretary of State
Two Martin Luther King, Jr. Drive, SE
Suite 313, West Tower
Atlanta, GA 30334
P: (404) 654-6034
E: NZaharis@sos.ga.gov

HAWAII
Ms. Ty Nohara
Commissioner
Business Registration Division
Commerce & Consumer Affairs
P.O. Box 40
Honolulu, HI 96810
P: (808) 586-2744
F: (808) 586-2733
E: breg@dcca.hawaii.gov

IDAHO
Mr. Jim Burns
Securities Bureau Chief
Department of Finance
800 Park Boulevard, Suite 200
P.O. Box 83720
Boise, ID 83720
P: (208) 332-8080
F: (208) 332-8099
E: jim.burns@finance.idaho.gov

ILLINOIS
Ms. Tanya Solov
Director of Securities
Securities Department
Office of the Secretary of State
69 West Washington Street, Suite 1220
Chicago, IL 60602
P: (312) 793-3384
F: (312) 793-1202

INDIANA
Mr. Alex Glass
Securities Commissioner
Securities Division
Office of the Secretary of State
302 West Washington, Room E111
Indianapolis, IN 46204
P: (317) 232-6681
F: (317) 233-3675
E: aglass@sos.in.gov

IOWA
Ms. Rosanne Mead
Securities Administrator
Insurance Division
Securities Bureau
601 Locust, 4th Floor
Des Moines, IA 50309
P: (515) 281-4242
F: (515) 281-3059
E: rosanne.mead@iid.iowa.gov

KANSAS
Mr. Josh Ney
Securities Commissioner
Office of the Securities Commissioner
109 Southwest 9th Street, Suite 600
Topeka, KS 66612
P: (785) 296-3307
F: (785) 296-6872
E: josh.ney@ks.gov

KENTUCKY
Ms. Shonita Bossier
Director, Division of Securities
Department of Financial Institutions
1025 Capital Center Drive, Suite 200
Frankfort, KY 40601
P: (502) 573-3390
F: (502) 573-2182
E: shonita.bossier@ky.gov

LOUISIANA
Mr. Len Riviere
Deputy Commissioner of Securities
Securities Division
Office of Financial Institutions
8660 United Plaza Boulevard, 2nd Floor
Baton Rouge, LA 70809
P: (225) 925-4512
F: (225) 925-4511
E: lriviere@ofi.la.gov

MAINE
Ms. Judith M. Shaw
Securities Administrator
Department of Professional & Financial Regulation
Office of Securities
121 State House Station
Augusta, ME 04333
P: (207) 624-8551
F: (207) 624-8590
E: judith.m.shaw@maine.gov

MARYLAND
Ms. Melanie Senter Lubin
Securities Commissioner
Division of Securities
Office of the Attorney General
200 Saint Paul Place
Baltimore, MD 21202
P: (410) 576-6365
F: (410) 576-6532
E: mlubin@oag.state.md.us

MASSACHUSETTS
The Honorable William F. Galvin (D)
Secretary of the Commonwealth
Office of the Secretary of the Commonwealth
State House, Room 337
24 Beacon Street
Boston, MA 02133
P: (617) 727-9180
F: (617) 742-4722
E: cis@sec.state.ma.us

MICHIGAN
Ms. Julia Dale
Director
Corporations, Securities & Commercial Licensing Bureau
Licensing & Regulatory Affairs
P.O. Box 30018
Lansing, MI 48909
P: (517) 241-6345
F: (517) 241-6356
E: CSCL-sec-registration@michigan.gov

Mr. Patrick M. McPharlin
Director
Department of Insurance & Financial Services
530 West Allegan Street, 7th Floor
P.O. Box 30220
Lansing, MI 48909
P: (517) 284-8800
F: (517) 284-8837
E: difs-info@michigan.gov

MINNESOTA
Mr. Mike Rothman
Commissioner
Department of Commerce
85 7th Place East, Suite 280
St. Paul, MN 55101
P: (651) 539-1441
F: (651) 539-1547
E: commerce.commissioner@state.mn.us

MISSISSIPPI
Ms. Jessica Long
Assistant Secretary of State
Securities Division
Office of the Secretary of State
125 South Congress Street, P.O. Box 136
Jackson, MS 39205
P: (601) 359-1334
F: (601) 359-9070

MISSOURI
Colonel Sandra K. Karsten
Superintendent
State Highway Patrol
1510 East Elm Street
Jefferson City, MO 65101
P: (573) 751-3313
F: (573) 751-9419

Mr. David M. Minnick
Commissioner of Securities
Securities Division
Office of the Secretary of State
600 West Main Street, Room 229
Jefferson City, MO 65101
P: (573) 751-4136
F: (573) 526-3124
E: securities@sos.mo.gov

MONTANA
Ms. Lynne Egan
Deputy Securities Commissioner
Commissioner of Securities & Insurance, State Auditor's Office
Securities Department
840 Helena Avenue
Helena, MT 59601
P: (406) 444-4388
F: (406) 444-3497

NEBRASKA
Ms. Claire McHenry
Deputy Director, Bureau of Securities
Department of Banking & Finance
1526 K Street, Suite 300
P.O. Box 95006
Lincoln, NE 68509
P: (402) 471-3445
E: claire.mchenry@nebraska.gov

NEVADA
Ms. Diana Foley
Securities Administrator
Securities Division
Office of the Secretary of State
555 East Washington Avenue, Suite 5200
Las Vegas, NV 89101
P: (702) 486-2440
F: (702) 486-2452
E: nvsec@sos.nv.gov

NEW HAMPSHIRE
Mr. Barry J. Glennon
Director of Securities Regulation
Bureau of Securities Regulation
Department of State
107 North Main Street, # 204
Concord, NH 03301
P: (603) 271-1463
F: (603) 271-7933
E: securities@sos.nh.gov

NEW JERSEY
Mr. Christopher W. Gerold
Bureau Chief
Bureau of Securities
Office of the Attorney General
153 Halsey Street, 6th Floor
Newark, NJ 07102
P: (973) 504-3600
E: njbos@dca.lps.state.nj.us

NEW MEXICO
Ms. Alexis Lotero
Acting Director
Securities Division
Regulation & Licensing Department
P.O. Box 25101
Santa Fe, NM 87504
P: (505) 554-9478
E: Alexis.Lotero@state.nm.us

NORTH CAROLINA
Mr. Kevin Harrington
Deputy Securities Administrator
Department of the Secretary of State
Securities Division
P.O. Box 29622
Raleigh, NC 27626
P: (919) 733-3924
F: (919) 807-2183
E: secdiv@sosnc.gov

NORTH DAKOTA
Ms. Karen Tyler
Commissioner
Securities Department
600 East Boulevard Avenue
State Capitol, 5th Floor
Bismarck, ND 58505
P: (701) 328-2910
F: (701) 328-2946
E: ndsecurities@nd.gov

OHIO
Ms. Andrea L. Seidt
Commissioner
Division of Securities
77 South High Street, 22nd Floor
Columbus, OH 43215
P: (614) 644-7381
F: (614) 466-3316
E: securitiesgeneral.questions@com.state.oh.us

OKLAHOMA
Mr. Irving L. Faught
Administrator
Securities Commission
204 North Robinson Avenue, Suite 400
Oklahoma City, OK 73102
P: (405) 280-7700
F: (405) 280-7742

OREGON
Ms. Laura N. Cali Robison
Insurance Commissioner/Chief Actuary
Department of Consumer & Business Services
Financial Regulation, P.O. Box 14480
350 Winter Street, Northeast
Salem, OR 97309
P: (503) 947-7980
F: (503) 378-4351
E: laura.n.cali@oregon.gov

PENNSYLVANIA
Ms. Robin Weissmann
Secretary
Department of Banking & Securities
Market Square Plaza
17 North 2nd Street, Suite 1300
Harrisburg, PA 17101
P: (717) 787-2665
F: (717) 787-8773
E: dobssecretary@pa.gov

PUERTO RICO
Mr. Damaris Mendoza
Assistant Commissioner
Commissioner of Financial Institutions
P.O. Box 11855
San Juan, PR 00910
P: (787) 723-3131 Ext. 2222
F: (787) 723-4042
E: damarism@ocif.pr.gov

RHODE ISLAND
Ms. Maria D'Alessandro
Deputy Director & Superintendent
Department of Business Regulation
1511 Pontiac Avenue
Cranston, RI 02920
P: (401) 462-9527
F: (401) 462-9645
E: maria.dalessandro@dbr.ri.gov

SOUTH CAROLINA
Mr. Stephen Lynch
Deputy, Securities Division
Office of the Attorney General
Rembert Dennis Building, Room 519
1000 Assembly Street, P.O. Box 11549
Columbia, SC 29211
P: (803) 734-9916
F: (803) 253-6283

Securities

SOUTH DAKOTA
Mr. Larry Deiter
Director
Division of Securities
State Department of Labor & Regulation
124 South Euclid Avenue, 2nd Floor
Pierre, SD 57501
P: (605) 773-3563
F: (605) 773-5369

TENNESSEE
Mr. Frank Borger-Gilligan
Assistant Commissioner for Securities
Securities Division
Department of Commerce & Insurance
500 James Robertson Parkway, 8th Floor
Nashville, TN 37243
P: (615) 741-2947
F: (615) 532-8375
E: frank.borger-gilligan@tn.gov

TEXAS
Mr. John Morgan
Securities Commissioner
State Securities Board
208 East 10th Street, 5th Floor
P.O. Box 13167
Austin, TX 78711
P: (512) 305-8300
F: (512) 305-8310

U.S. VIRGIN ISLANDS
Ms. Gwendolyn Hall Brady
Director of Banking & Insurance
Division of Banking, Insurance & Financial Regulation
5049 Kongens Gade
Charlotte Amalie
St. Thomas, VI 00802
P: (340) 774-7166
F: (340) 774-9458
E: gwendolyn.brady@lgo.vi.gov

UTAH
Mr. Keith Woodwell
Director
Department of Commerce, Division of Securities
160 East 300 South, 2nd Floor
P.O. Box 146760
Salt Lake City, UT 84114
P: (801) 530-6600
F: (801) 530-6980
E: kwoodwell@utah.gov

VERMONT
Mr. William R. Carrigan
Deputy Commissioner
Securities Division
Department of Financial Regulation
89 Main Street
Montpelier, VT 05620
P: (802) 828-4858
F: (802) 828-2896
E: william.carrigan@vermont.gov

VIRGINIA
Mr. Ronald W. Thomas
Director
State Corporation Commission, Division of Securities & Retail Franchising
Tyler Building, 1300 East Main Street
P.O. Box 1197
Richmond, VA 23218
P: (804) 371-9051
F: (804) 371-9911
E: ron.thomas@scc.virginia.gov

WASHINGTON
Mr. William M. Beatty
Director of Securities
Division of Securities
Department of Financial Institutions
P.O. Box 41200
Olympia, WA 98504
P: (360) 902-8760
F: (360) 902-0524
E: Bill.Beatty@dfi.wa.gov

WEST VIRGINIA
Ms. Lisa Hopkins
Senior Deputy Commissioner of Securities
Securities Commission, Office of the State Auditor
1900 Kanawha Boulevard, East
Building 1, Room W-100
Charleston, WV 25305
P: (304) 558-2251
F: (304) 558-4211
E: securities@wvsao.gov

WYOMING
Ms. Kelly Janes
Division Director
Compliance Division
Office of the Secretary of State
2020 Carey Avenue, Suite 700
Cheyenne, WY 82002
P: (307) 777-6621
F: (307) 777-7640
E: Compliance@wyo.gov

Small and Minority Business Assistance

Provides assistance and information on financing and government procurement opportunities to small and minority business ventures.

ALABAMA
Mr. Greg Canfield
Secretary
Department of Commerce
401 Adams Avenue
P.O. Box 304106
Montgomery, AL 36130
P: (334) 242-0421
F: (334) 242-0415
E: greg.canfield@commerce.alabama.gov

ALASKA
Ms. Britteny Cioni-Haywood
Division Director
Division of Economic Development
P.O. Box 110804
Juneau, AK 99811
P: (907) 465-2510
F: (907) 465-3767
E: britteny.cioni-haywood@alaska.gov

AMERICAN SAMOA
Mr. Keniseli Lafaele
Director
Department of Commerce
American Samoa Government
Executive Office Building, Utulei
Pago Pago, AS 96799
P: (684) 633-5155 Ext. 222
F: (684) 633-4195
E: keniseli.lafaele@doc.as

ARIZONA
Ms. Sandra Watson
President & CEO
Commerce Authority
118 North 7th Avenue, Suite 400
Phoenix, AZ 85007
P: (602) 845-1215
F: (602) 845-1201
E: commerce@azcommerce.com

ARKANSAS
Ms. Patricia Nunn Brown
Director, Small and Minority Business
Economic Development Commission
900 West Capitol Avenue, Suite 400
Little Rock, AR 72201
P: (501) 682-2559
F: (501) 682-7499
E: pbrown@arkansasedc.com

COLORADO
Ms. Kelly Manning
Director
Small Business Development Center
1625 Broadway, Suite 2700
Denver, CO 80202
P: (303) 892-3864
F: (303) 892-3848
E: kelly.manning@state.co.us

Ms. Rosy McDonough
Director
Office of Economic Development & International Trade
Minority Business Office
1625 Broadway, Suite 2700
Denver, CO 80202
P: (303) 892-3840
F: (303) 892-3848
E: rosy.mcdonough@state.co.us

DISTRICT OF COLUMBIA
Ms. Monica Palacio
Director
Office of Human Rights
441 4th Street, Northwest
Suite 570 North
Washington, DC 20001
P: (202) 727-4559
F: (202) 727-9589
E: ohr@dc.gov

GEORGIA
Mr. Pat Wilson
Commissioner
Department of Economic Development
75 5th Street Northwest
Suite 1200
Atlanta, GA 30308
P: (404) 962-4003
F: (404) 962-4009
E: ccarr@georgia.org

HAWAII
Mr. Luis P. Salaveria
Director
Department of Business, Economic Development & Tourism
250 South Hotel Street, 5th Floor
Honolulu, HI 96813
P: (808) 586-2355
F: (808) 586-2377
E: director@dbedt.hawaii.gov

IDAHO
Ms. Megan Ronk
Director
Department of Commerce
700 West State Street
P.O. Box 83720
Boise, ID 83720
P: (208) 334-2470
F: (208) 334-2631
E: megan.ronk@commerce.idaho.gov

ILLINOIS
Mr. Sean McCarthy
Director
Department of Commerce & Economic Opportunity
100 West Randolph Street, Suite 3-400
Chicago, IL 60601
P: (312) 814-2811

INDIANA
Ms. Terrie F. Daniel
Deputy Commissioner
Minority & Women's Business Enterprises
Department of Administration
402 West Washington Street, Room W479
Indianapolis, IN 46204
P: (317) 232-3061
F: (317) 233-6921
E: mwbe@idoa.in.gov

IOWA
Ms. Debi Durham
Director
Economic Development Authority
200 East Grand Avenue
Des Moines, IA 50309
P: (515) 725-3022
F: (515) 725-3010
E: director@iowaeda.com

KANSAS
Ms. Rhonda F. Harris
Director
Office of Minority & Women Business Development
Department of Commerce
1000 Southwest Jackson Street, Suite 100
Topeka, KS 66612
P: (785) 296-3425
F: (785) 296-3490
E: rharris@kansascommerce.com

KENTUCKY
Ms. Mandy Lambert
Commissioner
Department for Business Development
Old Capitol Annex, 300 West Broadway
Frankfort, KY 40601
P: (502) 564-7140
F: (502) 564-3256
E: Mandy.Lambert@ky.gov

LOUISIANA
Mr. Donald Pierson Jr.
Secretary of Economic Development
Louisiana Economic Development
617 North Third Street
Baton Rouge, LA 70802
P: (225) 342-5388
E: don.pierson@la.gov

MAINE
Mr. George C. Gervais
Commissioner
Department of Economic & Community Development
59 State House Station
Augusta, ME 04333
P: (207) 624-9800

MARYLAND
Celester Hall
Program Manager
Small Business, Office of Finance Programs
Department of Commerce
401 East Pratt Street
Baltimore, MD 21202
P: (410) 767-6356
E: celester.hall@maryland.gov

MASSACHUSETTS
Ms. Sandra E. Borders
Director
Office of Diversity & Equal Opportunity
One Ashburton Place, Room 213
Boston, MA 02108
P: (617) 727-7441
F: (617) 878-9830

Small and Minority Business Assistance

MICHIGAN
Mr. Steve Arwood
CEO
Economic Development Corporation
300 North Washington Square
Lansing, MI 48913
P: (517) 241-1400
F: (517) 241-3683
E: arwoods1@michigan.org

MINNESOTA
Mr. Matt Massman
Commissioner
Department of Administration
116 Veterans Service Building
20 West 12 Street
St. Paul, MN 55155
P: (651) 201-3421
F: (651) 297-7909
E: Matt.Massman@state.mn.us

MISSISSIPPI
Mr. Bob Covington
Chief Community Development & Leadership Officer
Development Authority
501 North West Street
P.O. Box 849
Jackson, MS 39205
P: (601) 359-9226
F: (601) 359-5290
E: rcovington@mississippi.org

Mr. Glenn L. McCullough Jr.
Chief Executive Officer
Development Authority
501 North West Street
P.O. Box 849
Jackson, MS 39205
P: (601) 359-3449
F: (601) 359-3832
E: gmccullough@mississippi.org

MISSOURI
Mr. Seth Bauman
Director
Office of Equal Opportunity
301 West High Street, Room 630
P.O. Box 809
Jefferson City, MO 65102
P: (573) 751-8130
F: (573) 522-8078

NEBRASKA
Ms. Courtney Dentlinger
Director
Department of Economic Development
301 Centennial Mall South
P.O. Box 94666
Lincoln, NE 68509
P: (402) 471-3746
F: (402) 471-3778
E: courtney.dentlinger@nebraska.gov

NEVADA
Ms. Jane Lee
Chair
Commission on Minority Affairs
Department of Business & Industry
555 East Washington Avenue, Suite 4900
Las Vegas, NV 89101
P: (702) 486-2750
F: (702) 486-2758
E: biinfo@business.nv.gov

NEW HAMPSHIRE
Mr. James Key-Wallace
Executive Director
Business Finance Authority
2 Pillsbury Street, Suite 201
Concord, NH 03301
P: (603) 415-0191
F: (603) 415-0194
E: JamesKW@nhbfa.com

NEW JERSEY
Ms. Melissa Orsen
Chief Executive Officer
Economic Development Authority
36 West State Street
P.O. Box 990
Trenton, NJ 08625
P: (609) 858-6700
F: (609) 292-0885
E: CustomerCare@njeda.com

NEW MEXICO
Mr. Matthew Geisel
Secretary
Economic Development Department
1100 South Saint Francis Drive
P.O. Box 20003
Santa Fe, NM 87504
P: (505) 827-0305
F: (505) 827-0328
E: Matthew.Geisel@state.nm.us

NEW YORK
Mr. Howard Zemsky
President & CEO
Empire State Development
633 Third Avenue, Floor 37
New York, NY 10017
P: (212) 803-3100
F: (212) 803-3715

NORTH CAROLINA
Mr. Scott Daugherty
Assistant Vice Chancellor/State Director
Small Business & Technology Development Center
5 West Hargett Street, Suite 600
Raleigh, NC 27601
P: (919) 715-7272
F: (919) 715-7777
E: sdaugherty@nccommerce.com

NORTH DAKOTA
Mr. Jay Schuler
Commissioner
Department of Commerce
1600 East Century Avenue, Suite 2
P.O. Box 2057
Bismarck, ND 58503
P: (701) 328-5300
F: (701) 328-5320
E: commerce@nd.gov

NORTHERN MARIANA ISLANDS
Mr. Manuel A. Sablan
Executive Director
Commonwealth Development Authority
P.O. Box 502149
Saipan, MP 96950
P: (670) 234-6245
F: (670) 235-7147
E: administration@cda.gov.mp

OKLAHOMA
Mr. Ken Talley
Small & Minority Business Coordinator
Business Customer Services
Department of Commerce
900 North Stiles Avenue
Oklahoma City, OK 73104
P: (405) 815-5218
F: (405) 605-2811
E: ken.talley@okcommerce.gov

PENNSYLVANIA
Mr. Dennis Davin
Secretary
Department of Community & Economic Development
Commonwealth Keystone Building
400 North Street, 4th Floor
Harrisburg, PA 17120
P: (866) 787-3003
F: (717) 787-6866

SOUTH CAROLINA
Ms. Pam Green
Director
Division of Small & Minority Business Contracting & Certification
Department of Administration
1205 Pendleton Street, Suite 453C
Columbia, SC 29201
P: (803) 734-0507
F: (803) 734-4061
E: Pamela.Green@admin.sc.gov

SOUTH DAKOTA
Mr. Scott Stern
Commissioner
Governor's Office of Economic Development
711 East Wells Avenue
Pierre, SD 57501
P: (800) 872-6190
F: (605) 773-3256
E: goedinfo@state.sd.us

TENNESSEE
Mr. Bob Rolfe
Commissioner
Department of Economic & Community Development
312 Rosa L. Parks Avenue, 11th Floor
Nashville, TN 37243
P: (615) 741-1888
F: (615) 741-7306
E: Bob.Rolfe@tn.gov

TEXAS
Mr. Harvey Hilderbran
Executive Director
Facilities Commission
1711 San Jacinto
Austin, TX 78701
P: (512) 463-3446
E: Harvey.Hilderbran@tfc.state.tx.us

U.S. VIRGIN ISLANDS
Mr. Wayne L. Biggs Jr.
Acting Chief Executive Officer
Economic Development Authority
8000 Nisky Shopping Center, Suite 620
P.O. Box 305038
St. Thomas, VI 00802
P: (340) 714-1700
F: (340) 773-6499

UTAH
Mr. Q. Vale Hale
Executive Director
Governor's Office of Economic Development
60 East South Temple, 3rd Floor
Salt Lake City, UT 84111
P: (801) 538-8769
F: (801) 538-8888

VIRGINIA
Ms. Tracey Wiley
Director
Department of Small Business & Supplier Diviersity
101 North 14th Street, 11th Floor
Richmond, VA 23219
P: (804) 786-6585
F: (804) 786-9736
E: tracey.jeter@sbsd.virginia.gov

WASHINGTON
Mr. Brian Bonlender
Director
Department of Commerce
1011 Plum Street, Southeast
P.O. Box 42525
Olympia, WA 98504
P: (360) 725-4000
E: brian.bonlender@commerce.wa.gov

WEST VIRGINIA
Mr. H. Wood Thrasher
Cabinet Secretary
Department of Commerce
Capitol Complex Building 6, Room 525
1900 Kanawha Boulevard East
Charleston, WV 25305
P: (304) 558-2234
F: (304) 558-1189
E: W.Thrasher@wv.gov

WISCONSIN
Mr. Mark Hogan
Chief Executive Officer
Economic Development Corporation
201 West Washington Avenue
P.O. Box 1687
Madison, WI 53701
P: (608) 210-6701
E: Mark.Hogan@wedc.org

WYOMING
Mr. Shawn Reese
Chief Executive Officer
Business Council
214 West 15th Street
Cheyenne, WY 82002
P: (307) 777-2862
F: (307) 777-2837
E: shawn.reese@wyo.gov

Social Services

Responsible for the delivery of services to children, disabled, and elderly.

ALABAMA
Ms. Nancy T. Buckner
Commissioner
Department of Human Resources
Gordon Persons Building, Suite 2104
50 North Ripley Street
Montgomery, AL 36130
P: (334) 242-1310
F: (334) 353-1115
E: Nancy.Buckner@dhr.alabama.gov

ALASKA
Ms. Valerie Davidson
Commissioner
Department of Health & Social Services
3601 C Street, Suite 902
P.O. Box 240249
Anchorage, AK 99503
P: (907) 269-7800
F: (907) 269-0060
E: val.davidson@alaska.gov

AMERICAN SAMOA
Dr. Taeaoafua Meki Solomona
Director
Department of Human & Social Services
P.O. Box 997534
Pago Pago, AS 96799
P: (684) 633-1664
F: (684) 633-7449
E: mtsolomona@dhss.as

ARIZONA
Mr. Henry Darwin
Interim Director
Department of Economic Security
1789 West Jefferson Street
Phoenix, AZ 85007
P: (602) 542-4791

ARKANSAS
Ms. Mary Franklin
Interim Director
Division of County Operations
Department of Human Services
P.O. Box 1437, Slot S301
Little Rock, AR 72203
P: (501) 682-8375
F: (501) 682-6836
E: mary.franklin@dhs.arkansas.gov

CALIFORNIA
Mr. Will Lightbourne
Director
Department of Social Services
744 P Street
Sacramento, CA 95814
P: (916) 657-2598
F: (916) 651-6569

COLORADO
Mr. Reginald L. Bicha
Executive Director
Department of Human Services
1575 Sherman Street
Denver, CO 80203
P: (303) 866-3475
F: (303) 866-2606
E: reginald.bicha@state.co.us

CONNECTICUT
Mr. Roderick L. Bremby
Commissioner
Department of Social Services
55 Farmington Avenue
Hartford, CT 06105
P: (860) 424-5053
E: roderick.bremby@ct.gov

DELAWARE
Ms. Kara Odom Walker
Secretary
Department of Health & Social Services
1901 North DuPont Highway
Main Building
New Castle, DE 19720
P: (302) 255-9040
F: (302) 255-4429

DISTRICT OF COLUMBIA
Ms. Laura Zeilinger
Director
Department of Human Services
64 New York Avenue, Northeast
6th Floor
Washington, DC 20002
P: (202) 671-4200
F: (202) 671-4326
E: dhs@dc.gov

FLORIDA
Mr. Mike Carroll
Secretary
Department of Children & Families
1317 Winewood Boulevard
Building 1, Room 202
Tallahassee, FL 32399
P: (850) 487-1111
F: (850) 922-2993
E: mike.carroll@myflfamilies.com

GEORGIA
Ms. Robyn A. Crittenden
Commissioner
Department of Human Services
2 Peachtree Street, Northwest
Suite 29-250
Atlanta, GA 30303
P: (404) 656-5680
F: (404) 651-8669

HAWAII
Mr. Pankaj Bhanot
Director
Department of Human Services
1390 Miller Street, Room 209
P.O. Box 339
Honolulu, HI 96809
P: (808) 586-4993
F: (808) 586-4890
E: dhs@dhs.hawaii.gov

IDAHO
Mr. Gary Moore
Administrator
Division of Family & Community Services
Department of Health & Welfare
450 West State Street
Boise, ID 83720
P: (208) 334-0641
F: (208) 332-7331
E: mooreg@dhw.idaho.gov

ILLINOIS
Mr. George H. Sheldon
Director
Department of Children & Family Services
406 East Monroe Street
Springfield, IL 62701
P: (217) 785-2509
F: (217) 785-1052

INDIANA
Ms. Adrienne Shields
Director of Family Resources
Family & Social Services Administration
402 West Washington Street, Room W392
P.O. Box 7083
Indianapolis, IN 46204
P: (317) 234-2373
F: (317) 232-4490
E: Adrienne.Shields@fssa.IN.gov

IOWA
Ms. Sally Titus
Deputy Director
Department of Human Services
Hoover State Office Building
1305 East Walnut Street
Des Moines, IA 50319
P: (515) 281-6360
F: (515) 281-4597
E: stitus@dhs.state.ia.us

KANSAS
Ms. Phyllis Gilmore
Secretary
Department for Children & Families
555 South Kansas Avenue
Topeka, KS 66603
P: (785) 296-3274
F: (785) 296-2173

KENTUCKY
Ms. Vickie Yates Brown Glisson
Secretary
Cabinet for Health & Family Services
275 East Main Street, 5W-A
Frankfort, KY 40621
P: (502) 564-7042
F: (502) 564-7091

LOUISIANA
Ms. Marketa Garner Walters
Secretary
Department of Children & Family Services
627 North Fourth Street
Baton Rouge, LA 70802
P: (225) 342-7475
F: (225) 342-8636
E: DCFS.Secretary@la.gov

MAINE
Mr. Ricker Hamilton
Deputy Commissioner of Programs
Department of Health & Human Services
221 State Street
11 State House Station
Augusta, ME 04333
P: (207) 287-3707
F: (207) 287-3005
E: ricker.hamilton@maine.gov

MASSACHUSETTS
Ms. Linda Spears
Commissioner
Department of Children & Families
Office of Health & Human Services
600 Washington Street
Boston, MA 02111
P: (617) 748-2000
F: (617) 261-7435
E: dcfcommissioner@state.ma.us

MICHIGAN
Mr. Nick Lyon
Director
Department of Health & Human Services
333 South Grand Avenue
P.O. Box 30195
Lansing, MI 48909
P: (517) 335-0267
F: (517) 335-6101
E: LyonN2@michigan.gov

MISSISSIPPI
Ms. Leigh Washington
Director
Office of Social Services Block Grant
Department of Human Services
750 North State Street
Jackson, MS 39202
P: (601) 359-4416

MISSOURI
Ms. Jennifer Tidball
Acting Director
Department of Social Services
Broadway State Office Building
P.O. Box 1527
Jefferson City, MO 65102
P: (573) 751-4815
F: (573) 751-3203

NEBRASKA
Mr. Douglas J. Weinberg
Director
Division of Children & Family Services
Department of Health & Human Services
P.O. Box 95026
Lincoln, NE 60509
P: (402) 471-1757
E: doug.weinberg@nebraska.gov

NEW HAMPSHIRE
Mr. Jeffrey A. Meyers
Commissioner
Department of Health & Human Services
129 Pleasant Street
Concord, NH 03301
P: (603) 271-9200
F: (603) 271-4912
E: Jeffrey.Meyers@dhhs.nh.gov

NEW JERSEY
Ms. Elizabeth Connolly
Acting Commissioner
Department of Human Services
222 South Warren Street
P.O. Box 700
Trenton, NJ 08625
P: (609) 292-3717

NEW MEXICO
Mr. Brent Earnest
Cabinet Secretary
Human Services Department
P.O. Box 2348
Santa Fe, NM 87504
P: (505) 827-7750
F: (505) 827-6286

NEW YORK
Mr. Samuel D. Roberts
Commissioner
Office of Temporary & Disability Assistance
40 North Pearl Street
Albany, NY 12243
P: (518) 473-1090
E: nyspio@otda.ny.gov

NORTH CAROLINA
Mr. Wayne E. Black
Director
Division of Social Services
Department of Health & Human Services
2401 Mail Service Center
Raleigh, NC 27699
P: (919) 527-6335
F: (919) 334-1018
E: wayne.black@dhhs.nc.gov

NORTH DAKOTA
Mr. Christopher Jones
Executive Director
Department of Human Services
600 East Boulevard Avenue
Department 325
Bismarck, ND 58505
P: (701) 328-2538
F: (701) 328-2359
E: dhseo@nd.gov

NORTHERN MARIANA ISLANDS
Ms. Roxanne P. Diaz
Director
Division of Public Health Services
P.O. Box 500409
Saipan, MP 96950
P: (670) 236-8703
E: chcpublichealth@gmail.com

OHIO
Ms. Cynthia C. Dungey
Director
Department of Job & Family Services
30 East Broad Street, 32nd Floor
Columbus, OH 43215
P: (614) 466-6283
F: (614) 466-2815

OREGON
Mr. Clyde Saiki
Director
Department of Human Services
500 Summer Street, Northeast
Salem, OR 97301
P: (503) 945-7001
F: (503) 581-6198
E: clyde.saiki@oregon.gov

PENNSYLVANIA
Mr. Theodore Dallas
Secretary
Department of Human Services
Health & Welfare Building
625 Forster Street, P.O. Box 2675
Harrisburg, PA 17105
P: (717) 787-2600
F: (717) 772-2062

PUERTO RICO
Ms. Glorimar Andujar Matos
Secretary
Department of the Family
P.O. Box 11398
Hato Rey, PR 00917
P: (787) 294-4900
F: (787) 297-0732

RHODE ISLAND
Mr. Eric J. Beane
Acting Director
Department of Human Services
Louis Pasteur Building
57 Howard Avenue
Cranston, RI 2920
P: (401) 462-2121

SOUTH CAROLINA
Ms. V. Susan Alford
Director
Department of Social Services
1535 Confederate Avenue
P.O. Box 1520
Columbia, SC 29202
P: (803) 898-7360
F: (803) 898-7277

SOUTH DAKOTA
Ms. Lynne A. Valenti
Cabinet Secretary
Department of Social Services
700 Governors Drive
Pierre, SD 57501
P: (605) 773-3165
F: (605) 773-4855
E: DSSInfo@state.sd.us

TENNESSEE
Ms. Danielle W. Barnes
Commissioner
Department of Human Services
400 Deaderick Street
Nashville, TN 37243
P: (615) 313-4700
F: (615) 741-4165
E: danielle.w.barnes@tn.gov

TEXAS
Mr. Gary Jessee
Deputy Executive Commissioner for Medicail & Social Services
Health & Human Services Commission
4900 North Lamar Boulevard
P.O. Box 13247
Austin, TX 78711
P: (512) 424-6500
F: (512) 424-6587

U.S. VIRGIN ISLANDS
Mr. Felicia Blyden
Commissioner
Department of Human Services
3011 Golden Rock
Christiansted
St. Croix, VI 00802
P: (340) 718-2980

UTAH
Ms. Ann S. Williamson
Executive Director
Department of Human Services
195 North 1950 West
Salt Lake City, UT 84116
P: (801) 538-4001
F: (801) 538-4016
E: annwilliamson@utah.gov

VIRGINIA
Ms. Margaret Ross Schultze
Commissioner
Department of Social Services
801 East Main Street
Richmond, VA 23219
P: (804) 726-7011
E: margaret.schultze@dss.virginia.gov

WASHINGTON
Mr. Bill Moss
Acting Secretary
Department of Social & Health Services
1115 Washington Street, Southeast
Olympia, WA 98504
P: (800) 737-0617
F: (360) 407-0304

Social Services

WEST VIRGINIA
Mr. Bill J. Crouch
Cabinet Secretary
Department of Health & Human Resources
One Davis Square, Suite 100 East
Charleston, WV 25301
P: (304) 558-0684
F: (304) 558-1130
E: DHHRSecretary@wv.gov

WYOMING
Dr. Steve Corsi
Director
Department of Family Services
Hathaway Building, 3rd Floor
2300 Capitol Avenue
Cheyenne, WY 82002
P: (307) 777-6597
F: (307) 777-7747
E: steve.corsi@wyo.gov

State Data Center

Center that acts as an information clearinghouse for the Census Bureau and other data sources within the state.

ALABAMA
Ms. Susannah Robichaux
Socioeconomic Analyst II
State Data Center
Center for Business & Economic Research
University of Alabama, Box 870221
Tuscaloosa, AL 35487
P: (205) 348-3781
E: scrobichaux@culverhouse.ua.edu

ALASKA
Ms. Heidi Drygas
Commissioner
Department of Labor & Workforce Development
P.O. Box 111149
Juneau, AK 99811
P: (907) 465-2700
F: (907) 465-2784
E: heidi.drygas@alaska.gov

AMERICAN SAMOA
Mr. Meleisea Vai Filiga
Chief Statistician
Research & Statistics Division
Department of Commerce
Executive Office Building, Utulei
Pago Pago, AS 96799
P: (684) 633-5155
F: (684) 633-4195
E: vai.filiga@doc.as

ARIZONA
Mr. Gary Hensley
Chief Operations Officer
State Data Center
Strategic Enterprise Technology Division
100 North 15th Avenue, Suite 440
Phoenix, AZ 85007
P: (602) 771-6401

ARKANSAS
Ms. Phyllis Poche
Director
Census State Data Center
UALR Institute for Economic Advancement
2801 South University Avenue
Little Rock, AR 72204
P: (501) 569-8530
F: (501) 569-8538
E: pnpoche@ualr.edu

CALIFORNIA
Mr. William Schooling
Chief
Demographic Research Unit
915 L Street
Sacramento, CA 95814
P: (916) 323-4086
F: (916) 327-0222
E: ficalpop@dof.ca.gov;webmaster@dof.

COLORADO
Ms. Elizabeth Garner
State Demographer
Demography Office
Department of Local Affairs
1313 Sherman Street, Room 521
Denver, CO 80203
P: (303) 864-7750
F: (303) 864-7759
E: elizabeth.garner@state.co.us

CONNECTICUT
Mr. Michael Howser
Director
State Data Center, University of Connecticut
Homer Babbidge Library
369 Fairfield Road, Unit 1005M
Storrs, CT 06269
P: (860) 570-9028
E: ctsdc@uconn.edu

DELAWARE
Ms. Miriam Pomilio
Principal Planner/GIS Coordination
Office of State Planning Coordination
Haslet Armory
122 Martin Luther King Jr. Blvd., South
Dover, DE 19901
P: (302) 739-3090
E: miriam.pomilio@state.de.us

DISTRICT OF COLUMBIA
Ms. Joy E. Phillips
Associate Director
State Data Center
1100 4th Street, Southwest
Suite 650 East
Washington, DC 20024
P: (202) 442-7630
F: (202) 442-7638
E: joy.phillips@dc.gov

FLORIDA
Mr. Eric Larson
Acting Executive Director & Chief Information Officer & Chief Operations Officer
Agency for State Technology
4050 Esplanade Way, Suite 115
Tallahassee, FL 32399
P: (850) 717-9506

GEORGIA
Mr. Robert Giacomini
Director of Research
Governor's Office of Planning & Budget
2 Capitol Square
Atlanta, GA 30334
P: (404) 656-3820
F: (404) 656-3828
E: robert.giacomini@opb.state.ga.us

GUAM
Mr. William C. McDonald
Acting Director
Bureau of Statistics & Plans
P.O. Box 2950
Hagatna, GU 96932
P: (671) 472-4201
F: (671) 477-1812

HAWAII
Dr. Eugene Tian
Administrator & Chief State Economist
Research & Economic Analysis Division
Business, Economic Development & Tourism
P.O. Box 2359
Honolulu, HI 96804
P: (808) 586-2470
F: (808) 586-8449
E: xtian@dbedt.hawaii.gov

IDAHO
Ms. Megan Ronk
Director
Department of Commerce
700 West State Street
P.O. Box 83720
Boise, ID 83720
P: (208) 334-2470
F: (208) 334-2631
E: megan.ronk@commerce.idaho.gov

ILLINOIS
Ms. Sue Ebetsch
Coordinator
State Data Center Cooperative
Commerce & Economic Opportunity
500 East Monroe Street
Springfield, IL 62701
P: (217) 782-1381
F: (217) 558-5146
E: Sue.Ebetsch@illinois.gov

INDIANA
Mr. Jacob Speer
State Librarian
State Library
315 West Ohio Street
Indianapolis, IN 46202
P: (317) 232-3692
E: director@library.in.gov

IOWA
Mr. Gary Krob
Data Warehouse Analyst
State Data Center
Ola Babcock Miller Building
1112 East Grand Avenue
Des Moines, IA 50319
P: (515) 281-6618
F: (515) 242-6543
E: gary.krob@iowa.gov

KENTUCKY
Dr. Matthew Ruther
Executive Director
State Data Center
426 West Bloom Street
Louisville, KY 40208
P: (502) 852-8151
E: matthew.ruther@louisville.edu

MAINE
Ms. Amanda Rector
State Economist
Office of Policy & Management
181 State House Station
Augusta, ME 04333
P: (207) 480-3090
F: (207) 287-6489
E: OPM@maine.gov

MARYLAND
Mr. Alfred P. Sundara
Director
Projections & State Data Center, Planning Data & Research Section
Department of Planning
301 West Preston Street
Baltimore, MD 21201
P: (410) 767-4394
F: (410) 767-4480
E: alfred.sundara@maryland.gov

State Data Center

MASSACHUSETTS
Ms. Carrie Bernstein
Manager
State Data Center
UMASS Donahue Institute
100 Venture Way, Suite 9
Hadley, MA 01035
P: (413) 545-6655
F: (413) 545-3420

MICHIGAN
Mr. David Behen
Director
Department of Technology, Management & Budget
320 South Walnut Street, 2nd Floor
P.O. Box 30026
Lansing, MI 48909
P: (517) 373-1004
E: behend@michigan.gov

MINNESOTA
Mr. Matt Massman
Commissioner
Department of Administration
116 Veterans Service Building
20 West 12 Street
St. Paul, MN 55155
P: (651) 201-3421
F: (651) 297-7909
E: Matt.Massman@state.mn.us

MISSISSIPPI
Dr. John J. Green
Director
Center for Population Studies
Department of Sociology & Anthropology
537 Lamar Hall
University, MS 38677
P: (662) 915-7295
F: (662) 915-5372
E: jjgreen@olemiss.edu

MISSOURI
Terry Blauvelt
Statistical Research Analyst
Census Data Center
State Library
600 West Main Street
Jefferson City, MO 65101
P: (417) 895-6670
E: Terry.Blauvelt@sos.mo.gov

MONTANA
Mr. Ron Baldwin
Chief Information Officer
Information Technology Services Division
Department of Administration
P.O. Box 200113
Helena, MT 59620
P: (406) 444-2777
F: (406) 444-2701

NEBRASKA
Mr. Jerome Deichart
Director & Senior Research Associate
Center for Public Affairs Research
CPACS 108
6001 Dodge Street
Omaha, NE 68182
P: (402) 554-2133
F: (402) 554-4946
E: jdeicher@unomaha.edu

NEVADA
Mr. William D. Anderson
Chief Economist
Department of Employment, Training & Rehabilitation
Research & Analysis Bureau
1937 North Carson Street
Carson City, NV 89701
P: (775) 684-0387
F: (775) 684-3850
E: wdanderson@nvdetr.org

NEW HAMPSHIRE
Mr. Ken Gallager
Principal Planner
State Data Center
Johnson Hall, 3rd Floor
107 Pleasant Street
Concord, NH 03301
P: (603) 271-1773
F: (603) 271-2615
E: ken.gallager@nh.gov

NEW JERSEY
Mr. Len Preston
Director
State Data Center
Labor & Workforce Development
P.O. Box 388
Trenton, NJ 08625
P: (609) 984-2595
F: (609) 984-6833
E: lpreston@dol.state.nj.us

NEW MEXICO
Ms. Elizabeth Davis
Research & Marketing Director
Economic Development Department
1100 South Saint Francis Drive
P.O. Box 20003
Santa Fe, NM 87504
P: (505) 827-0333
F: (505) 827-0328
E: Elizabeth.Davis@state.nm.us

NEW YORK
Ms. Laura Close
State Data Center
Department of Labor
30 South Pearl Street
Albany, NY 12207
P: (518) 292-5300
E: nysdatacenter@labor.ny.gov

NORTH CAROLINA
Mr. Michael Cline
State Demographer
Department of State Budget & Management
Demographic & Economic Analysis
20320 Mail Service Center
Raleigh, NC 27699
P: (919) 807-4756
E: michael.cline@osbm.nc.gov

NORTH DAKOTA
Mr. Shawn Riley
Chief Information Officer
Information Technology Department
4201 Normandy Street
Bismarck, ND 58503
P: (701) 328-1001
F: (701) 328-1075
E: sriley@nd.gov

OKLAHOMA
Mr. Jon Chiappe
Director
Research & Economic Analysis
Department of Commerce
900 North Stiles Avenue
Oklahoma City, OK 73104
P: (405) 815-5210
F: (405) 605-2807
E: jon.chiappe@okcommerce.gov

OREGON
Mr. Alex Pettit
Chief Information Officer
Department of Administrative Services
Executive Building
155 Cottage Street Northeast, 4th Floor
Salem, OR 97301
P: (503) 378-2128
F: (503) 378-3795
E: alex.pettit@das.state.or.us

PENNSYLVANIA
Ms. Sue Copella
Director
State Data Center
777 West Harrisburg Pike
Middletown, PA 17057
P: (717) 948-6427
F: (717) 948-6754
E: sdc3@psu.edu

PUERTO RICO
Mr. Luis F. Batista Cruz
Director
Office of Management & Budget
P.O. Box 9023228
San Juan, PR 00902
P: (787) 725-9420
F: (787) 722-0299

SOUTH CAROLINA
Mr. Frank Rainwater
Executive Director
Revenue & Fiscal Affairs Office
Rembert Dennis Building
1000 Assembly Street, Suite 402
Columbia, SC 29201
P: (803) 734-2265
E: frank.rainwater@rfa.sc.gov

TENNESSEE
Mr. Mark Bengel
Chief Information Officer
Office for Information Resources
Department of Finance & Administration
901 5th Avenue, North
Nashville, TN 37243
P: (615) 741-7951
F: (615) 532-0471

TEXAS
Ms. Stacey Napier
Executive Director
Department of Information Resources
300 West 15th Street, Suite 1300
P.O. Box 13564
Austin, TX 78711
P: (512) 475-4700
F: (512) 475-4759

U.S. VIRGIN ISLANDS
Mr. Stevie Henry
Data Manager
Conservation Data Center
University of the Virgin Islands
#2 John Brewer's Bay
St. Thomas, VI 00802
P: (340) 693-1020
F: (340) 693-1025
E: shenry@uvi.edu

UTAH
Ms. Kristen Cox
Executive Director
Governor's Office of Management & Budget
State Capitol, Suite 150
P.O. Box 132210
Salt Lake City, UT 84114
P: (801) 538-1705
F: (801) 538-1547
E: kristencox@utah.gov

VIRGINIA
Ms. Ellen Marie Hess
Commissioner
Employment Commission
703 East Main Street
P.O. Box 1358
Richmond, VA 23219
P: (866) 832-2363
E: ellenmarie.hess@vec.virginia.gov

WEST VIRGINIA
Mr. H. Wood Thrasher
Cabinet Secretary
Department of Commerce
Capitol Complex Building 6, Room 525
1900 Kanawha Boulevard East
Charleston, WV 25305
P: (304) 558-2234
F: (304) 558-1189
E: W.Thrasher@wv.gov

WISCONSIN
Mr. Phil Wells
Program & Policy Analyst-Advanced
Demographic Services Center
101 East Wilson, 9th Floor
P.O. Box 8944
Madison, WI 53708
P: (608) 266-1927
F: (608) 264-6104
E: DIR_Demo@wi.gov

State and Public Libraries

Serves the information and research needs of state executive and legislative branch officials. Also oversees the development of public libraries in the state and federal programs related to such libraries.

ALABAMA
Ms. Nancy Pack
Director
Public Library Service
6030 Monticello Drive
Montgomery, AL 36130
P: (334) 213-3901
F: (334) 213-3993
E: npack@apls.state.al.us

ALASKA
Ms. Linda Thibodeau
State Librarian & Director
Division of Libraries, Archives & Museums
P.O. Box 110571
Juneau, AK 99811
P: (907) 465-2911
F: (907) 465-2151
E: linda.thibodeau@alaska.gov

AMERICAN SAMOA
Mr. Justin Maga
Acting Territorial Librarian
American Samoa Government
P.O. Box 997687
Pago Pago, AS 96799
E: justinmaga@gmail.com

ARIZONA
Ms. Holly Henley
State Librarian
State of Arizona
State Capitol, Room 200
1700 West Washington
Phoenix, AZ 85007
P: (602) 926-3366
F: (602) 256-7983

ARKANSAS
Ms. Carolyn Ashcraft
State Librarian
State Library
900 West Capitol Avenue
Suite 100
Little Rock, AR 72201
P: (501) 682-1526
F: (501) 682-1899
E: carolyn@library.arkansas.gov

CALIFORNIA
Mr. Greg Lucas
Librarian
State of California
P.O. Box 942837
Sacramento, CA 94237
P: (916) 323-9759
E: Greg.Lucas@library.ca.gov

COLORADO
Mr. Gene Hainer
Assistant Commissioner
State Library
201 East Colfax Avenue, Room 309
Denver, CO 80203
P: (303) 594-4780
F: (303) 866-6940
E: hainer_g@cde.state.co.us

CONNECTICUT
Mr. Kendall F. Wiggin
State Librarian
State Library
231 Capitol Avenue
Hartford, CT 06106
P: (860) 757-6510
F: (860) 757-6503
E: kendall.wiggin@ct.gov

DELAWARE
Dr. Anne E.C. Norman
Director & State Librarian
Division of Libraries
121 Duke of York Street
Dover, DE 19901
P: (302) 739-4748
F: (302) 739-6787
E: annie.norman@state.de.us

DISTRICT OF COLUMBIA
Mr. Richard Reyes-Gavilan
Executive Director
District of Columbia
901 G Street, Northwest
Suite 400
Washington, DC 20001
P: (202) 727-1101
E: rrg@dc.gov

FLORIDA
Ms. Amy Johnson
Director
Division of Library & Information Services
R.A. Gray Building
500 South Bronough Street
Tallahassee, FL 32399
P: (850) 245-6622
F: (850) 245-6735
E: amy.johnson@dos.myflorida.com

GEORGIA
Ms. Julie Walker
State Librarian
Public Library Service
1800 Century Place, Northeast
Suite 150
Atlanta, GA 30345
P: (404) 406-4519
F: (404) 235-7201
E: jwalker@georgialibraries.org

HAWAII
Ms. Stacey A. Aldrich
State Librarian
State Public Library System
44 Merchant Street
Honolulu, HI 96813
P: (717) 783-2466
F: (717) 772-3265
E: stacey.aldrich@librarieshawaii.org

IDAHO
Ms. Ann Joslin
State Librarian
Commission for Libraries
325 West State Street
Boise, ID 83702
P: (208) 334-2150
F: (208) 334-4016
E: ann.joslin@libraries.idaho.gov

ILLINOIS
Ms. Anne Craig
Director
State Library
300 South Second Street
Gwendolyn Brooks Building
Springfield, IL 62701
P: (217) 782-2994
F: (217) 785-4326
E: acraig@ilsos.net

INDIANA
Mr. Jacob Speer
State Librarian
State of Indiana
315 West Ohio Street
Indianapolis, IN 46202
P: (317) 232-3692
E: director@library.in.gov

IOWA
Mr. Michael Scott
Chief Library Officer
State of Iowa
State Library
1112 East Grand Avenue
Des Moines, IA 50319
P: (515) 281-4105
F: (515) 242-6543
E: michael.scott@lib.state.ia.us

KANSAS
Ms. Jo Budler
State Librarian
State Library
Capitol Building, Room 343-N
300 Southwest 10th Avenue
Topeka, KS 66612
P: (785) 506-4563
F: (785) 368-7291
E: jo.budler@library.ks.gov

KENTUCKY
Mr. Terry Manuel
Acting State Librarian & Commissioner
Department for Libraries & Archives
P.O. Box 537
Frankfort, KY 40602
P: (502) 564-1730
E: terry.manuel@ky.gov

LOUISIANA
Ms. Rebecca Hamilton
State Librarian
State Library
P.O. Box 131
Baton Rouge, LA 70821
P: (225) 342-4923
F: (225) 219-4804
E: rhamilton@crt.la.gov

MAINE
Mr. James Ritter
State Librarian
State Library
64 State House Station
Augusta, ME 04333
P: (207) 287-5604
F: (207) 287-5624
E: james.ritter@maine.gov

MARYLAND
Ms. Irene M. Padilla
Assistant State Superintendent for Libraries
Division of Library Development & Services
200 West Baltimore Street
Baltimore, MD 21201
P: (410) 767-0435
F: (410) 333-2507
E: irene.padilla@maryland.gov

MASSACHUSETTS
Ms. Dianne Carty
Director
Board of Library Commissioners
98 North Washington Street, Suite 401
Boston, MA 02114
P: (617) 725-1860 Ext. 222
E: dianne.carty@state.ma.us

MICHIGAN
Mr. Randy Riley
State Librarian
State Library & Historical Center
P.O. Box 30007
Lansing, MI 48909
P: (517) 373-5860
F: (517) 373-4480
E: rileyr1@michigan.gov

MINNESOTA
Ms. Jennifer Nelson
State Librarian & Director
State Library Services
Department of Education
1500 Highway 36 West
Roseville, MN 55113
P: (651) 582-8791
E: Jennifer.R.Nelson@state.mn.us

MISSOURI
Ms. Barbara Reading
State Librarian
State Library
P.O. Box 387
Jefferson City, MO 65102
P: (573) 526-4783
E: Barbara.reading@sos.mo.gov

MONTANA
Ms. Jennie Stapp
State Librarian
State Librarian's Office
1515 East 6th Avenue
P.O. Box 201800
Helena, MT 59620
P: (406) 444-4799
F: (406) 444-0266
E: jstapp2@mt.gov

NEBRASKA
Mr. Rod Wagner
Director
Library Commission
The Atrium
1200 N Street, Suite 120
Lincoln, NE 68508
P: (402) 471-4001
F: (402) 471-2083
E: rod.wagner@nebraska.gov

NEVADA
Mr. Jeffrey M. Kintop
Acting Division Administrator
State Library & Archives
100 North Stewart Street
Carson City, NV 89701
P: (775) 684-3410
F: (775) 684-3311
E: jkintop@admin.nv.gov

NEW HAMPSHIRE
Mr. Michael York
State Librarian
State Library
20 Park Street
Concord, NH 03301
P: (603) 271-2397
F: (603) 271-6826
E: michael.york@dcr.nh.gov

NEW JERSEY
Ms. Mary Chute
State Librarian
State of New Jersey
185 West State Street
Trenton, NJ 08625
P: (609) 278-2640 Ext. 101
F: (609) 278-2647
E: mchute@njstatelib.org

NEW MEXICO
Ms. Kathleen Moeller-Peiffer
State Librarian
State of New Mexico
1209 Camino Carlos Rey
Santa Fe, NM 87507
P: (505) 476-9762
E: Kathleen.Peiffer@state.nm.us

NEW YORK
Mr. Bernard A. Margolis
State Librarian & Assistant Commissioner for Libraries
State Library
Cultural Education Center
10C34
Albany, NY 12230
P: (518) 474-5930
F: (518) 486-6880
E: bernard.margolis@nysed.gov

NORTH CAROLINA
Ms. Cal Shepard
State Librarian
State Library
4640 Mail Service Center
Raleigh, NC 27699
P: (919) 807-7410
F: (919) 733-8748
E: cal.shepard@ncdcr.gov

NORTH DAKOTA
Ms. Mary Soucie
State Librarian
State of North Dakota
604 East Boulevard Avenue
Department 250
Bismarck, ND 58505
P: (701) 328-4654
F: (701) 328-2040
E: msoucie@nd.gov

OHIO
Ms. Beverly Cain
State Librarian
State Library
274 East 1st Avenue, Suite 100
Columbus, OH 43201
P: (614) 644-6843
F: (614) 466-3584
E: bcain@library.ohio.gov

OKLAHOMA
Ms. Susan C. McVey
State Librarian
Department of Libraries
200 Northeast 18th Street
Oklahoma City, OK 73105
P: (405) 522-3173
F: (405) 521-1077
E: susan.mcvey@libraries.ok.gov

OREGON
Ms. MaryKay Dahlgreen
State Librarian
State Of Oregon
250 Winter Street, Northeast
Salem, OR 97301
P: (503) 378-4367
F: (503) 585-8059
E: marykay.dahlgreen@state.or.us

PENNSYLVANIA
Mr. Glenn Miller
Deputy Secretary/Commissioner for Libraries/State Librarian
Office of Commonwealth Libraries
Department of Education
Forum 203, 607 South Drive
Harrisburg, PA 17120
P: (717) 783-2466
F: (717) 223-3121
E: glennmille@pa.gov

RHODE ISLAND
Ms. Karen Mellor
Chief Library Officer
Office of Library & Information Services
1 Capitol Hill, Floor 2
Providence, RI 02908
P: (401) 574-9304
E: Karen.Mellor@olis.ri.gov

SOUTH CAROLINA
Ms. Leesa Aiken
Interim Director
State of South Carolina
P.O. Box 11469
Columbia, SC 29211
P: (803) 734-8668
F: (803) 734-0822
E: laiken@statelibrary.sc.gov

SOUTH DAKOTA
Ms. Daria Bossman
State Librarian
State of South Dakota
MacKay Building
800 Governors Drive
Pierre, SD 57501
P: (605) 773-3131
E: daria.bossman@state.sd.us

TENNESSEE
Mr. Charles A. Sherrill
State Librarian & Archivist
State Library & Archives
403 7th Avenue, North
Nashville, TN 37243
P: (615) 741-7996
F: (615) 532-9293
E: Chuck.Sherrill@tn.gov

TEXAS
Mr. Mark Smith
Director & State Librarian
State Library & Archives
P.O. Box 12516
Austin, TX 78711
P: (512) 463-5460
E: msmith@tsl.texas.gov

U.S. VIRGIN ISLANDS
Ms. Ingrid Bough
Territorial Director of Libraries, Archives & Museums
Territory of the Virgin Islands
C/o Florence Williams Public Library
1122 King Street, Christiansted
St. Croix, VI 00820
P: (304) 773-5715
F: (304) 773-5327
E: ingrid.bough@dpnr.vi.gov

UTAH
Ms. Donna Morris
State Librarian
State Library
250 North 1950 West, Suite A
Salt Lake City, UT 84116
P: (801) 715-6770
F: (801) 715-6767
E: dmorris@utah.gov

State and Public Libraries

VERMONT
Mr. Scott Murphy
Acting State Librarian
Department of Libraries
109 State Street
Montpelier, VT 05609
P: (802) 828-3261
F: (802) 828-2199
E: scott.murphy@vermont.gov

VIRGINIA
Ms. Sandra Treadway
State Librarian
The Library of Virginia
800 East Broad Street
Richmond, VA 23219
P: (804) 692-3535
F: (804) 692-3594
E: Sandra.Treadway
@lva.virginia.gov

WASHINGTON
Mr. Greg Lane
Deputy Secretary of State &
Acting State Librarian
State Library
Office of the Secretary of State
P.O. Box 42460
Tumwater, WA 98504
P: (360) 902-4141
E: greg.lane@sos.wa.gov

WEST VIRGINIA
Ms. Karen E. Goff
Secretary
State of West Virginia
1900 Kanawha Boulevard, East
Cultural Center
Charleston, WV 25305
P: (304) 558-2041
F: (304) 558-2044
E: karen.e.goff@wv.gov

WISCONSIN
Mr. Kurt Kiefer
State Librarian
Division for Libraries,
Technology & Community
Learning
Department of Public Instruction
P.O. Box 7841
Madison, WI 53707
P: (608) 266-2205
F: (608) 266-8770
E: Kurt.Kiefer@dpi.wi.gov

WYOMING
Ms. Jamie Markus
Interim State Librarian
State Library
2800 Central Avenue
Cheyenne, WY 82002
P: (307) 777-5914
F: (307) 777-5920
E: jamie.markus@wyo.gov

State Police

Patrols the state's highways and enforces the motor vehicle laws of the state.

ALABAMA
Mr. Stan Stabler
Acting Secretary of Law Enforcement
Law Enforcement Agency
301 South Ripley Street
P.O. Box 1511
Montgomery, AL 36102
P: (334) 517-2800
F: (334) 242-0512

ALASKA
Mr. Walt Monegan
Commissioner
Department of Public Safety
5700 East Tudor Road
Anchorage, AK 99507
P: (907) 269-5086
F: (907) 269-4543
E: walt.monegan@alaska.gov

AMERICAN SAMOA
Mr. Le'i S. Thompson
Commissioner
Department of Public Safety
American Samoa Government
P.O. Box 1086
Pago Pago, AS 96799
P: (684) 633-1111
F: (684) 633-7296
E: lei.thompson@dps.as.gov

ARIZONA
Colonel Frank Milstead
Director
Department of Public Safety
2222 West Encanto Boulevard
Phoenix, AZ 85009
P: (602) 223-2000
F: (602) 223-2917

ARKANSAS
Colonel Bill Bryant
Director
State Police
1 State Police Plaza Drive
Little Rock, AR 72209
P: (501) 618-8299
F: (501) 618-8222
E: info@asp.arkansas.gov

CALIFORNIA
Mr. Joseph A. Farrow
Commissioner
Highway Patrol
601 North 7th Street
P.O. Box 942898
Sacramento, CA 94298
P: (916) 843-3001
F: (916) 843-3264

COLORADO
Colonel Scott G. Hernandez
Chief
State Patrol
Department of Public Safety
700 Kipling Street, #1000
Denver, CO 80215
P: (303) 239-4404
F: (303) 239-4670
E: scott.hernandez@state.co.us

CONNECTICUT
Ms. Dora B. Schriro
Commissioner
Department of Emergency Services & Public Protection
1111 Country Club Road
Middletown, CT 06457
P: (860) 685-8000
F: (860) 685-8354
E: dora.schriro@ct.gov

DELAWARE
Colonel Nathaniel McQueen Jr.
Commissioner
State Police
1441 North DuPont Highway
Dover, DE 19901
P: (302) 739-5960

DISTRICT OF COLUMBIA
Mr. Peter Newsham
Chief of Police
Metropolitan Police Department
300 Indiana Avenue, Northwest
Room 5059
Washington, DC 20001
P: (202) 727-9099
F: (202) 727-4106
E: mpd@dc.gov

FLORIDA
Mr. Rick Swearingen
Commissioner
Department of Law Enforcement
2331 Phillips Road
P.O. Box 1489
Tallahassee, FL 32302
P: (850) 410-7011
E: RickSwearingen@fdle.state.fl.us

GEORGIA
Colonel Mark W. McDonough
Commissioner
Department of Public Safety
959 East Confederate Avenue, Southeast
P.O. Box 1456
Atlanta, GA 30371
P: (404) 624-7477
F: (404) 624-6706

ILLINOIS
Mr. Leo P. Schmitz
Director
State Police
801 South 7th Street, Suite 1100 – S
Springfield, IL 62703
P: (217) 782-7263
E: askisp@isp.state.il.us

INDIANA
Mr. Douglas G. Carter
Superintendent
State Police
Indiana Government Center North
100 North Senate Avenue
Indianapolis, IN 46204
P: (317) 232-8248
E: ISP@isp.in.gov

IOWA
Colonel Patrick J. Hoye
Bureau Chief
Governor's Traffic Safety Bureau
Department of Public Safety
215 East 7th Street
Des Moines, IA 50319
P: (515) 725-6120
F: (515) 725-6133
E: hoye@dps.state.ia.us

KANSAS
Colonel Mark Bruce
Superintendent
Highway Patrol
122 Southwest 7th Street
Topeka, KS 66603
P: (785) 296-6800
F: (785) 296-3049

KENTUCKY
Mr. Richard Sanders
Commissioner
State Police
919 Versailles Road
Frankfort, KY 40601
F: (502) 573-1479

LOUISIANA
Colonel Kevin W. Reeves
Superintendent
State Police
Public Safety Services
7919 Independence Boulevard
Baton Rouge, LA 70806
P: (225) 925-6118

MAINE
Colonel Robert A. Williams
Chief
State Police
42 State House Station
45 Commerce Drive
Augusta, ME 04333
P: (207) 624-7200
E: robert.a.williams@maine.gov

MARYLAND
Colonel William Pallozzi
Superintendent
Department of State Police
1201 Reisterstown Road
Pikesville, MD 21208
P: (410) 653-4219
E: msp.superintendent@maryland.gov

MASSACHUSETTS
Colonel Richard D. McKeon
Superintendent
State Police
Office of Public Safety & Security
470 Worcester Road
Framingham, MA 01702
P: (508) 820-2300
F: (617) 727-6874

MICHIGAN
Colonel Kriste Kibbey Etue
Director
State Police
P.O. Box 30634
Lansing, MI 48909
P: (517) 332-2521
F: (517) 241-0991
E: EtueK@michigan.gov

MINNESOTA
Colonel Matt Langer
Chief
State Patrol
445 Minnesota Street
St. Paul, MN 55101
P: (651) 201-7100
F: (651) 296-5937
E: matthew.langer@state.mn.us

MISSISSIPPI
Mr. Jimmy Jordan
Director
Bureau of Investigation
P.O. Box 958
Jackson, MS 39205
P: (601) 987-1573

State Police

MONTANA
The Honorable Tim Fox (R)
Attorney General
Department of Justice
Justice Building
215 North Sanders
Helena, MT 59620
P: (406) 444-2026
F: (406) 444-3549
E: contactdoj@mt.gov

NEBRASKA
Colonel Bradley Rice
Superintendent of Law Enforcement & Public Safety
State Patrol
1600 Highway 2
Lincoln, NE 68502
P: (402) 471-4545
F: (402) 479-4002
E: Brad.Rice@nebraska.gov

NEVADA
Colonel Dennis S. Osborn
Chief
Highway Patrol
Department of Public Safety
555 Wright Way
Carson City, NV 89711
P: (775) 687-5300

NEW HAMPSHIRE
Colonel Robert L. Quinn
Director
Division of State Police
Department of Safety
33 Hazen Drive
Concord, NH 03305
P: (603) 223-8813
F: (603) 271-0336
E: SPHeadquarters@dos.nh.gov

NEW JERSEY
Colonel Joseph R. Fuentes
Superintendent
State Police
P.O. Box 7068
West Trenton, NJ 08628
P: (609) 882-2000
F: (609) 530-4383

NEW MEXICO
Mr. Pete N. Kassetas
Chief of Police
Department of Public Safety
4491 Cerrillos Road
P.O. Box 1628
Santa Fe, NM 87504
P: (505) 827-9219
F: (505) 827-3395
E: NMSP.Chief@state.nm.us

NEW YORK
Mr. Joseph D'Amico
Superintendent
State Police
1220 Washington Avenue, Building 22
Albany, NY 12226
P: (518) 457-6721
E: nyspmail@troopers.ny.gov

NORTH CAROLINA
Colonel Glenn McNeill
Commander
State Highway Patrol
512 North Salisbury Street
Raleigh, NC 27604
P: (919) 733-7952
E: glenn.mcneill@ncdps.gov

NORTH DAKOTA
Colonel Michael Gerhart
Superintendent
Highway Patrol
600 East Boulevard Avenue
Department 504
Bismarck, ND 58505
P: (701) 328-2455
F: (701) 328-1717
E: ndhpinfo@nd.gov

NORTHERN MARIANA ISLANDS
Mr. Robert A. Guerrero
Commissioner
Department of Public Safety
Jose M. Sablan Building
Caller Box 10007
Saipan, MP 96950
P: (670) 664-9022
F: (670) 664-9027

OHIO
Colonel Paul A. Pride
Superintendent
State Highway Patrol
1970 West Broad Street
P.O. Box 182074
Columbus, OH 43223
P: (614) 466-2990
E: wwwohp@dps.ohio.gov

OKLAHOMA
Mr. Michael C. Thompson
Commissioner
Department of Public Safety
P.O. Box 11415
Oklahoma City, OK 73136
P: (405) 425-2424
E: mike.thompson@dps.state.ok.us

PENNSYLVANIA
Colonel Tyree C. Blocker
Commissioner
State Police
1800 Elmerton Avenue
Harrisburg, PA 17110
P: (717) 783-5599
F: (717) 787-2948

PUERTO RICO
Ms. Michelle M. Hernandez De Fraley
Superintendent
Puerto Rico Police
601 Franklin Delano Roosevelt Avenue
San Juan, PR 00936
P: (787) 793-1234

RHODE ISLAND
Colonel Ann Claire Assumpico
Director
Department of Public Safety
311 Danielson Pike
North Scituate, RI 02857
P: (401) 444-1000
F: (401) 444-1105

SOUTH CAROLINA
Colonel Michael Oliver
Commander
Highway Patrol
10311 Wilson Boulevard
P.O. Box 1993
Blythewood, SC 29016
P: (803) 896-7920
F: (803) 896-7922

SOUTH DAKOTA
Colonel Craig Price
Superintendent
Highway Patrol
Department of Public Safety
118 West Capitol Avenue
Pierre, SD 57501
P: (605) 773-3105
F: (605) 773-6046

TENNESSEE
Mr. David Purkey
Commissioner
Department of Safety & Homeland Security
1150 Foster Avenue
P.O. Box 945
Nashville, TN 37202
P: (615) 251-5166
E: email.safety@tn.gov

TEXAS
Mr. Steve McCraw
Director
Department of Public Safety
5805 North Lamar Boulevard
P.O. Box 4087
Austin, TX 78773
P: (512) 424-2000
F: (512) 483-5708

U.S. VIRGIN ISLANDS
Mr. Delroy Richards Sr.
Commissioner
Police Department
Farrelly Criminal Justice Center
Charlotte Amalie
St. Thomas, VI 00802
P: (340) 774-2211
F: (340) 715-5517

UTAH
Mr. Michael Rapich
Superintendent
State Highway Patrol
Department of Public Safety
South 4501 South 2700 West
Salt Lake City, UT 84129
P: (801) 965-4458
E: mrapich@utah.gov

VERMONT
Colonel Matthew Birmingham
Director
State Police
45 State Drive
Waterbury, VT 05671
P: (802) 241-5260
E: Matthew.Birmingham@vermont.gov

VIRGINIA
Colonel W. Steven Flaherty
Superintendent
Department of State Police
7700 Midlothian Turnpike
P.O. Box 27472
Richmond, VA 23261
P: (804) 674-2000
F: (804) 674-2936
E: steve.flaherty@vsp.virginia.gov

WASHINGTON
Mr. John R. Batiste
Chief
State Patrol
General Administration Building
P.O. Box 42600
Olympia, WA 98504
P: (360) 596-4000
F: (360) 596-4128
E: john.batiste@wsp.wa.gov

WEST VIRGINIA
Colonel J. L. Cahill
Superintendent
State Police
725 Jefferson Road
South Charleston, WV 25309
P: (304) 746-2115

WISCONSIN
Mr. J.D. Lind
Superintendent
Division of State Patrol
4802 Sheboygan Avenue, Room 551
P.O. Box 7912
Madison, WI 53707
P: (608) 266-3212
F: (608) 267-4495
E: JD.Lind@dot.wi.gov

WYOMING
Colonel Kebin Haller
Administrator
Highway Patrol
5300 Bishop Boulevard
Cheyenne, WY 82009
P: (307) 777-4301
F: (307) 777-3897

State Security

Develops and oversees operations to insure the safety of state citizens from threats of violence and terrorism.

ALABAMA
Mr. Art Faulkner
Director
Emergency Management Agency
5898 County Road 41
P.O. Box 2160
Clanton, AL 35046
P: (205) 280-2201
F: (334) 224-9142
E: art.faulkner@ema.alabama.gov

ALASKA
Major General Laurel J. Hummel
Adjutant General & Commissioner
Department of Military & Veterans Affairs
P.O. Box 5800
Fort Richardson, AK 99505
P: (907) 428-6003
F: (907) 428-6019
E: laurie.hummel@alaska.gov

AMERICAN SAMOA
Mr. Le'i S. Thompson
Commissioner
Department of Public Safety
American Samoa Government
P.O. Box 1086
Pago Pago, AS 96799
P: (684) 633-1111
F: (684) 633-7296
E: lei.thompson@dps.as.gov

ARIZONA
Colonel Frank Milstead
Director
Department of Public Safety
2222 West Encanto Boulevard
Phoenix, AZ 85009
P: (602) 223-2000
F: (602) 223-2917

ARKANSAS
A.J. Gary
Director & State Homeland Security Advisor
Department of Emergency Management
Building 9501, Camp Joseph T. Robinson
North Little Rock, AR 72199
P: (501) 683-7834
F: (501) 680-7961
E: AJ.Gary@adem.arkansas.gov

CALIFORNIA
Mr. Joseph A. Farrow
Commissioner
Highway Patrol
601 North 7th Street
P.O. Box 942898
Sacramento, CA 94298
P: (916) 843-3001
F: (916) 843-3264

Mr. Mark Ghilarducci
Director
Governor's Office of Emergency Services
3650 Schriever Avenue
Mather, CA 95655
P: (916) 845-8506
F: (916) 662-3155
E: mark.ghilarducci@caloes.ca.gov

COLORADO
Mr. Dane Matthew
Director
Office of Emergency Preparedness & Response
4300 Cherry Creek Drive, South
Denver, CO 80246
P: (303) 692-2954
F: (303) 691-7811
E: nicole.comstock@state.co.us

CONNECTICUT
Ms. Dora B. Schriro
Commissioner
Department of Emergency Services & Public Protection
1111 Country Club Road
Middletown, CT 06457
P: (860) 685-8000
F: (860) 685-8354
E: dora.schriro@ct.gov

DELAWARE
Colonel Robert M. Coupe
Cabinet Secretary
Department of Safety & Homeland Security
303 Transportation Circle
P.O. Box 818
Dover, DE 19903
P: (302) 744-2680
F: (302) 739-4874

DISTRICT OF COLUMBIA
Mr. Peter Newsham
Chief of Police
Metropolitan Police Department
300 Indiana Avenue, Northwest
Room 5059
Washington, DC 20001
P: (202) 727-9099
F: (202) 727-4106
E: mpd@dc.gov

FLORIDA
Mr. Rick Swearingen
Commissioner
Department of Law Enforcement
2331 Phillips Road
P.O. Box 1489
Tallahassee, FL 32302
P: (850) 410-7011
E: RickSwearingen@fdle.state.fl.us

GEORGIA
Colonel Mark W. McDonough
Commissioner
Department of Public Safety
959 East Confederate Avenue, Southeast
P.O. Box 1456
Atlanta, GA 30371
P: (404) 624-7477
F: (404) 624-6706

GUAM
Mr. Roderick R. Leon Guerrero
Adjutant General
National Guard
430 Army Drive, Building 300
Barrigada, GU 96913
P: (671) 735-0400
F: (671) 734-4081

HAWAII
Major General Arthur "Joe" Logan
Adjutant General
Department of Defense
3949 Diamond Head Road
Honolulu, HI 96816
P: (808) 733-4246
F: (808) 733-4499

IDAHO
Major General Gary L. Sayler
Adjutant General
Military Division
4040 West Guard Street, Building 600
Boise, ID 83705
P: (208) 272-5755
F: (208) 422-6179
E: saylerg@imd.idaho.gov

ILLINOIS
Mr. James Joseph
Director
State Emergency Management Agency
2200 South Dirksen Parkway
Springfield, IL 62703
P: (217) 782-2700
F: (217) 670-4206
E: james.joseph@illinois.gov

Mr. Leo P. Schmitz
Director
State Police
801 South 7th Street, Suite 1100 – S
Springfield, IL 62703
P: (217) 782-7263
E: askisp@isp.state.il.us

INDIANA
Mr. Douglas G. Carter
Superintendent
State Police
Indiana Government Center North
100 North Senate Avenue
Indianapolis, IN 46204
P: (317) 232-8248
E: ISP@isp.in.gov

IOWA
Mr. Mark J. Schouten
Director
Homeland Security & Emergency Management Department
7900 Hickmand Road, Suite 500
Windsor Heights, IA 50324
P: (515) 725-3223
F: (515) 975-4382
E: mark.schouten@iowa.gov

KANSAS
Major General Lee E. Tafanelli (R)
Adjutant General
Adjutant General's Department
5920 Southeast Coyote Drive
Building 2005, Room 229
Topeka, KS 66619
P: (785) 646-1190
F: (785) 274-1682
E: ng.ks.ksarng.list.staff-pao@mail.mil

KENTUCKY
Major General Stephen Hogan
Adjutant General
Department of Military Affairs
100 Minuteman Parkway
Frankfort, KY 40601
P: (502) 607-1713
F: (502) 607-1271

LOUISIANA
Mr. James Waskom
Director
Governor's Office of Homeland Security & Emergency Preparedness
7667 Independence Boulevard
Baton Rouge, LA 70608
P: (225) 925-7345
F: (337) 780-5383
E: james.waskom@la.gov

MAINE
Mr. Bruce Fitzgerald
Director
State Emergency Management Agency
45 Commerce Drive, Suite #2
Augusta, ME 04333
P: (207) 624-4400
F: (207) 287-3178
E: bruce.fitzgerald@maine.gov

MARYLAND
Mr. Walter Landon
Director of Homeland Security
Governor's Office of Homeland Security
Fred L. Wineland Building
16 Francis Street
Annapolis, MD 21401
P: (410) 974-3901
F: (410) 539-1117
E: dlgohs_gov@maryland.gov

MASSACHUSETTS
Mr. Daniel Bennett
Secretary
Executive Office of Public Safety & Security
One Ashburton Place, Suite 2133
Boston, MA 02108
P: (617) 727-7775
F: (617) 727-4764
E: eopsinfo@state.ma.us

MICHIGAN
Colonel Kriste Kibbey Etue
Director
State Police
P.O. Box 30634
Lansing, MI 48909
P: (517) 332-2521
F: (517) 241-0991
E: EtueK@michigan.gov

Captain Chris A. Kelenske
Deputy State Director
State Emergency Management & Homeland Security Division
7150 Harris Drive
Dimondale, MI 48821
P: (517) 284-3966
F: (517) 719-1194
E: kelenskec@michigan.gov

MINNESOTA
Ms. Ramona Dohman
Commissioner
Department of Public Safety
445 Minnesota Street, Suite 199
St. Paul, MN 55101
P: (651) 201-7160
F: (651) 297-5728
E: Mona.Dohman@state.mn.us

MISSISSIPPI
Mr. Lee Smithson
Executive Director
Emergency Management Agency
#1 MEMA Drive
P.O. Box 5644
Pearl, MS 39288
P: (601) 933-6882
F: (601) 850-6362
E: lsmithson@mema.ms.gov

MISSOURI
Mr. Charles A. Juden
Director
Department of Public Safety
Office of the Director
P.O. Box 749
Jefferson City, MO 65102
P: (573) 751-4905
F: (573) 751-5399

MONTANA
Mr. Ed Tinsley
Continuity of Government Program Manager
Office of State Continuity & Emergency Management
P.O. Box 200113
Helena, MT 59620
P: (406) 444-0125
F: (406) 444-2939
E: Continuity@mt.gov

NEBRASKA
Colonel Bradley Rice
Superintendent of Law Enforcement & Public Safety
State Patrol
1600 Highway 2
Lincoln, NE 68502
P: (402) 471-4545
F: (402) 479-4002
E: Brad.Rice@nebraska.gov

NEVADA
Mr. Caleb Cage
Chief
Division of Emergency Management/Homeland Security
2478 Fairview Drive
Carson City, NV 89701
P: (775) 687-0300
F: (775) 443-8814
E: cscage@dps.state.nv.us

NEW HAMPSHIRE
Colonel Robert L. Quinn
Director
Division of State Police
Department of Safety
33 Hazen Drive
Concord, NH 03305
P: (603) 223-8813
F: (603) 271-0336
E: SPHeadquarters@dos.nh.gov

NEW JERSEY
Mr. Jared Maples
Acting Director
Office of Homeland Security & Preparedness
P.O. Box 091
Trenton, NJ 08625
P: (609) 584-4000
E: communications@njohsp.gov

NEW MEXICO
Mr. Jay Mitchell
Secretary
State Department of Homeland Security & Emergency Management
13 Bataan Boulevard
P.O. Box 27111
Santa Fe, NM 87502
P: (505) 476-9655
E: jay.mitchell@state.nm.us

NEW YORK
Mr. John Melville
Commissioner
Division of Homeland Security & Emergency Services
1220 Washington Avenue
Building 7A Suite 710
Albany, NY 12242
P: (518) 242-5000
F: (518) 322-4978

NORTH CAROLINA
Mr. Erik A. Hooks
Secretary of Public Safety
Department of Public Safety
512 North Salisbury Street
Raleigh, NC 27604
P: (919) 662-4500
E: erik.hooks@ncdps.gov

NORTH DAKOTA
Colonel Michael Gerhart
Superintendent
Highway Patrol
600 East Boulevard Avenue
Department 504
Bismarck, ND 58505
P: (701) 328-2455
F: (701) 328-1717
E: ndhpinfo@nd.gov

Mr. Greg Wilz
Director, Division of Homeland Security
Department of Emergency Services
Fraine Barracks Lane, Building 35
P.O. Box 5511
Bismarck, ND 58506
P: (701) 328-8100 Ext. 8101
F: (701) 995-0446
E: gwilz@nd.gov

NORTHERN MARIANA ISLANDS
Mr. Gerald Deleon Guerrero
Special Assistant for Homeland Security & Emergency Management
Homeland Security & Emergency Management
Office of the Governor
Caller Box 1007, 1313 Anatahan Drive
Saipan, MP 96950
P: (670) 664-2216
F: (670) 287-7166
E: gerald.guerrero@cnmihsem.gov.mp

OHIO
Colonel John Born
Director
Department of Public Safety
1970 West Broad Street
P.O. Box 182081
Columbus, OH 43218
P: (614) 466-3383
F: (614) 466-0433

OKLAHOMA
Mr. Michael C. Thompson
Commissioner
Department of Public Safety
P.O. Box 11415
Oklahoma City, OK 73136
P: (405) 425-2424
E: mike.thompson@dps.state.ok.us

PENNSYLVANIA
Mr. Richard Flinn Jr.
Director
State Emergency Management Agency
2605 Interstate Drive
Harrisburg, PA 17110
P: (717) 651-2007
F: (717) 317-1741
E: rflinn@pa.gov

State Security

PUERTO RICO
Ms. Michelle M. Hernandez De Fraley
Superintendent
Puerto Rico Police
601 Franklin Delano Roosevelt Avenue
San Juan, PR 00936
P: (787) 793-1234

RHODE ISLAND
Mr. Christopher Callahan
Adjutant General
National Guard
645 New London Avenue
Cranston, RI 02920
P: (401) 275-4102
F: (401) 275-4338

SOUTH CAROLINA
Mr. Mark A. Keel
Chief
State Law Enforcement Division
4400 Broad River Road
Columbia, SC 29210
P: (803) 896-9223
F: (803) 896-7588

SOUTH DAKOTA
Mr. Trevor Jones
Secretary
Department of Public Safety
118 West Capitol Avenue
Pierre, SD 57501
P: (605) 773-3178
F: (605) 773-3018
E: DPSInfo@state.sd.us

Mr. Stefan Pluta
Homeland Security Director
Office of Homeland Security
Department of Public Safety
118 West Capitol Avenue
Pierre, SD 57501
P: (605) 773-3450
F: (605) 773-6631
E: dpshomelandsecurity@state.sd.us

TENNESSEE
Mr. David Purkey
Commissioner
Department of Safety & Homeland Security
1150 Foster Avenue
P.O. Box 945
Nashville, TN 37202
P: (615) 251-5166
E: email.safety@tn.gov

TEXAS
Mr. Steve McCraw
Director
Department of Public Safety
5805 North Lamar Boulevard
P.O. Box 4087
Austin, TX 78773
P: (512) 424-2000
F: (512) 483-5708

U.S. VIRGIN ISLANDS
Brigadier General Deborah Howell
Adjutant General
National Guard
RR#1, Box 9201
Kingshill, VI 00850
P: (340) 712-7711
F: (340) 712-7709

UTAH
Mr. Kris J. Hamlet
Director
Division of Emergency Management
Department of Public Safety
1110 State Office Building
Salt Lake City, UT 84114
P: (801) 538-9553
F: (801) 243-0147
E: krishamlet@utah.gov

WASHINGTON
Major General Bret D. Daugherty
Adjutant General
Department of Military
Building 1, 1 Militia Drive
Camp Murray, WA 98430
P: (253) 512-8000
F: (253) 512-8497
E: bret.daughtery@mil.wa.gov

WEST VIRGINIA
Mr. Jeff Sandy
Cabinet Secretary
Department of Military Affairs & Public Safety
Building 1, Room W-400
1900 Kanawha Boulevard, East
Charleston, WV 25305
P: (304) 558-2930
E: Jeff.Sandy@wv.gov

WISCONSIN
Mr. Brian M. Satula
Administrator
Division of Emergency Management
2400 Wright Street
P.O. Box 7865
Madison, WI 53704
P: (608) 242-3210
F: (608) 514-3461
E: brian.satula@wisconsin.gov

WYOMING
Mr. Guy Cameron
Director
Office of Homeland Security
5500 Bishop Boulevard
Cheyenne, WY 82002
P: (307) 777-8511
F: (307) 630-0566
E: guy.cameron@wyo.gov

Telecommunications

Responsible for communications planning and organizing a statewide plan for total communications, especially with local government emergency matters.

ALABAMA
Mr. Andy Cannon
Assistant Director, Network & Operations
Information Services Division
Folsom Administrative Building
64 North Union Street
Montgomery, AL 36130
P: (334) 242-2222
F: (334) 242-7002
E: andy.cannon@isd.alabama.gov

ALASKA
Mr. Bill Vajda
Chief Information Officer
Office of Information Technology
Department of Administration
333 Willoughby Avenue, 10th Floor
Juneau, AK 99801
P: (907) 465-8461
E: bill.vajda@alaska.gov

ARIZONA
Mr. Morgan Reed
Chief Information Officer
Strategic Enterprise Technology
100 North 15th Avenue, Suite 400
Phoenix, AZ 85007
P: (602) 540-8831
F: (602) 542-4272

ARKANSAS
Mr. Don McDaniel
Enterprise Network Services Director
Department of Information Services
One Capitol Mall
P.O. Box 3155
Little Rock, AR 72203
P: (501) 682-4310
F: (501) 682-4316
E: don.mcdaniel@arkansas.gov

CALIFORNIA
Ms. Amy Tong
Director & Chief Information Officer
Department of Technology
1325 J Street, Suite 1600
Sacramento, CA 95814
P: (916) 319-9223
F: (916) 324-1734
E: amy.tong@state.ca.gov

COLORADO
Ms. Suma Nallapati
Secretary of Technology & Chief Information Officer
Governor's Office of Information Technology
601 East 18th Avenue, Suite 250
Denver, CO 80203
P: (303) 764-7707
E: oit@state.co.us

CONNECTICUT
Mr. Mark D. Raymond
Chief Information Officer
Department of Administrative Services
55 Farmington Avenue
Hartford, CT 06105
P: (860) 622-2419
F: (860) 291-8665
E: mark.raymond@ct.gov

DELAWARE
Mr. James L. Collins
Chief Information Officer
Department of Technology & Information
801 Silver Lake Boulevard
Dover, DE 19904
P: (302) 739-9500
F: (302) 739-9686
E: james.collins@state.de.us

GEORGIA
Mr. Tom Fruman
Director
Enterprise Governance & Planning
Georgia Technology Authority
47 Trinity Avenue
Atlanta, GA 30334
P: (404) 463-6815
F: (404) 463-2380
E: thomas.fruman@gta.ga.gov

HAWAII
Ms. Sharon Wong
Branch Chief
Telecommunications Services Branch
Office of Enterprise Technology Services
1177 Alakea Street
Honolulu, HI 96813
P: (808) 586-1930
F: (808) 586-1882
E: ets@hawaii.gov

ILLINOIS
Mr. Jonelle Brent
Chief Administrative Officer
Department of Innovation & Technology
100 West Randolph, 4th Floor
Chicago, IL 60601
P: (217) 785-1943
E: rich_fetter@cms.state.il.us

INDIANA
Mr. Dewand Neely
Chief Information Officer & Director
Office of Technology
1000 North Senate Avenue
IGCN, Room N551
Indianapolis, IN 46204
P: (317) 234-0835

IOWA
Mr. Ric Lumbard
Executive Director
Iowa Communications Network
Grimes State Office Building
400 East 14th Street
Des Moines, IA 50319
P: (515) 725-4692
F: (515) 725-4727

KANSAS
Mr. Jay Coverdale
Director
Network & Telecommunication Services
Information Technology Services
700 Southwest Harrison Street, Room 1015
Topeka, KS 66603
P: (785) 296-3937
E: jay.coverdale@ks.gov

LOUISIANA
Mr. Richard Howze
State Chief Information Officer
Office of Technology Services
Division of Administration
Claiborne Building, Suite 2-130
Baton Rouge, LA 70804
P: (225) 342-7105
F: (225) 219-9465
E: cio@la.gov

MAINE
Ms. Ellen Lee
Director, Vendor Management Office
Office of Information Technology
51 Commerce Drive
145 State House Station
Augusta, ME 04333
P: (207) 624-8800
F: (207) 287-4563
E: ellen.lee@maine.gov

MASSACHUSETTS
Mr. Mark Nunnelly
Executive Director
Executive Office for Administration & Finance
MassIT
One Ashburton Place, Room 804
Boston, MA 02108
P: (617) 626-4671

MICHIGAN
Mr. David Behen
Director
Department of Technology, Management & Budget
320 South Walnut Street, 2nd Floor
P.O. Box 30026
Lansing, MI 48909
P: (517) 373-1004
E: behend@michigan.gov

MINNESOTA
Mr. Dan Oehmke
Information Systems Manager
MN.IT Services Office
540 Cedar Street
St. Paul, MN 55155
P: (651) 431-4997
F: (651) 297-5368
E: Dan.Oehmke@state.mn.us

MISSISSIPPI
Mr. Steven Walker
Telecom Services Director
Information Technology Services
3771 Eastwood Drive
Jackson, MS 39211
P: (601) 432-8004
F: (601) 713-6380
E: Steven.Walker@its.ms.gov

MONTANA
Ms. Jody Troupe
Network Technology Services Bureau Chief
Department of Administration
Mitchell Building, 125 North Roberts
P.O. Box 200113
Helena, MT 59620
P: (406) 444-2666

Telecommunications

NEBRASKA
Ms. Jayne Scofield
Network Services IT Administrator
Office of the Chief Information Officer
501 South 14th Street
Lincoln, NE 68508
P: (402) 471-3454
F: (402) 471-3339
E: jayne.scofield@nebraska.gov

NEVADA
Mr. Ken Adams
Chief IT Manager, Telecommunications
Enterprise IT Services
100 North Stewart Street, Suite 100
Carson City, NV 89701
P: (775) 684-5800
F: (775) 684-7345

NEW JERSEY
Mr. Dave Weinstein
Chief Information Officer
Office of Information Technology
300 Riverview Plaza
Trenton, NJ 08625
P: (609) 777-5865

NEW MEXICO
Mr. Estevan J. Lujan
Deputy Secretary
Department of Information Technology
715 Alta Vista Street
P.O. Box 22550
Santa Fe, NM 87502
P: (505) 827-0000

NEW YORK
Mr. Peter J. Arment
First Deputy Director
Office of Information Technology Services
Empire State Building
P.O. Box 2062
Albany, NY 12220
P: (518) 402-2324
F: (518) 473-7145
E: peter.arment@oft.state.ny.us

NORTH CAROLINA
Mr. Eric Boyette
Secretary & State Chief Information Officer
Department of Information Technology
P.O. Box 17209
Raleigh, NC 27619
P: (919) 707-2134
E: eric.boyette@nc.gov

NORTH DAKOTA
Mr. Shawn Riley
Chief Information Officer
Information Technology Department
4201 Normandy Street
Bismarck, ND 58503
P: (701) 328-1001
F: (701) 328-1075
E: sriley@nd.gov

OHIO
Mr. Spencer Wood
Chief Operating Officer
Infrastructure Services Division
Office of Information Technology
30 East Broad Street, 39th Floor
Columbus, OH 43215
P: (614) 644-9245
F: (614) 466-7345
E: spencer.wood@das.ohio.gov

OREGON
Mr. Alex Pettit
Chief Information Officer
Department of Administrative Services
Executive Building
155 Cottage Street Northeast, 4th Floor
Salem, OR 97301
P: (503) 378-2128
F: (503) 378-3795
E: alex.pettit@das.state.or.us

Mr. Alex Pettit
Chief Information Officer
Department of Administrative Services
Executive Building
155 Cottage Street Northeast, 4th Floor
Salem, OR 97301
P: (503) 378-2128
F: (503) 378-3795
E: alex.pettit@das.state.or.us

PENNSYLVANIA
Mr. John MacMillan
Deputy Secretary for Information Technology & Chief Information Officer
Office for Information Technology
Governor's Office of Administration
613 North Street, Room 210
Harrisburg, PA 17109
P: (717) 787-5440
F: (717) 787-4523
E: cio@pa.gov

RHODE ISLAND
Mr. Christopher Antonellis
Chief Information Officer
Office of Information Technology
Department of Administration
50 Service Avenue
Warwick, RI 02886
P: (401) 462-2185

SOUTH CAROLINA
Mr. Keith Osman
Chief Information Officer
Division of Technology
Department of Administration
4430 Broad River Road
Columbia, SC 29210
P: (803) 896-0222

SOUTH DAKOTA
Mr. Dennis Nincehelser
Director of Telecommunications
Bureau of Information & Telecommunications
700 Governors Drive
Pierre, SD 57501
P: (605) 773-7277
F: (605) 773-3741
E: dennis.nincehelser@state.sd.us

TENNESSEE
Mr. Mark Bengel
Chief Information Officer
Office for Information Resources
Department of Finance & Administration
901 5th Avenue, North
Nashville, TN 37243
P: (615) 741-7951
F: (615) 532-0471

TEXAS
Mr. John Hoffman
Chief Technology Officer
Chief Technology Office
Department of Information Resources
300 West 15th Street, Suite 1300
Austin, TX 78701
P: (512) 936-2501
F: (512) 475-4759
E: john.hoffman@dir.texas.gov

UTAH
Mr. Michael Hussey
Chief Information Officer
Department of Technology Services
1 State Office Buidling, Floor 6
Salt Lake City, UT 84114
P: (801) 538-3298
F: (801) 538-3622
E: mhussey@utah.gov

VERMONT
Mr. John Quinn
Secretary & Chief Information Officer
Agency of Digital Services
Department of Information & Innovation
133 State Street
Montpelier, VT 05633
P: (802) 828-2316
E: john.quinn@vermont.gov

VIRGINIA
Ms. Dana Smith
Director, Internal Technology & Portfolio Management
Information Technologies Agency
11751 Meadowville Lane
Chester, VA 23836
P: (804) 416-6009
E: Dana.Smith@vita.virginia.gov

WASHINGTON
Jing Roth
Assistant Director, Telecommunications
Utilities & Transportation Commission
P.O. Box 47250
Olympia, WA 98504
P: (360) 664-1291

WEST VIRGINIA
Mr. John Dunlap
Chief Technology Officer
Office of Technology
Capitol Complex, Building 5, 10th Floor
Charleston, WV 25305
P: (304) 558-8100
F: (304) 558-0136
E: John.D.Dunlap@wv.gov

WISCONSIN
Ms. Trina Zanow
Bureau Director
Bureau of Infrastructure Support
101 East Wilson Street
P.O. Box 7844
Madison, WI 53707
P: (608) 224-4002
E: trina.zanow@wisconsin.gov

WYOMING
Mr. Rick Imbrogno
Administrator
Information Technology Division
Emerson Building, Room 237
2001 Capitol Avenue
Cheyenne, WY 82002
P: (307) 777-5101
F: (307) 777-6725

Tourism

Coordinates promotional and advertising programs for the tourism industry in the state.

ALABAMA
Mr. Lee Sentell
Director
Tourism Department
401 Adams Avenue
P.O. Box 4927
Montgomery, AL 36103
P: (334) 242-4413
E: Lee.Sentell@tourism.alabama.gov

ALASKA
Ms. Caryl McConkie
Development Specialist
Division of Economic Development
Commerce, Community & Economic Developme
Juneau, AK 99811
P: (907) 465-5478
F: (907) 465-3767
E: caryl.mcconkie@alaska.gov

AMERICAN SAMOA
Mr. Keniseli Lafaele
Director
Department of Commerce
American Samoa Government
Executive Office Building, Utulei
Pago Pago, AS 96799
P: (684) 633-5155 Ext. 222
F: (684) 633-4195
E: keniseli.lafaele@doc.as

Ms. Virginia Samuelu
Administrator To the Director
Department of Commerce
American Samoa Government
Executive Office Building, Utulei
Pago Pago, AS 96799
P: (684) 633-5155
F: (684) 633-4195
E: virginia.samuelu@doc.as

ARIZONA
Ms. Debbie Johnson
Executive Director
Office of Tourism
118 North 7th Avenue, Suite 400
Phoenix, AZ 85007
P: (602) 364-3717
F: (602) 364-3702
E: djohnson@tourism.az.gov

ARKANSAS
Mr. Richard Davies
Executive Director
Department of Parks & Tourism
#1 Capitol Mall, Room 4A900
Little Rock, AR 72201
P: (501) 682-2535
F: (501) 682-2383
E: richard.davies@arkansas.gov

CALIFORNIA
Ms. Caroline Beteta
President & Chief Executive Officer
Visit California
P.O. Box 101711
Pasadena, CA 91189
P: (916) 444-0410
F: (916) 322-3402
E: cbeteta@commerce.ca.gov

COLORADO
Ms. Cathy Ritter
Director
Tourism Office
1625 Broadway, Suite 2700
Denver, CO 80202
P: (303) 892-3840
F: (303) 892-3885
E: Cathy.Ritter@state.co.us

CONNECTICUT
Mr. Randy Fiveash
Director of Tourism
Offices of Culture & Tourism
One Constitution Plaza, 2nd Floor
Hartford, CT 06103
P: (860) 256-2769
F: (860) 256-2811
E: Randall.Fiveash@ct.gov

FLORIDA
Mr. Karl Blischke
Director
Division of Strategic Business Development
Department of Economic Opportunity
107 East Madison St., Caldwell Building
Tallahassee, FL 32399
P: (850) 245-7105
F: (850) 921-3223
E: karl.blischke@deo.myflorida.com

GEORGIA
Mr. Kevin Langston
Deputy Commissioner of Tourism
Department of Economic Development
Technology Square
75 5th Street Northwest, Suite 1200
Atlanta, GA 30308
P: (404) 962-4093
F: (404) 962-4083
E: klangston@georgia.org

GUAM
Mr. Jon Nathan P. Denight
President & CEO
Visitor's Bureau
401 Pale San Vitores Road
Tumon, GU 96913
P: (671) 646-5278
F: (671) 646-8861
E: info@visitguam.org

IDAHO
Ms. Diane Norton
Tourism Manager
Department of Commerce
700 West State Street
P.O. Box 83720
Boise, ID 83720
P: (208) 287-0785
F: (208) 334-2631
E: diane.norton@tourism.idaho.gov

ILLINOIS
Mr. Sean McCarthy
Director
Department of Commerce & Economic Opportunity
100 West Randolph Street, Suite 3-400
Chicago, IL 60601
P: (312) 814-2811

IOWA
Ms. Shawna Lode
Manager
Tourism Office
200 East Grand Avenue
Des Moines, IA 50309
P: (515) 725-3090
F: (515) 242-4718
E: shawna.lode@iowaeda.com

KANSAS
Ms. Linda Craghead
Assistant Secretary for Parks & Tourism
Tourism Division
Department of Wildlife, Parks & Tourism
1020 South Kansas Avenue, Room 200
Topeka, KS 66612
P: (785) 296-3870
E: linda.craghead@ks.gov

KENTUCKY
Ms. Kristen Branscum
Commissioner
Department of Tourism
100 Airport Road, 2nd Floor
Frankfort, KY 40601
P: (502) 892-3222
F: (502) 564-5695
E: kristen.branscum@ky.gov

Mr. Don Parkinson
Secretary
Tourism, Arts & Heritage Cabinet
100 Airport Road, Second Floor
Frankfort, KY 40601
P: (502) 564-4270
F: (502) 564-1512
E: Don.Parkinson@ky.gov

LOUISIANA
The Honorable Billy Nungesser (R)
Lieutenant Governor
Office of the Lieutenant Governor
1051 North 3rd Street, Capitol Annex
P.O. Box 44243
Baton Rouge, LA 70804
P: (225) 342-7009
F: (225) 342-1949
E: ltgov@crt.la.gov

MAINE
Mr. Steve Lyons
Acting Director
Office of Tourism
59 State House Station
Augusta, ME 04333
P: (207) 624-9815
E: steve.lyons@maine.gov

MARYLAND
Mr. R. Michael Gill
Secretary
Department of Commerce
Office of the Secretary
401 East Pratt Street
Baltimore, MD 21202
P: (410) 767-6301
F: (410) 333-8628
E: Mike.Gill@maryland.gov

MASSACHUSETTS
Mr. Francois-Laurent Nivaud
Executive Director
Office of Travel & Tourism
10 Park Plaza, Suite 4510
Boston, MA 02116
P: (617) 973-8500
F: (617) 973-8525
E: execdirector.mott@state.ma.us

MICHIGAN
Ms. Emily Guerrant
Vice President
Marketing, Communications & Public Relations
Economic Development Corporation
300 North Washington Square
Lansing, MI 48913
P: (517) 373-5689
E: guerrante@michigan.org

MINNESOTA
Mr. John Edman
Director
Explore Minnesota Tourism
121 7th Place East, Suite 100
St. Paul, MN 55101
P: (651) 757-1844
F: (651) 296-7095
E: john.edman@state.mn.us

MISSISSIPPI
Mr. Daron Wilson
Deputy Director/Chief Administrative Officer
State Development Authority
501 North West Street
P.O. Box 849
Jackson, MS 39205
P: (601) 359-2378
F: (601) 359-2832
E: dwilson@mississippi.org

MONTANA
Mr. Sean Becker
Division Administrator
Office of Tourism & Business Development
301 South Park Avenue
P.O. Box 200533
Helena, MT 59620
P: (406) 841-2707
F: (406) 841-2871

NEBRASKA
Ms. Courtney Dentlinger
Director
Department of Economic Development
301 Centennial Mall South
P.O. Box 94666
Lincoln, NE 68509
P: (402) 471-3746
F: (402) 471-3778
E: courtney.dentlinger@nebraska.gov

NEVADA
Ms. Claudia Vecchio
Director
Division of Tourism & Cultural Affairs
401 North Carson Street
Carson City, NV 89701
P: (775) 687-0607
F: (775) 687-6779
E: cvecchio@travelnevada.com

NEW HAMPSHIRE
Ms. Victoria Cimino
Director, Travel & Tourism Development
Department of Resources & Economic Development
172 Pembroke Road
Concord, NH 03301
P: (603) 271-2629
F: (603) 271-6870
E: travel@dred.nh.gov

NEW MEXICO
Ms. Rebecca Latham
Cabinet Secretary
Tourism Department
491 Old Santa Fe Trail
Santa Fe, NM 87501
P: (505) 827-7469
F: (505) 827-7402
E: Susan.Kavanaugh@state.nm.us

NEW YORK
Mr. Howard Zemsky
President & CEO
Empire State Development
633 Third Avenue, Floor 37
New York, NY 10017
P: (212) 803-3100
F: (212) 803-3715

NORTH CAROLINA
Mr. Wit Tuttell
Executive Director
VisitNC
Department of Commerce
15000 Weston Parkway
Cary, NC 27513
P: (919) 447-7740
F: (919) 733-8582
E: wit.tuttell@visitnc.com

NORTH DAKOTA
Ms. Sarah Otte-Coleman
Director
Tourism Division
1600 East Century Avenue, Suite 2
Century Center, P.O. Box 2057
Bismarck, ND 58502
P: (701) 328-2525
F: (701) 328-4878
E: socoleman@nd.gov

NORTHERN MARIANA ISLANDS
Mr. Christopher A. Concepcion
Managing Director
Visitor's Authority
P.O. Box 500861
Saipan, MP 96950
P: (670) 664-3200
F: (670) 664-3237
E: mva@mymarianas.com

OHIO
Ms. Mary Cusick
Director
Tourism Ohio
P.O. Box 1001
Columbus, OH 43216
P: (614) 466-3704
F: (614) 466-6744
E: Mary.Cusick@development.ohio.gov

OREGON
Mr. Todd Davidson
Chief Executive Officer
Tourism Commission/Travel Oregon
250 Church Street, Southeast Suite 100
Salem, OR 97301
P: (503) 967-1568
F: (503) 967-1579
E: Todd@TravelOregon.com

PENNSYLVANIA
Mr. Michael Chapaloney
Executive Director
Office of Travel, Tourism & Film
Commonwealth Keystone Building
400 North Street, 4th Floor
Harrisburg, PA 17120
P: (717) 720-7327
E: mchapalone@pa.gov

PUERTO RICO
Mr. Jose R. Izquierdo II
Executive Director
Puerto Rico Tourism Company
P.O. Box 9023960
San Juan, PR 00902
P: (787) 721-2400 Ext. 2071
F: (787) 722-6238
E: contact@tourism.pr.gov

RHODE ISLAND
Mr. Mark Brodeur
Director of Tourism
Commerce Corporation
315 Iron Horse Way, Suite 101
Providence, RI 02908
P: (401) 278-9100
F: (401) 273-8270
E: mbrodeur@commerceri.com

SOUTH CAROLINA
Mr. Duane Parrish
Director
Department of Parks, Recreation & Tourism
1205 Pendleton Street
Columbia, SC 29201
P: (803) 734-0166
F: (803) 734-1409
E: dparrish@scprt.com

SOUTH DAKOTA
Mr. James D. Hagen
Secretary
Office of Tourism
711 East Wells Avenue
Pierre, SD 57501
P: (605) 773-3301
F: (605) 773-5977
E: sdinfo@state.sd.us

TENNESSEE
Mr. Kevin Triplett
Commissioner
Department of Tourist Development
312 Rosa L. Parks Avenue
Tennessee Tower, 13th Floor
Nashville, TN 37243
P: (615) 741-9001
E: Kevin.Triplett@tn.gov

Tourism

TEXAS
Mr. Brad Smyth
Director
Texas Tourism
Economic Development & Tourism Division
P.O. Box 12428
Austin, TX 78711
P: (512) 936-0100
F: (512) 936-0080

U.S. VIRGIN ISLANDS
Ms. Beverly Nicholson Doty
Commissioner
Department of Tourism
Elainco Building
78 Contant 1-2-3
St. Thomas, VI 00802
P: (340) 774-8784
F: (340) 773-0495

UTAH
Ms. Vicki Varela
Managing Director of Tourism, Film & Global Branding
Governor's Office of Economic Office
60 East South Temple, 3rd Floor
Salt Lake City, UT 84111
P: (801) 538-3395
F: (801) 538-8888
E: vvarela@utah.gov

VERMONT
Ms. Wendy Knight
Commissioner
Department of Tourism & Marketing
Commerce & Community Development
One National Life Drive, 6th Floor
Montpelier, VT 05620
P: (802) 798-2191
E: wendy.knight@vermont.gov

VIRGINIA
Ms. Rita McClenny
President & CEO
Tourism Corporation
901 East Cary Street, Suite 900
Richmond, VA 23219
P: (804) 545-5510
F: (804) 545-5501
E: president@virginia.org

WEST VIRGINIA
Ms. Chelsea Ruby
Commissioner
Division of Tourism
Department of Commerce
90 MacCorkle Avenue, Southwest
South Charleston, WV 25303
P: (304) 957-9345
F: (304) 558-2956
E: Chelsea.A.Ruby@wv.gov

WISCONSIN
Ms. Stephanie Klett
Secretary
Department of Tourism
201 West Washington Avenue
P.O. Box 8690
Madison, WI 53708
P: (608) 266-2345
F: (608) 266-3403
E: sklett@travelwisconsin.com

WYOMING
Ms. Diane Shober
Executive Director
Office of Tourism
5611 High Plains Road
Cheyenne, WY 82007
P: (307) 777-2808
F: (307) 777-2877
E: Diane.Shober@wyo.gov

Training and Development

Responsible for the training and development of state employees.

ALABAMA
Ms. Norma L. Taylor
Manager of Training
State Personnel Department
300 Folsom Administration Building
64 North Union Street
Montgomery, AL 36130
P: (334) 242-3494
F: (334) 242-1110

ALASKA
Ms. Kate Sheehan
Director
Division of Personnel & Labor Relations
Department of Administration
P.O. Box 110201
Juneau, AK 99811
P: (907) 465-4430
F: (907) 465-3415
E: kate.sheehan@alaska.gov

AMERICAN SAMOA
Mr. Esenaeiaso J. Liu
Director
Department of Human Resources
Executive Office Building
AP Lutali, 2nd Floor
Pago Pago, AS 96799
P: (684) 644-4485
F: (684) 633-1139
E: eseneiaso.liu@hr.as.gov

CALIFORNIA
Mr. Stewart Knox
Executive Director
Employment Training Panel
1100 J Street, 4th Floor
Sacramento, CA 95814
P: (916) 327-5640
F: (916) 445-5972
E: stewart.knox@etp.ca.gov

COLORADO
Ms. Kim Burgess
Chief Human Resources Officer
Division of Human Resources
Department of Personnel & Administration
1313 Sherman Street, 1st Floor
Denver, CO 80203
P: (303) 866-2105
F: (303) 866-2021
E: kim.burgess@state.co.us

CONNECTICUT
Ms. Melody A. Currey
Commissioner
Department of Administrative Services
450 Columbus Boulevard
Hartford, CT 06103
P: (860) 713-5100
F: (860) 713-7481
E: Melody.Currey@ct.gov

DELAWARE
Ms. Lori Reeder
Director
Department of Labor
Division of Employment & Training
4425 North Market Street
Wilmington, DE 19802
P: (302) 761-8085
E: lori.reeder@state.de.us

DISTRICT OF COLUMBIA
Ms. Ventris C. Gibson
Director
Department of Human Resources
441 4th Street Northwest
Suite 300 South
Washington, DC 20001
P: (202) 442-9700
F: (202) 727-6827
E: ventris.gibson@dc.gov

GUAM
Ms. Christine Baleto
Director
Department of Administration
P.O. Box 884
Hagatna, GU 96928
P: (671) 475-1101
F: (671) 477-6788

HAWAII
Dr. James K. Nishimoto
Director
Department of Human Resources Development
Leiopapa A. Kamehameha Building
235 South Beretania Street
Honolulu, HI 96813
P: (808) 587-1100
F: (808) 587-1106
E: dhrd@hawaii.gov

IDAHO
Mr. Roy Valdez
Council Liaison & Deputy Director
Workforce Development Council
Department of Labor
317 West Main Street
Boise, ID 83735
P: (208) 332-3570 Ext. 3163
F: (208) 334-3454
E: roy.valdez@labor.idaho.gov

ILLINOIS
Ms. Roneta Taylor
Division Manager
Technical Services & Agency Training Division
Stratton Office Building, Room 504
401 South Spring
Springfield, IL 62706
P: (217) 557-0225

INDIANA
Nereida Williams
Director
Employee Engagement Division
State Personnel Department
402 West Washington Street, Room W161
Indianapolis, IN 46204
P: (317) 234-3111
F: (317) 232-3089
E: NeWilliams@spd.IN.gov

KANSAS
Mr. Antonio J. Soave
Secretary
Department of Commerce
1000 Southwest Jackson Street, Suite 100
Topeka, KS 66612
P: (785) 296-2994
F: (785) 296-5055
E: asoave@kansascommerce.com

KENTUCKY
Mr. Thomas Stephens
Secretary
Personnel Cabinet
State Office Building, 3rd Floor
501 High Street
Frankfort, KY 40601
P: (502) 564-7430
F: (502) 564-7603
E: thomasb.stephens@ky.gov

LOUISIANA
Ms. Dana LeBherz
Training Division Administrator
Workforce Planning & Development
Department of State Civil Service
P.O. Box 94111
Baton Rouge, LA 70804
P: (225) 342-8540
F: (225) 342-8058
E: Dana.LeBherz@La.Gov

MARYLAND
Ms. Cynthia Kollner
Executive Director
Office of Personnel Services & Benefits
Department of Budget & Management
301 West Preston Street, Room 609
Baltimore, MD 21201
P: (410) 767-4715
F: (410) 333-5262
E: cindy.kollner@maryland.gov

MASSACHUSETTS
Mr. Ronald Arigo
Chief Human Resources Officer
Human Resources Division
Office for Administration and Finance
1 Ashburton Palce, Room 301
Boston, MA 02108
P: (617) 878-9703
E: ronald.arigo@MassMail.State.MA.US

MICHIGAN
Ms. Janine Winters
State Personnel Director
State Civil Service Commission
Capitol Commons Center
400 South Pine Street
Lansing, MI 48933
P: (517) 373-3020
F: (517) 284-9950
E: wintersj@michigan.gov

MINNESOTA
Mr. Myron Frans
Commissioner
Management & Budget
658 Cedar Street, Suite 400
St. Paul, MN 55155
P: (651) 201-8011
F: (651) 296-8685
E: myron.frans@state.mn.us

Training and Development

MISSOURI
Ms. Nancy Johnston
Director, Division of Personnel
Office of Administration
301 West High Street, Suite 430
P.O. Box 388
Jefferson City, MO 65101
P: (573) 751-4162
F: (573) 751-8641
E: persmail@oa.mo.gov

MONTANA
Mr. John Lewis
Director
Department of Administration
125 North Roberts Street, Room 155
P.O. Box 200101
Helena, MT 59620
P: (406) 444-3033
F: (406) 444-6194
E: johnlewis@mt.gov

NEBRASKA
Ms. Marjory Bell
Director
State Personnel Division
Department of Administrative Services
1526 K Street, Suite 100
Lincoln, NE 68508
P: (402) 471-2075
F: (402) 471-3754
E: margie.bell@nebraska.gov

NEW HAMPSHIRE
Ms. Sara J. Willingham
Director
Division of Personnel
Department of Administrative Services
28 School Street
Concord, NH 03301
P: (603) 271-3261
F: (603) 271-1422
E: sara.willingham@nh.gov

NEW JERSEY
Mr. Dennis M. Bone
Chair
State Employment & Training Commission
One John Fitch Way, P.O. Box 940
Trenton, NJ 08625
P: (609) 633-0605
F: (609) 633-1359
E: SETC@dol.state.nj.us

NEW MEXICO
Mr. Justin Najaka
Director
State Personnel Office
2600 Cerrillos Road
Santa Fe, NM 87505
P: (505) 490-2414
F: (505) 476-7806
E: Justin.Najaka@state.nm.us

NORTH CAROLINA
Ms. Sarah Harris
Director
Talent Management Division
Office of State Human Resources
1331 Mail Service Center
Raleigh, NC 27699
P: (919) 733-8343
E: sarah.w.harris@nc.gov

OKLAHOMA
Ms. Lisa Fortier
Director
Human Resource Development Services Division
Human Capital Management Division
2101 North Lincoln Boulevard
Oklahoma City, OK 73105
P: (405) 521-6345
F: (405) 524-6942
E: lisa.fortier@opm.ok.gov

OREGON
Ms. Madilyn Zike
Chief HR Officer
Human Resources Office
Department of Administrative Services
155 Cottage Street, Northeast
Salem, OR 97301
P: (503) 378-3020
F: (503) 373-7684
E: madilyn.zike@state.or.us

PENNSYLVANIA
Ms. Sharon Minnich
Secretary
Governor's Office of Administration
207 Finance Building
Harrisburg, PA 17102
P: (717) 783-0247
E: sminnich@pa.gov

PUERTO RICO
Mr. Harry O. Diaz Vega
Director
Labor Affairs & Human Resource Administration
P.O. Box 8476
San Juan, PR 00919
P: (787) 274-4300
F: (787) 250-1145

Mr. Carlos J. Saavedra Gutierrez
Secretary
Department of Labor & Human Resources
P.O. Box 195540
San Juan, PR 00919
P: (787) 754-5353
F: (787) 753-9550

RHODE ISLAND
Ms. Melissa Day
Assistant Administrative Officer
Office of Training & Development
Department of Administration
One Capitol Hill
Providence, RI 02908
P: (401) 222-2178
F: (401) 222-6378
E: Melissa.Day@hr.ri.gov

SOUTH CAROLINA
Ms. Kim Aydlette
Director
Division of Human Resources
Department of Administration
8301 Parklane Road, Suite A220
Columbia, SC 29223
P: (803) 896-5300
F: (803) 896-5050
E: kim.aydlette@admin.sc.gov

SOUTH DAKOTA
Ms. Ellen Zeller
Director of Training
Bureau of Human Resources - Training
Becker-Hansen Building
700 East Broadway Avenue
Pierre, SD 57501
P: (605) 773-3461
F: (605) 773-4344
E: ctr@state.sd.us

TENNESSEE
Dr. Trish Holliday
Assistant Commissioner & Chief Learning Officer
Strategic Learning Solutions
James K. Polk Building
505 Deaderick Street
Nashville, TN 37243
P: (615) 741-4156
F: (615) 532-0728
E: Trish.Holliday@tn.gov

U.S. VIRGIN ISLANDS
Mr. Milton E. Potter
Director
Division of Personnel
GERS Building, 3rd Floor
3438 Kronprindsens Gade
St. Thomas, VI 00802
P: (340) 774-8588
F: (340) 714-5040
E: info@dopusvi.net

UTAH
Mr. Rich Hughes
Director, Learning & Development
Department of Human Resource Management
State Office Building, Room 2120
Salt Lake City, UT 84114
P: (801) 641-6075
F: (801) 538-3081
E: rhughes@utah.gov

VERMONT
Ms. Rose Lucenti
Director of Workforce Development
Department of Labor
5 Green Mountain Drive
P.O. Box 488
Montpelier, VT 05601
P: (802) 828-4151
F: (802) 828-4022
E: rose.lucenti@vermont.gov

VIRGINIA
Mrs. Sara Redding Wilson
Director
Department of Human Resource Management
101 North 14th Street, 12th Floor
Richmond, VA 23219
P: (804) 225-2237
F: (804) 371-7401
E: sara.wilson@dhrm.virginia.gov

WASHINGTON
Mr. Franklin Plaistowe
Assistant Director
State Human Resources
128th 10th Avenue
P.O. Box 47500
Olympia, WA 98504
P: (360) 407-4104
E: StateHR@ofm.wa.gov

WISCONSIN
Mr. Robert A. Rodriguez
Administrator
Division of Equal Rights
201 East Washington Avenue
P.O. Box 8928
Madison, WI 53708
P: (608) 266-3345
F: (608) 267-4592
E: erinfo@dwd.wisconsin.gov

WYOMING
Mr. John F. Cox
Director
Department of Workforce
Services
614 South Greeley Highway
Cheyenne, WY 82002
P: (307) 777-8728
F: (307) 777-5857
E: john.cox@wyo.gov

Transportation and Highways

Umbrella agency responsible for planning, designing, constructing and maintaining public transportation services, highways and facilities throughout the state.

ALABAMA
Mr. John R. Cooper
Transportation Director
Department of Transportation
1409 Coliseum Boulevard
P.O. Box 303050
Montgomery, AL 36130
P: (334) 242-6311
F: (334) 262-8041
E: cooperjr@dot.state.al.us

ALASKA
Mr. Marc Luiken
Commissioner
Department of Transportation & Public Facilities
3132 Channel Drive
P.O. Box 112500
Juneau, AK 99811
P: (907) 465-3901
F: (907) 586-8365
E: marc.luiken@alaska.gov

ARIZONA
Mr. John Halikowski
Director
Department of Transportation
206 South 17th Avenue
Phoenix, AZ 85007
P: (602) 712-7011
F: (602) 712-6941
E: jhalikowski@azdot.gov

ARKANSAS
Mr. Scott Bennett
Director of Highways & Transportation
State Highway & Transportation Department
10324 Interstate 30
P.O. Box 2261
Little Rock, AR 72203
P: (501) 569-2211
F: (501) 569-2400
E: scott.bennett@arkansashighways.com

CALIFORNIA
Mr. Malcolm Dougherty
Director
Department of Transportation
1120 N Street
P.O. Box 942873
Sacramento, CA 94273
P: (916) 654-5266
F: (916) 654-6608
E: Malcolm.Dougherty@dot.ca.gov

COLORADO
Mr. Shailen Bhatt
Executive Director
Department of Transportation
4201 East Arkansas Avenue
Denver, CO 80222
P: (303) 757-9201
F: (303) 757-9656
E: shailen.bhatt@state.co.us

CONNECTICUT
Mr. James Redeker
Commissioner
Department of Transportation
2800 Berlin Turnpike
P.O. Box 317546
Newington, CT 06131
P: (860) 594-3000
F: (860) 594-3008
E: james.redeker@ct.gov

DELAWARE
Ms. Jennifer L. Cohan
Secretary
Department of Transportation
800 Bay Road, Route 113
P.O. Box 778
Dover, DE 19903
P: (302) 760-2303
F: (302) 739-2895
E: jennifer.cohan@state.de.us

DISTRICT OF COLUMBIA
Mr. Leif A. Dormsjo
Director of Transportation
Department of Transportation
55 M Street Southeast, #400
Washington, DC 20003
P: (202) 673-6813
F: (202) 671-0642
E: leif.dormsjo@dc.gov

FLORIDA
Ms. Rachel D. Cone
Secretary
Department of Transportation
605 Suwannee Street
Tallahassee, FL 32399
P: (850) 414-5200
F: (850) 414-5201
E: rachel.cone@dot.state.fl.us

GEORGIA
Mr. Russell McMurry
Commissioner
Department of Transportation
600 West Peachtree Street, Northwest
Atlanta, GA 30308
P: (404) 631-1000
F: (404) 631-1022
E: rmcmurry@dot.ga.gov

HAWAII
Mr. Ford Fuchigami
Director
Department of Transportation
869 Punchbowl Street
Honolulu, HI 96813
P: (808) 587-2150
F: (808) 587-2167
E: ford.n.fuchigami@hawaii.gov

IDAHO
Mr. Brian W. Ness
Director
Transportation Department
3311 West State Street
P.O. Box 7129
Boise, ID 83707
P: (208) 334-8820
F: (208) 334-3858
E: brian.ness@itd.idaho.gov

ILLINOIS
Mr. Randall S. Blankenhorn
Secretary
Department of Transportation
2300 South Dirksen Parkway
Springfield, IL 62764
P: (217) 782-5597
F: (217) 782-6828
E: randy.blankenhorn@illinois.gov

INDIANA
Mr. Joe McGuinness
Commissioner
Department of Transportation
Indiana Government Center North
100 North Senate Avenue, Room N 758
Indianapolis, IN 46204
P: (317) 232-5525
F: (317) 232-0238
E: jmcguinness@indot.in.gov

IOWA
Mr. Mark Lowe
Director
Department of Transportation
800 Lincoln Way
Ames, IA 50010
P: (515) 237-3210
F: (515) 817-6508
E: mark.lowe@dot.iowa.gov

KANSAS
Mr. Richard Carlson
Secretary of Transportation
Department of Transportation
Eisenhower State Office Building
700 Southwest Harrison
Topeka, KS 66603
P: (785) 296-3461
F: (785) 296-1095
E: richard.carlson@ks.gov

KENTUCKY
Mr. Greg Thomas
Acting Secretary
Transporation Cabinet
200 Mero Street
Frankfort, KY 40622
P: (502) 564-4890
F: (502) 564-4809
E: gregory.thomas@ky.gov

LOUISIANA
Dr. Shawn Wilson
Secretary
Department of Transportation & Development
1201 Capitol Access Road
P.O. Box 94245
Baton Rouge, LA 70804
P: (225) 379-1200
F: (225) 379-1851
E: shawn.wilson@la.gov

MAINE
Mr. David Bernhardt
Commissioner
Department of Transportation
24 Child Street
16 State House Station
Augusta, ME 04333
P: (207) 624-3000
F: (207) 624-3001
E: david.bernhardt@maine.gov

MARYLAND
Mr. Pete K. Rahn
Secretary
Department of Transportation
Office of the Secretary, P.O. Box 548
7201 Corporate Center Drive
Hanover, MD 21076
P: (888) 713-1414
F: (410) 865-1334
E: prahn@mdot.state.md.us

MASSACHUSETTS
Ms. Stephanie Pollack
Secretary of Transportation & Public Works
Department of Transportation
10 Park Plaza, Suite 3170
Boston, MA 02116
P: (617) 973-7000
F: (617) 973-8031
E: stephanie.pollack@dot.state.ma.us

MICHIGAN
Mr. Kirk T. Steudle
Director
Department of Transportation
Murray D. Van Wagoner Building
425 West Ottawa Street, P.O. Box 30050
Lansing, MI 48933
P: (517) 373-2114
F: (517) 373-8841
E: steudlek@michigan.gov

MINNESOTA
Mr. Charles A. Zelle
Commissioner
Department of Transportation
Transportation Building
395 John Ireland Boulevard
St. Paul, MN 55155
P: (651) 366-4800
F: (651) 366-4795
E: charlie.zelle@state.mn.us

MISSISSIPPI
Ms. Melinda LittleJohn McGrath
Executive Director
Department of Transportation
Administrative Office Building
401 North West Street, P.O. Box 1850
Jackson, MS 39215
P: (601) 359-7001
F: (601) 359-7050
E: mmcgrath@mdot.state.ms.us

MISSOURI
Mr. Patrick McKenna
Director
Department of Transportation
105 West Capitol Avenue
P.O. Box 270
Jefferson City, MO 65102
P: (573) 751-4622
F: (573) 751-6555
E: patrick.mckenna@modot.mo.gov

MONTANA
Mr. Michael T. Tooley
Director
Department of Transportation
2701 Prospect Avenue
P.O. Box 201001
Helena, MT 59620
P: (406) 444-6201
F: (406) 444-7643
E: mitooley@mt.gov

NEBRASKA
Mr. Kyle Schneweis
Director
Department of Roads
1500 Highway 2
P.O. Box 94759
Lincoln, NE 68509
P: (402) 479-4615
F: (402) 479-4325
E: kyle.schneweis@nebraska.gov

NEVADA
Mr. Rudy Malfabon
Director
Department of Transportation
1263 South Stewart Street
Carson City, NV 89712
P: (775) 888-7440
F: (775) 888-7201
E: rmalfabon@dot.state.nv.us

NEW HAMPSHIRE
Ms. Victoria Sheehan
Commissioner
Department of Transportation
John O. Morton Building
7 Hazen Drive, P.O. Box 483
Concord, NH 03302
P: (603) 271-1484
F: (603) 271-3914
E: vsheehan@dot.state.nh.us

NEW JERSEY
Mr. Richard T. Hammer
Acting Commissioner
Department of Transportation
1035 Parkway Avenue
P.O. Box 600
Trenton, NJ 08625
P: (609) 530-3536
F: (609) 530-3894
E: rick.hammer@dot.nj.gov

NEW MEXICO
Mr. Tom Church
Cabinet Secretary
Department of Transportation
Joe M. Anaya Building
1120 Cerrilos Road, P.O. Box 1149
Santa Fe, NM 87504
P: (505) 827-5110
F: (505) 827-5469
E: tom.church@state.nm.us

NEW YORK
Mr. Matthew Driscoll
Commissioner
Department of Transportation
50 Wolf Road
Albany, NY 12232
P: (518) 457-4422
F: (518) 457-5583
E: commissioner@dot.ny.gov

NORTH CAROLINA
Mr. Nick Tennyson
Secretary
Department of Transportation
1507 Mail Service Center
1 South Wilmington Street
Raleigh, NC 27699
P: (919) 707-2800
F: (919) 733-9150
E: njtennyson@ncdot.gov

NORTH DAKOTA
Mr. Grant Levi
Director
Department of Transportation
608 East Boulevard Avenue
Bismarck, ND 58505
P: (701) 328-2581
F: (701) 328-0310
E: glevi@nd.gov

OHIO
Mr. Jerry Wray
Director
Department of Transportation
1980 West Broad Street
Columbus, OH 43223
P: (614) 466-7170
F: (614) 466-8662
E: Terri.Barnhart@dot.ohio.gov

OKLAHOMA
Mr. J. Michael Patterson
Director
Department of Transportation
200 Northeast 21st Street
Oklahoma City, OK 73105
P: (405) 522-1800
F: (405) 522-1805
E: mpatterson@odot.org

OREGON
Mr. Matthew Garrett
Director
Department of Transportation
355 Capitol Street, Northeast
Salem, OR 97301
P: (503) 986-3452
F: (503) 986-3432
E: matthew.l.garrett@odot.state.or.us

PENNSYLVANIA
Ms. Leslie S. Richards
Secretary
Department of Transportation
Keystone Building
400 North Street, Fifth Floor
Harrisburg, PA 17120
P: (717) 787-2838
F: (717) 787-5491
E: lsrichards@pa.gov

PUERTO RICO
Mr. Carlos Contreras
Secretary of Transportation & Public Works
Department of Transportation & Public Works
Office of the Secretary
P.O. Box 41269, Minillas Station
San Juan, PR 00940
P: (787) 722-2929
F: (787) 728-1620
E: ccontreras@dtop.pr.gov

RHODE ISLAND
Mr. Peter Alviti
Director
Department of Transportation
State Office Building
2 Capitol Hill
Providence, RI 02903
P: (401) 222-2481
F: (401) 222-2086
E: peter.alviti@dot.ri.gov

SOUTH CAROLINA
Ms. Christy Hall
Interim Secretary of Transportation
Department of Transportation
Silas N. Pearman Building
955 Park Street
Columbia, SC 29201
P: (803) 737-2314
F: (803) 737-2038
E: HallCA@dot.state.sc.us

Transportation and Highways

SOUTH DAKOTA
Mr. Darin Bergquist
Secretary
Department of Transportation
700 East Broadway Avenue
Pierre, SD 57501
P: (605) 773-3265
F: (605) 773-3921
E: darin.bergquist@state.sd.us

TENNESSEE
Mr. John Schroer
Commissioner
Department of Transportation
700 James K. Polk Building
505 Deaderick Street
Nashville, TN 37243
P: (615) 741-2848
F: (615) 741-2508
E: John.Schroer@tn.gov

TEXAS
Mr. James Bass
Executive Director
Department of Transportation
Dewitt C. Greer Highway Building
125 East 11th Street
Austin, TX 78701
P: (512) 305-9501
F: (512) 305-9567
E: James.Bass@txdot.gov

UTAH
Mr. Carlos Braceras
Executive Director
Department of Transportation
4501 South 2700, West
Salt Lake City, UT 84129
P: (801) 965-4000
F: (801) 965-4338
E: cbraceras@utah.gov

VERMONT
Mr. Joe Flynn
Secretary of Transportation
Agency of Transportation
One National Life Drive
Montpelier, VT 05633
P: (802) 828-2657
F: (802) 828-3522
E: Joe.Flynn@vermont.gov

VIRGINIA
Mr. Aubrey Layne Jr.
Secretary of Transportation
Department of Transportation
1401 East Broad Street
Richmond, VA 23219
P: (804) 786-2801
F: (804) 786-2940
E: aubrey.layne@governor.virginia.gov

WASHINGTON
Mr. Roger Millar
Secretary of Transportation
Department of Transportation
310 Maple Park Avenue, Southeast
P.O. Box 47316
Olympia, WA 98504
P: (360) 705-7054
F: (360) 705-6800
E: millarr@wsdot.wa.gov

WEST VIRGINIA
Mr. Thomas J. Smith
Secretary of Transportation/Commissioner of Highways
Department of Transportation
1900 Kanawha Boulevard, East
Building 5, Room 110
Charleston, WV 25305
P: (304) 558-0444
F: (304) 558-1004
E: thomas.j.smith@wv.gov

WISCONSIN
Mr. Dave Ross
Secretary
Department of Transportation
4802 Sheboygan Avenue
P.O. Box 7910
Madison, WI 53707
P: (608) 266-1114
F: (608) 266-9912
E: daveb.ross@dot.wi.gov

WYOMING
Mr. Bill Panos
Director
Department of Transportation
5300 Bishop Boulevard
Cheyenne, WY 82009
P: (307) 777-4484
F: (307) 777-4163
E: bill.panos@wyo.gov

Treasurer

The custodian of all state funds and securities belonging to and held in trust by the state.

ALABAMA
The Honorable Young Boozer III (R)
State Treasurer
Office of the State Treasurer
600 Dexter Avenue
State Capitol, Room S-106
Montgomery, AL 36104
P: (334) 242-7501
F: (334) 242-7592
E: young.boozer@treasury.alabama.gov

ALASKA
The Honorable Pamela Leary (appointed)
State Treasurer
Department of Revenue
P.O. Box 110400
Juneau, AK 99811
P: (907) 465-3669
F: (907) 465-2389
E: pam.leary@alaska.gov

AMERICAN SAMOA
The Honorable Ueli Tonumaipea
Treasurer
Department of Treasury
American Samoa Government
Pago Pago, AS 96799
P: (684) 633-4155
F: (684) 633-4100
E: ueli.tonumaipea@tr.as.gov

ARIZONA
The Honorable Jeff De Wit (R)
State Treasurer
Office of the State Treasurer
1700 West Washington Street
Phoenix, AZ 85007
P: (602) 542-7800
F: (602) 542-7176

ARKANSAS
The Honorable Dennis Milligan
State Treasurer
Office of the State Treasurer
220 State Capitol
Little Rock, AR 72201
P: (501) 682-5888
F: (501) 682-3842

CALIFORNIA
The Honorable John Chiang (D)
State Treasurer
Office of the State Treasurer
915 Capitol Mall, Room 110
Sacramento, CA 95814
P: (916) 653-2995
F: (916) 653-3125

COLORADO
The Honorable Walker Stapleton (R)
State Treasurer
Office of the State Treasurer
140 State Capitol Building
Denver, CO 80203
P: (303) 866-2441
F: (303) 866-2123
E: treasurer.stapleton@state.co.us

CONNECTICUT
The Honorable Denise L. Nappier (D)
State Treasurer
Office of State Treasurer
55 Elm Street, 7th Floor
Hartford, CT 06106
P: (860) 702-3010
F: (860) 702-3043
E: denise.nappier@ct.gov

DELAWARE
The Honorable Ken Simpler (R)
State Treasurer
Office of the State Treasurer
820 Silver Lake Boulevard, Suite 100
Dover, DE 19904
P: (302) 672-6700
F: (302) 739-5635
E: statetreasurer@state.de.us

DISTRICT OF COLUMBIA
Mr. Jeffrey Barnette (appointed)
Deputy CFO & Treasurer
Office of Finance & Treasury
1101 4th Street, Southwest
Suite 850
Washington, DC 20024
P: (202) 727-6055
F: (202) 727-6963

FLORIDA
The Honorable Jeffrey H. Atwater (R)
Chief Financial Officer
Department of Financial Services
200 East Gaines Street
Tallahassee, FL 32399
P: (850) 413-2850
F: (850) 413-2950
E: allison@jeffatwater.com

GEORGIA
The Honorable Steve McCoy (appointed)
Treasurer & Director
Office of the State Treasurer
200 Piedmont Avenue
Suite 1204, West Tower
Atlanta, GA 30334
P: (404) 656-2168
F: (404) 656-9048
E: OSTWeb@treasury.ga.gov

GUAM
The Honorable Rosita T. Fejeran
Treasurer
Department of Administration, Treasury
P.O. Box 884
Hagatna, GU 96932
P: (671) 475-1101
F: (671) 477-6788
E: rtfejeran@doa.guam.gov

HAWAII
The Honorable Wesley Machida (appointed)
Director of Finance
Department of Budget & Finance
P.O. Box 150
Honolulu, HI 96810
P: (808) 586-1518
F: (808) 586-1976
E: hi.budgetandfinance@hawaii.gov

IDAHO
The Honorable Ron G. Crane (R)
State Treasurer
Office of the State Treasurer
700 West Jefferson Street, Suite E-126
P.O. Box 83720
Boise, ID 83720
P: (208) 334-3200
F: (208) 332-2959
E: idahotreasurer@sto.idaho.gov

ILLINOIS
The Honorable Michael W. Frerichs (D)
State Treasurer
Office of the State Treasurer
Statehouse
Executive Office 203
Springfield, IL 62706
P: (217) 782-2211
F: (217) 785-2777

INDIANA
The Honorable Kelly Mitchell (R)
State Treasurer
Office of the State Treasurer
242 State House
Indianapolis, IN 46204
P: (317) 232-6386
F: (317) 233-1780

IOWA
The Honorable Michael L. Fitzgerald (D)
State Treasurer
Office of the State Treasurer
State Capitol Building
Des Moines, IA 50319
P: (515) 281-5368
F: (515) 281-7562
E: treasurer@iowa.gov

KANSAS
The Honorable Jacob LaTurner (R)
State Treasurer
Office of the State Treasurer
900 Southwest Jackson Street
Suite 201
Topeka, KS 66612
P: (785) 296-3171
F: (785) 296-7950
E: jacob@treasurer.ks.gov

KENTUCKY
The Honorable Allison Ball (R)
State Treasurer
Office of the State Treasurer
1050 U.S. Highway 127 South
Suite 100
Frankfort, KY 40601
P: (502) 564-4722
F: (502) 564-6545
E: allison.ball@ky.gov

LOUISIANA
The Honorable Ron J. Henson (R)
State Treasurer
Office of the State Treasurer
P.O. Box 44154
Baton Rouge, LA 70804
P: (225) 342-0010
F: (225) 342-0046
E: rhenson@treasury.state.la.us

Treasurer

MAINE
The Honorable Terry Hayes (I)
State Treasurer
Office of the State Treasurer
39 State House Station
Augusta, ME 04333
P: (207) 624-7477
F: (207) 287-2367
E: terry.hayes@maine.gov

MARYLAND
The Honorable Nancy K. Kopp (D)
(elected by the Legislature)
State Treasurer
Office of the State Treasurer
Goldstein Treasury Building
80 Calvert Street
Annapolis, MD 21401
P: (410) 260-7160
F: (410) 260-6056
E: nkopp@treasurer.state.md.us

MASSACHUSETTS
The Honorable Deborah B. Goldberg (D)
State Treasurer
Office of the State Treasurer
State House, Room 227
Boston, MA 02133
P: (617) 367-3900
F: (617) 248-0372

MICHIGAN
The Honorable Nick Khouri
(appointed)
State Treasurer
Department of Treasury
430 West Allegan Street
Lansing, MI 48922
P: (517) 373-3223
F: (517) 335-1785
E: KhouriN@michigan.gov

MINNESOTA
Mr. Myron Frans
Commissioner
Management & Budget
658 Cedar Street, Suite 400
St. Paul, MN 55155
P: (651) 201-8011
F: (651) 296-8685
E: myron.frans@state.mn.us

MISSISSIPPI
The Honorable Lynn Fitch (R)
State Treasurer
Office of the State Treasurer
P.O. Box 138
Jackson, MS 39205
P: (601) 359-3600
F: (601) 576-4495
E: ms.treasurydept@treasury.ms.gov

MISSOURI
The Honorable Eric Schmitt (R)
State Treasurer
Office of the State Treasurer
State Capitol, Room 229
P.O. Box 210
Jefferson City, MO 65102
P: (573) 751-2411
F: (573) 751-9443
E: eric.schmitt@treasurer.mo.gov

MONTANA
Mr. John Lewis
(appointed)
Director
Department of Administration
125 North Roberts Street, Room 155
P.O. Box 200101
Helena, MT 59620
P: (406) 444-3033
F: (406) 444-6194
E: johnlewis@mt.gov

NEBRASKA
The Honorable Don B. Stenberg (R)
State Treasurer
Office of the State Treasurer
State Capitol, Room 2005
P.O. Box 94788
Lincoln, NE 68509
P: (402) 471-2455
F: (402) 471-4390
E: Don.Stenberg@nebraska.gov

NEVADA
The Honorable Dan Schwartz (R)
State Treasurer
Office of the State Treasurer
101 North Carson Street, Suite 4
Carson City, NV 89701
P: (775) 684-7109
F: (775) 684-5623
E: statetreasurer@nevadatreasurer.gov

NEW HAMPSHIRE
The Honorable William Dwyer
(elected by the Legislature)
State Treasurer
State Treasury
25 Capitol Street
Concord, NH 03301
P: (603) 271-2621
F: (603) 271-3922
E: bdwyer@treasury.state.nh.us

NEW JERSEY
The Honorable Ford M. Scudder
(appointed)
State Treasurer
Department of the Treasury
State House, First Floor
P.O. Box 002
Trenton, NJ 08625
P: (609) 292-6748
F: (609) 984-3888

NEW MEXICO
The Honorable Tim Eichenberg (D)
State Treasurer
Office of the State Treasurer
2055 South Pacheco Street, Suite 100
P.O. Box 5135
Santa Fe, NM 87502
P: (505) 955-1120
F: (505) 955-1180
E: Tim.Eichenberg@state.nm.us

NEW YORK
The Honorable Christopher Curtis
(appointed)
Deputy Commissioner & Treasurer
Department of Taxation & Finance
110 State Street, 2nd Floor
Albany, NY 12207
P: (518) 474-4250
F: (518) 402-4118
E: christopher.curtis@tax.ny.gov

NORTH CAROLINA
The Honorable Dale R. Folwell (R)
State Treasurer
Office of the State Treasurer
3200 Atlantic Avenue
Raleigh, NC 27604
P: (919) 814-4000
F: (919) 855-5805
E: assistantsecretary@nccommerce.com

NORTH DAKOTA
The Honorable Kelly L. Schmidt (R)
State Treasurer
Office of State Treasurer
600 East Boulevard, Department 120
State Capital, 3rd Floor
Bismarck, ND 58505
P: (701) 328-2643
F: (701) 328-3002
E: treasurer@nd.gov

NORTHERN MARIANA ISLANDS
Mr. Mark O. Rabauliman
Secretary of Commerce
Department of Commerce
Office of the Insurance Commissioner
Caller Box 10007 CK
Saipan, MP 96950
P: (670) 664-3077
F: (670) 664-3067
E: info@commerce.gov.mp

OHIO
The Honorable Josh Mandel (R)
Treasurer of State
Office of the State Treasurer
30 East Broad Street
9th Floor
Columbus, OH 43215
P: (614) 466-2160
F: (614) 644-7313

OKLAHOMA
The Honorable Ken Miller (R)
State Treasurer
Office of the State Treasurer
2300 North Lincoln Boulevard
State Capital Building, Room 217
Oklahoma City, OK 73105
P: (405) 521-3191
F: (405) 521-4994

OREGON
The Honorable Tobias Read (D)
State Treasurer
Office of the State Treasurer
900 Court Street Northeast, Room 159
Salem, OR 97301
P: (503) 378-4329
F: (503) 373-7051
E: oregon.treasurer@ost.state.or.us

PENNSYLVANIA
The Honorable Joseph Torsella (D)
State Treasurer
Office of the State Treasurer
129 Finance Building
Harrisburg, PA 17120
P: (717) 787-2465
F: (717) 783-9760

PUERTO RICO
The Honorable Raul Maldonado-Gautier
Secretary of Treasury
Department of the Treasury
P.O. Box 9024140
San Juan, PR 00902
P: (787) 721-2020
F: (787) 721-6213

RHODE ISLAND
The Honorable Seth Magaziner (D)
General Treasurer
Office of the General Treasurer
102 State House
Providence, RI 02903
P: (401) 222-2397
F: (401) 222-6140
E: generaltreasurer@treasury.ri.gov

SOUTH CAROLINA
The Honorable Curtis M. Loftis Jr. (R)
State Treasurer
Office of the State Treasurer
P.O. Box 11778
Columbia, SC 29211
P: (803) 734-2101
F: (803) 734-2690
E: treasurer@sto.sc.gov

SOUTH DAKOTA
The Honorable Rich L. Sattgast (R)
State Treasurer
Office of the State Treasurer
500 East Capitol Avenue
Pierre, SD 57501
P: (605) 773-3378
F: (605) 773-3115
E: rich.sattgast@state.sd.us

TENNESSEE
The Honorable David H. Lillard Jr. (elected by the Legislature)
State Treasurer
Department of Treasury
State Capitol, First Floor
600 Charlotte Avenue
Nashville, TN 37243
P: (615) 741-2956
F: (615) 253-1591
E: david.lillard@tn.gov

TEXAS
The Honorable Glenn Hegar (R)
Comptroller of Public Accounts
Office of the Comptroller of Public Accounts
LBJ State Office Building, 1st Floor
111 East 17th Street
Austin, TX 78774
P: (512) 463-4444
F: (512) 463-4902
E: glenn.hegar@cpa.state.tx.us

U.S. VIRGIN ISLANDS
The Honorable Laurel Payne (appointed)
Director of Treasury
Department of Finance
Treasury Division
2314 Kronprindsens Gade
St. Thomas, VI 00802
P: (340) 774-4750
F: (340) 776-4028

UTAH
The Honorable David Damschen (R)
State Treasurer
Office of the State Treasurer
350 North State Street, Suite 180
Salt Lake City, UT 84114
P: (801) 538-1042
F: (801) 538-1465
E: sto@utah.gov

VERMONT
The Honorable Elizabeth Pearce
State Treasurer
Office of the State Treasurer
109 State Street
Montpelier, VT 05609
P: (802) 828-3322
F: (802) 828-2301
E: Beth.Pearce@state.vt.us

VIRGINIA
The Honorable Manju Ganeriwala (appointed)
State Treasurer
Department of the Treasury
P.O. Box 1879
Richmond, VA 23219
P: (804) 225-3131
F: (804) 786-0833
E: Manju.Ganeriwala@trs.virginia.gov

WASHINGTON
The Honorable Duane Davidson (R)
State Treasurer
Office of the State Treasurer
P.O. Box 40200
Olympia, WA 98504
P: (360) 902-9001
F: (360) 902-9044
E: Duane.Davidson@tre.wa.gov

WEST VIRGINIA
The Honorable John D. Perdue (D)
State Treasurer
Office of the State Treasurer
State Capitol Complex
Building 1, Room E-145
Charleston, WV 25305
P: (304) 558-5000
F: (304) 558-4097

WISCONSIN
The Honorable Matt Adamczyk (R)
State Treasurer
Office of the State Treasurer
B41 West, State Capitol
Madison, WI 53701
P: (608) 266-1714
F: (608) 266-2647
E: Matt.Adamczyk@wisconsin.gov

WYOMING
The Honorable Mark Gordon
State Treasurer
Office of the State Treasurer
200 West 24th Street
Cheyenne, WY 82002
P: (307) 777-7408
F: (307) 777-5411
E: treasurer@wyo.gov

Tribal Affairs

Acts as a liaison between state and tribal officials and advances the concerns of Native Americans.

ALABAMA
Ms. Eloise P. Josey
Executive Director
Indian Affairs Commission
771 South Lawrence Street, Suite 106
Montgomery, AL 36130
P: (334) 240-0998
F: (334) 240-3408
E: aiac@att.net

ARIZONA
Ms. Kristine M. FireThunder
Executive Director
Governor's Office of Tribal Relations
1700 West Washington Street, Suite 235
Phoenix, AZ 85007
P: (602) 542-4426
F: (602) 542-4428
E: gotrinfo@az.gov

CALIFORNIA
Mr. Cynthia Gomez
Executive Secretary
Native American Heritage Commission
1550 Harbor Boulevard, Suite 100
West Sacramento, CA 95691
P: (916) 373-3710
F: (916) 373-5471
E: nahc@nahc.ca.gov

COLORADO
The Honorable Donna Lynne (D)
Lieutenant Governor
Office of the Lieutenant Governor
130 State Capitol
Denver, CO 80203
P: (303) 866-2087
F: (303) 866-5469

FLORIDA
Mr. Curtis Osceola
Executive Director
Governor's Council on Indian Affairs
625 North Adams Street
Tallahassee, FL 32301
P: (850) 488-0730
E: cosceola@fgcia.org

IOWA
Ms. Jill Avery
Division Administrator
Commission on Native American Affairs
Lucas State Office Building
321 East 12th Street
Des Moines, IA 50319
P: (515) 242-6334
E: jill.avery@iowa.gov

KENTUCKY
Ms. Tressa Brown
Native American Heritage Coordinator
State Heritage Council
State Historic Preservation Office
300 Washington Street
Frankfort, KY 40601
P: (502) 564-7005 Ext. 125
F: (502) 564-5820
E: tressa.brown@ky.gov

MAINE
Mr. John Dieffenbacher-Krall
Executive Director
Indian Tribal-State Commission
P.O. Box 241
Stillwater, ME 04489
P: (207) 944-8376
F: (207) 394-9230
E: mitsced@roadrunner.com

MARYLAND
Mr. E. Keith Colston
Assistant Director
Commission on Indian Affairs
State Executive Department
301 West Preston Street, Suite 1500
Baltimore, MD 21201
P: (410) 767-7631
F: (410) 333-7542
E: keith.colston@maryland.gov

MICHIGAN
Mr. Agustin V. Arbulu
Executive Director
Department of Civil Rights
Capital Tower Building
110 West Michigan Avenue, Suite 800
Lansing, MI 48933
P: (517) 335-3165
F: (517) 241-0546
E: ArbuluA@michigan.gov

MINNESOTA
Mr. Dennis Olson Jr.
Executive Director
Indian Affairs Council
161 St. Anthony Avenue, Suite 919
St. Paul, MN 55103
P: (651) 539-2202
E: Dennis.W.Olson@state.mn.us

MONTANA
Mr. Jason Smith
Director of Indian Affairs
Governor's Office of Indian Affairs
Capitol Building, 2nd Floor, Room 202
P.O. Box 200801
Helena, MT 59620
P: (406) 444-3702
F: (406) 444-1350
E: oia@mt.gov

NEBRASKA
Ms. Judi M. Gaiashkibos
Executive Director
Commission on Indian Affairs
1445 K Street, 6th Floor, East
P.O. Box 94981
Lincoln, NE 68509
P: (402) 471-3475
F: (402) 471-3392
E: judi.gaiashkibos@nebraska.gov

NEVADA
Ms. Sherry L. Rupert
Executive Director
Indian Commission
5366 Snyder Avenue
Carson City, NV 89701
P: (775) 687-8333
F: (775) 687-8330
E: srupert@govmail.state.nv.us

NEW JERSEY
Ms. Rowena Madden
Lt. Governor's Designee
Commission on American Indian Affairs
Office of the Secretary of State
P.O. Box 300
Trenton, NJ 08625
P: (609) 633-9627
F: (609) 777-2939
E: Feedback@sos.nj.gov

NEW MEXICO
Ms. Kelly Zunie
Secretary
Indian Affairs Department
Wendell Chino Building, 2nd Floor
1220 South St. Francies Drive
Santa Fe, NM 87505
P: (505) 476-1600
F: (505) 476-1601
E: Nicole.Macias@state.nm.us

NORTH CAROLINA
Mr. Furnie Lambert
Chair
Commission of Indian Affairs
Department of Administration
1317 Mail Service Center
Raleigh, NC 27699
P: (919) 807-4440
E: daphne.pinto@doa.nc.gov

NORTH DAKOTA
Mr. Scott J. Davis
Executive Director
Indian Affairs Commission
600 East Boulevard Avenue
Judicial Wing, Room #117
Bismarck, ND 58505
P: (701) 328-2428
F: (701) 328-1537
E: sjdavis@nd.gov

OREGON
Ms. Karen Quigley
Executive Director
Legislative Commission on Indian Services
900 Court Street Northeast, Room 167
Salem, OR 97301
P: (503) 986-1067
F: (503) 986-1071
E: karen.m.quigley@oregonlegislature.gov

SOUTH CAROLINA
Mr. Raymond Buxton II
Commissioner
Human Affairs Commission
1026 Sumter Street
Columbia, SC 29201
P: (803) 737-7800
E: rbuxton@schac.sc.gov

SOUTH DAKOTA
Mr. Steve Emery
Secretary of Tribal Relations
Department of Tribal Relations
302 East Dakota Street
Pierre, SD 57501
P: (605) 773-3415
F: (605) 773-6592

UTAH
Ms. Shirlee Silversmith
Director
Division of Indian Affairs
Department of Heritage & Arts
250 North 1950 West, Suite A
Salt Lake City, UT 84116
P: (801) 715-6701
F: (801) 521-4727
E: ssilversmith@utah.gov

WASHINGTON
Mr. Craig A. Bill
Executive Director
Governor's Office of Indian Affairs
210 - 11th Avenue, Southwest, Suite 415
P.O. Box 40909
Olympia, WA 98504
P: (360) 902-8826
F: (360) 902-8829
E: craig.bill@goia.wa.gov

WISCONSIN
Ms. Dawn Vick
Intergovernmental Services Team Leader
State Tribal Relations Initiative
101 East Wilson Street, 9th Floor
P.O. Box 8944
Madison, WI 53708
P: (608) 266-7043
F: (608) 267-6917
E: dawn.vick@wisconsin.gov

Unclaimed Property

Responsible for the marshaling, administration and disposition of unclaimed or abandoned property.

ALABAMA
The Honorable Young Boozer III (R)
State Treasurer
Office of the State Treasurer
600 Dexter Avenue
State Capitol, Room S-106
Montgomery, AL 36104
P: (334) 242-7501
F: (334) 242-7592
E: young.boozer@treasury.alabama.gov

Ms. Daria Story
Assistant Treasurer/Chief Operating Officer
State Treasury
600 Dexter Avenue, S-100
Montgomery, AL 36130
P: (334) 242-7500
F: (334) 353-4080
E: daria.story@treasury.alabama.gov

ALASKA
The Honorable Pamela Leary
State Treasurer
Department of Revenue
P.O. Box 110400
Juneau, AK 99811
P: (907) 465-3669
F: (907) 465-2389
E: pam.leary@alaska.gov

Ms. Rachel Lewis
Unclaimed Property Manager
Unclaimed Property Section
Department of Revenue, Treasury Division
P.O. Box 110420
Juneau, AK 99811
P: (907) 465-5885
F: (907) 465-2394
E: rachel.lewis@alaska.gov

ARIZONA
Mr. David Briant
Director
Department of Revenue
1600 West Monroe
Phoenix, AZ 85007
P: (602) 716-6090
F: (602) 542-2072

Mr. Joshua Joyce
Administrator
Unclaimed Property
Department of Revenue
1600 West Monroe
Phoenix, AZ 85007
P: (602) 716-6033
F: (602) 716-7997
E: JJoyce@azdor.gov

ARKANSAS
Mr. Bradley Earl
Unclaimed Property Division Manager
State Auditor's Office
P.O. Box 251906
Little Rock, AR 72225
P: (501) 371-2124
F: (501) 683-4285

The Honorable Andrea Lea (R)
Auditor of State
Office of the Auditor of State
State Capitol Building, Room 230
Little Rock, AR 72201
P: (501) 682-6030
F: (501) 682-2521

CALIFORNIA
Ms. Nancy Hollins
Chief
Unclaimed Property Division
State Controller's Office
10600 White Rock Road, Building A
Rancho Cordova, CA 95670
P: (916) 464-6263
F: (916) 322-4404

COLORADO
The Honorable Walker Stapleton (R)
State Treasurer
Office of the State Treasurer
140 State Capitol Building
Denver, CO 80203
P: (303) 866-2441
F: (303) 866-2123
E: treasurer.stapleton@state.co.us

Ms. Patty White
Program Director
Unclaimed Property Division
State Treasury
1580 Logan Street, Suite 500
Denver, CO 80203
P: (303) 866-6070
F: (303) 866-6154
E: patty.white@state.co.us

CONNECTICUT
Ms. Maria M. Greenslade
Assistant Deputy Treasurer
Unclaimed Property
State Treasury
55 Elm Street
Hartford, CT 06106
P: (860) 702-3125
E: maria.greenslade@po.state.ct.us

The Honorable Denise L. Nappier (D)
State Treasurer
Office of State Treasurer
55 Elm Street, 7th Floor
Hartford, CT 06106
P: (860) 702-3010
F: (860) 702-3043
E: denise.nappier@ct.gov

DELAWARE
Mr. Richard J. Geisenberger
Secretary of Finance
Department of Finance
Carvel State Building, 8th Floor
820 North French Street
Wilmington, DE 19801
P: (302) 577-8987
F: (302) 577-8982

Mr. David Gregor
Director
Division of Revenue
Carvel State Office Building
820 North French Street
Wilmington, DE 19801
P: (302) 577-8686
F: (302) 577-8202
E: david.gregor@state.de.us

DISTRICT OF COLUMBIA
Mr. Jeffrey Barnette
Deputy CFO & Treasurer
Office of Finance & Treasury
1101 4th Street, Southwest
Suite 850
Washington, DC 20024
P: (202) 727-6055
F: (202) 727-6963

Mr. Gracie B. Musher
Manager, Unclaimed Property
Office of Finance & Treasury
1101 4th Street, Southwest
Suite W 800-B
Washington, DC 20024
P: (202) 442-8195
F: (202) 442-8180
E: gracie.musher@dc.gov

FLORIDA
The Honorable Jeffrey H. Atwater (R)
Chief Financial Officer
Department of Financial Services
200 East Gaines Street
Tallahassee, FL 32399
P: (850) 413-2850
F: (850) 413-2950
E: allison@jeffatwater.com

Mr. Walter Graham
Chief of Unclaimed Property
Department of Financial Services
200 East Gaines Street
353 Fletcher Building
Tallahassee, FL 32399
P: (850) 413-5522
F: (850) 413-3017
E: Walter.Graham@myfloridacfo.com

GEORGIA
Mr. Steve Harbin
Program Manager
Unclaimed Property Program
4125 Welcome All Road
Atlanta, GA 30349
P: (404) 724-7058
E: Steve.Harbin@dor.ga.gov

Ms. Lynnette Riley
Revenue Commissioner
Department of Revenue
1800 Century Center Boulevard
Atlanta, GA 30345
P: (404) 417-2100

HAWAII
Mr. Scott Kami
Administrator
Financial Administration Division
Department of Budget & Finance
P.O. Box 150
Honolulu, HI 96810
P: (808) 586-1612
F: (808) 586-1644
E: scott.a.kami@hawaii.gov

The Honorable Wesley Machida
Director of Finance
Department of Budget & Finance
P.O. Box 150
Honolulu, HI 96810
P: (808) 586-1518
F: (808) 586-1976
E: hi.budgetandfinance@hawaii.gov

IDAHO
The Honorable Ron G. Crane (R)
State Treasurer
State Treasurer's Office
700 West Jefferson Street, Suite E-126
P.O. Box 83720
Boise, ID 83720
P: (208) 334-3200
F: (208) 332-2959
E: idahotreasurer@sto.idaho.gov

Ms. Cozette Haley
Administrator
Unclaimed Property
State Treasurer's Office
P.O. Box 83720
Boise, ID 83720
P: (208) 332-2979
F: (208) 332-2970
E: cozette.haley@sto.idaho.gov

ILLINOIS
The Honorable Michael W. Frerichs (D)
State Treasurer
Office of the State Treasurer
Statehouse
Executive Office 203
Springfield, IL 62706
P: (217) 782-2211
F: (217) 785-2777

INDIANA
Ms. Lindsey R. Mayes
Director
Unclaimed Property Division
P.O. Box 2504
Greenwood, IN 46142
P: (317) 883-4557
F: (317) 883-4520
E: lindsey.mayes@atg.in.gov

IOWA
Ms. Karen Austin
Deputy Treasurer
Office of the State Treasurer
Lucas State Office Building
321 East 12th Street
Des Moines, IA 50319
P: (515) 281-7677
F: (515) 281-6962
E: karen.austin@iowa.gov

The Honorable Michael L. Fitzgerald (D)
State Treasurer
State Treasurer's Office
State Capitol Building
Des Moines, IA 50319
P: (515) 281-5368
F: (515) 281-7562
E: treasurer@iowa.gov

KANSAS
Ms. Katherine Priest
Director of Unclaimed Property
Unclaimed Property Division
900 Southwest Jackson, Suite 201
Topeka, KS 66612
P: (785) 291-3171
F: (785) 296-7950
E: kathy@treasurer.ks.gov

KENTUCKY
The Honorable Allison Ball (R)
State Treasurer
Office of the State Treasurer
1050 U.S. Highway 127 South
Suite 100
Frankfort, KY 40601
P: (502) 564-4722
F: (502) 564-6545
E: allison.ball@ky.gov

Mr. Samara Heavrin
Director
Unclaimed Property Division
1050 U.S. Highway 127 South, Suite 100
Frankfort, KY 40601
P: (502) 564-4722
F: (502) 564-4200
E: unclaimed.property@ky.gov

LOUISIANA
The Honorable Ron J. Henson (R)
State Treasurer
Office of the State Treasurer
P.O. Box 44154
Baton Rouge, LA 70804
P: (225) 342-0010
F: (225) 342-0046
E: rhenson@treasury.state.la.us

Ms. Kathleen Lobell
Director of Unclaimed Property
State Treasury
P.O. Box 44154
Baton Rouge, LA 70804
P: (225) 219-9400
E: klobell@treasury.state.la.us

MAINE
The Honorable Terry Hayes (I)
State Treasurer
Office of the State Treasurer
39 State House Station
Augusta, ME 04333
P: (207) 624-7477
F: (207) 287-2367
E: terry.hayes@maine.gov

MARYLAND
Mr. Eric Eichler
Manager
Unclaimed Property
301 West Preston Street, Room 310
Baltimore, MD 21201
P: (410) 767-2985
F: (410) 333-7150
E: eeichler@comp.state.md.us

The Honorable Peter Franchot (D)
Comptroller
Office of the Comptroller
L.L. Goldstein Treasury Building
80 Calvert Street, P.O. Box 466
Annapolis, MD 21404
P: (410) 260-7801
F: (410) 974-3808
E: mdcomptroller@comp.state.md.us

MASSACHUSETTS
Mr. Mark W. Bracken
Director of Abandoned Property
State Treasury
One Ashburton Place, 12th Floor
Boston, MA 02108
P: (617) 367-0400
F: (617) 367-3645
E: mwbracken@tre.state.ma.us

The Honorable Deborah B. Goldberg (D)
State Treasurer
Office of the State Treasurer
State House, Room 227
Boston, MA 02133
P: (617) 367-3900
F: (617) 248-0372

MICHIGAN
Mr. Terry Stanton
Manager
Unclaimed Property Division
State Treasury
P.O. Box 30756
Lansing, MI 48909
P: (517) 636-5320
F: (517) 322-5986

MINNESOTA
Mr. Robert Commodore
Senior Director
Consumer & Industry Services
Department of Commerce
85 7th Place East, Suite 500
St. Paul, MN 55101
P: (651) 296-2508
E: Robert.Commodore@state.mn.us

Mr. Mike Rothman
Commissioner
Department of Commerce
85 7th Place East, Suite 280
St. Paul, MN 55101
P: (651) 539-1441
F: (651) 539-1547
E: commerce.commissioner@state.mn.us

MISSISSIPPI
The Honorable Lynn Fitch (R)
State Treasurer
Office of the State Treasurer
P.O. Box 138
Jackson, MS 39205
P: (601) 359-3600
F: (601) 576-4495
E: ms.treasurydept@treasury.ms.gov

Mr. Tony Geiger
Director
Unclaimed Property
P.O. Box 138
Jackson, MS 39205
P: (601) 359-3600
F: (601) 576-4495
E: Tony.Geiger@treasury.ms.gov

MISSOURI
Mr. Scott Harper
Director of Unclaimed Property & General Services
Division of Unclaimed Property
State Treasury
P.O. Box 1272
Jefferson City, MO 65102
P: (573) 751-2082
F: (573) 526-6027
E: scott.harper@treasurer.mo.gov

Unclaimed Property

The Honorable Eric Schmitt (R)
State Treasurer
Office of the State Treasurer
State Capitol, Room 229
P.O. Box 210
Jefferson City, MO 65102
P: (573) 751-2411
F: (573) 751-9443
E: eric.schmitt@treasurer.mo.gov

MONTANA
Mr. Mike Kadas
Director
Department of Revenue
P.O. Box 5805
Helena, MT 59604
P: (406) 444-6900
F: (406) 444-3696

Mr. Mark Schoefeld
Unclaimed Property Program Manager
Department of Revenue
P.O. Box 5805
Helena, MT 59604
P: (406) 444-6900
F: (406) 444-0722
E: UnclaimedProperty@mt.gov

NEBRASKA
Ms. Meaghan Aguirre
Unclaimed Property Coordinator
State Treasury
809 P Street
Lincoln, NE 68509
P: (402) 471-1089
F: (402) 471-1167
E: meaghan.aguirre@nebraska.gov

The Honorable Don B. Stenberg (R)
State Treasurer
Office of the State Treasurer
State Capitol, Room 2005
P.O. Box 94788
Lincoln, NE 68509
P: (402) 471-2455
F: (402) 471-4390
E: Don.Stenberg@nebraska.gov

NEVADA
Ms. Tara Hagan
Chief Deputy Treasurer
Office of the State Treasurer
555 East Washington Avenue
Suite 4200
Las Vegas, NV 89101
P: (702) 486-4140
E: trhagan@nevadatreasurer.gov

The Honorable Dan Schwartz (R)
State Treasurer
Office of the State Treasurer
101 North Carson Street, Suite 4
Carson City, NV 89701
P: (775) 684-7109
F: (775) 684-5623
E: statetreasurer@nevadatreasurer.gov

NEW HAMPSHIRE
The Honorable William Dwyer
State Treasurer
State Treasury
25 Capitol Street
Concord, NH 03301
P: (603) 271-2621
F: (603) 271-3922
E: bdwyer@treasury.state.nh.us

Ms. Melissa VanSickle
Assistant Director
Unclaimed Property Division
25 Capitol Street, Room 205
Concord, NH 03301
P: (603) 271-2619
F: (603) 271-2730

NEW JERSEY
Mr. Steven Harris
Chief of Unclaimed Property Operations
Division of Taxation
P.O. Box 214
50 Barrack Street, 6th Floor
Trenton, NJ 08695
P: (609) 777-4655
F: (609) 984-0595
E: steven.harris@treas.state.nj.us

The Honorable Ford M. Scudder
State Treasurer
Department of the Treasury
State House, First Floor
P.O. Box 002
Trenton, NJ 08625
P: (609) 292-6748
F: (609) 984-3888

NEW MEXICO
Ms. Stephanie Dennis
Tax Compliance Specialist Supervisor
Taxation & Revenue Department
P.O. Box 25123
Santa Fe, NM 87504
P: (505) 827-0762
F: (505) 827-1759
E: stephanie.dennis@state.nm.us

Mr. John Monforte
Acting Secretary
Taxation & Revenue Department
1100 South St. Francis Drive
Santa Fe, NM 87504
P: (505) 827-0700
F: (505) 827-0331

NEW YORK
The Honorable Thomas P. DiNapoli (D)
Comptroller
Office of the State Comptroller
110 State Street
Albany, NY 12236
P: (518) 474-4040
F: (518) 474-3004
E: tdinapoli@osc.state.ny.us

Mr. Lawrence Schantz
Director
Office of Unclaimed Funds
State Comptroller's Office
110 State Street, 8th Floor
Albany, NY 12236
P: (518) 473-6318
F: (518) 474-7016
E: lschantz@osc.state.ny.us

NORTH CAROLINA
The Honorable Dale R. Folwell (R)
State Treasurer
Office of the State Treasurer
3200 Atlantic Avenue
Raleigh, NC 27604
P: (919) 814-4000
F: (919) 855-5805
E: assistantsecretary@nccommerce.com

Ms. Brenda Williams
Deputy Treasurer
Unclaimed Property Division
325 North Salisbury Street
Raleigh, NC 27603
P: (919) 508-5929
F: (919) 508-5181
E: brenda.williams@nctreasurer.com

NORTH DAKOTA
Ms. Linda Fisher
Unclaimed Property Administrator
Department of Trust Lands
P.O. Box 5523
Bismarck, ND 58506
P: (701) 328-2800
F: (701) 328-3650
E: llfisher@state.nd.us

Mr. Lance Gaebe
Land Commissioner
State Land Department
P.O. Box 5523
Bismarck, ND 58506
P: (701) 328-2800
F: (701) 328-3650
E: lancegaebe@nd.gov

OHIO
Mr. Yaw Obeng
Superintendent
Division of Unclaimed Funds
Department of Commerce
77 South High Street, 20th Floor
Columbus, OH 43266
P: (614) 644-6094
F: (614) 752-5078
E: Yaw.O'Beng@com.state.oh.us

OKLAHOMA
Ms. Kathy Janes
Director of Unclaimed Property
State Treasurer's Office
2401 Northwest 23rd Street, Suite 42
Oklahoma City, OK 73107
P: (405) 522-6743
F: (405) 521-2677
E: Kathy.Janes@treasurer.ok.gov

The Honorable Ken Miller (R)
State Treasurer
Office of the State Treasurer
2300 North Lincoln Boulevard
State Capital Building, Room 217
Oklahoma City, OK 73105
P: (405) 521-3191
F: (405) 521-4994

OREGON
Mr. Patrick Tate
Trust Property Manager
Finance & Administration
Department of State Lands
775 Summer Street, Northeast, Suite 100
Salem, OR 97301
P: (503) 986-5248
F: (503) 378-4844
E: patrick.tate@state.or.us

PENNSYLVANIA
Mr. Brian Munley
Director
Bureau of Unclaimed Property
State Treasury
Room 127, Finance Building
Harrisburg, PA 17120
P: (717) 783-3236
E: bmunley@patreasury.gov

The Honorable Joseph Torsella (D)
State Treasurer
Office of the State Treasurer
129 Finance Building
Harrisburg, PA 17120
P: (717) 787-2465
F: (717) 783-9760

PUERTO RICO
Ms. Salva Valentin
Unclaimed Property Supervisor
Commissioner of Financial Institutions
P.O. Box 11855
San Juan, PR 00910
P: (787) 723-3131 Ext. 2330
F: (787) 723-4225
E: salvad@ocif.gobierno.pr

RHODE ISLAND
The Honorable Seth Magaziner (D)
General Treasurer
Office of the General Treasurer
102 State House
Providence, RI 02903
P: (401) 222-2397
F: (401) 222-6140
E: generaltreasurer@treasury.ri.gov

Mr. Lammis Vargas
Director of Unclaimed Property
Office of the Treasury
P.O. Box 1435
Providence, RI 02901
P: (401) 462-7639
F: (401) 274-3865
E: lvargas@treasury.ri.gov

SOUTH CAROLINA
Mr. Dayle DeLong
Senior Assistant State Treasurer
Office of the State Treasurer
P.O. Box 11778
Columbia, SC 29211
P: (803) 734-2683
E: Dayle.DeLong@sto.sc.gov

The Honorable Curtis M. Loftis Jr. (R)
State Treasurer
Office of the State Treasurer
P.O. Box 11778
Columbia, SC 29211
P: (803) 734-2101
F: (803) 734-2690
E: treasurer@sto.sc.gov

SOUTH DAKOTA
Ms. Anissa Grambihler
Compliance Manager
State Treasury
State Capitol
500 East Capitol Avenue
Pierre, SD 57501
P: (605) 773-3379
F: (605) 773-3115
E: anissa.grambihler@state.sd.us

The Honorable Rich L. Sattgast (R)
State Treasurer
Office of the State Treasurer
500 East Capitol Avenue
Pierre, SD 57501
P: (605) 773-3378
F: (605) 773-3115
E: rich.sattgast@state.sd.us

TENNESSEE
Mr. John Gabriel
Director of Unclaimed Property
State Treasury
Andrew Jackson Building, 9th Floor
502 Deaderick Street
Nashville, TN 37243
P: (615) 253-5354
F: (615) 734-6458
E: john.gabriel@tn.gov

The Honorable David H. Lillard Jr.
State Treasurer
Department of Treasury
State Capitol, First Floor
600 Charlotte Avenue
Nashville, TN 37243
P: (615) 741-2956
F: (615) 253-1591
E: david.lillard@tn.gov

TEXAS
The Honorable Glenn Hegar (R)
Comptroller of Public Accounts
Office of the Comptroller of Public Accounts
LBJ State Office Building, 1st Floor
111 East 17th Street
Austin, TX 78774
P: (512) 463-4444
F: (512) 463-4902
E: glenn.hegar@cpa.state.tx.us

Ms. Frances Torres
Director
Unclaimed Property Division
P.O. Box 12019
Austin, TX 78711
P: (512) 936-6246

UTAH
The Honorable David Damschen (R)
State Treasurer
Office of the State Treasurer
350 North State Street, Suite 180
Salt Lake City, UT 84114
P: (801) 538-1042
F: (801) 538-1465
E: sto@utah.gov

Mr. Dennis Johnston
Administrator
Division of Unclaimed Property
P.O. Box 140530
Salt Lake City, UT 84114
P: (801) 715-3321
F: (801) 715-3309
E: dljohnston@utah.gov

VERMONT
Mr. Albert LaPerle
Director of Unclaimed Property
State Treasury
109 State Street, 4th Floor
Montpelier, VT 05609
P: (802) 828-1452
F: (802) 828-2772
E: al.laperle@state.vt.us

The Honorable Elizabeth Pearce
State Treasurer
Office of the State Treasurer
109 State Street
Montpelier, VT 05609
P: (802) 828-3322
F: (802) 828-2301
E: Beth.Pearce@state.vt.us

VIRGINIA
Ms. Vicki D. Bridgeman
Director of Unclaimed Property
State Treasury
P.O. Box 2478
Richmond, VA 23218
P: (804) 225-3156
F: (804) 786-4653
E: vicki.bridgeman@trs.virgina.gov

The Honorable Manju Ganeriwala
State Treasurer
Department of the Treasury
P.O. Box 1879
Richmond, VA 23219
P: (804) 225-3131
F: (804) 786-0833
E: Manju.Ganeriwala@trs.virginia.gov

WASHINGTON
Ms. Celeste Monahan
Program Manager
Department of Revenue
P.O. Box 47454
Olympia, WA 98504
P: (360) 534-1301
F: (360) 664-8438
E: celestem@dor.wa.gov

Ms. Vikki Smith
Director
Department of Revenue
Executive Office
P.O. Box 47450
Olympia, WA 98504
P: (360) 534-1605

WEST VIRGINIA
Ms. Carolyn Atkinson
Deputy Treasurer of Unclaimed Property
State Treasury
One Player's Club Drive
Charleston, WV 25311
P: (304) 341-0703
F: (304) 558-5063
E: carolyn.atkinson@wvsto.com

The Honorable John D. Perdue (D)
State Treasurer
State Treasurer's Office
State Capitol Complex
Building 1, Room E-145
Charleston, WV 25305
P: (304) 558-5000
F: (304) 558-4097

WISCONSIN
The Honorable Matt Adamczyk (R)
State Treasurer
Office of the State Treasurer
B41 West, State Capitol
Madison, WI 53701
P: (608) 266-1714
F: (608) 266-2647
E: Matt.Adamczyk@wisconsin.gov

Unclaimed Property

Ms. Erin Egan
Director
Bureau of Tax Operations
P.O. Box 8982
Madison, WI 53708
P: (608) 264-6997
E: ErinB.Egan
@revenue.wi.gov

WYOMING
The Honorable Mark Gordon
State Treasurer
Office of the State Treasurer
200 West 24th Street
Cheyenne, WY 82002
P: (307) 777-7408
F: (307) 777-5411
E: treasurer@wyo.gov

Veterans Affairs

Provides services and information to the state's veterans, their dependents and survivors.

ALABAMA
Mr. W. Clyde Marsh
Commissioner
Department of Veterans Affairs
P.O. Box 1509
Montgomery, AL 36102
P: (334) 242-5077
F: (334) 242-5102
E: clyde.marsh@va.alabama.gov

ALASKA
Mr. Verdie Bowen
Director
Office of Veterans Affairs
4600 DeBarr Road, Suite 180
Anchorage, AK 99508
P: (907) 334-0874
F: (907) 334-0869
E: verdie.bowen@alaska.gov

ARIZONA
Ms. Wanda Wright
Director
Department of Veterans' Services
3839 North Third Street
Phoenix, AZ 85012
P: (602) 255-3373
F: (602) 255-1038
E: wwright@azdvs.gov

ARKANSAS
Colonel Nathaniel Todd
Director
Department of Veterans Affairs
501 Woodlane Street, Suite 230C
Little Rock, AR 72201
P: (501) 683-2382

CALIFORNIA
Dr. Vito Imbasciani
Secretary
Department of Veterans Affairs
1227 O Street
Sacramento, CA 95814
P: (916) 653-2158
E: vito.imbasciani@calvet.ca.gov

COLORADO
Mr. Ruben Mestas
Director
Division of Veteran Affairs
1355 South Colorado Boulevard
Building C, Suite 113
Denver, CO 80222
P: (303) 284-6077
E: reuben.mestas@dmva.state.co.us

CONNECTICUT
Lieutenant Colonel Sean Connolly
Commissioner
Department of Veterans Affairs
287 West Street
Rocky Hill, CT 06067
P: (860) 616-3602
F: (860) 721-5919
E: Fausto.Parra@ct.gov

DELAWARE
Mr. Lawrence Kirby
Executive Director
Commission of Veterans Affairs
802 Silver Lake Boulevard, Suite 100
Dover, DE 19904
P: (302) 739-2792
F: (302) 739-2794
E: Lawrence.Kirby@state.de.us

DISTRICT OF COLUMBIA
Mr. Ely S. Ross
Director
Office of Veterans Affairs
441 4th Street, Northwest
Suite 870
Washington, DC 20001
P: (202) 724-5454
E: ova@dc.gov

FLORIDA
Mr. Glenn Sutphin
Executive Director
Department of Veterans Affairs
The Capitol, Suite 2105
400 South Monroe Street
Tallahassee, FL 32399
P: (850) 487-1533
E: ExDir@fdva.state.fl.us

GEORGIA
Mr. Mike Roby
Commissioner
Department of Veterans Service
Floyd Veterans Memorial Building
Suite E-970
Atlanta, GA 30334
P: (404) 656-2300
F: (404) 657-9738
E: mroby@vs.state.ga.us

GUAM
Mr. Joe A. San Agustin
Administrator
Veterans Affairs Office
Office of the Governor
P.O. Box 2950
Hagatna, GU 96932
P: (671) 475-8388
E: joe.san.agustin@gvao.guam.gov

HAWAII
Mr. Ron Han
Director
Office of Veterans Services
459 Patterson Road
E-Wing, Room 1-A103
Honolulu, HI 96819
P: (808) 433-0420
F: (808) 433-0385
E: ovs@ovs.hawaii.gov

IDAHO
Mr. David Brasuell
Administrator
Division of Veterans Affairs
351 Collins Road
Boise, ID 83702
P: (208) 780-1300
F: (208) 334-2627
E: david.brasuell@veterans.idaho.gov

ILLINOIS
Ms. Erica Jeffries
Director
Department of Veterans Affairs
P.O. Box 19432
Springfield, IL 62794
P: (217) 782-6641
F: (217) 524-0344
E: erica.jeffries@illinois.gov

INDIANA
Sergeant James M. Brown
Director
Department of Veterans Affairs
302 West Washington Street, Room E-120
Indianapolis, IN 46204
P: (317) 232-3910
F: (317) 232-7721
E: jbrown@dva.in.gov

IOWA
Ms. Jodi Tymeson
Executive Director
Department of Veterans Affairs
Camp Dodge, Building 3465
7105 Northwest 70th Avenue
Johnston, IA 50131
P: (515) 727-3444
F: (515) 242-5659
E: Jodi.Tymeson@iowa.gov

KANSAS
Mr. Gregg Burden
Director
Commission on Veterans' Affairs
700 Southwest Jackson Street
Jayhawk Towers, Suite 1004
Topeka, KS 66603
P: (785) 296-3976
F: (785) 296-1462
E: gburden@kvva.org

KENTUCKY
Brigadier General Norman E. Arflack
Commissioner
Department of Veterans Affairs
1111B Louisville Road
Frankfort, KY 40601
P: (502) 564-9203

LOUISIANA
Mr. Joey Strickland
Secretary
Department of Veterans Affairs
P.O. Box 94095
Baton Rouge, LA 70804
P: (225) 219-5000
F: (225) 922-0511
E: veteran@la.gov

MAINE
Ms. Adria O. Horn
Director
Bureau of Veterans Services
117 State House Station
Augusta, ME 04333
P: (207) 430-6035
F: (207) 626-4471
E: mainebvs@maine.gov

MARYLAND
Mr. George W. Owings III
Secretary
Department of Veterans Affairs
The Wineland Building, 4th Floor
16 Francis Street
Annapolis, MD 21401
P: (410) 260-3838
F: (410) 216-7928
E: secretary.mdva@maryland.gov

MASSACHUSETTS
Mr. Francisco Urena
Secretary
Department of Veterans Services
600 Washington Street, 7th Floor
Boston, MA 02111
P: (617) 210-5779
F: (617) 210-5755
E: MDVS@vet.state.ma.us

Veterans Affairs

MICHIGAN
Mr. James Robert Redford
Director
Veterans Affairs Agency
222 North Washington Square, 5th Floor
P.O. Box 30104
Lansing, MI 48909
P: (800) 642-4838

MINNESOTA
Major General Larry W. Shellito
Commissioner
Department of Veterans Affairs
Central Office
20 West 12th Street, Room 206
St. Paul, MN 55155
P: (651) 296-2562
F: (651) 296-3954
E: larry.shellito@state.mn.us

MISSISSIPPI
Mr. Randy Reeves
Executive Director
Veterans Affairs Board
P.O. Box 5947
Pearl, MS 39288
P: (601) 576-4850
F: (601) 576-4868
E: rreeves@vab.ms.gov

MISSOURI
Mr. Larry D. Kay
Executive Director
Veterans Commission
205 Jefferson Street
12th Floor, Jefferson Building
Jefferson City, MO 65102
P: (573) 751-3779
F: (573) 751-6836
E: larry.kay@mvc.dps.mo.gov

MONTANA
Mr. Joseph S. Foster
Administrator
Veterans Affairs Division
1900 Williams Street
P.O. Box 5715
Helena, MT 59604
P: (406) 324-3741
F: (406) 324-3745
E: jofoster@mt.gov

NEBRASKA
Mr. John Hilgert
Director
Department of Veterans Affairs
301 Centennial Mall South, 1st Floor
P.O. Box 95083
Lincoln, NE 68509
P: (402) 471-2458
F: (402) 471-2491
E: john.hilgert@nebraska.gov

NEVADA
Colonel Katherine Miller
Director
Department of Veterans Services
6880 South McCarran Boulevard
Building A, Suite 12
Reno, NV 89509
P: (775) 688-1653
F: (775) 688-1656
E: millerk@veterans.nv.gov

NEW HAMPSHIRE
Mr. Bobby Broneske
Director
Office of Veterans Services
275 Chestnut Street, Room 517
Manchester, NH 03101
P: (603) 624-9230
E: bobby.broneske@va.gov

NEW JERSEY
Mr. Raymond Zawacki
Deputy Commissioner for Veterans Affairs
Department of Military & Veterans Affairs
P.O. Box 340
Trenton, NJ 08625
P: (609) 530-7045
F: (609) 530-7075
E: raymond.zawacki@njdmava.state.nj.us

NEW MEXICO
Mr. Jack Fox
Secretary
Department of Veterans Services
407 Galisteo Street, Room 142
Santa Fe, NM 87504
P: (866) 433-8387

NEW YORK
Mr. Eric Hesse
Director
Division of Veterans Affairs
Corning Tower, Suite 2836
5 Empire State Plaza
Albany, NY 12223
P: (518) 474-6114
F: (518) 474-6924

NORTH CAROLINA
Mr. Ilario Pantano
Director
Division of Veterans Affairs
1315 Mail Service Center
325 North Salisbury Street
Raleigh, NC 27699
P: (919) 807-4250
F: (919) 807-4260
E: ilario.pantano@doa.nc.gov

NORTH DAKOTA
Mr. Lonnie Wangen
Commissioner
Department of Veterans Affairs
4201 38th Street Southwest, Suite 104
Fargo, ND 58104
P: (701) 239-7165
F: (701) 239-7166
E: lwangen@nd.gov

OHIO
Mr. Chip Tansill
Director
Department of Veterans Services
77 South High Street, 7th Floor
Columbus, OH 43215
P: (614) 644-0898
F: (614) 728-9498
E: chip.tansill@dvs.ohio.gov

OKLAHOMA
Major General Myles L. Deering
Director
Department of Veterans Affairs
2311 North Central
Oklahoma City, OK 73105
P: (405) 523-4000
F: (405) 521-6533
E: mdeering@odva.state.ok.us

OREGON
Mr. Cameron Smith
Director
Department of Veterans Affairs
700 Summer Street, Northeast
Salem, OR 97301
P: (503) 373-2000
F: (503) 373-2362
E: smithc@odva.state.or.us

PENNSYLVANIA
Brigadier General Jerry G. Beck Jr.
Deputy Adjutant General
Department of Military & Veterans Affairs
Fort Indiantown Gap
Building 0-47
Annville, PA 17003
P: (717) 861-8910
F: (717) 861-8589

RHODE ISLAND
Mr. Kasim Yarn
Director
Office of Veterans Affairs
560 Jefferson Boulevard
Warwick, RI 02886
P: (401) 921-2119

SOUTH CAROLINA
Mr. Howard Metcalf
Director
Division of Veterans Affairs
1205 Pendleton Street, Suite 463
Columbia, SC 29201
P: (803) 734-0200
F: (803) 734-0197
E: hmetcalf@oepp.sc.gov

SOUTH DAKOTA
Mr. Larry Zimmerman
Zimmerman
Department of Veterans Affairs
2525 West Main Street, Suite 303A #4
Rapid City, SD 57702
P: (605) 593-7781
F: (605) 773-5380
E: larry.zimmerman@state.sd.us

TENNESSEE
Ms. Many-Bears Grinder
Commissioner
Department of Veterans Services
315 Rosa L. Parks Avenue
Nashville, TN 37243
P: (615) 741-2931
F: (615) 741-4785
E: TN.Veterans@tn.gov

TEXAS
Mr. Thomas Palladino
Executive Director
Veterans Commission
P.O. Box 12277
Austin, TX 78711
P: (512) 463-6564
F: (512) 475-2395
E: executiveoffice@tvc.texas.gov

UTAH
Mr. Gary R. Harter
Executive Director
Department of Veterans & Military Affairs
550 Foothill Drive, Suite 105
Salt Lake City, UT 84113
P: (801) 326-2372
F: (801) 326-2369
E: gharter@utah.gov

VERMONT
Mr. Robert Burke
Director
Office of Veterans Affairs
118 State Street
Montpelier, VT 05620
P: (802) 828-3379
F: (802) 828-5932
E: robert.burke@state.vt.us

VIRGINIA
Mr. John Newby
Commissioner
Department of Veterans Services
101 North 14th Street, 17th Floor
Richmond, VA 23219
P: (804) 786-0286
F: (804) 786-0302
E: Kendra.Ellison@dvs.virginia.gov

WASHINGTON
Ms. Lourdes Alvarado-Ramos
Director
Department of Veterans Affairs
1102 Quince Street, Southeast
P.O. Box 41150
Olympia, WA 98504
P: (800) 562-2308
F: (360) 586-4393

WEST VIRGINIA
Mr. Dennis Davis
Cabinet Secretary
Department of Veterans Assistance
1514-B Kanawha Boulevard, East
Charleston, WV 25311
P: (304) 558-3661
E: dennis.e.davis@wv.gov

WISCONSIN
Mr. Daniel J. Zimmerman
Secretary
Department of Veterans Affairs
201 West Washington Avenue
P.O. Box 7843
Madison, WI 53707
P: (800) 947-8387

WYOMING
Mr. Larry Barttlebort
Director
Veterans Commission
5500 Bishop Boulevard
Cheyenne, WY 82009
P: (307) 777-8151
F: (307) 772-5202
E: larry.barttelbort@wyo.gov

Vital Statistics

Maintains a statewide file of birth, death, marriage and divorce records, and issues certified copies of those records.

ALABAMA
Ms. Catherine Donald
Director
Center for Health Statistics
Department of Public Health
P.O. Box 5625
Montgomery, AL 36103
P: (334) 206-5429
F: (334) 206-2666

ALASKA
Ms. Heidi Lengdorfer
Chief
Health Analytics & Vital Records
Department of Health & Social Services
P.O. Box 110675
Juneau, AK 99811
P: (907) 465-8643
E: heidi.lengdorfer@alaska.gov

ARIZONA
Dr. Cara M. Christ
Director
Department of Health Services
150 North 18th Avenue
Phoenix, AZ 85007
P: (602) 542-1025
F: (602) 542-0833

ARKANSAS
Ms. Martha Robinson
Branch Chief
Division of Vital Records
Department of Health
4815 West Markham Street, Slot 44
Little Rock, AR 72205
P: (501) 661-2336
F: (501) 661-2717
E: martha.robinson@arkansas.gov

CALIFORNIA
Mr. James Clark
Chief
Vital Records Issuance & Preservation Branch
Department of Public Health
P.O. Box 997410
Sacramento, CA 95899
P: (916) 552-8129

COLORADO
Mr. Bob O'Doherty
Director & Chief Information Officer
Health Statistics & Evaluation Branch
Public Health & Environment
4300 Cherry Creek Drive, South
Denver, CO 80246
P: (303) 692-2160
F: (303) 691-7821
E: cdphe.healthstatistics@state.co.us

CONNECTICUT
Ms. Jane Purtill
State Registrar of Vital Records
Vital Records Office
Department of Public Health
410 Capitol Avenue, MS#11VRS
Hartford, CT 06134
P: (860) 509-7895
F: (860) 509-7964
E: jane.purtill@ct.gov

DELAWARE
Ms. Judy Chaconas
Director
Bureau of Health Planning & Resources Management
Jesse Cooper Building
417 Federal Street
Dover, DE 19901
P: (302) 744-4555
F: (302) 739-3313

DISTRICT OF COLUMBIA
Ms. Laura Zeilinger
Director
Department of Human Services
64 New York Avenue, Northeast
6th Floor
Washington, DC 20002
P: (202) 671-4200
F: (202) 671-4326
E: dhs@dc.gov

FLORIDA
Mr. Ken T. Jones
Deputy State Registrar
Bureau of Vital Statistics
Department of Health
P.O. Box 210
Jacksonville, FL 32231
P: (904) 359-6900
F: (904) 359-6931
E: ken.jones@flhealth.gov

GEORGIA
Dr. Brenda C. Fitzgerald
Commissioner & State Health Officer
Department of Public Health
Two Peachtree Street, Northwest
Suite 15-470
Atlanta, GA 30303
P: (404) 657-2703

HAWAII
Dr. Alvin T. Onaka
Chief & State Registrar
Office of Health Status Monitoring
Health Planning & Development Agency
1177 Alakea Street, Room 402
Honolulu, HI 96813
P: (808) 586-4600
F: (808) 586-4606

IDAHO
Mr. James Aydelotte
Chief & State Registrar
Bureau of Vital Records & Health Statistics
450 West State Street
Boise, ID 83702
P: (208) 334-4969
F: (208) 332-8260
E: james.aydelotte@dhw.idaho.gov

ILLINOIS
Dr. Nirav D. Shah
Director of Public Health
Department of Public Health
525-535 West Jefferson Street
Springfield, IL 62761
P: (217) 557-2556
F: (217) 782-3987

INDIANA
Mr. Brian Carnes
Director
Vital Records Division
Department of Health
2 North Meridian Street, Room 2NLL077
Indianapolis, IN 46204
P: (317) 233-7523
F: (317) 233-5956
E: bcarnes@isdh.IN.gov

IOWA
Ms. Jill France
Bureau Chief
Bureau of Health Statistics
Lucas State Office Building
321 East 12th Street
Des Moines, IA 50319
P: (515) 281-4944
E: jill.france@idph.iowa.gov

KANSAS
Dr. Elizabeth W. Saadi
State Registrar
Office of Vital Statistics
Department of Health & Environment
1000 Southwest Jackson
Topeka, KS 66612
P: (785) 296-1400
F: (785) 296-8075
E: kdhe.VitalRecords@ks.gov

LOUISIANA
Ms. Devin D. George
Administrator
Vital Records Registry Program
Department of Health
P.O. Box 629
Baton Rouge, LA 70821
P: (504) 593-5182
F: (504) 568-8716
E: devin.george@la.gov

MAINE
Ms. Roberta L. Fogg
Deputy State Registrar & Supervisor
Office of Data, Research & Vital Statistics
Department of Health & Human Services
11 SHS, 220 Capitol Street
Augusta, ME 04333
P: (207) 287-3181
F: (207) 287-5470
E: roberta.l.fogg@maine.gov

MARYLAND
Dr. Isabelle L. Horon
Director
Vital Statistics Administration
Department of Health & Mental Hygiene
4201 Patterson Avenue, 5th Floor
Baltimore, MD 21215
P: (410) 764-3513
F: (410) 358-4750
E: isabelle.horon@maryland.gov

MASSACHUSETTS
Dr. Monica Bharel
Commissioner
Department of Public Health
250 Washington Street, 2nd Floor
Boston, MA 02108
P: (617) 624-6000

MICHIGAN
Mr. Glenn Copeland
State Registrar & Division Director
Department of Health & Human Services
333 South Grand Avenue
P.O. Box 30195
Lansing, MI 48909
P: (517) 335-8677
F: (517) 335-8711
E: CopelandG@michigan.gov

MINNESOTA
Dr. Edward Ehlinger
Commissioner of Health
Department of Health
625 North Robert Street
P.O. Box 64975
St. Paul, MN 55164
P: (651) 201-5810
F: (651) 201-4986
E: Ed.Ehlinger@state.mn.us

MISSISSIPPI
Ms. Judy Moulder
State Registrar
Public Health Statistics
571 Stadium Drive
P.O. Box 1700
Jackson, MS 39215
P: (601) 206-8200
F: (601) 206-8272
E: jmoulder
@msdh.state.ms.us

MISSOURI
Ms. Michelle Zeilman
Chief
Bureau of Vital Records
Department of Health & Senior Services
P.O. Box 570
Jefferson City, MO 65102
P: (573) 751-6387
F: (573) 526-3846
E: VitalRecordsInfo
@health.mo.gov

MONTANA
Mr. Dean Vig
Vital Records Supervisor
Office of Vital Statistics
111 North Sanders, Room 6
P.O. Box 4210
Helena, MT 59604
P: (406) 444-5249
F: (406) 444-1803
E: dvig@mt.gov

NEVADA
Mr. Jason L. Lewis
Vital Records Program Manager
Division of Public & Behavioral Health
Department of Health & Human Services
4150 Technology Way
Carson City, NV 89706
P: (775) 684-4162
F: (775) 684-4156
E: jalewis@health.nv.gov

NEW HAMPSHIRE
Mr. Steven M. Wurtz
Acting Registrar
Division of Vital Records
Department of State
71 South Fruit Street
Concord, NH 03301
P: (603) 271-4650
F: (603) 271-3447
E: vitalrecords@sos.nh.gov

NEW JERSEY
Ms. Cathleen Bennett
Commissioner
Department of Health
P.O. Box 360
Trenton, NJ 08625
P: (609) 292-7838
F: (609) 292-0053

NEW YORK
Mr. Robert LoCicero
Director, Vital Records
Division of Administration
Department of Health
Corning Tower, Empire State Plaza
Albany, NY 12237
P: (518) 474-5245

NORTH CAROLINA
Ms. Catherine Ryan
Director & State Registrar
Department of Health & Human Services
Vital Records Division
1903 Mail Service Center
Raleigh, NC 27699
P: (919) 733-3000
F: (919) 733-1511
E: catherine.c.ryan
@dhhs.nc.gov

NORTH DAKOTA
Mr. Darin J. Meschke
State Registrar, Director
Division of Vital Records
600 East Boulevard Avenue
Department 301
Bismarck, ND 58505
P: (701) 328-2360
F: (701) 328-1850
E: dmeschke@nd.gov

NORTHERN MARIANA ISLANDS
Mr. John G. Moore
Commonwealth Recorder
Vital Records Section
P.O. Box 500307
Saipan, MP 96950
P: (670) 236-9830
F: (670) 236-9831

OHIO
Ms. Karen Sorrell
Office of Vital Statistics
Department of Health
225 Neilston Street
Columbus, OH 43215
P: (614) 466-2531
E: VitalStat@odh.ohio.gov

OKLAHOMA
Mr. Derek Pate
Director
Center for Health Statistics
State Department of Health
1000 Northeast 10th Street
Oklahoma City, OK 73117
P: (405) 271-6225
F: (405) 270-9061

OREGON
Ms. Jennifer A. Woodward
Section Manager/State Registrar
Center for Health Statistics
State Health Authority
800 Northeast Oregon Street, Suite 205
Portland, OR 97232
P: (971) 673-1190
F: (971) 673-1203
E: jennifer.a.woodward
@state.or.us

PENNSYLVANIA
Ms. Debra Romberger
Director
Division of Vital Records
101 South Mercer Street, Room 401
P.O. Box 1528
New Castle, PA 16103
P: (724) 656-3100
F: (724) 656-3079

PUERTO RICO
Mr. Nicolas
Fernandez-Cornier
Executive Director
Demographic Registry
P.O. Box 11854
San Juan, PR 00910
P: (787) 281-8867
F: (787) 751-5003

RHODE ISLAND
Ms. Roseann Giorgianni
Chief & State Registrar
Center for Vital Records
Department of Health
3 Capitol Hill
Providence, RI 02908
P: (401) 222-2811
F: (401) 222-6548
E: doh.website
@health.ri.gov

SOUTH CAROLINA
Ms. Shae Sutton
Director
Public Health Statistics & Information Services
Health & Environmental Control
2600 Bull Street
Columbia, SC 29201
P: (803) 898-1808

SOUTH DAKOTA
Ms. Mariah Pokorny
State Registrar
Vital Records
Department of Health
207 East Missouri Avenue, Suite 1A
Pierre, SD 57501
P: (605) 773-4961
F: (605) 773-2680
E: vitalrecords@state.sd.us

TENNESSEE
Ms. Catherine Haralson
State Registrar & Director
Vital Records
1st Floor, Andrew Johnson Tower
710 James Robertson Parkway
Nashville, TN 37243
P: (615) 741-1763

TEXAS
Dr. Tara Das
Vital Statistics
Department of State Health Services
P.O.Box 149347
Austin, TX 78714
P: (512) 776-7368
F: (512) 458-7711
E: registrar
@dshs.state.tx.us

Dr. Lisa Wyman
Director
Center for Health Statistics
Department of State Health Services
1100 West 49th Street
Austin, TX 78756
P: (512) 776-7261
F: (512) 776-7332
E: chs-info
@dshs.state.tx.us

U.S. VIRGIN ISLANDS
Ms. Michelle Davis
Commissioner
Department of Health
Charles Harwood Complex
3500 Estate Richmond
Christiansted, VI 00820
P: (340) 718-1311

Vital Statistics

UTAH
Mr. Richard Oborn
Director
Office of Vital Records & Statistics
288 North 1460 West
P.O. Box 141012
Salt Lake City, UT 84114
P: (801) 538-6262
F: (801) 538-7012
E: roborn@utah.gov

VERMONT
Ms. Helen Reid
Director
Division of Health Surveillance
Department of Health
108 Cherry Street, Suite 306
Burlington, VT 05402
P: (802) 863-7300
E: helen.reid@vermont.gov

VIRGINIA
Dr. Marissa J. Levine
Commissioner of Health
Department of Health
109 Governor Street
P.O. Box 2448
Richmond, VA 23218
P: (804) 864-7009
F: (804) 864-7022
E: Marissa.Levine@vdh.virginia.gov

WASHINGTON
Mr. Jerrod Davis
Assistant Secretary
Disease Control & Health Statistics Division
State Department of Health
101 Israel Road, Southeast
Tumwater, WA 98504
P: (360) 236-4204

WEST VIRGINIA
Mr. Gary L. Thompson
State Registrar & Assistant Director
Health Statistics Center
350 Capitol Street, Room 165
Charleston, WV 25301
P: (304) 558-2931
F: (304) 558-1051
E: Gary.L.Thompson@wv.gov

WYOMING
Dr. Guy Beaudoin
Deputy State Registrar
Vital Statistics Services
Department of Health
2300 Capitol Avenue
Cheyenne, WY 82002
P: (307) 777-7591
F: (307) 777-2483

Vocational Rehabilitation

Assists and encourages disabled persons to find suitable employment through training programs.

ALABAMA
Ms. Jane Burdeshaw
Commissioner
Department of Rehabilitation Services
602 South Lawrence Street
P.O. Box 4280
Montgomery, AL 36103
P: (334) 293-7200

ALASKA
Mr. John Cannon
Director
State Rehabilitation Services
Juneau Central Office
801 West 10th Street, Suite A
Juneau, AK 99801
P: (907) 465-6927

AMERICAN SAMOA
Mr. Pete Galea'i
Director
Vocational Rehabilitation
American Samoa Government
ASG Mail 3492
Pago Pago, AS 96799
P: (684) 699-1371
F: (864) 633-2393

ARIZONA
Ms. Kristen Mackey
State Rehabilitation Services
1789 West Jefferson, 2nd Floor Northwest
P.O. Box 6123
Phoenix, AZ 85005
P: (602) 364-2907

ARKANSAS
Mr. Alan McClain
Commissioner
State Rehabilitation Services
525 West Capitol Avenue
Little Rock, AR 72201
P: (501) 296-1616

Ms. Katy Morris
Director
Division of Services for the Blind
700 Main Street, Slot S101
Little Rock, AR 72201
P: (501) 682-0360
F: (501) 682-0366
E: katy.morris@arkansas.gov

CALIFORNIA
Mr. Joe Xavier
Director
Department of Rehabilitation
721 Capitol Mall
Sacramento, CA 95814
P: (916) 558-5800

COLORADO
Mr. Steve Anton
Division of Vocational Rehabilitation
Department of Human Services
1575 Sherman Street, 4th Floor
Denver, CO 80203
P: (303) 866-4889

CONNECTICUT
Mr. David Doukas
Director
State Rehabilitation Services
Department of Social Services
25 Sigourney Street, 11th Floor
Hartford, CT 06106
P: (860) 424-4862

Mr. Brian S. Sigman
Director of Education & Rehabilitation
Bureau of Education & Services for the Blind
184 Windsor Avenue
Windsor, CT 06095
P: (860) 602-4008
F: (860) 602-4030
E: brian.sigman@ct.gov

DELAWARE
Ms. Andrea Guest
Director
Division of Vocational Rehabilitation
Department of Labor
4425 North Market Street, P.O. Box 9969
Wilmington, DE 19809
P: (302) 761-8275
F: (302) 761-6611

Ms. Elisha Jenkins
Division for the Visually Impaired
Health & Social Services, Biggs Building
1901 North DuPont Highway
New Castle, DE 19720
P: (302) 255-9800

DISTRICT OF COLUMBIA
Ms. Pamela Downing-Hosten
Department on Disability Services
One Independence Square
250 E Street, Southwest
Washington, DC 20024
P: (202) 442-8663

FLORIDA
Mr. Robert Doyle
Director
Division of Blind Services
325 West Gaines Street
Turlington Building, Room 1114
Tallahassee, FL 32399
P: (850) 245-0331

Ms. Aleisa McKinlay
Director
Division of Vocational Rehabilitation
Department of Education
4070 Esplanade Way, 2nd Floor
Tallahassee, FL 32399
P: (850) 245-3311
F: (850) 245-3316

GEORGIA
Mr. Sean Casey
Executive Director
Vocational Rehabilitation Agency
200 Piedmont Avenue
West Tower Suite 1408
Atlanta, GA 30334
P: (404) 232-1880

GUAM
Ms. Rita Sotomayor
Director, Division of Vocational Rehabilitation
Department of Integrated Services for Individuals with Disabilities
Suite 602 DNA Building
238 AFC Flores Street
Hagatna, GU 96910
P: (671) 475-5735

HAWAII
Mr. Albert Perez
Administrator
State Rehabilitation Services
1901 Bachelot Street
Honolulu, HI 96817
P: (808) 586-9741

IDAHO
Ms. Beth Cunningham
Administrator
Commission for the Blind & Visually Impaired
341 West Washington Street
P.O. Box 83720
Boise, ID 83720
P: (208) 334-3220 Ext. 123

Ms. Jane Donnellan
Administrator
Division of Vocational Rehabilitation
650 West State Street, Room 150
P.O. Box 83720-0096
Boise, ID 83720
P: (208) 287-6477

ILLINOIS
Ms. Quinetta Wade
Director, Division of Rehabilitation Services
Department of Human Services
100 South Grand Avenue
P.O. Box 19429
Springfield, IL 62704
P: (217) 557-0401

INDIANA
Ms. Theresa Koleszar
Director
Bureau of Rehabilitation Services
402 West Washington Street
IGCS/W453/MS 20
Indianapolis, IN 46204
P: (317) 232-1432

IOWA
Mr. David Mitchell
Administrator
Vocational Rehabilitation Services
Department of Education
510 East 12th Street
Des Moines, IA 50319
P: (515) 281-6731
F: (515) 281-4703
E: david.mitchell@iowa.gov

Ms. Emily Wharton
Director
Department for the Blind
524 Fourth Street
Des Moines, IA 50309
P: (515) 281-1334

KENTUCKY
Ms. Becky Cabe
Assistant Director of Consumer Services
Office of Vocational Rehabilitation
Education Cabinet
275 East Main Street, Mail Drop 2-EK
Frankfort, KY 40621
P: (502) 782-3417
E: Becky.Cabe@ky.gov

Vocational Rehabilitation

Ms. Cora McNabb
VR Administrator, Training & HRD
Office for the Blind
275 East Main Street, Mail Stop 2 E-J
Frankfort, KY 40621
P: (502) 564-3416
E: Cora.McNabb@ky.gov

LOUISIANA
Mr. Mark Martin
Director
Rehabilitation Services
P.O. Box 91297
Baton Rouge, LA 70821
P: (225) 219-2231
F: (225) 219-2942

MAINE
Ms. Brenda Drummond
Division for the Blind & Visually Impaired
150 State House Station
Augusta, ME 04333
P: (207) 623-7956

Ms. Elizabeth Hopkins
Director
Division of Vocational Rehabilitation
150 State House Station
Augusta, ME 04333
P: (207) 623-6745
F: (207) 287-5292

MARYLAND
Ms. Suzanne Page
Assistant State Superintendent
Division of Rehabilitation Services
Department of Education
2301 Argonne Drive
Baltimore, MD 21218
P: (410) 554-9385
F: (410) 554-9384

MASSACHUSETTS
Ms. Adelaide Nicky Osborn
State Rehabilitation Commission
27 Wormwood Street
Boston, MA 02210
P: (617) 204-3600
F: (617) 727-1354

Mr. Paul Saner
Commissioner
Commission for the Blind
48 Boylston Street
Boston, MA 02210
P: (617) 626-7503

MICHIGAN
Ms. Suzanne Howell
Director
Rehabilitation Services
201 North Washington Square
P.O. Box 30010
Lansing, MI 48909
P: (517) 373-7457

Mr. William Robinson
Bureau of Services for Blind Persons
201 North Washington Square
P.O. Box 30652
Lansing, MI 48909
P: (517) 335-4265

MINNESOTA
Ms. Carol Pankow
Director
State Services for the Blind
2200 University Avenue West, Suite 240
St. Paul, MN 55114
P: (651) 539-2272

Ms. Kimberley T. Peck
Director, Rehabilitation Services Branch
Department of Employment & Economic Development
First National Bank Building
332 Minnesota Street, Suite #E200
St. Paul, MN 55101
P: (651) 259-7345
F: (651) 297-5159

MISSISSIPPI
Mr. Chris Howard
Executive Director
Department of Rehabilitation Services
1281 Highway 51 (Madison, MN 39110)
P.O. Box 1698
Jackson, MS 39215
P: (601) 853-5203

MISSOURI
Mr. Kevin Faust
Deputy Director
Rehabilitation Services for the Blind
615 Howerton Court
P.O. Box 2320
Jefferson City, MO 65102
P: (573) 751-4249
F: (573) 751-4984

Dr. C. Jeanne Loyd
Assistant Commissioner
Vocational Rehabilitation
3024 Dupont Circle
Jefferson City, MO 65109
P: (573) 751-3251
F: (573) 751-1441
E: info@vr.dese.mo.gov

MONTANA
Mr. Jim Marks
Administrator, Vocational Rehabilitation
Disability Transitions Programs
111 North Last Chance Gulch, Suite 4C
P.O. Box 4210
Helena, MT 59604
P: (406) 444-2591
F: (406) 444-3632

NEBRASKA
Mr. Mark Schultz
Assistant Commissioner & Director, Vocational Rehabilitation
Department of Education
6th Floor, 301 Centennial Mall South
P.O. Box 94987
Lincoln, NE 68509
P: (402) 471-3649
F: (402) 471-0788

Ms. Pearl VanZandt
Executive Director
Commission for the Blind & Visually Impaired
4600 Valley Road, Suite 100
Lincoln, NE 68510
P: (402) 471-2891
F: (402) 471-3009

NEVADA
Ms. Shelley Hendren
Administrator, Rehabilitation Division
Department of Employment, Training & Rehabilitation
3016 West Charleston Boulevard Suite 215
Las Vegas, NV 89102
P: (702) 486-0372

NEW HAMPSHIRE
Ms. Lisa K. Hinson-Hatz
State Director
State Rehabilitation Services
21 South Fruit Street, Suite 20
Concord, NH 03301
P: (603) 271-7080
F: (603) 271-7095
E: lhatz@ed.state.nh.us

NEW JERSEY
Mr. Daniel Frye
Executive Director
Commission for the Blind & Visually Impaired
153 Halsey Street
P.O. Box 47017
Newark, NJ 07101
P: (973) 648-2324

Ms. Alice Hunnicut
Director
Division of Vocational Rehabilitation Services
135 East State Street
P.O. Box 398
Trenton, NJ 08625
P: (609) 292-7318
F: (609) 292-4033

NEW MEXICO
Mr. Joe Cordova
Division of Vocational Rehabilitation
435 St. Michael's Drive, Building D
Santa Fe, NM 87505
P: (505) 954-8517

Mr. Greg Trapp
Executive Director
Commission for the Blind
2200 Yale Boulevard, Southeast
Albuquerque, NM 87106
P: (505) 827-4479
F: (505) 827-4475

NEW YORK
Ms. Debora Brown-Johnson
Assistant Commissioner
Vocational & Educational Services for People with Disabilities
State Education Department
One Commerce Plaza, Room 1606
Albany, NY 12234
P: (518) 474-2714

Mr. Brian Daniels
Director
Commission for the Blind & Visually Impaired
40 North Pearl Street
Albany, NY 12243
P: (518) 474-6812
F: (518) 486-5819

NORTH CAROLINA
Ms. Tara Myers
Division of Vocational Rehabilitation Services
Department of Health & Human Services
2801 Mail Service Center
Raleigh, NC 27699
P: (919) 855-3563

Ms. Cynthia Speight
Interim Director
Division of Services for the Blind
309 Ashe Avenue, Fisher Building
2601 Mail Service Center
Raleigh, NC 27699
P: (919) 733-9822 Ext. 212

NORTH DAKOTA
Mr. Russell Cusack
Director
Division of Vocational Rehabilitation
Prairie Hills Plaza
1237 West Divide Avenue, Suite #1B
Bismarck, ND 58501
P: (701) 328-8926
F: (701) 328-8969

NORTHERN MARIANA ISLANDS
Ms. Arlene Kay Yamagata
Director
Office of Vocational Rehabilitation
Navy Hill Building, N-2
P.O. Box 501521
Saipan, MP 96950
P: (670) 322-6448

OHIO
Mr. Kevin Miller
Executive Director
Opportunities for Ohioians with Disabilities
400 East Campus View Boulevard
Columbus, OH 43235
P: (614) 438-1200
F: (614) 985-7906

OKLAHOMA
Mr. Noel Tyler
Department of Rehabilitation Services
3535 Northwest 58th Street, Suite 500
Oklahoma City, OK 73112
P: (405) 951-3400

OREGON
Ms. Dacia Johnson
Administrator
State Commission for the Blind
535 Southeast 12th Avenue
Portland, OR 97214
P: (971) 673-1588

Ms. Trina Lee
Administrator
Office of Vocational Rehabilitation Services
Department of Human Services
500 Summer Street, Northeast, E-87
Salem, OR 97301
P: (503) 945-5949

PENNSYLVANIA
Mr. David DeNotaris
Deputy Secretary
Office of Vocational Rehabilitation
Department of Labor & Industry
1521 North 6th Street
Harrisburg, PA 17102
P: (717) 787-7312

PUERTO RICO
Mr. Jose Ortiz
Vocational Rehabilitation Administration
P.O. Box 191118
San Juan, PR 00919
P: (787) 729-0160

RHODE ISLAND
Mr. Ronald Racine
Administrator
Office of Rehabilitation Services
Department of Human Services
40 Fountain Street
Providence, RI 02903
P: (401) 462-7888

SOUTH CAROLINA
Mr. Neil Getsinger
Commissioner
Vocational Rehabilitation Department
1410 Boston Avenue
P.O. Box 15
West Columbia, SC 29170
P: (803) 896-6504

Mr. James Kirby
Commissioner
Commission for the Blind
1430 Confederate Avenue
P.O. Box 2467
Columbia, SC 29202
P: (803) 898-8700
F: (803) 898-8852

SOUTH DAKOTA
Ms. Gaye Mattke
Director
Services for the Blind
East Highway 34
C/o 500 East Capitol
Pierre, SD 57501
P: (605) 773-5114
F: (605) 773-5483

Mr. Eric Weiss
Director
Division of Rehabilitation Services
3800 East Highway 34
C/o 500 East Capitol
Pierre, SD 57501
P: (605) 773-3195
F: (605) 773-5483

TENNESSEE
Ms. Cherrell Campbell-Street
Rehabilitation & Community Social Services
10th Floor, Citizens Plaza Building
400 Deaderick Street
Nashville, TN 37243
P: (615) 313-4713

TEXAS
Mr. Cheryl Fuller
Assistant Commissioner
State Workforce Commission
4900 North Lamar Boulevard, Suite 5667
Austin, TX 78751
P: (512) 424-4220

U.S. VIRGIN ISLANDS
Mr. Felicia Blyden
Commissioner
Department of Human Services
3011 Golden Rock
Christiansted
St. Croix, VI 00802
P: (340) 718-2980

UTAH
Mr. Darin Brush
Director
State Office of Rehabilitation
250 East 500, South
P.O. Box 144200
Salt Lake City, UT 84114
P: (801) 538-7547

VERMONT
Mr. Fred Jones
Director
Divsion of Services for the Blind & Visually Impaired
Department of Aging
HC 2 South, 280 State Drive
Waterbury, VT 05671
P: (802) 241-0326
F: (802) 241-2210
E: Fred.Jones@ahs.state.vt.us

VIRGINIA
Mr. Ray Hopkins
Commissioner
Department for the Blind & Vision Impaired
397 Azalea Avenue
Richmond, VA 23227
P: (804) 371-3145
F: (804) 371-3157

Mr. James Rothrock
Commissioner
Department of Rehabilitative Services
8004 Franklin Farms Drive
Henrico, VA 23229
P: (804) 662-7010
F: (804) 662-7644

WASHINGTON
Ms. Lou Durand
Director
Department of Services for the Blind
P.O. Box 40933
Olympia, WA 98504
P: (360) 725-3835
F: (360) 407-0679
E: loudurand@dsb.wa.gov

Mr. Robert Hines
Division of Vocational Services
P.O. Box 45340
Olympia, WA 98504
P: (360) 725-3610

WEST VIRGINIA
Ms. Marijane Waldron
Division of Rehabilitation Services
State Capitol
P.O. Box 50890
Charleston, WV 25305
P: (304) 356-2058

Vocational Rehabilitation

WISCONSIN
Ms. Delora Newton
Administrator
Division of Vocational Rehabilitation
201 East Washington Avenue, #G100
P.O. Box 7852
Madison, WI 53707
P: (608) 261-0050

WYOMING
Mr. Jim McIntosh
Administrator
Division of Vocational Rehabilitation
Department of Employment
1100 Herschler Building
Cheyenne, WY 82002
P: (307) 777-7389
F: (307) 777-5939

Waste Management

Develops and maintains a comprehensive waste management program in the state.

ALABAMA
Ms. Debi Thomas
Executive Assistant
Environmental Management Commission
1400 Coliseum Boulevard
P.O. Box 301463
Montgomery, AL 36130
P: (334) 271-7706
F: (334) 279-3052

ARIZONA
Ms. Laura L. Malone
Waste Programs Division Director
Department of Environmental Quality
1110 West Washington Street
Phoenix, AZ 85007
P: (602) 771-4208
F: (602) 771-2302
E: malone.laura@azdeq.gov

CALIFORNIA
Mr. Scott Smithline
Director
Department of Resources, Recycling & Recovery
1001 I Street
P.O. Box 4025
Sacramento, CA 95812
P: (916) 322-4032
F: (916) 319-7227
E: Scott.Smithline@CalRecycle.ca.gov

COLORADO
Mr. Gary Baughman
Director
Hazardous Materials & Waste Management Division
Public Health & Environment
4300 Cherry Creek Drive, South
Denver, CO 80246
P: (303) 692-3338
F: (303) 759-5355
E: gary.baughman@state.co.us

CONNECTICUT
Mr. Robert Isner
Director
Waste Engineering & Enforcement Division
Energy & Environmental Protection
79 Elm Street
Hartford, CT 06106
P: (860) 424-3023
F: (860) 424-4059
E: robert.isner@ct.gov

DELAWARE
Ms. Nancy C. Marker
Administrator
Solid & Hazardous Waste Management Section
89 Kings Highway
Dover, DE 19901
P: (302) 739-9403
F: (302) 739-5060
E: nancy.marker@state.de.us

DISTRICT OF COLUMBIA
Mr. Christopher Shorter
Director
Department of Public Works
Frank D. Reeves Municipal Center
2000 14th Street, Northwest
Washington, DC 20009
P: (202) 673-6833
F: (202) 671-0642
E: dpw@dc.gov

FLORIDA
Mr. Joe Ullo
Director
Division of Waste Management
Department of Environmental Protection
2600 Blair Stone Road
Tallahassee, FL 32399
P: (850) 245-8693
E: joseph.ullo@dep.state.fl.us

GEORGIA
Mr. Jeff Cown
Branch Chief
Land Protection Branch
2 Martin Luther King Jr. Drive Southeast
Suite 1054, East Floyd Tower
Atlanta, GA 30334
P: (404) 463-8509
F: (404) 362-2693
E: jeff.cown@dnr.ga.gov

HAWAII
Mr. Steven Y.K. Chang
Branch Chief
Solid & Hazardous Waste Branch
Department of Health
919 Ala Moana Boulevard, #212
Honolulu, HI 96814
P: (808) 586-4226
F: (808) 586-7509
E: schang@eha.health.state.hi.us

IDAHO
Mr. Michael McCurdy
Administrator
Waste Management & Remediation Division
DEQ State Office
1410 North Hilton
Boise, ID 83706
P: (208) 373-0188
F: (208) 373-0154
E: michael.mccurdy@deq.idaho.gov

ILLINOIS
Mr. Alec Messina
Director
Environmental Protection Agency
1021 North Grand Avenue, East
P.O. Box 19276
Springfield, IL 62794
P: (217) 782-3397

INDIANA
Ms. Peggy Dorsey
Assistant Commissioner, Office of Land Quality
Department of Environmental Management
Government Center North
100 North Senate Avenue
Indianapolis, IN 46204
P: (317) 234-0337
F: (317) 233-6647
E: PDorsey@idem.IN.gov

KANSAS
Mr. William L. Bider
Director
Bureau of Waste Management
Department of Health & Environment
1000 Southwest Jackson Street, Suite 320
Topeka, KS 66612
P: (785) 296-1600
F: (785) 296-1612
E: William.Bider@ks.gov

KENTUCKY
Mr. Jon Maybriar
Division Director
Division of Waste Management
Department for Environmental Protection
300 Sower Boulevard, 2nd Floor
Frankfort, KY 40601
P: (502) 564-6702
F: (502) 564-4245
E: jon.maybriar@ky.gov

LOUISIANA
Ms. Lourdes Iturralde
Assistant Secretary
Office of Environmental Compliance
Department of Environmental Quality
P.O. Box 4312
Baton Rouge, LA 70821
P: (225) 219-3710
F: (225) 219-3708
E: deqoec@la.gov

MARYLAND
Ms. Hilary Miller
Director
Land Management Administration
Department of the Environment
1800 Washington Boulevard
Baltimore, MD 21230
P: (410) 537-3314
F: (410) 537-3321
E: hilary.miller@maryland.gov

MASSACHUSETTS
Mr. Martin Suuberg
Commissioner
Department of Environmental Protection
One Winter Street
Boston, MA 02108
P: (617) 292-5500
F: (617) 574-6880

MINNESOTA
Mr. John Linc Stine
Commissioner
Pollution Control Agency
520 Lafayette Road, North
St. Paul, MN 55155
P: (651) 757-2014
F: (651) 296-6334
E: john.stine@state.mn.us

Waste Management

MISSISSIPPI
Mr. Gary Rikard
Executive Director
Department of Environmental Quality
P. O. Box 2261
Jackson, MS 39225
P: (601) 961-5000
F: (601) 961-5093
E: gary_rikard@deq.state.ms.us

MISSOURI
Mr. Chris Nagel
Program Director
Solid Waste Management Program
Department of Natural Resources
P.O. Box 176
Jefferson City, MO 65102
P: (573) 751-5401
F: (573) 526-3902
E: swmp@dnr.mo.gov

NEBRASKA
Mr. Jim Macy
Director
Department of Environmental Quality
1200 N Street, Suite 400
P.O. Box 98922
Lincoln, NE 68509
P: (402) 471-2186
F: (402) 471-2909
E: Jim.Macy@nebraska.gov

NEVADA
Mr. Bradley Crowell
Director
Department of Conservation & Natural Resources
901 South Stewart Street, Suite 1003
Carson City, NV 89701
P: (775) 684-2700
F: (775) 684-2715
E: bcrowell@dcnr.nv.gov

Mr. Eric Noack
Bureau Chief
Bureau of Waste Management
Division of Environmental Protection
901 South Stewart Street, Suite 4001
Carson City, NV 89701
P: (775) 687-9366
F: (775) 687-6396
E: enoack@ndep.nv.gov

NEW HAMPSHIRE
Mr. John Duclos
Bureau Administrator
Hazardous Waste Management Bureau
Department of Environmental Services
29 Hazen Drive, P.O. Box 95
Concord, NH 03301
P: (603) 271-1998
F: (603) 271-2456
E: john.duclos@des.nh.gov

NEW JERSEY
Mr. Ray Bukowski
Assistant Commissioner, Compliance & Enforcement
Department of Environmental Protection
401 East State Street
P.O. Box 420
Trenton, NJ 08625
P: (609) 984-3285
F: (609) 292-9938

NEW MEXICO
Mr. John E. Kielng
Chief
Hazardous Waste Bureau
State Environment Department
2905 Rodeo Park Drive East, Building 1
Santa Fe, NM 87505
P: (505) 476-6035
F: (505) 476-6030
E: john.kielng@state.nm.us

NEW YORK
Mr. Basil Seggos
Commissioner
Department of Environmental Conservation
625 Broadway
Albany, NY 12233
P: (518) 402-8545
F: (518) 402-8541

NORTH CAROLINA
Mr. Michael Scott
Director
Department of Environment & Natural Resources
Division of Waste Management
217 West Jones Street
Raleigh, NC 27603
P: (919) 707-8246
E: michael.scott@ncdenr.gov

NORTH DAKOTA
Mr. Scott Radig
Director
Division of Waste Management
Department of Health
918 East Divide Avenue, 3rd Floor
Bismark, ND 58501
P: (701) 328-5166
F: (701) 328-5200
E: sradig@nd.gov

NORTHERN MARIANA ISLANDS
Mr. James A. Ada
Secretary
Department of Public Works
Caller Box 10007, Capitol Hill
Saipan, MP 96950
P: (670) 235-5827
F: (670) 235-6346

OHIO
Ms. Terrie TerMeer
Chief
Division of Materials & Waste Management
50 West Town Street, Suite 700
P.O. Box 1049
Columbus, OH 43216
P: (614) 728-0017
F: (614) 728-5315
E: terrie.termeer@epa.ohio.gov

OKLAHOMA
Ms. Kelly Dixon
Division Director
Land Protection Division
Department of Environmental Quality
P.O. Box 1677
Oklahoma City, OK 73101
P: (405) 702-5100
F: (405) 702-5101
E: kelly.dixon@deq.ok.gov

OREGON
Mr. Richard Whitman
Interim Director
Department of Environmental Quality
700 Northeast Multnomah Street Suite 600
Portland, OR 97232
P: (503) 229-5696
F: (503) 229-5850

PENNSYLVANIA
Mr. Walt Harner
Bureau Director
Bureau of Waste Management
Department of Environmental Protection
P.O. Box 69170
Harrisburg, PA 17106
P: (717) 783-2388
F: (717) 787-1904
E: ra-epwaste@pa.gov

PUERTO RICO
Mr. Nelson J. Santiago Marrero
Executive Director
Solid Waste Management Authority
P.O. Box 40285
San Juan, PR 00940
P: (787) 765-7575
F: (787) 753-2220

RHODE ISLAND
Ms. Janet Coit
Director
Department of Environmental Management
235 Promenade Street
Providence, RI 02908
P: (401) 222-6800
F: (401) 222-6802
E: janet.coit@dem.ri.gov

SOUTH CAROLINA
Ms. Myra Reece
Director of Environmental Affairs
Department of Health & Environmental Control
2600 Bull Street
Columbia, SC 29201
P: (803) 898-3432
F: (803) 896-4001
E: info@dhec.sc.gov

SOUTH DAKOTA
Ms. Vonni Kallemeyn
Environmental Scientist Manager
Department of Environment & Natural Resources
Waste Management Program
523 East Capitol Avenue
Pierre, SD 57501
P: (605) 773-3153
F: (605) 773-6035
E: denrinternet@state.sd.us

TENNESSEE
Mr. Patrick J. Flood
Environmental Program Administrator
Division of Solid Waste Management
312 Rosa L. Parks Avenue
Nashville, TN 37243
P: (615) 532-0792
F: (615) 532-0886
E: Pat.Flood@tn.gov

TEXAS
Mr. Brent Wade
Deputy Director
Office of Waste
12100 Park 35 Circle
P.O. Box 13087
Austin, TX 78711
P: (512) 239-6566
F: (512) 239-0659

U.S. VIRGIN ISLANDS
Mr. Gustav James
Commissioner
Department of Public Works
6002 Estate Anna's Hope
Christiansted
St. Croix, VI 00820
P: (340) 773-1290
F: (340) 778-8906

UTAH
Mr. Scott Anderson
Director
Division of Waste Management & Radiation Control
Department of Environmental Quality
P.O. Box 144880
Salt Lake City, UT 84114
P: (801) 536-0203
F: (801) 536-0222
E: standerson@utah.gov

VERMONT
Mr. Chuck Schwer
Director
Waste Management & Prevention Division
One National Life Drive
Davis Building, 1st Floor
Montpelier, VT 05620
P: (802) 249-5324
F: (802) 828-1011
E: chuck.schwer@vermont.gov

VIRGINIA
Mr. David K. Paylor
Director
Department of Environmental Quality
629 East Main Street
P.O. Box 1105
Richmond, VA 23219
P: (804) 698-4000
F: (804) 698-4019
E: david.paylor@deq.virginia.gov

WASHINGTON
Ms. Maia Bellon
Ecology Director
Department of Ecology
300 Desmond Drive, Southeast
Lacey, WA 98503
P: (360) 407-6000
F: (360) 407-6989
E: maib461@ecy.wa.gov

WEST VIRGINIA
Mr. Scott G. Mandirola
Division Director
Division of Water & Waste Management
Department of Environmental Protection
601 57th Street Southeast, Room 2119
Charleston, WV 25304
P: (304) 926-0499
F: (304) 926-0463
E: Scott.G.Mandirola@wv.gov

WISCONSIN
Mr. Pat Stevens
Division Administrator
Division of Air, Waste & Remediation & Redevelopment
P.O. Box 7921
Madison, WI 53707
P: (608) 264-9210
F: (608) 267-2768
E: Patrick.Stevens@Wisconsin.gov

WYOMING
Mr. Luke Esch
Administrator
Solid & Hazardous Waste Division
Department of Environmental Quality
200 West 17th Street, 2nd Floor
Cheyenne, WY 82002
P: (307) 777-7192
F: (307) 635-1784
E: luke.esch1@wyo.gov

Water Resources

Responsible for water conservation, development, use and planning in the state.

ALABAMA
Mr. James Atkins
Division Chief
Office of Water Resources
401 Adams Avenue
P.O. Box 5690
Montgomery, AL 36103
P: (334) 242-5499
F: (334) 242-5099
E: James.Atkins@adeca.alabama.gov

ALASKA
Mr. David W. Schade
Chief of the Water Resources Section
Division of Mining, Land & Water
Department of Natural Resources
550 West 7th Avenue, Suite 1020
Anchorage, AK 99501
P: (907) 269-8645
F: (907) 269-8904
E: david.w.schade@alaska.gov

AMERICAN SAMOA
Mr. Ute Abe Malae
Executive Director
American Samoa Power Authority
P.O Box PPB
1st Road Airport
Pago Pago, AS 96799
P: (684) 699-1234
F: (684) 699-4329
E: utum@aspower.com

ARIZONA
Mr. Thomas Buschatzke
Director
Department of Water Resources
1110 West Washington, Suite 310
Phoenix, AZ 85007
P: (602) 771-8426
F: (602) 771-8678
E: tbuschatzke@azwater.gov

ARKANSAS
Mr. Bruce Holland
Executive Director
Natural Resources Commission
101 East Capitol Avenue, Suite 350
Little Rock, AR 72201
P: (501) 682-3961
F: (501) 682-3991
E: bruce.holland@arkansas.gov

CALIFORNIA
Mr. Mark W. Cowin
Director
Department of Water Resources
1416 Ninth Street, Room 1115-1
P.O. Box 942836
Sacramento, CA 94236
P: (916) 653-5791
F: (916) 653-4684
E: Janiene.friend@water.ca.gov

COLORADO
Ms. Lauren Ris
Assistant Director for Water
Department of Natural Resources
1313 Sherman Street, Room 718
Denver, CO 80203
P: (303) 866-3311
E: lauren.ris@state.co.us

CONNECTICUT
Mr. Brian Thompson
Director
Land & Water Resources Division
Energy & Environmental Protection
79 Elm Street
Hartford, CT 06106
P: (860) 424-3019
F: (860) 424-4075
E: brian.thompson@ct.gov

DELAWARE
Mr. Virgil R. Holmes
Director
Division of Water
89 Kings Highway
Dover, DE 19901
P: (302) 739-9949
F: (302) 739-7864
E: Virgil.Holmes@state.de.us

DISTRICT OF COLUMBIA
Mr. George S. Hawkins
CEO & General Manager
Water & Sewer Authority
5000 Overlook Avenue, Southwest
P.O. Box 97200
Washington, DC 20090
P: (202) 787-2000
F: (202) 787-2333
E: info@dcwater.com

FLORIDA
Mr. Justin Green
Director
Water Resource Management
Department of Environmental Protection
2600 Blair Stone Road, M.S. 3500
Tallahassee, FL 32399
P: (850) 245-8336
F: (850) 245-8356
E: justin.b.green@dep.state.fl.us

GEORGIA
Mr. James A. Capp
Branch Chief
Watershed Protection Branch
2 Martin Luther King Jr. Drive
Suite 1152 East
Atlanta, GA 30334
P: (404) 463-4911
F: (404) 651-8455

GUAM
Mr. Miguel C. Bordallo
General Manager
Waterworks Authority
P.O. Box 3010
Hagatna, GU 96932
P: (671) 300-6845
F: (671) 648-3290
E: mcbordallo@guamwaterworks.org

HAWAII
Mr. Jeffrey T. Pearson
Deputy Director
Commission on Water Resource Management
Department of Land & Water Resources
1151 Punchbowl Street, Room 227
Honolulu, HI 96813
P: (808) 587-0214
F: (808) 587-0219
E: dlnr.cwrm@hawaii.gov

IDAHO
Mr. Gary Spackman
Director
Department of Water Resources
322 East Front Street
P.O. Box 83720
Boise, ID 83720
P: (208) 287-4800
F: (208) 287-6700
E: gary.spackman@idwr.idaho.gov

ILLINOIS
Mr. Dan Injerd
Director
Office of Water Resources
1 Natural Resources Way
Springfield, IL 62702
P: (217) 785-3334
F: (217) 785-5014

IOWA
Mr. Jon Tack
Bureau Chief
Water Quality Bureau
Department of Natural Resources
502 East 9th Street
Des Moines, IA 50319
P: (515) 725-8401
F: (515) 725-8202
E: jon.tack@dnr.iowa.gov

KANSAS
Mr. David W. Barfield
Chief Engineer
Division of Water Resources
Department of Agriculture
900 Southwest Jackson, Room 456
Topeka, KS 66612
P: (785) 564-6640
F: (785) 564-6778
E: David.Barfield@ks.gov

Mr. Tracy D. Streeter
Director
Kansas Water Office
900 Southwest Jackson Street, Suite 404
Topeka, KS 66612
P: (785) 296-3185
F: (785) 296-0878
E: tracy.streeter@kwo.ks.gov

KENTUCKY
Mr. Pete Goodmann
Director
Division of Water
Department for Environmental Protection
200 Fair Oaks Lane, Fourth Floor
Frankfort, KY 40601
P: (502) 564-3410
F: (502) 564-0111
E: water@ky.gov

LOUISIANA
The Honorable Richard P. Ieyoub (D)
Commissioner of Conservation
Office of Conservation
Department of Natural Resources
P.O. Box 94275
Baton Rouge, LA 70804
P: (225) 342-5540
F: (225) 342-3705
E: richard.ieyoub@la.gov

MAINE
Mr. Paul Mercer
Commissioner
Department of Environmental Protection
17 State House Station
28 Tyson Drive
Augusta, ME 04333
P: (207) 287-7688
F: (207) 287-2814
E: paul.mercer@maine.gov

MARYLAND
Mr. William C. Anderson
Assistant Secretary for Aquatic Resources
Department of Natural Resources
Tawes State Office Building
580 Taylor Avenue
Annapolis, MD 21401
P: (410) 260-8109
E: bill.anderson@maryland.gov

MASSACHUSETTS
Mr. Matthew A. Beaton
Secretary of Energy and Environmental Affairs
Executive Office of Energy & Environmental Affairs
100 Cambridge Street, Suite 900
Boston, MA 02114
P: (614) 626-1000
F: (614) 626-4900
E: env.internet@state.ma.us

MINNESOTA
Mr. John Linc Stine
Commissioner
Pollution Control Agency
520 Lafayette Road, North
St. Paul, MN 55155
P: (651) 757-2014
F: (651) 296-6334
E: john.stine@state.mn.us

MISSISSIPPI
Mr. Kay Whittington
Director
Office of Land & Water Resources
700 North State Street
P.O. Box 2309
Jackson, MS 39225
P: (601) 961-5729
F: (601) 961-5228

MONTANA
Mr. John Tubbs
Director
Department of Natural Resources & Conservation
1539 Eleventh Avenue
P.O. Box 201601
Helena, MT 59620
P: (406) 444-2074
F: (406) 444-2684

NEBRASKA
Mr. Gordon W. Fassett
Director
Department of Natural Resources
301 Centennial Mall South
P.O. Box 94676
Lincoln, NE 68509
P: (402) 471-2366
F: (402) 471-2900
E: jeff.fassett@nebraska.gov

NEVADA
Mr. Jason King
State Engineer
Department of Conservation & Natural Resources
Division of Water Resources
901 South Stewart Street, Suite 2002
Carson City, NV 89701
P: (775) 684-2861
F: (775) 684-2811
E: jking@water.nv.gov

NEW HAMPSHIRE
Mr. Eugene Forbes
Director
Water Division
Department of Environmental Services
29 Hazen Drive, P.O. Box 95
Concord, NH 03302
P: (603) 271-3434
F: (603) 271-2982
E: eugene.forbes@des.nh.gov

NEW JERSEY
Mr. Fred Sickels
Acting Director
Division of Water Supply & Geoscience
Department of Environmental Protection
P.O. Box 420
Trenton, NJ 08625
P: (609) 292-7219
F: (609) 292-1654

NEW MEXICO
Mr. Tom Blaine
State Engineer/Secretary, Interstate Stream Commission
Office of the State Engineer/Interstate Stream Commission
130 South Capitol Street, Pino Building
P.O. Box 25102
Santa Fe, NM 87504
P: (505) 827-6091
F: (505) 827-3806

NEW YORK
Mr. Mark Klotz
Director
Division of Water
625 Broadway
Albany, NY 12233
P: (518) 402-8233
F: (518) 402-9029
E: DOWinformation@dec.ny.gov

NORTH CAROLINA
Mr. Jay Zimmerman
Director
Department of Environment & Natural Resources
Division of Water Resources
217 West Jones Street
Raleigh, NC 27603
P: (919) 707-9027
F: (919) 733-3558
E: jay.zimmerman@ncdenr.gov

NORTH DAKOTA
Mr. Garland Erbele
State Engineer
Water Commission
900 East Boulevard Avenue
Department 770
Bismarck, ND 58505
P: (701) 328-4940
F: (701) 328-3696
E: gerbele@nd.gov

NORTHERN MARIANA ISLANDS
Mr. Jesus B. Castro
Division Manager
Water Division
P.O. Box 501220
Saipan, MP 96950
P: (670) 235-7025
F: (670) 235-7053

OHIO
Mr. Steven J. Grossman
Executive Director
Water Development Authority
480 South High Street
Columbus, OH 43215
P: (614) 466-5822
F: (614) 644-9964
E: steve@owda.org

OKLAHOMA
Ms. Julie Cunningham
Executive Director
Water Resources Board
3800 North Classen Boulevard
Oklahoma City, OK 73118
P: (405) 530-8800
F: (405) 530-8900

Mr. J.D. Strong
Director
Water Resources Board
P.O. Box 53465
Oklahoma City, OK 73152
P: (405) 522-6279
F: (405) 521-6505

OREGON
Mr. Tom Byler
Director
Water Resources Department
725 Summer Street, Northeast, Suite A
Salem, OR 97301
P: (503) 986-0876
F: (503) 986-0903
E: thomas.m.byler@oregon.gov

Water Resources

PENNSYLVANIA
Ms. Cindy Adams Dunn
Secretary
Department of Conservation & Natural Resources
400 Market Street, 7th Floor
Harrisburg, PA 17105
P: (717) 787-2869
F: (717) 705-2832

PUERTO RICO
Mr. Javier Velez-Arocho
Secretary
Department of Natural & Environmental Resources
P.O. Box 366147
San Juan, PR 00936
P: (787) 999-2200
F: (787) 999-2303

SOUTH CAROLINA
Mr. Joe Gellici
Section Chief
Hydrology Section
Department of Natural Resources
1000 Assembly Street
Columbia, SC 29201
P: (803) 734-6428
F: (803) 734-9200
E: gellicij@dnr.sc.gov

TENNESSEE
Mr. John McClurkan
Administrator
Water Resources Program
Department of Agriculture
440 Hogan Road
Nashville, TN 37220
P: (615) 837-5305
F: (615) 837-5025
E: john.mcclurkan@tn.gov

TEXAS
Ms. Jessica Zuba
Deputy Executive Administrator
Water Supply & Infrastructure
Water Development Board
1700 North Congress, P.O. Box 13231
Austin, TX 78711
P: (512) 475-3734
F: (512) 475-2053
E: jessica.zuba@twdb.texas.gov

U.S. VIRGIN ISLANDS
Mr. David Simon
Director
Division of Environmental Protection
Cyril E. King Airport
Terminal Building, 2nd Floor
St. Thomas, VI 00802
P: (340) 774-3320
E: david.simon@dpnr.gov.vi

UTAH
Mr. Eric Millis
Director
Division of Water Resources
Department of Natural Resources
P.O. Box 146201
Salt Lake City, UT 84114
P: (801) 538-7230
F: (801) 538-7279
E: ericmillis@utah.gov

VERMONT
Mr. Peter LaFlamme
Director
Watershed Management Division
One National Life Drive
Main Building, 2nd Floor
Montpelier, VT 05620
P: (802) 828-1535
F: (802) 828-1544
E: pete.laflamme@vermont.gov

VIRGINIA
Mr. David K. Paylor
Director
Department of Environmental Quality
629 East Main Street
P.O. Box 1105
Richmond, VA 23219
P: (804) 698-4000
F: (804) 698-4019
E: david.paylor@deq.virginia.gov

WASHINGTON
Mr. Tom Loranger
Program Manager
Water Resources Programs
Department of Ecology
300 Desmond Drive, Southeast
Lacey, WA 98503
P: (360) 407-6672
F: (360) 407-6574
E: tlor461@ecy.wa.gov

WEST VIRGINIA
Mr. Scott G. Mandirola
Division Director
Division of Water & Waste Management
Department of Environmental Protection
601 57th Street Southeast, Room 2119
Charleston, WV 25304
P: (304) 926-0499
F: (304) 926-0463
E: Scott.G.Mandirola@wv.gov

WISCONSIN
Mr. Russell Rasmussen
Special Adviser To the Secretary
Division of Water
101 South Webster Street
P.O. Box 7921
Madison, WI 53707
P: (608) 264-6278
F: (608) 261-4380
E: russell.rasmussen@wisconsin.gov

WYOMING
Mr. Kevin Frederick
Administrator
Water Quality Division
Department of Environmental Quality
200 West 17th Street, Suite 400
Cheyenne, WY 82002
P: (307) 777-7781
F: (307) 777-5973
E: Kevin.Frederick@wyo.gov

Welfare

Administers the delivery of financial and medical benefits to low-income families and individuals.

ALABAMA
Ms. Nancy T. Buckner
Commissioner
Department of Human Resources
Gordon Persons Building, Suite 2104
50 North Ripley Street
Montgomery, AL 36130
P: (334) 242-1310
F: (334) 353-1115
E: Nancy.Buckner@dhr.alabama.gov

ALASKA
Ms. Monica Windom
Director
Division of Public Assistance
Department of Health & Social Services
P.O. Box 110640
Juneau, AK 99811
P: (907) 465-2680
E: monica.windom@alaska.gov

AMERICAN SAMOA
Dr. Taeaoafua Meki Solomona
Director
Department of Human & Social Services
P.O. Box 997534
Pago Pago, AS 96799
P: (684) 633-1664
F: (684) 633-7449
E: mtsolomona@dhss.as

ARIZONA
Mr. Bryon Winston
Acting Director
Division of Benefits & Medical Eligibility
Department of Economic Security
1789 West Jefferson Street
Phoenix, AZ 85007
P: (602) 542-7596

ARKANSAS
Ms. Mary Franklin
Interim Director
Division of County Operations
Department of Human Services
P.O. Box 1437, Slot S301
Little Rock, AR 72203
P: (501) 682-8375
F: (501) 682-6836
E: mary.franklin@dhs.arkansas.gov

CALIFORNIA
Mr. Will Lightbourne
Director
Department of Social Services
744 P Street
Sacramento, CA 95814
P: (916) 657-2598
F: (916) 651-6569

COLORADO
Mr. Reginald L. Bicha
Executive Director
Department of Human Services
1575 Sherman Street
Denver, CO 80203
P: (303) 866-3475
F: (303) 866-2606
E: reginald.bicha@state.co.us

CONNECTICUT
Mr. Roderick L. Bremby
Commissioner
Department of Social Services
55 Farmington Avenue
Hartford, CT 06105
P: (860) 424-5053
E: roderick.bremby@ct.gov

DELAWARE
Ms. Kara Odom Walker
Secretary
Department of Health & Social Services
1901 North DuPont Highway
Main Building
New Castle, DE 19720
P: (302) 255-9040
F: (302) 255-4429

DISTRICT OF COLUMBIA
Ms. Laura Zeilinger
Director
Department of Human Services
64 New York Avenue, Northeast
6th Floor
Washington, DC 20002
P: (202) 671-4200
F: (202) 671-4326
E: dhs@dc.gov

FLORIDA
Mr. Mike Carroll
Secretary
Department of Children & Families
1317 Winewood Boulevard
Building 1, Room 202
Tallahassee, FL 32399
P: (850) 487-1111
F: (850) 922-2993
E: mike.carroll@myflfamilies.com

GEORGIA
Mr. Bobby Cagle
Division Director
Division of Family & Children Services
Department of Human Services
Two Peachtree Street, Northwest
Atlanta, GA 30303
P: (404) 657-8986
F: (404) 657-5105
E: bobby.cagle@dhs.ga.gov

HAWAII
Mr. Pankaj Bhanot
Director
Department of Human Services
1390 Miller Street, Room 209
P.O. Box 339
Honolulu, HI 96809
P: (808) 586-4993
F: (808) 586-4890
E: dhs@dhs.hawaii.gov

IDAHO
Ms. Lori Wolff
Administrator
Division of Welfare
Department of Health & Welfare
450 West State Street
Boise, ID 83702
P: (208) 334-7258
F: (208) 334-5817
E: lori.wolff@dhw.idaho.gov

ILLINOIS
Ms. Felicia F. Norwood
Director
Department of Healthcare & Family Services
201 South Grand Avenue East, 3rd Floor
Springfield, IL 62763
P: (217) 782-1200

INDIANA
Mr. Joe Moser
Director of Medicaid
Office of Medicaid Policy & Planning
402 West Washington Street
P.O. Box 7083
Indianapolis, IN 46207
P: (317) 233-4454
E: Joe.Moser@fssa.IN.gov

IOWA
Ms. Ann Wiebers
Bureau Chief
Bureau of Financial, Health & Work Supports
Hoover State Office Building
1305 East Walnut Street
Des Moines, IA 50319
P: (515) 248-1243
F: (515) 281-7791
E: awieber@dhs.state.ia.us

KANSAS
Ms. Sandra Kimmons
Director
Economic & Employment Services
Department for Children & Families
555 South Kansas Avenue
Topeka, KS 66603
P: (785) 296-8867
F: (785) 296-6960

KENTUCKY
Ms. Adria Johnson
Commissioner
Department for Community Based Services
275 East Main Street
Mail Stop 3W-A
Frankfort, KY 40621
P: (502) 564-3703
F: (502) 564-6907

MAINE
Ms. Stefanie Nadeau
Director
Office of MaineCare Services
Department of Health & Human Services
11 State House Station
Augusta, ME 04333
P: (207) 287-2674
F: (207) 287-2675
E: Stefanie.Nadeau@maine.gov

MASSACHUSETTS
Mr. Jeff McCue
Commissioner
Department of Transitional Assistance
Office of Health & Human Services
600 Washington Street
Boston, MA 02111
P: (617) 348-8400
F: (617) 348-8575

MICHIGAN
Mr. Nick Lyon
Director
Department of Health & Human Services
333 South Grand Avenue
P.O. Box 30195
Lansing, MI 48909
P: (517) 335-0267
F: (517) 335-6101
E: LyonN2@michigan.gov

Welfare

MISSISSIPPI
Ms. Cathy Sykes
Director
Division of Economic Assistance
Department of Human Services
750 North State Street
Jackson, MS 39202
P: (601) 359-4093

MISSOURI
Mr. Patrick Luebbering
Acting Director
Family Support Division
Department of Social Services
P.O. Box 2320
Jefferson City, MO
P: (573) 751-3221

NEW HAMPSHIRE
Mr. Jeffrey A. Meyers
Commissioner
Department of Health & Human Services
129 Pleasant Street
Concord, NH 03301
P: (603) 271-9200
F: (603) 271-4912
E: Jeffrey.Meyers@dhhs.nh.gov

NEW JERSEY
Ms. Natasha Johnson
Director
Division of Family Development
Department of Human Services
P.O. Box 716
Trenton, NJ 08625
P: (609) 588-2400
F: (609) 584-4404

NEW MEXICO
Mr. Sean Pearson
Interim Director
Income Support Division
Human Services Department
2009 South Pacheco Street, P.O. Box 2348
Santa Fe, NM 87505
P: (505) 827-7250

NEW YORK
Mr. Samuel D. Roberts
Commissioner
Office of Temporary & Disability Assistance
40 North Pearl Street
Albany, NY 12243
P: (518) 473-1090
E: nyspio@otda.ny.gov

NORTH CAROLINA
Mr. Wayne E. Black
Director
Division of Social Services
Department of Health & Human Services
2401 Mail Service Center
Raleigh, NC 27699
P: (919) 527-6335
F: (919) 334-1018
E: wayne.black@dhhs.nc.gov

NORTH DAKOTA
Mr. Christopher Jones
Executive Director
Department of Human Services
600 East Boulevard Avenue
Department 325
Bismarck, ND 58505
P: (701) 328-2538
F: (701) 328-2359
E: dhseo@nd.gov

NORTHERN MARIANA ISLANDS
Ms. Eleanor S. Dela Cruz
Administrator
Nutrition Assistance Program
JTV Building
P.O. Box 501488
Saipan, MP 96950
P: (670) 280-2883
F: (670) 664-2850

OHIO
Ms. Cynthia C. Dungey
Director
Department of Job & Family Services
30 East Broad Street, 32nd Floor
Columbus, OH 43215
P: (614) 466-6283
F: (614) 466-2815

OKLAHOMA
Mr. Jim Struby
Director
Adult & Family Services
Department of Human Services
P.O. Box 25352
Oklahoma City, OK 73125
P: (405) 521-3076
F: (405) 521-4158
E: fssinquiries@okdhs.org

OREGON
Mr. Clyde Saiki
Director
Department of Human Services
500 Summer Street, Northeast
Salem, OR 97301
P: (503) 945-7001
F: (503) 581-6198
E: clyde.saiki@oregon.gov

PENNSYLVANIA
Mr. Theodore Dallas
Secretary
Department of Human Services
Health & Welfare Building
625 Forster Street, P.O. Box 2675
Harrisburg, PA 17105
P: (717) 787-2600
F: (717) 772-2062

PUERTO RICO
Ms. Glorimar Andujar Matos
Secretary
Department of the Family
P.O. Box 11398
Hato Rey, PR 00917
P: (787) 294-4900
F: (787) 297-0732

RHODE ISLAND
Mr. Eric J. Beane
Acting Director
Department of Human Services
Louis Pasteur Building
57 Howard Avenue
Cranston, RI 2920
P: (401) 462-2121

SOUTH DAKOTA
Ms. Lynne A. Valenti
Cabinet Secretary
Department of Social Services
700 Governors Drive
Pierre, SD 57501
P: (605) 773-3165
F: (605) 773-4855
E: DSSInfo@state.sd.us

TENNESSEE
Ms. Danielle W. Barnes
Commissioner
Department of Human Services
400 Deaderick Street
Nashville, TN 37243
P: (615) 313-4700
F: (615) 741-4165
E: danielle.w.barnes@tn.gov

TEXAS
Mr. Charles Smith
Executive Commissioner
Health & Human Services Commission
4900 North Lamar Boulevard
P.O. Box 13247
Austin, TX 78711
P: (512) 424-6500
F: (512) 424-6587

Mr. Jon Weizenbaum
Commissioner
Department of Aging & Disability Services
701 West 51st Street
P.O. Box 149030
Austin, TX 78714
P: (512) 438-3011
F: (512) 438-3011

U.S. VIRGIN ISLANDS
Mr. Felicia Blyden
Commissioner
Department of Human Services
3011 Golden Rock
Christiansted
St. Croix, VI 00802
P: (340) 718-2980

UTAH
Mr. Jon S. Pierpont
Executive Director
Department of Workforce Services
P.O. Box 45249
Salt Lake City, UT 84145
P: (801) 526-9210
F: (801) 526-9211
E: jpierpo@utah.gov

VERMONT
Mr. Ken Schatz
Commissioner
Department for Children & Families
280 State Drive, HC 1 North
Waterbury, VT 05671
P: (802) 241-0929
E: ken.schatz@vermont.gov

VIRGINIA
Ms. Margaret Ross Schultze
Commissioner
Department of Social Services
801 East Main Street
Richmond, VA 23219
P: (804) 726-7011
E: margaret.schultze@dss.virginia.gov

WASHINGTON
Mr. Bill Moss
Acting Secretary
Department of Social & Health Services
1115 Washington Street, Southeast
Olympia, WA 98504
P: (800) 737-0617
F: (360) 407-0304

WEST VIRGINIA
Mr. Bill J. Crouch
Cabinet Secretary
Department of Health & Human Resources
One Davis Square, Suite 100 East
Charleston, WV 25301
P: (304) 558-0684
F: (304) 558-1130
E: DHHRSecretary@wv.gov

WYOMING
Dr. Steve Corsi
Director
Department of Family Services
Hathaway Building, 3rd Floor
2300 Capitol Avenue
Cheyenne, WY 82002
P: (307) 777-6597
F: (307) 777-7747
E: steve.corsi@wyo.gov

Workers Compensation

Administers laws providing insurance and compensation for workers for job-related illnesses, injury or death.

ALABAMA
Mr. Charles Delamar
Director
Workers Compensation Division
649 Monroe Street
Montgomery, AL 36131
P: (334) 353-0970
E: Charles.Delamar@labor.alabama.gov

ALASKA
Ms. Marie Marx
Director
Division of Workers' Compensation
Labor & Workforce Development
P.O. Box 115512
Juneau, AK 99811
P: (907) 465-2790
F: (907) 465-2797
E: marie.marx@alaska.gov

AMERICAN SAMOA
Mr. Esenaeiaso J. Liu
Director
Department of Human Resources
Executive Office Building
AP Lutali, 2nd Floor
Pago Pago, AS 96799
P: (684) 644-4485
F: (684) 633-1139
E: eseneiaso.liu@hr.as.gov

ARIZONA
Mr. James Ashley
Director
Industrial Commission
800 West Washington Street
Phoenix, AZ 85007
P: (602) 542-4411
F: (602) 542-7889

ARKANSAS
Ms. Barbara Womack Webb
Chief Executive Officer
Workers' Compensation Commission
324 South Spring Street
P.O. Box 950
Little Rock, AR 72203
P: (501) 682-3930
F: (501) 682-2786
E: bwebb@awcc.state.ar.us

CALIFORNIA
Mr. George Parisotto
Acting Administrative Director
Division of Workers' Compensation
1515 Clay Street, 17th Floor
P.O. Box 420603
Oakland, CA 94612
P: (510) 286-7100

COLORADO
Mr. Paul Tauriello
Director
Division of Workers Compensation
Department of Labor & Employment
633 17th Street, Suite 400
Denver, CO 80202
P: (303) 318-8700
F: (303) 318-8710
E: workers.comp@state.co.us

CONNECTICUT
Mr. John A. Mastropietro
Chair
Workers' Compensation Commission
Capitol Place
21 Oak Street
Hartford, CT 06106
P: (860) 493-1500
F: (860) 247-1361
E: wcc.chairmansoffice@po.state.ct.us

DELAWARE
Mr. John F. Kirk III
Administrator
Office of Workers' Compensation
4425 North Market Street, 3rd Floor
Wilmington, DE 19802
P: (302) 761-8200
F: (302) 736-9170
E: jkirk@state.de.us

DISTRICT OF COLUMBIA
Mr. Odie Donald II
Director
Department of Employment Services
4058 Minnesota Avenue, Northeast
Washington, DC 20019
P: (202) 724-7000
F: (202) 673-6993
E: does@dc.gov

FLORIDA
Mr. Tanner Holloman
Director
Division of Workers' Compensation
Department of Financial Services
200 East Gaines Street
Tallahassee, FL 32399
P: (850) 413-1600
E: Tanner.Holloman@myfloridacfo.com

GEORGIA
Delece A. Brooks
Executive Director/Chief Operating Officer
State Board of Workers' Compensation
270 Peachtree Street, Northwest
Atlanta, GA 30303
P: (404) 656-2048

GUAM
Mr. Manuel Q. Cruz
Director
Department of Labor
Government of Guam
P.O. Box 9970
Tamuning, GU 96931
P: (671) 475-7044
F: (671) 674-6517

HAWAII
Ms. JoAnn Vidinhar
Administrator
Disability Compensation Division
830 Punchbowl Street, Room 209
P.O. Box 3769
Honolulu, HI 96812
P: (808) 586-9151
F: (808) 586-9219

IDAHO
Mr. Thomas E. Limbaugh
Chair
Industrial Commission
P.O. Box 83720
Boise, ID 83720
P: (208) 334-6000
F: (208) 334-2321
E: tom.limbaugh@iic.idaho.gov

ILLINOIS
Ms. Carolyn Parks
Executive Director
Workers' Compensation Commission
100 West Randolph Street, Suite 8-200
Chicago, IL 60601
P: (312) 814-6638
E: carolyn.parks@illinois.gov

INDIANA
Ms. Linda Hamilton
Chair
Worker's Compensation Board
402 West Washington Street, Room W-196
Indianapolis, IN 46204
P: (317) 232-3811
F: (317) 233-5493
E: lhamilton@wcb.in.gov

IOWA
Mr. Joseph S. Cortese II
Commissioner
Division of Workers' Compensation
Workforce Development
1000 East Grand Avenue
Des Moines, IA 50319
P: (515) 725-3820
F: (515) 281-6501
E: joseph.cortese@iwd.iowa.gov

KANSAS
Mr. Larry Karns
Director
Division of Workers Compensation
Department of Labor
401 Southwest Topeka Boulevard, Suite 2
Topeka, KS 66603
P: (785) 296-4000
F: (785) 296-0025
E: wc@dol.ks.gov

KENTUCKY
Mr. Robert Swisher
Acting Commissioner
Department of Workers' Claims
657 Chamberlin Avenue
Frankfort, KY 40601
P: (502) 782-4439
F: (502) 564-5934

LOUISIANA
Ms. Sheral Kellar
Director
Office of Workers' Compensation Administration
Workforce Commission
P.O. Box 94040
Baton Rouge, LA 70804
P: (225) 342-7555
F: (225) 342-5665
E: owca@lwc.la.gov

MAINE
Mr. Paul H. Sighinolfi
Executive Director/Chair
Workers' Compensation Board
442 Civic Center Drive, Suite 100
Augusta, ME 04333
P: (207) 287-3751
F: (207) 287-7198
E: phil.sighinolfi@maine.gov

MARYLAND
Ms. Mary K. Ahearn
Chief Executive Officer
Workers' Compensation Commission
10 East Baltimore Street, 4th Floor
Baltimore, MD 21202
P: (410) 864-5300
F: (410) 333-8122
E: Mahearn@Wcc.state.md.us

MASSACHUSETTS
Dr. Linda Edmonds Turner
Director
Department of Industrial Accidents
Office of Labor & Workforce Development
1 Congress Street, Suite 100
Boston, MA 02114
P: (617) 727-4900
F: (617) 727-7470
E: Info2@massmail.state.ma.us

MICHIGAN
Mr. Mark C. Long
Director
Workers' Compensation Agency
P.O. Box 30016
Lansing, MI 48909
P: (517) 284-8902
F: (517) 284-8906
E: longm1@michigan.gov

MINNESOTA
Mr. Ken Peterson
Commissioner
Department of Labor & Industry
443 Lafayette Road North
St. Paul, MN 55155
P: (651) 284-5010
F: (651) 284-5720
E: DLI.workcomp@state.mn.us

MISSISSIPPI
Ms. Joyce Wells
Commission Secretary
Workers' Compensation Commission
1428 Lakeland Drive
Jackson, MS 39216
P: (601) 987-4252
E: jwells@mwcc.ms.gov

MISSOURI
Nasreen Esmail
Interim Director
Division of Workers' Compensation
Labor & Industrial Relations
P.O. Box 58
Jefferson City, MO 65102
P: (573) 751-4231
E: workerscomp@labor.mo.gov

MONTANA
Mr. Peter Van Nice
Bureau Chief
Workers' Compensation Regulations Bureau
Beck Building, 1805 Prospect Avenue
P.O. Box 8011
Helena, MT 59604
P: (406) 444-0566
F: (406) 444-7710

NEBRASKA
Ms. Tamra L. Walz
Administrator
Workers' Compensation Court
P.O. Box 98908
Lincoln, NE 68509
P: (402) 471-3602
F: (402) 471-2700
E: tamra.walz@nebraska.gov

NEVADA
Mr. Joseph D. Decker
Administrator
Division of Industrial Relations
400 West King Street, Suite 400
Carson City, NV 89703
P: (775) 684-7270
F: (775) 687-6305

NEW HAMPSHIRE
Ms. Kathryn J. Barger
Deputy Commissioner
Department of Labor
95 Pleasant Street
Concord, NH 03301
P: (603) 271-3176
F: (603) 271-2668
E: kathryn.barger@dol.nh.gov

NEW JERSEY
Mr. Russell Wojtenko Jr.
Chief Judge/Director
Division of Workers' Compensation
Labor & Workforce Development
P.O. Box 381
Trenton, NJ 08625
P: (609) 292-2414
F: (609) 984-2515
E: Russell.Wojtenko@dol.nj.gov

NEW MEXICO
Mr. Darin A. Childers
Director
Workers' Compensation Administration
2410 Centre Avenue, Southeast
P.O. Box 27198
Albuquerque, NM 87125
P: (505) 841-6000
F: (505) 841-6009

NEW YORK
Mr. Kenneth J. Munnelly
Chair
Workers' Compensation Board
328 State Street
Albany, NY 12305
P: (877) 632-4996
E: general_information@wcb.ny.gov

NORTH DAKOTA
Mr. Bryan Klipfel
Director
Workforce Safety & Insurance
1600 East Century Avenue, Suite 1
Bismarck, ND 58503
P: (800) 777-5033
F: (701) 328-3820
E: ndwsi@nd.gov

NORTHERN MARIANA ISLANDS
Mr. Mark O. Rabauliman
Secretary of Commerce
Department of Commerce
Office of the Insurance Commissioner
Caller Box 10007 CK
Saipan, MP 96950
P: (670) 664-3077
F: (670) 664-3067
E: info@commerce.gov.mp

OKLAHOMA
The Honorable Michael J. Harkey
Administrator
Workers' Compensation Court
1915 North Stiles Avenue, Suite 127
Oklahoma City, OK 73105
P: (405) 522-8600

OREGON
Mr. Lou Savage
Division Administrator
Workers' Compensation Division
350 Winter Street, Northeast
P.O. Box 14480
Salem, OR 97309
P: (503) 947-7810
F: (503) 947-7630

PENNSYLVANIA
Ms. Kelly Smith
Deputy Chief Counsel
Bureau of Workers' Compensation Division
1171 South Cameron Street
Harrisburg, PA 17104
P: (717) 783-4467
F: (717) 783-4469

RHODE ISLAND
Mr. Matthew P. Carey III
Assistant Director
Workers Compensation
Department of Labor & Training
Center General Complex, 1511 Pontiac Ave
Cranston, RI 02920
P: (401) 462-8100
F: (401) 462-8105
E: mcarey@dlt.ri.gov

SOUTH CAROLINA
Mr. Gary M. Cannon
Executive Director
Workers' Compensation Commission
1333 Main Street, Suite 500
P.O. Box 1715
Columbia, SC 29202
P: (803) 737-5744
F: (803) 737-5768
E: gcannon@wcc.sc.gov

Workers Compensation

SOUTH DAKOTA
Mr. James E. Marsh
Director
Division of Labor & Management
Department of Labor & Regulation
700 Governors Drive
Pierre, SD 57501
P: (605) 773-3681
F: (605) 773-4211
E: james.marsh@state.sd.us

TENNESSEE
Ms. Abbie Hudgens
Administrator
Workers' Compensation Division
Labor & Workforce Development
220 French Landing Drive
Nashville, TN 37243
P: (615) 741-2395
F: (615) 532-1468
E: wc.info@tn.gov

Mr. Burns Phillips
Commissioner
Department of Labor & Workforce Development
220 French Landing Drive
Nashville, TN 37243
P: (844) 224-5818
F: (615) 741-5078
E: burns.phillips@tn.gov

TEXAS
Mr. Ryan Brannan
Commissioner
Division of Workers' Compensation
Department of Insurance
7551 Metro Center Drive, Suite 100
Austin, TX 78744
P: (800) 252-7031

UTAH
Mr. Ron Dressler
Director
Industrial Accidents Division
Labor Commission
P.O. Box 146610
Salt Lake City, UT 84114
P: (801) 530-6841
F: (801) 530-6804
E: rdressler@utah.gov

VERMONT
Mr. J. Stephen Monahan
Director of Workers' Comp & Safety
Department of Labor
5 Green Mountain Drive
P.O. Box 488
Montpelier, VT 05601
P: (802) 828-2138
F: (802) 828-4022
E: stephen.monahan@vermont.gov

VIRGINIA
Ms. Evelyn McGill
Executive Director
Workers' Compensation Commission
1000 DMV Drive
Richmond, VA 23220
P: (804) 205-3060
F: (877) 262-3577

WASHINGTON
Mr. Frank E. Fennerty Jr.
Labor Member
Board of Industrial Insurance Appeals
2430 Chandler Court, Southwest
P.O. Box 42401
Olympia, WA 98504
P: (360) 753-6823
F: (360) 586-5611
E: fennerty@biia.wa.gov

WEST VIRGINIA
Mr. Allan L. McVey
Insurance Commissioner
Offices of the Insurance Commissioner
900 Pennsylvania Avenue
P.O. Box 50540
Charleston, WV 25305
P: (304) 558-3354
F: (304) 558-4965
E: Allan.L.McVey@wv.gov

WISCONSIN
Mr. B.J. Dernbach
Division Administrator
Workers Compensation Division
201 East Washington Avenue, Room C100
P.O. Box 7901
Madison, WI 53707
P: (608) 266-1340
F: (608) 267-0394
E: BJ.Dernbach@dwd.wisconsin.gov

WYOMING
Mr. Steven R. Czoschke
Executive Secretary
Workers' Compensation Medical Commission
CenturyLink Building, Suite 190
6101 Yellowstone Road
Cheyenne, WY 82002
P: (307) 777-5422
F: (307) 777-5201

Workforce Development

Administers job training and services for the unemployed, underemployed and economically disadvantaged in the state.

ALABAMA
Mr. Fitzgerald Washington
Secretary
Department of Labor
649 Monroe Street
Montgomery, AL 36131
P: (334) 242-8055
E: fwashington@labor.alabama.gov

ALASKA
Ms. Heidi Drygas
Commissioner
Department of Labor & Workforce Development
P.O. Box 111149
Juneau, AK 99811
P: (907) 465-2700
F: (907) 465-2784
E: heidi.drygas@alaska.gov

AMERICAN SAMOA
Mr. Esenaeiaso J. Liu
Director
Department of Human Resources
Executive Office Building
AP Lutali, 2nd Floor
Pago Pago, AS 96799
P: (684) 644-4485
F: (684) 633-1139
E: eseneiaso.liu@hr.as.gov

ARIZONA
Mr. Michael Wisehart
Director
Division of Employment & Rehabilitation Services
Department of Economic Security
1789 West Jefferson Street
Phoenix, AZ 85007
P: (602) 542-3596

ARKANSAS
Mr. Daryl Bassett
Director
Department of Workforce Services
#2 Capitol Mall
Little Rock, AR 72201
P: (501) 682-3394
F: (501) 682-8845
E: daryl.bassett@arkansas.gov

CALIFORNIA
Mr. Patrick W. Henning Jr.
Director
Employment Development Department
800 Capitol Mall
P.O. Box 826880
Sacramento, CA 94280
P: (916) 654-8210
F: (916) 654-9069
E: patrick.henning@edd.ca.gov

COLORADO
Ms. Ellen Golombek
Executive Director
Department of Labor & Employment
633 17th Street, Suite 201
Denver, CO 80202
P: (303) 318-8017
F: (303) 318-8047
E: Ellen.Golombek@state.co.us

Ms. Stephanie Veck
Director
Workforce Development Council
Department of Labor & Employment
633 17th Street, Suite 1200
Denver, CO 80202
P: (303) 318-8038
F: (303) 318-8049
E: stephanie.veck@state.co.us

CONNECTICUT
Mr. Scott D. Jackson
Commissioner
Department of Labor
200 Folly Brook Boulevard
Westerfield, CT 06109
P: (860) 263-6000
F: (850) 263-6529
E: scott.jackson@ct.gov

DELAWARE
Mr. John McMahon
Secretary of Labor
Department of Labor
4425 North Market Street
Wilmington, DE 19802
P: (302) 761-8000
F: (302) 761-6621
E: john.mcmahon@state.de.us

Ms. Lori Reeder
Director
Department of Labor
Division of Employment & Training
4425 North Market Street
Wilmington, DE 19802
P: (302) 761-8085
E: lori.reeder@state.de.us

DISTRICT OF COLUMBIA
Mr. Odie Donald II
Director
Department of Employment Services
4058 Minnesota Avenue, Northeast
Washington, DC 20019
P: (202) 724-7000
F: (202) 673-6993
E: does@dc.gov

FLORIDA
Ms. Cissy Proctor
Director
Department of Economic Opportunity
107 East Madison Street
Caldwell Building
Tallahassee, FL 32399
P: (850) 245-7105
F: (850) 921-3223
E: cissy.proctor@deo.myflorida.com

GEORGIA
The Honorable Mark Butler (R)
Commissioner
Department of Labor
148 International Boulevard Northeast
Atlanta, GA 30303
P: (404) 232-7300
F: (404) 656-2683
E: commissioner@gdol.ga.gov

HAWAII
Ms. Linda Chu Takayama
Director
Department of Labor & Industrial Relations
830 Punchbowl Street
Honolulu, HI 96813
P: (808) 586-8844
F: (808) 586-9099
E: dlir.director@hawaii.gov

IDAHO
Mr. Kenneth D. Edmunds
Director
Department of Labor
317 West Main Street
Boise, ID 83735
P: (208) 332-3570
F: (208) 334-6430
E: kenneth.edmunds@labor.idaho.gov

ILLINOIS
Mr. Julio Rodriguez
Deputy Director
Department of Commerce & Economic Opportunity
Office of Employment & Training
100 West Randolph Street, Suite 3-400
Chicago, IL 60601
P: (312) 814-7179

INDIANA
Mr. Steve Braun
Commissioner
Department of Workforce Development
Government Center South
10 North Senate Avenue
Indianapolis, IN 46204
P: (317) 232-7676
E: SBraun@dwd.IN.gov

IOWA
Ms. Beth Townsend
Executive Director
Workforce Development
1000 East Grand Avenue
Des Moines, IA 50319
P: (515) 281-5364
E: beth.townsend@iwd.iowa.gov

KANSAS
Ms. Lana Gordon
Secretary of Labor
Department of Labor
401 Southwest Topeka Boulevard
Topeka, KS 66603
P: (785) 296-5000
F: (785) 368-5289
E: lana.gordon@dol.ks.gov

Mr. Antonio J. Soave
Secretary
Department of Commerce
1000 Southwest Jackson Street, Suite 100
Topeka, KS 66612
P: (785) 296-2994
F: (785) 296-5055
E: asoave@kansascommerce.com

Workforce Development

KENTUCKY
Ms. Beth Kuhn
Commissioner
Department of Workforce Investment
500 Mero Street
3rd Floor Capital Plaza Tower
Frankfort, KY 40601
P: (502) 564-0372
E: Beth.Kuhn@ky.gov

LOUISIANA
Ms. Ava Dejoie
Executive Director
Workforce Commission
1001 North 23rd Street
P.O. Box 94094
Baton Rouge, LA 70804
P: (225) 342-3111
F: (225) 342-3778
E: owd@lwc.la.gov

Ms. Shannon Joseph
Director
Office of Workforce Development
1001 North 23rd Street
P.O. Box 94094
Baton Rouge, LA 70804
P: (225) 342-3111
F: (225) 342-7960
E: sjoseph@lwc.la.gov

MAINE
Ms. Jeanne Paquette
Commissioner
Department of Labor
54 State House Station
Augusta, ME 04333
P: (207) 623-7900
F: (207) 623-7934
E: jeanne.paquette@maine.gov

MARYLAND
Mr. James E. Rzepkowski
Assistant Secretary
Division of Workforce Development & Adult Learning
Labor, Licensing and Regulation
1100 North Eutaw Street
Baltimore, MD 21201
P: (410) 767-2924
E: james.rzepkowski@maryland.gov

MASSACHUSETTS
Mr. Ronald L. Walker II
Secretary
Executive Office of Labor & Workforce Development
One Ashburton Place, Suite 2112
Boston, MA 02108
P: (617) 626-7122

MICHIGAN
Ms. Stephanie Beckhorn
Director
Workforce Development Agency
Victor Office Center
201 North Washington Square
Lansing, MI 48913
P: (517) 335-5858
F: (517) 241-8217
E: beckhorns@michigan.gov

MINNESOTA
Mr. Jeremy Hanson Willis
Deputy Commissioner, Workforce Development
Department of Employment & Economic Development
1st National Bank Building
332 Minnesota Street, Suite E-200
St. Paul, MN 55101
P: (651) 259-7563

MISSISSIPPI
Mr. Mark Henry
Executive Director
Department of Employment Security
1235 Echelon Parkway
P.O. Box 1699
Jackson, MS 39215
P: (601) 321-6000
F: (601) 321-6104
E: mhenry@mdes.ms.gov

MISSOURI
Mr. Mike Downing
Acting Director
Department of Economic Development
P.O. Box 1157
Jefferson City, MO 65102
P: (573) 751-4770
F: (573) 526-7700
E: ecodev@ded.mo.gov

Ms. Anna Hui
Director
Department of Labor & Industrial Relations
421 East Dunklin Street
P.O. Box 504
Jefferson City, MO 65102
P: (573) 751-4091
F: (573) 751-4135
E: diroffice@labor.mo.gov

MONTANA
Ms. Pam Bucy
Commissioner
Department of Labor & Industry
P.O. Box 1728
Helena, MT 59624
P: (406) 444-2840
F: (406) 444-1419
E: dliquestions@mt.gov

Mr. Scott Eychner
Administrator
Workforce Services Division
Department of Labor & Industry
P.O. Box 1728
Helena, MT 59624
P: (406) 444-4100
F: (406) 444-3037

NEBRASKA
Ms. Courtney Dentlinger
Director
Department of Economic Development
301 Centennial Mall South
P.O. Box 94666
Lincoln, NE 68509
P: (402) 471-3746
F: (402) 471-3778
E: courtney.dentlinger@nebraska.gov

NEVADA
Mr. Joseph D. Decker
Administrator
Division of Industrial Relations
400 West King Street, Suite 400
Carson City, NV 89703
P: (775) 684-7270
F: (775) 687-6305

NEW HAMPSHIRE
Mr. George N. Copadis
Commissioner
Department of Employment Security
45 South Fruit Street
Concord, NH 03301
P: (603) 224-3311
E: george.n.copadis@nhes.nh.gov

NEW JERSEY
Dr. Aaron R. Fichtner
Acting Commissioner
Department of Labor & Workforce Development
1 John Fitch Plaza
P.O. Box 110
Trenton, NJ 08625
P: (609) 292-1070
E: aaron.fichtner@dol.state.nj.us

NEW MEXICO
Ms. Celina Bussey
Secretary
Department of Workforce Solutions
401 Broadway, Northeast
P.O. Box 1928
Albuquerque, NM 87103
P: (505) 841-8405
F: (505) 841-8491
E: celina.bussey@state.nm.us

NEW YORK
Ms. Roberta Reardon
Commissioner
Department of Labor
W. Averell Harriman State Office Campus
Building 12
Albany, NY 12240
P: (518) 457-9000
F: (518) 485-6297
E: roberta.reardon@labor.state.ny.us

NORTH CAROLINA
Mr. Danny Giddens
Executive Director of Operations
Division of Workforce Development
313 Chapanoke Road, Suite 120
4316 Mail Service Center
Raleigh, NC 27699
P: (919) 814-0325
F: (919) 662-4770
E: dgiddens@nccommerce.com

NORTH DAKOTA
Mr. Wayde Sick
Director
Workforce Development Division
1600 East Century Avenue, Suite 2
P.O. Box 2057
Bismarck, ND 58503
P: (701) 328-5345
F: (701) 328-5320
E: wsick@nd.gov

OHIO
Ms. Cynthia C. Dungey
Director
Department of Job & Family Services
30 East Broad Street, 32nd Floor
Columbus, OH 43215
P: (614) 466-6283
F: (614) 466-2815

Mr. Bruce Madson
Assistant Director, Employment Services
Department of Job & Family Services
30 East Broad Street, 32nd Floor
Columbus, OH 43215
P: (614) 466-6283
F: (614) 466-2815

Mr. John B. Weber
Deputy Director
Office of Workforce Development
Department of Job & Family Services
P.O. Box 1618
Columbus, OH 43216
P: (614) 466-9494
F: (614) 728-8366
E: john.weber@jfs.ohio.gov

OKLAHOMA
Mr. Richard McPherson
Executive Director
Employment Security Commission
P.O. Box 52003
Oklahoma City, OK 73152
P: (405) 557-7201
E: richard.mcpherson@oesc.state.ok.us

OREGON
Mr. Jim Middleton
Interim Executive Director
Department of Community Colleges & Workforce Development
Public Service Building
255 Capitol Street, Northeast, 3rd Floor
Salem, OR 97301
P: (503) 947-2433
F: (503) 378-3365
E: jim.middleton@state.or.us

PENNSYLVANIA
Ms. Kathy M. Manderino
Secretary
Department of Labor & Industry
651 Boas Street
Harrisburg, PA 17121
P: (717) 787-5279
F: (717) 787-8826

PUERTO RICO
Mr. Carlos J. Saavedra Gutierrez
Secretary
Department of Labor & Human Resources
P.O. Box 195540
San Juan, PR 00919
P: (787) 754-5353
F: (787) 753-9550

RHODE ISLAND
Mr. Scott Jensen
Director
Department of Labor & Training
Center General Complex
1511 Pontiac Avenue
Cranston, RI 02920
P: (401) 462-8000
F: (401) 462-8872
E: director-dlt@dlt.ri.gov

SOUTH CAROLINA
Ms. Cheryl M. Stanton
Executive Director
Department of Employment & Workforce
1550 Gadsden Street
P.O. Box 995
Columbia, SC 29202
P: (803) 737-2617
E: cstanton@dew.sc.gov

SOUTH DAKOTA
Ms. Marcia Hultman
Cabinet Secretary
Department of Labor & Regulation
123 West Missouri Avenue
Pierre, SD 57501
P: (605) 773-5395
F: (605) 773-6184
E: marcia.hultman@state.sd.us

TENNESSEE
Mr. Burns Phillips
Commissioner
Department of Labor & Workforce Development
220 French Landing Drive
Nashville, TN 37243
P: (844) 224-5818
F: (615) 741-5078
E: burns.phillips@tn.gov

Mr. Sterling Van Der Spuy
Administrator
Workforce Services Division
Labor & Workforce Development
220 French Landing Drive
Nashville, TN 37243
P: (615) 741-1031
F: (615) 741-5078

TEXAS
Ms. Courtney Arbour
Division Director
Workforce Development Division
Workforce Commission
101 East 15th Street
Austin, TX 78778
P: (512) 463-8326
E: courtney.arbour@twc.state.tx.us

Mr. Larry E. Temple
Executive Director
Workforce Commission
101 East 15th Street
Austin, TX 78778
P: (512) 463-0735
F: (512) 475-2321
E: larry.temple@twc.state.tx.us

UTAH
Mr. Jon S. Pierpont
Executive Director
Department of Workforce Services
P.O. Box 45249
Salt Lake City, UT 84145
P: (801) 526-9210
F: (801) 526-9211
E: jpierpo@utah.gov

VERMONT
Ms. Lindsay H. Kurrle
Commissioner
Department of Labor
5 Green Mountain Drive
P.O. Box 488
Montpelier, VT 05601
P: (802) 828-4301
F: (802) 828-4022
E: Labor.WebInput@vermont.gov

VIRGINIA
Ms. Ellen Marie Hess
Commissioner
Employment Commission
703 East Main Street
P.O. Box 1358
Richmond, VA 23219
P: (866) 832-2363
E: ellenmarie.hess@vec.virginia.gov

WASHINGTON
Ms. Eleni Papadakis
Executive Director
Workforce Training & Education Coordinating Board
128 10th Avenue, Southwest
P.O. Box 43105
Olympia, WA 98504
P: (360) 709-4600
F: (360) 586-5862
E: eleni.papadakis@wtb.wa.gov

WEST VIRGINIA
Mr. Russell Fry
Acting Executive Director
Workforce West Virginia
112 California Avenue
Charleston, WV 25305
P: (304) 558-7024
F: (304) 558-1343
E: Russell.L.Fry@wv.gov

WISCONSIN
Mr. Ray Allen
Secretary
Department of Workforce Development
201 East Washington Avenue (GEF-1)
Room A-400, P.O. Box 7946
Madison, WI 53707
P: (608) 266-3131
F: (608) 266-1784
E: sec@dwd.wisconsin.gov

WYOMING
Mr. John F. Cox
Director
Department of Workforce Services
614 South Greeley Highway
Cheyenne, WY 82002
P: (307) 777-8728
F: (307) 777-5857
E: john.cox@wyo.gov